DATE DU[illegible] MED BELOW

[illegible]ails in the panel

FUNDAMENTALS & TECHNIQUES
OF MATHEMATICS FOR SCIENTISTS

Edited by the late

Professor D. R. HARTREE, F.R.S.

and

DAPHNE G. PADFIELD, Ph.D.

Fundamentals & Techniques of Mathematics for Scientists

M. M. NICOLSON, Ph.D.

Late Lecturer in Physics in the University of Leeds

1724

LONGMANS

Longmans, Green and Co Ltd
48 Grosvenor Street, London W1
Railway Crescent, Croydon, Victoria, Australia
443 Lockhart Road, Hong Kong
Private Mail Bag 1036, Ikeja (Lagos)
44 Jalan Ampang, Kuala Lumpur
Accra, Auckland, Ibadan, Kingston (Jamaica)
Nairobi, Salisbury (Rhodesia)

Longmans Southern Africa (Pty) Ltd
Thibault House, Thibault Square, Cape Town

Longmans, Green and Co Inc
119 West 40th Street, New York 18

Longmans, Green and Co
137 Bond Street, Toronto 2

Orient Longmans Private Ltd
Calcutta, Bombay, Madras
Delhi, Hyderabad, Dacca

First Published 1961

Printed in Great Britain by
Robert MacLehose & Co. Ltd., University Press, Glasgow

FOREWORD

Shortly after the end of the war, I had an enquiry from Messrs. Longmans, Green & Co. Ltd. about the desirability of revising Mellor's *Higher Mathematics for Students of Chemistry and Physics*. My view was (and is) that a completely new book would be more satisfactory than an attempt to revise an old one, and Dr M. M. Nicolson, who during the war had been an Instructor in Mathematics at the Military College of Science, and had considerable experience of teaching mathematics to those for whom it was primarily a tool for use in applications rather than a subject for study for its own sake, was approached and undertook the task of writing such a book.

When he had nearly completed a first draft, Dr Nicolson was fatally injured in a tragic accident, and I undertook, with the help of Dr Daphne G. Padfield, to try to get the material in a suitable form for publication; the present book is the result. The editorial work has been considerable; the amount of material left by Dr Nicolson was about twice as much as the publishers were prepared to accept for the proposed book, so considerable pruning has been necessary. Also his material was in a very preliminary form; although divided into sections, many of these were not assembled into chapters, and there was no indication of the intended sequence of chapters; also it was in some respects incomplete. In particular there was nothing on functions of two and more variables, or on vector algebra and analysis,* although there were references indicating an intention to include these topics; and there was only a section heading to show that Dr Nicolson intended to include a section on Lebesgue integration.

In the work of editing this material, the help of Dr Padfield has been of the greatest value. She has provided almost all the material on the topics just mentioned as being missing from Dr Nicolson's draft, and has done much of the difficult, and often distasteful, work of deciding what parts of Dr Nicolson's material to omit, and also much of the work of tracing consequential modifications in those parts which have been

*Or tensors. D.G.P.

retained. This editorial work has been carried out in such spare time as both of us could find, and it has consequently taken some time to bring the book to its present stage.

Shortly before Dr Nicolson met his accident, I had heard that his first draft was nearly complete and that he hoped shortly to send it to me for comments. What modifications he would have made as a result of these comments must remain unknown; it is possible that he might have made more substantial alterations than we have felt ourselves justified in making without his authority. In particular, he seems deliberately to have avoided use of the ideas of differentiation and integration in the material of Chapters 2 to 5 (which suggests that he intended this material to come, as we have placed it, before the chapter on Calculus). My own preference would be to introduce these ideas in Chapter 2 and to use them freely thereafter. However, the point of view which Dr Nicolson's draft seems to imply is a tenable one; departure from it would involve such a substantial rewriting of Chapters 2 to 6 that this part of the book would cease to be his, and this would be a greater liberty than we considered we should take with his text.

One topic which, it seems from references in the text, Dr Nicolson had intended to include was the theory of servomechanisms and control systems, which was one of the important applications of mathematics with which he was concerned in his work at the Military College of Science. Just after the war, when there were few or no books on this subject available, there might have been a case for including a chapter on it; but there seems no reason now to put such emphasis on just this one application. Another topic which, after discussion with the publishers and their reader, we decided to omit on the ground that any adequate treatment would make the book unduly long, is the theory and practice of numerical methods, on which also there are now several books which were not available when Dr Nicolson wrote his draft.

D. R. Hartree

May 1957

Footnote: The work of preparing the manuscript was entering its final stages when, in January 1958, Professor Hartree died suddenly. Without his guidance in the last revision, the surviving editor is solely responsible for remaining shortcomings. D.G.P.

ACKNOWLEDGEMENTS

Thanks are due to Mr & Mrs M. McCaig and to Mr. J. C. Fletcher for help in proof-reading. The invaluable help of Mr H. D. Ursell of Leeds University in vetting much of the analysis and suggesting many improvements is most gratefully acknowledged.

ADVICE TO THE READER

This book may be read in any of three ways: complete as it stands; in shorter consecutive blocks of reading; or as a reference book. The first method is recommended to the more mature reader, the graduate or the long vacation reader. To the reader who wants a shorter programme we recommend any one or more of the following blocks of reading (according to the extent of his previous knowledge):

(1) Chapters 6–9 inclusive, and Chapters 17, 20.
(2) Chapters 10–12
(3) Chapters 13–16
(4) Chapters 18–19

Chapters 1–5 should be read unhurriedly, and the reader wanting quick results from his reading may delay reading them until he personally discovers a need of, or a curiosity about, their subject matter.

TABLE OF CONTENTS

CHAPTER ONE

NUMBERS AND THEIR USES

1.1 Mathematics and the experimental sciences

Mathematics does not come easily to scientists, or for that matter to mathematicians, and before beginning what may be a long and arduous but not necessarily wearisome journey it is a good plan to have some idea of what mathematics is, and why it is useful to the scientist. These of course are really very profound questions and it may be that there is no completely satisfactory answer to the first of them. It will, however, be of advantage to have in mind even an imperfect picture of the nature of mathematical knowledge, and the views to be put forward are intended to help in avoiding the confusion which often arises between mathematical or analytical expressions on the one hand and their physical representations on the other.

Mathematics began as an experimental science: the early mathematicians drew their inspiration from the sizes and shapes of everyday things. Euclidean geometry, for example, was the mathematical synthesis of the uncoordinated rules of thumb of the builders and craftsmen who by long experience had evolved methods for the construction of right angles, rectangles, pyramids, and the like.

The Greek geometers were able to show that these apparently unrelated rules could be deduced from a small number of simple statements by application of logical processes. The original statements or axioms of the system were regarded as the basic experimental facts of geometry, analogous to Newton's laws of motion for mechanics.

However, mathematics is not merely an instrument for compressing empirical knowledge into systematic order. The geometry of Euclid, whatever its humble origins, is not an experimental science in the sense that one's belief in its validity depends on the agreement of conclusions with experiment.

It forms a closed system of its own ; the only criterion for its validity is the self-consistency of its development by accepted rules from postulated axioms. If different sets of axioms are inserted in place of Euclid's, equally consistent systems may be obtained ; these are the non-Euclidean geometries in which the angles of a triangle do not add up to two right angles, and straight lines may meet at more than one point. There are many such geometries, and clearly not more than one of them can apply to the world of the physicist and engineer ; but they are all equally correct to the mathematician.

It seems, then, that mathematics does not necessarily apply to the external world. It is a mental game in which one is at liberty to choose one's own objects of thought and rules of play, the only condition being that of self-consistency, or the absence of inherent contradictions.

Freed in this way from such restrictions as counting and measuring, the mathematician devises algebras in which $a \times b$ is not equal to $b \times a$ (the non-commutative algebras as they are called), arithmetics in which numbers can be factorised into different sets of prime factors, the non-Euclidean geometries already mentioned, spaces of many dimensions, and so on.

It is a source of regret, however, to many pure mathematicians that no matter how remote and ethereal their creations are, sooner or later some horny-handed physicist or clay-footed engineer discovers that they are just what is required to simplify his mundane problems. (It is also, very occasionally, a matter of regret to some of the more conservative physicists and engineers that more and more of these new branches of mathematics are being thrust upon them.)

Why is it that mathematics, intentionally or otherwise, proves such a useful tool in practice? A number of reasons suggest themselves. First there is the economy of expression and ease of manipulation which arises from the use of symbols rather than the complexities which the symbols represent. Familiar examples will occur to the reader : the brick and a half that weighs a pound and a half plus half a brick, and similar schoolroom posers ; in algebraic form the numbing effect of the repeated words disappears and the problem becomes trivial. A second point is that when a problem is correctly expressed and solved, the solution may bring to light unexpected possibilities which owing to oversight or preconceived ideas would otherwise be missed. A simple example can be easily constructed: a circular table is placed in the corner of a room so that it touches both walls; a spot P on the circumference is then found to be 6 inches from one wall and 27 inches from the other: what is the radius of the table? The diagram that springs immediately to the mind is that of Fig. 1.1.

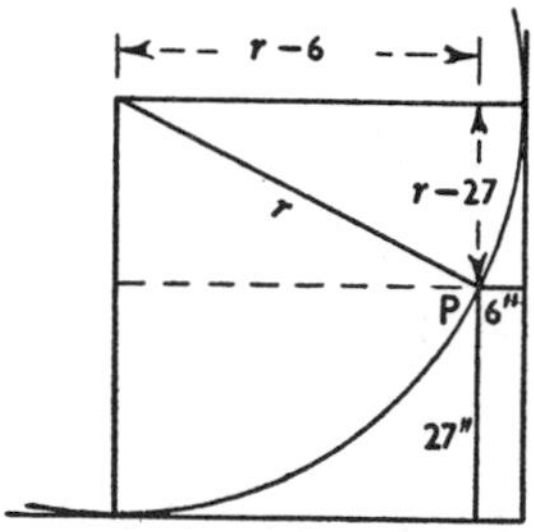

Fig. 1.1

Let the unknown radius be r inches. Then from the right-angled triangle with sides r, $r-6$, and $r-27$ inches we obtain

$$(r-6)^2+(r-27)^2=r^2$$

and hence $r^2-66r+765=0$.

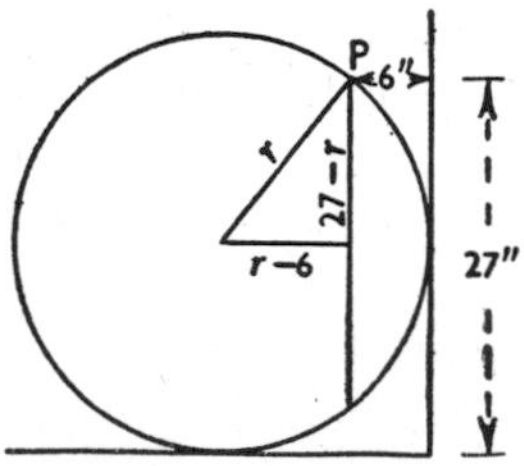

Fig. 1.2

This is a quadratic in r and therefore there are two solutions. They are $r=51$ and $r=15$. The first solution corresponds to Fig. 1.1. The second is illustrated by Fig. 1.2: it is an equally good solution of the original problem, and turns up in the mathematics whether we think of it beforehand or not. In other cases it is possible to prove that there is no solution, as in the famous problem of 'squaring the circle', or to prove that there is one and only one solution.

A third advantage of mathematical methods is their generality of application. A single piece of mathematics can be applied to several different physical problems, merely by a reinterpretation of the mathematical symbols. Thus the oscillations of an electric circuit, of a pendulum, and of a weighted spring can be treated as a single problem; similarly electrostatics, magnetostatics, the gravitational field, and the steady state distribution of heat in a solid are apparently dissimilar problems with a similar mathematical background.

In short, the scientist uses mathematical symbols and methods for economy in expression and ease of manipulation ; because of the way in which general and not merely particular solutions appear ; and because of the unification which is found to underlie very different problems when they are formulated.

Now a word of explanation about the difference between pure mathematics and the version used by the scientist, for there is a profound difference, lying largely in the notion of infinity and the corresponding notion of the infinitesimal. To the mathematician these two notions are crystal clear, sharp and definite—not, it may be said, because he understands them any better than the scientist, but because he is able to define them in his own terms. To the scientist, thinking in terms of the actualities of nature, infinity is a vague concept not clearly distinguished from 'extremely large', and the infinitesimal nearly always means simply 'small compared with some fixed quantity' rather than 'smaller than any pre-assigned non-zero quantity': when such common-sense attitudes fail to give reliable guidance, he will often find it rewarding to supplement them by the mathematician's precise idealisations ; but when the mathematician is more concerned with rooting out logical difficulties than with obtaining useful results, the scientist need not follow him. To the mathematician, for example, the number π can be defined only by indirect and sophisticated methods : it is only in the last hundred years that he has been able to refine his techniques sufficiently to deal with it and other similar numbers to his own satisfaction. The point is that π, e, $\surd 2$, and so on cannot be related to the positive integers, which we may take as an acceptable starting point for discussion, except by infinite processes, infinite decimals, infinite series, definite integrals, and the like. To the scientist, however, the number π is hardly ever anything more than the number 3·14159, or even 22/7, and he uses it with the same nonchalance as he does the integers.

The slight loss of precision which the scientist permits himself means that a large part of what the pure mathematician regards as essential to a strict proof is irrelevant to the scientist. This does not of course mean that any piece of loose reasoning is good enough in science, but simply that the scientist can afford to ignore the more formidable techniques of mathematical introspection.

1.2. The real variable

A good example of the way in which the scientist uses mathematical concepts is the real variable. To the scientist this is simply a variable or symbol which represents any number, positive or negative, and his picture of it is usually a geometrical one in which a moving point may take up any position along a graduated line. The distance of the point from a fixed origin can have any value whatever and so forms a geometrical or graphical representation of the real variable.

Notice, first of all, the ease with which one says ‘ positive and negative ’. It is with a touch of surprise that we remember early arguments at school about whether a number can be ‘ less than nothing ’ or not. The negative number is in fact the simplest example of a mathematical abstraction which, because of its usefulness at all stages of scientific thought, has become as real as the positive integers. The usefulness lies, of course, in that it halves the terminology required to express the results of measurement. Thus the scientist does not speak of 10 feet up and 8 feet down in formulating a problem but having chosen ‘ up ’ as his positive direction, speaks of $+10$ feet and -8 feet. Similarly he uses only one of such pairs as : left, right ; north, south ; push, pull ; pressure, tension ; acceleration, retardation ; and so on. This however is not the meaning of negative numbers to the mathematician. To him they are pure inventions, obtained as follows. Starting with the positive integers 0, 1, 2, 3, 4 ... as his objects of thought he defines operations for combining two or more integers to produce further integers ; these are the familiar arithmetical operations of addition and multiplication. He sees that to every pair of integers a and b he can find new quantities c and d, also positive integers, such that

$$a+b=c$$
$$a\times b=d$$

He now defines the inverse operations, subtraction and division ; thus, the result of subtracting b from a is by definition a quantity $(a-b)$ which obeys

$$(a-b)+b=a$$

Similarly the result of dividing a by b is a quantity (a/b) defined by

$$(a/b)\times b=a$$

Unlike the direct operations of addition and multiplication, which never lead to anything new, the inverse operations may lead to quantities which are not positive integers. Thus $4-6$ is a quantity n which satisfies

$$n+6=4$$

and there is no positive integer n which satisfies this equation. Rather than say that $4-6$ is meaningless, the mathematician invents the negative integers ; since they are not otherwise defined, he is at liberty to say that these new quantities also obey the laws of addition and multiplication, and the inverse laws of subtraction and division. Similarly he finds that 4/6 is not a positive integer and rather than say ' 6 into 4 won't go ' is led to define the rational fraction p/q, as the number which satisfies

$$(p/q)\times q=p$$

Division by 0, however, is excluded—a necessary precaution, not so much because there is no finite number equal to say $(p/0)$, but to avoid the consequences of cancelling the zero factors from an equation of the form $a\,.\,0=b\,.\,0$.

The mathematician has therefore invented these numbers ; but their applications to measurement and other physical interpretations are so simply made in early life that one is apt to forget that the properties of these numbers do not follow from analogies based on the lengths of pieces of string, or slices of cake etc., etc. The number 3/2 is certainly more easily explained to the uninitiated by dividing 3 loaves equally between 2 people, and so on, but its definition is essentially that it has the property

$$2\times(3/2)=3$$

This simple example illustrates the way in which the scientist borrows abstract concepts from the mathematician, and gives them an interpretation in terms of observable or measurable quantities. It will save a good deal of confusion if it is remembered that many of the concepts borrowed in this way have an existence of their own, which is independent of their interpretation, or of their representation which is usually in graphical terms. This confusion is particularly noticeable in many treatments of complex numbers.

The integers and rational fractions, positive and negative, cover practically all the needs of the scientist, but they do not fulfil the requirements of the mathematician. There is for example no rational fraction p/q such that $(p/q)^2 = 2$ exactly, in other words the square root of 2 does not find a place among the numbers so far defined. (The student may like to test his mathematical acumen by proving this statement.) The scientist makes no *numerical* use of irrational numbers: if $\sqrt{2}$ occurs in a formula which he wants to evaluate numerically, he replaces it by a rational approximation, such as 1·414 or 1·4142136 according to the number of figures he is prepared to carry (and is justified in regarding as significant) in the subsequent working. The irrational numbers are nevertheless essential to the concepts of continuity and of limits of functions (e.g. in differentiation) which the scientist would find it almost impossible to do without, so in what follows we shall make use of the whole field of real numbers, rational and irrational. The omission of a rigorous definition† of irrational numbers is unlikely to cause any difficulty to the reader who is familiar with the representation of numbers by the points of a straight line.

1.3. The complex variable

Complex numbers are also widely used by the scientist; it is particularly important here to distinguish carefully between the mathematical or analytical concept and its graphical representation.

Complex numbers are introduced into mathematics to fill a role for which real numbers are not sufficiently flexible. In spite of the addition of rational and irrational numbers to the original integers, there are no values of the real variable x which will satisfy equations such as

$$x^2 + 1 = 0 \tag{1}$$

$$5x^2 + 6x + 2 = 0 \tag{2}$$

$$x^4 + 4n^4 = 0 \tag{3}$$

In accordance with his usual practice, the mathematician does not say these are insoluble; he introduces a new 'number' i, defined as a solution of equation (1). Apart from the property

† Such a definition can be found in Hardy, *Pure Mathematics* (Cambridge University Press), Chapter 1.

that $i^2+1=0$, this new number is required to obey the same laws of addition and multiplication as the real numbers. He then finds that the solutions of (2) are

$$x=-(3-i)/5 \quad \text{and} \quad x=-(3+i)/5$$

and the student, whether he has already met complex numbers or not, will readily verify that when x is given either of these values equation (2) is in fact satisfied. Similarly the four solutions of (3) can be verified to be

$$x=n(1+i),\ x=n(1-i),\ x=n(-1+i),\ x=n(-1-i)$$

The typical complex number is thus of the form $x+iy$ where x and y are ordinary real numbers. If a variable z is allowed to range over all such values, it is called a complex variable. It may well be wondered how such an artificial creation can be of use to the scientist, and why he should be expected to become familiar with its properties. If we try to obtain a representation of it, similar to those which make the real variable such a familiar thing, we shall certainly dismiss it as meaningless or, to use the term of opprobrium which is still attached to the number i, as 'imaginary'. Thus 2 loaves, 16/5 loaves, and even π loaves, can be readily interpreted ; with a more perceptible pause we can also attach a meaning to -2 loaves but we can make nothing whatever of $(5+i8)$ loaves.

This, however, is not the point. The real variable is useful to the scientist because it is the natural and convenient way of representing physical quantities which can be expressed by a single number : heights, components of force, and acceleration and so on. The complex variable is useful because it can carry, in one symbol, the two pieces of information which are required for quantities which are defined by two measurements. The position of a point on a plane is an example of such a quantity. A single real variable can handle the position of a point on a line, but two real variables x and y are required to fix a position in a plane : the single complex variable $z=x+iy$ will do the job equally well. The part played by i is simply that of keeping the x and y separate. Similarly two real variables are required to define the instantaneous value of a steady alternating current (of given frequency), e.g. the amplitude of the current and its instantaneous phase. Here again a single complex variable can carry both pieces of information.

The use of the complex variable does not as a rule enable the scientist to solve problems which cannot be solved otherwise ; more often it simply enables him to do so with a marked economy of effort. It is not, of course, yet obvious how this is to be done ; at this stage we are simply pointing out that the complex variable, like the real variable, is essentially a mathematical invention which the scientist exploits because he finds that its symbolism can be used, with a little ingenuity, to handle the relations between physical quantities involving two independent measurements.

The student should now compare the concept of negative integers with that of complex numbers. The negative integer is in the first place an invention brought in to make subtraction of one integer from another possible in all circumstances. The graphical representation of positive numbers on the right and negative numbers on the left of a given point on a straight line gives the negative numbers a representation which makes them immediately acceptable. The complex number is introduced so as to provide analytical solutions to certain equations such as $x^2 = -1$ which cannot be satisfied by any real number. A graphical representation of the complex number is given in Chapter 6. Knowing the rules for operating with complex numbers (the ordinary rules of algebra plus the additional fact that $i^2 = -1$) and having a graphical representation, the student should approach the study of the complex variable not with the feeling that he is tampering with the supernatural, but with the knowledge that he is adapting a mathematical invention which will assist him very powerfully in dealing with 'two-variable' problems.

Summary

Mathematical concepts are regarded as being in the first place dissociated from the world of science. The scientist finds that some of these concepts can be given an interpretation in terms of physical quantities ; the relations between physical quantities can then be explored in a compact and systematic manner with the aid of the mathematical symbolism.

Thus the real variable, although a more complete concept than the scientist requires, provides an adequate symbolism for expressing relations between lengths, components of force, masses, and in general any quantities that are specified completely by a single measurement.

Similarly the complex variable provides a symbolism capable of handling the relationship between quantities which require two independent measurements, e.g. the position of a point on a plane.

CHAPTER TWO

FUNCTIONS OF A REAL VARIABLE

2.1. Relations between physical quantities

In the physical sciences we usually represent physical variables, length, mass, time, force, pressure, volume and so on, by means of numbers. There is of course no unique way of doing this ; the number representing a given length will depend on the particular length to which we assign the value unity. In other words we first choose a unit of length, the foot, centimetre, metre, etc., and then express any other length as a number of these units. Similarly for any other physical quantity ; we first define a unit amount of the quantity and then any other amount can be represented by a number.

In this way a relation between physical quantities becomes a relation between numbers. The numbers are not the physical quantities themselves but the 'measures' of these quantities in a particular system of units.

2.2. Relations between numbers

Let x, y be real variables, i.e. x (or y) is a non-committal symbol which can represent any real number, i.e. can stand for any integer, positive or negative or zero, a rational fraction (i.e. p/q where p and q are integers but $q \neq 0$), or an irrational number. Let us suppose that they are related in some way ; that is, for a given value of x there is some rule which enables us to calculate a corresponding value of y. The rule is very frequently an algebraic formula such as

$$y = 5x^2 + 2x - 3 \qquad (1)$$

but any relation which enables y to be calculated from the given value of x will suffice. Thus

$$\left.\begin{aligned} y &= 4x \quad \text{for } x > 0 \\ y &= -3x \text{ for } x \leqslant 0 \end{aligned}\right\} \qquad (2)$$

in spite of its awkwardness, specifies a quite definite relation between x and y.

Other examples of relations between x and y are

$$x^2+y^2=a^2 \tag{3}$$

$$\sin y \quad = \sin x \tag{4}$$

$$\left\{\begin{array}{ll} y=1/|\,q\,| & \text{if } x=p/q, \text{ where } p, q \text{ are non-zero} \\ & \text{integers without a common factor} \\ y=0 & \text{if } x \text{ is irrational or zero} \end{array}\right\} \tag{5}$$

Note : The modulus sign | | is the non-negative symbol or function ; its meaning is defined : $|\,x\,|=x$ if $x\geqslant 0$, $|\,x\,|=-x$ if $x<0$.

$$\log\left[(x-1)^2+y^2\right]=(x^2+y^2)^{-\frac{1}{2}} \tag{6}$$

$$\left.\begin{array}{l} y=2 \text{ when } x=6 \\ y=4 \text{ when } x=8,\ 10,\ 12,\ \ldots \\ y \text{ undefined for other values of } x \end{array}\right\} \tag{7}$$

When values of y are associated with values of x, by some relation such as (1)–(7), y is said to be a function of x. A notation which expresses this in general terms is

$$y=\mathrm{f}(x)$$

x is usually called the ‘ argument ’ of the function $\mathrm{f}(x)$.

The following convention should be noticed. To find the value of a function at $x=a$, we must replace x wherever it occurs by a, and evaluate the result according to the directions specified by the formula $y=\mathrm{f}(a)$. If division by 0 is entailed, the result can often be interpreted in some other way depending on the nature of the physical problem, but to avoid ambiguity the mathematician regards the function as indeterminate in such a case. Thus the function $y=x/x$ is equal to 1 at all points except $x=0$: it would generally be inappropriate to adopt any other value at $x=0$, but it must be clearly recognised that y is not in fact defined at $x=0$ by this relationship.

It will be seen from the examples above that the definition of function is an extremely wide one, and it is convenient to have names for functions of more limited types. First there is the *explicit* function in which y is given directly in terms of x, as in (1), (2), (5), and (7) above. Any other function is *implicit*, a term covering equations such as (3) and (4) which can be made explicit immediately, and also (6) which, although it establishes a relationship between x and y, does not enable us to calculate y for a given x except by a lengthy numerical process of trial and error.

Two special classes of functions, called ' odd functions ' and ' even functions ', are worth distinguishing, although the majority of functions belong to neither of these classes. If for all x, $\mathrm{f}(-x)=\mathrm{f}(x)$, the function f is said to be ' even ', while if for all x, $\mathrm{F}(-x)=-\mathrm{F}(x)$, the function F is said to be ' odd '. For example, $\mathrm{f}(x)=x^2$ and $\mathrm{f}(x)=\cos x$ are even functions of x since $(-x)^2=x^2$ and $\cos(-x)=\cos x$; similarly $\mathrm{f}(x)=\text{constant}$ is an even function. On the other hand $\mathrm{F}(x)=x^3+4x$ and $\mathrm{F}(x)=\tan x$ are odd functions of x. The function $\phi(x)=x+x^2$ is neither even nor odd, since $\phi(-x)=-x+x^2$ is equal neither to $+\phi(x)$ nor to $-\phi(x)$; however, this function $\phi(x)$ is the sum of an even function and an odd function of x, and indeed this is true of *any* function which is defined for all values of x. For, whatever the function $\phi(x)$,

$\frac{1}{2}[\phi(x)+\phi(-x)]$ is an even function of x, say $\mathrm{f}(x)$

and $\frac{1}{2}[\phi(x)-\phi(-x)]$ is an odd function of x, say $\mathrm{F}(x)$;

and $\phi(x)=\mathrm{f}(x)+\mathrm{F}(x)$,

which expresses $\phi(x)$ as the sum of an even and an odd function of x.

Another simple sub-grouping of functions is into *single-valued* and *many-valued* functions. For each value of x a single-valued function defines a single value of y. Examples are (1), (2), (5) and (7). Equation (3) however defines a *double-valued* function : for a given x, there are two values of y, $y=+\sqrt{(a^2-x^2)}$ and $y=-\sqrt{(a^2-x^2)}$. Equation (4) defines an infinitely many-valued function : the general solution is $y=n\pi+(-1)^n x$ where n is any integer positive, zero, or negative.

The function defined by 2.2 eqn. (5) although explicit and single valued is not likely to occur in a physical problem. It is an example of what has been called a ' pathological ' function, for reasons which appear when we try to represent it graphically.

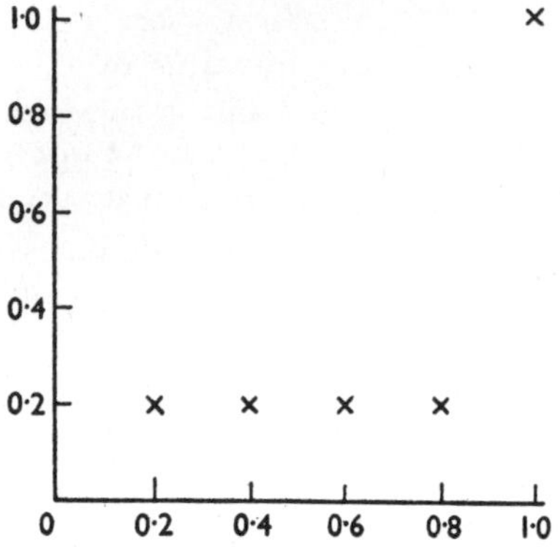

FIG. 2.1

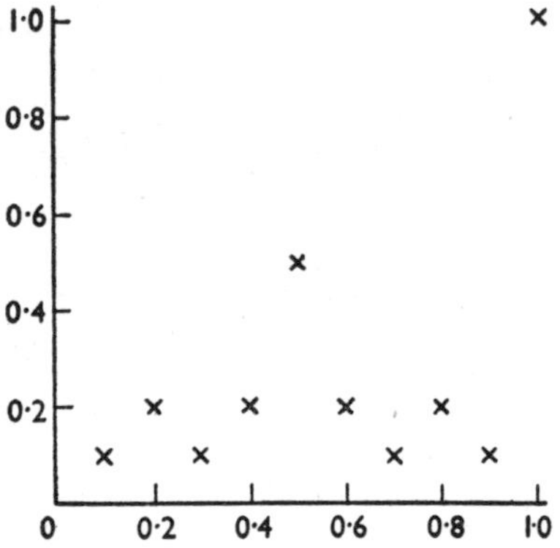

FIG. 2.2

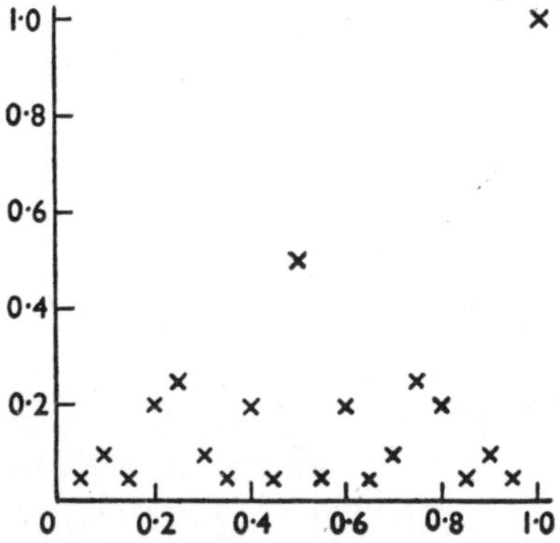

FIG. 2.3

The values of this function for $x=0{\cdot}2$, $0{\cdot}4$, $0{\cdot}6$, ... are shown in Fig. 2.1 ; the values for $x=0{\cdot}1$, $0{\cdot}2$, $0{\cdot}3$, ... in Fig. 2.2 ; the values for $x=0{\cdot}05$, $0{\cdot}1$, $0{\cdot}15$, ... in Fig. 2.3. The reader may verify that, however small an interval is chosen for plotting the values of this function, a curve can never be drawn so that intermediate values can be correctly estimated from the graph. In other words this function cannot be adequately represented, even in a short interval, by a graph.

We have dwelt on this example to emphasize that the concept of a function is very wide : we mean *only* that there is a rule associating values of y with some or all values of x, and we imply no other properties at all.

2.21. *Continuity*

A function $f(x)$ is said to be *continuous* at $x=x_0$ if for any non-zero, positive number ϵ there exists a number $\delta>0$ such that

$$|f(x)-f(x_0)| < \epsilon$$

whenever $x_0-\delta<x<x_0+\delta$, i.e. for *all* values of x in the range $|x-x_0|<\delta$.

This may be roughly interpreted : in a small interval about $x=x_0$, $f(x)$ is approximately equal to $f(x_0)$.

A better way of conveying the gist of the definition is to say that if a function is continuous at a point, its variation ($\pm\epsilon$) in a small range ($\pm\delta$) about that point can be made as small as we please by sufficiently restricting the range. If the function were discontinuous, there would be a limit (the size of the step constituting the discontinuity) below which ϵ could not be reduced no matter how small the range.

To the reader coming to such work for the first time the formal definition of continuity may seem unnecessarily cumbrous, and he may fail to see the point of exercises in its use such as the examples below. However, similar definitions and methods form the foundation of all discussions of convergence, and these in turn are essential in those parts of mathematics which are most vital for the scientist, such as infinite series, calculus etc. For these reasons, a clear appreciation of the significance of the phraseology is desirable.

First note that the value of δ cannot be discussed until it is known how small it is desired that $|f(x)-f(x_0)|$ shall be. In other words it is necessary to mention ϵ before talking about δ. This is the reason why so many of our definitions, both here and in later chapters, begin rather awkwardly with a conditional clause 'if for any $\epsilon>0$ . . .' instead of using a more natural-seeming phraseology.

The second pitfall to be avoided in the definition is that of specifying a *particular* value of ϵ. The inequality must be satisfied for *any* $\epsilon>0$. Since a particular value cannot be given to ϵ, neither can the numerical value of δ ever be found. In establishing continuity the value of δ will always be a function of the variable ϵ whose numerical value is only restricted by the condition $\epsilon>0$. To establish *discontinuity*, of course, it would be sufficient to find a single value of ϵ for which the continuity condition failed.

In the examples, the reader may at first be discouraged by the apparent lack of any general method of approach. But the guide to method will come, not so much from the subtlety of the mathematician as from the common-sense of the scientist. No very general prescriptions are possible, though the examples given cover the commonest types. The scientist can guess from a graph whether his function is likely to be continuous or discontinuous at any point: when the graph is smooth, as in

Example 1, and a tangent can be drawn at the point x_0, it is likely that a linear factor $(x-x_0)$ can be taken out of $|\,f(x)-f(x_0)\,|$; infinite or finite discontinuities can nearly always be discussed along the lines of Examples 2, 3, and so on. Having studied the examples the student should have a sufficient background of knowledge (and insight) about continuity to serve him when it is called for in subsequent work involving limiting processes etc.

Example 1

The function $f(x)=x^n$ where n is a positive integer is continuous for all x.

For $|\,f(x)-f(x_0)\,|=|\,x^n-x_0{}^n\,|$

$$=|\,x-x_0\,|\,|x^{n-1}+x_0x^{n-2}+x_0{}^2x^{n-3}+\dots+x_0{}^{n-1}\,|$$

$$\leqslant|\,x-x_0\,|\,|\,nX^{n-1}\,|$$

where X is the larger of $|\,x\,|$ and $|\,x_0\,|$. Thus by taking $\delta<\epsilon/\,nX^{n-1}$ we can make $|\,f(x)-f(x_0)\,|<\epsilon$ whenever $x_0-\delta<x<x_0+\delta$.

Example 2

The function $f(x)=(1/x)$ (Fig. 2.4) is discontinuous at $x=0$. For to begin with $f(0)$ is not defined; but if we define $f(0)$ separately, e.g. $f(0)=k$, then, no matter what value δ has, we can always find an x in the range $-\delta<x<\delta$ such that $|\,f(x)-f(0)\,|=|\,(1/x)-f(0)\,|>\epsilon$. There is an infinite discontinuity at the origin.

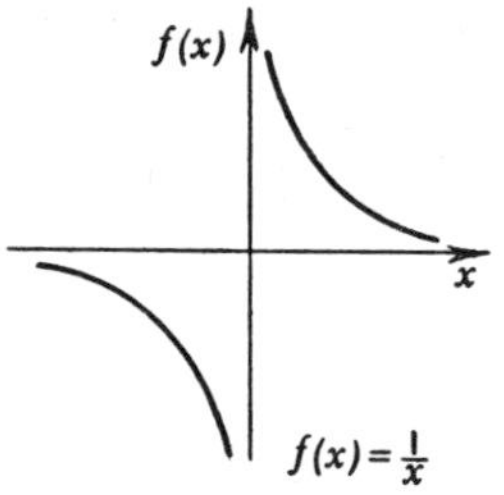

FIG. 2.4

Example 3

The function $f(x)=0, \quad x\leqslant 0$

$\qquad\qquad\qquad\;\; =1, \quad x>0$

(Fig. 2.5) is discontinuous at $x=0$. For, let us choose $\epsilon<1$. Then as $f(x)=1$ for all $0<x<\delta$, $f(x)-f(0)=1$, i.e. $|\,f(x)-f(0)\,|>\epsilon$ no matter what value of δ is chosen. This is an example of a jump discontinuity.

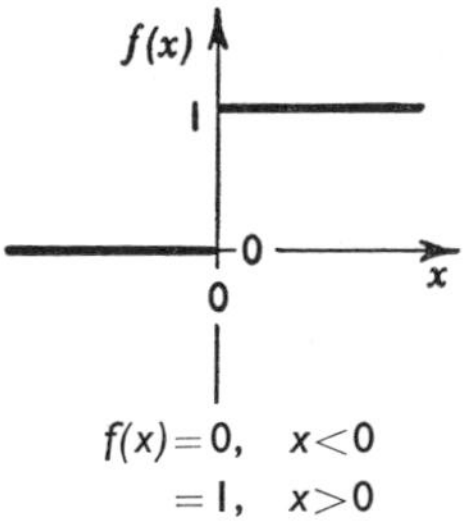

FIG. 2.5

Example 4

The function $f(x)=\lim\limits_{n\to\infty}(x^2)^{1/n}$, which has the value 1 when $x\neq 0$ and the value 0 when $x=0$, is similarly discontinuous, but here the discontinuity is usually unimportant. It can be removed by redefining the function at the single point $x=0$.

Example 5

The function $f(x)=1$ when x is rational and $f(x)=0$ when x is irrational is discontinuous everywhere. For, any range of x such as $x_0-\delta<x<x_0+\delta$ must contain a rational number x_1 and an irrational x_2, and clearly if $\epsilon<\frac{1}{2}$, $|f(x)-f(x_0)|$ cannot be less than ϵ both at x_1 and at x_2.

Example 6

The function $f(x)=-3x, \quad x<0 \qquad f(x)=4x, \quad x\geqslant 0$ is continuous. The only doubtful point is $x=0$, $f(0)=0$; but $|f(x)-f(0)|<\epsilon$ whenever $|x|<\delta$ where $\delta=\frac{1}{4}\epsilon$. Continuity thus implies the absence of 'breaks' rather than smoothness in the sense of freedom from abrupt changes in slope.

If the function $f(x)$ is continuous at every point x_0 in the range $a<x_0<b$, it is said to be continuous in the interval $a<x<b$. If $f(x)$ is continuous in each of the intervals $a<x<b$, $b<x<c$, $c<x<d$ ... $l<x<m$, there being a finite number of these intervals, it is said to be sectionally continuous in the interval $a<x<m$.

From the definition of continuity it can be proved that the sum of a *finite* number of continuous functions is itself continuous.

2.22. *Bounded functions, monotonic functions*

If there exists a number M such that $-M<f(x)<M$ for all x, then $f(x)$ is called a *bounded* function.

If $f(x_1)\leqslant f(x_2)$ whenever $x_1<x_2$ the function $f(x)$ is said to be *monotonic and increasing* in the wide sense. If $f(x_1)<f(x_2)$ without the equality $f(x)$ is said to be *strictly* increasing. If $f(x_2)\leqslant f(x_1)$ whenever $x_1<x_2$, the function $f(x)$ is said to be monotonic decreasing (or a steadily increasing function).

2.23. *Inverse functions*

Under certain conditions the equation $y=f(x)$ can be solved to give x in terms of y, in the form $x=\phi(y)$, say. The function $\phi(x)$ is then said to be the inverse of the function $f(x)$ and vice versa. For example if $y=mx+c$, $x=\dfrac{1}{m}(y-c)$ and thus the inverse of $f(x)=mx+c$ is $\phi(x)=\dfrac{1}{m}(x-c)$. Other pairs are:

$$f(x)=x^3, \qquad \phi(x)=x^{\frac{1}{3}}; \qquad f(x)=1/x, \qquad \phi(x)=1/x$$

$$f(x)=\frac{ax+b}{cx+d}, \qquad \phi(x)=\frac{b-dx}{cx-a}; \qquad f(x)=\log_{10}x, \qquad \phi(x)=10^x$$

If $x=\phi(y)$ is the inverse of a continuous function $z=f(x)$

which is strictly increasing in the range $x_1 < x < x_2$, then $\phi(y)$ is a unique and strictly increasing function of y in the range $f(x_1) < y < f(x_2)$.)

Not every function has an inverse. Consider, for example, the function

$$\begin{aligned} y = f(x) &= +1 \quad \text{if } x > 1 \\ &= -2 \quad \text{if } x \leqslant 1 \end{aligned}$$

Here we see that although for any value of x a unique value of y is defined, the converse is quite untrue ; if y has the value $+1$, the value of x may be any number at all which is greater than 1, and if y has neither of the values $+1$ or -2, there is no value of x for which $f(x) = y$; thus in this case x cannot be regarded as a function of y ; that is this function $f(x)$ has no inverse function $\phi(x)$.

2.24. *Graph of a function*

The usual method of representing a function graphically is to take two mutually perpendicular lines in a plane as x-axis and y-axis and to plot points representing corresponding values of x and $y = f(x)$. This can always be done, but the points should only be joined up by a smooth curve if there is reason to believe the function and its slope to be continuous, and the plotted points are sufficiently close together to represent adequately the behaviour of the function. In any case, if it is required to represent the values of a function with an error less than about 1 part in 100, a graphical representation has to give way to a numerical tabulation.

The purpose of a graph is often to deduce the relationship between two quantities from a set of observed values. Usually this cannot be achieved by a single graph, but the first attempt gives a clue to a new and more profitable way of plotting the results. If, for example, a graph like one of the lower curves on the right-hand side of Fig. 2.6 were obtained when the two quantities were first plotted one against the other, we might well suspect a relationship $y = x^n$, but $n = 3, 4, 5, 6, \ldots$ might well look all equally plausible from the shape of the graph, and even the possibility $y = e^x - 1$ might not be entirely ruled out. To test the suspected relationship $y = x^n$, a second plot of $\log y$ against $\log x$ would be made. If $\log y = n \log x$, this second graph would be a straight line through the origin whose slope would give the value of n. Deviations from a straight line are far easier to recognize than deviations from a curved form, so the second representation offers a far better test of the relation $y=x^n$ than the first.

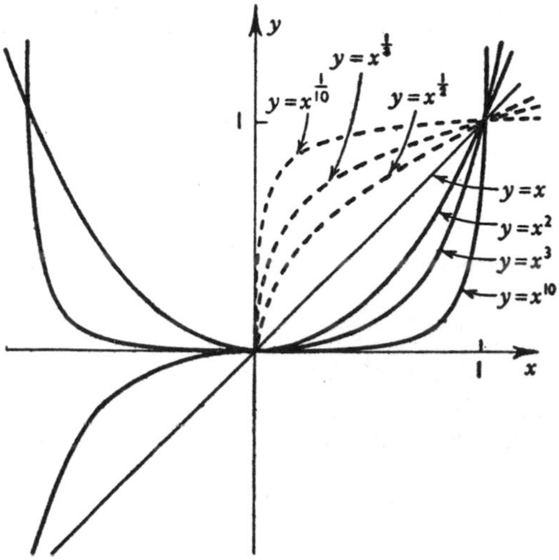

FIG. 2.6

The uses of special graph papers should not be overlooked. There are, for instance, logarithmic graph papers: the unequally spaced logarithmic scales in one or both directions automatically ‘take logarithms’ of the numbers plotted, thus dispensing with the need for looking up the logarithms in tables. Probability paper has a similar usefulness when it is suspected that one variable is the ordinate of a ‘normal distribution’.

2.3. Functions of more than one real variable

A physical quantity may depend on more than one independent variable. The volume occupied by a fixed mass of gas depends on the pressure exerted on it, and on the temperature to which it is raised. The pressure and temperature are independent variables, in the sense that any pair of values may be assigned to them (apart from physical limitations such as the pressure remaining positive and the temperature being above absolute zero). Similarly the value of g, the acceleration due to gravity, at the earth's surface depends on the latitude and longitude of the point considered ; the potential at a point near a bar magnet depends on the distance of the point from the magnet and on the angle that the line from the point to the magnet makes with the axis of the magnet. The most frequently occurring example of a function of several variables is that of a physical quantity which can be measured at all points in a certain region of space ; the temperature at different points in a furnace ; the electric field near a transmitter ; the velocity at different points in a fluid, and so on.

The interdependence of the physical quantities is expressed by an equation between numbers, in which one number say is specified explicitly or implicitly as a function of two or more other numbers. For example, z may be related to x and y by

$$z = ax + by$$

or by

$$x^2 + y^2 + z^2 = a^2$$

Similarly a number u may depend on three or more independent variables,

$$u = \mathrm{f}(x, y, z), \quad u = \mathrm{f}(x, y, z, t) \text{ etc.}$$

A representation of a function of two variables $z = \mathrm{f}(x, y)$ can be obtained by means of a three-dimensioned model. A pair of axes are drawn on a plane and at each point (x, y) or in practice at a sufficient number of points, an ordinate perpendicular to the plane is erected, equal to $\mathrm{f}(x, y)$. The surface (or surfaces if the function is many valued) formed by the tips of these ordinates then represents the function.

A more convenient representation is obtained by the method of contours used to represent height on maps. Instead of erecting an ordinate at the point (x, y), the value of z is calculated from the formula and noted down. The curves along which z is constant are then drawn and labelled ; the resulting contour map is a two-dimensional representation of the function, equivalent in most respects to the three-dimensional model.

When there are more than two variables, valuable simplifications can often be obtained by replacing the original variables by functions of themselves : in some cases the number of variables which have to be retained can be reduced by such a technique, e.g. the chemist considering a mixture of three components may be well advised to change his variables so that instead of actual weights or volumes of each component he uses only the fraction of the total weight or volume contributed by each : then if two weight fractions or volume fractions are known, the third can be deduced, and the number of variables has in effect been reduced from three to two.

2.4. Functions of a discrete variable

The scientist not only measures but counts. Sometimes, as in the case of a revolution counter, the quantity which is being counted—the rotation of a shaft—may be continuously varying ; more rarely the quantity may have no meaning except for discrete values. Thus the electric charge on an atomic nucleus, or for that matter the total charge on any body whatever, is expressible by an integer, if the electronic charge e is taken as the unit ; a total charge of $2{\cdot}5e$ for example does not appear to be a physical possibility. An important example of a function whose existence at intermediate values is usually implied even though actual values are only given at a discrete set of points, is provided by the numerical table of a function. This of necessity defines the function only at discrete values of the argument or entry. The estimation of the function at intermediate points is a constantly occurring problem.

If a physical quantity depends on a discrete variable, as for example the force between two similar charged particles at a fixed distance apart depends on the number of electronic charges which each carries, the relation may be expressed by means of a function of a discrete variable. The graphical representation of such a function may be effected as for functions of a continuous variable, by erecting ordinates at the points on the x-axis for which the function is defined. It is often convenient to draw a smooth curve through the extremities of the ordinates, but it should always be borne in mind that there may be no meaning in the interpolated parts of such a curve. Alternatively blocks centred on the known ordinates may be drawn. This version of the representation is called a histogram of which Figs. 2.7 and 2.8 are examples.

When a variable assumes only integral values it is common (though not invariable) practice to denote it by m or n rather than x or y.

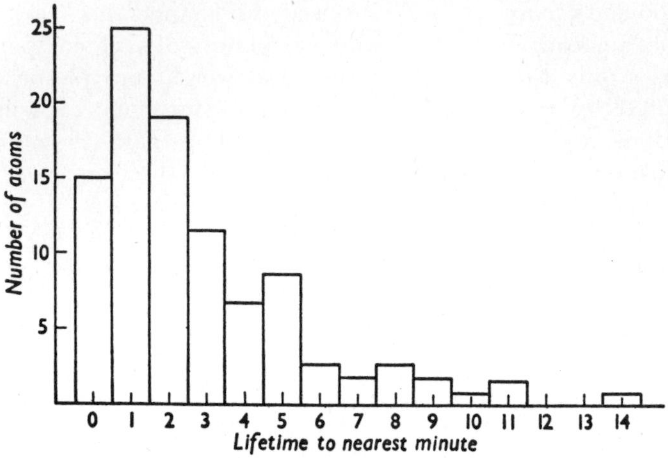

Number of atoms
25
20
15
10
5
0 1 2 3 4 5 6 7 8 9 10 11 12 13 14
Lifetime to nearest minute

Fig. 2.7

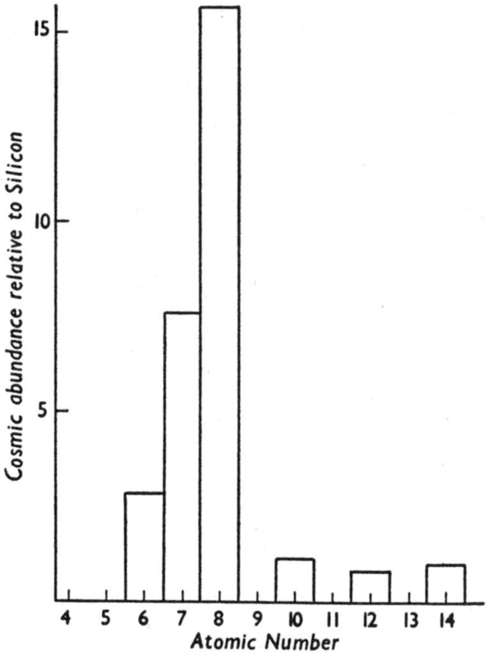

Cosmic abundance relative to Silicon
15
10
5
4 5 6 7 8 9 10 11 12 13 14
Atomic Number

Fig. 2.8

2.41. *Functions of an integral variable. Mathematical induction*

It frequently happens that a relation between two functions of an integral variable, n, is suspected as a result of trials with small values of n. The method of induction is a powerful method which can often be used in such circumstances to establish the relation for all values of n.

The method will be illustrated by an example. By actual multiplication one finds

$$(1+x)^2 = 1 + 2x + x^2$$

$$(1+x)^3 = 1 + 3x + 3x^2 + x^3$$

$$(1+x)^4 = 1 + 4x + 6x^2 + 4x^3 + x^4$$

and as a result of pondering on the structure of the coefficients which appear on the right-hand side one might, if one's perseverance or mathematical aptitude were sufficiently great, be led to suspect the existence of the following relation, valid for all values of x :

$$(1+x)^n = 1 + nx + \tfrac{1}{2}n(n-1)x^2 + \ldots + \binom{n}{r} x^r + \ldots + x^n \qquad (1)$$

where $$\binom{n}{r} = \frac{n(n-1)\ldots(n-r+1)}{r(r-1)(r-2)\ldots 3\,.\,2\,.\,1} = \frac{n!}{(n-r)!\,r!}$$

and $$n! = n(n-1)(n-2)\ldots 3\,.\,2\,.\,1$$

Note : $\binom{n}{r}$ replaces the notation ${}^nC_r$ used in older text-books.

To verify this speculation, let us suppose that it is true for a particular value of n, say $n=m$. Then

$$(1+x)^m = 1 + mx + \tfrac{1}{2}m(m-1)x^2 + \ldots + \binom{m}{r} x^r + \ldots + x^m \qquad (2)$$

Now calculate $(1+x)^{m+1}$, for example by multiplying (2) by x and adding the result to (2).

$$x(1+x)^m = x + mx^2 + \ldots + \binom{m}{r-1} x^r + \ldots + x^{m+1} \qquad (3)$$

Adding (2) and (3)

$$(1+x)^{m+1} = 1 + (m+1)x + \tfrac{1}{2}(m+1)mx^2 + \ldots$$

$$+ \left[\binom{m}{r} + \binom{m}{r-1}\right] x^r + \ldots + x^{m+1} \qquad (4)$$

The coefficient of x^r is

$$\binom{m}{r}+\binom{m}{r-1}=\frac{m!}{(m-r)!\,r!}+\frac{m!}{(m-r+1)!(r-1)!}$$
$$=\frac{m!}{(m-r+1)!\,r!}\,[(m-r+1)+r]$$
$$=\frac{(m+1)!}{(m+1-r)!\,r!}$$

Hence (4) may be written

$$(1+x)^{m+1}=1+(m+1)x+\,\dots\,+\frac{(m+1)!}{(m+1-r)!\,r!}x^r+\dots+x^{m+1}$$

which is the form taken by (1) when $n=m+1$. Hence if (1) is true for just one particular value of n, say m, it is also true for the value $n=m+1$. But (1) is true for $n=1$, therefore it is true for $n=2$; and therefore for $n=3$; and therefore for all integral values of n.

The identity (1) is known as the Binomial theorem.

Example 1

Use the method of induction to verify the formula for the sum of an arithmetic progression. If the first n terms of the A.P. are

$$a,\ a+d,\ a+2d,\ \dots,\ a+(n-1)d,$$

the formula to be verified by induction is that the sum S_n of these terms is

$$S_n=\tfrac{1}{2}n[2a+(n-1)\,d]$$

Example 2

Use the method to verify the formula for the sum of a geometric progression. If the terms of the G.P. are a, ar, ar^2, ... , ar^{n-1}, the sum to be verified is $S_n=a\,\dfrac{1-r^n}{1-r}$.

The main application of functions of a discrete variable is to the study of infinite sets of numbers and infinite sets of functions. These sets, which the reader may have encountered already as infinite sequences and infinite series, are of extreme importance in both pure and applied mathematics.

2.42. *Infinite sequences*

An infinite sequence of numbers may be expressed in general in the form $\phi(1)$, $\phi(2)$, $\phi(3)$, ... This emphasises the fact that the numbers of the sequence can be regarded as values of a function which we may write $\phi(n)$, defined only at integral values, $n=1, 2, 3, \ldots$. It is more usual, however, to use a subscript and to reserve the bracket notation for continuous variables. The sequence will therefore be written $\phi_1, \phi_2, \phi_3. \ldots$ and the general term, ϕ_n

In many cases we are particularly interested in the behaviour of ϕ_n as n increases indefinitely. Before considering the possible varieties of behaviour, we introduce a few convenient terms and phrases. The phrase 'n tends to infinity', written $n\to\infty$, means that the integer n is allowed to assume a sequence of values $n_1, n_2, \ldots, n_r, \ldots$ such that for any finite number N there is a member of the sequence, n_s say, beyond which all the n's are greater than N, i.e. $n_{s+1}>N$, $n_{s+2}>N$, etc.

The second phrase 'ϕ_n tends to a limit l as n tends to infinity', written $\lim_{n\to\infty} \phi_n=l$, can be best interpreted in two stages. Roughly speaking it means that the difference between ϕ_n and the fixed number l can be made as small as we please by choosing a sufficiently large value of n, and, conversely, for all large n, ϕ_n differs little from l. Such a statement is not precise enough for mathematical use, however, so we must proceed to the more exact, if less readily appreciated, definition.

2.43. *Definition of the limit of a sequence*

The sequence ϕ_n is said to converge to a limit l as n tends to infinity if for any positive number ϵ, not equal to zero, there is a number n_0 such that, for all $n \geqslant n_0$

$$|\phi_n - l| < \epsilon$$

The additional detail conveyed by this statement is that the difference $|\phi_n - l|$ has to be smaller than ϵ for *all* values $n \geqslant n_0$, not merely for some values or even most values. The reader should also notice that we first mention the variable ϵ, and then prove the existence of a corresponding n_0 which is a function of ϵ.

Example 1

The sequence $1, \frac{1}{2}, \frac{1}{3}, \frac{1}{4}, \ldots$. Here $\phi_n = 1/n$. As n tends to infinity, ϕ_n tends to zero. To prove this consider any number ϵ; we have to establish the existence of a number n_0 such that $|\phi_n - 0|$, i.e. $1/n$ is less than ϵ for all values of n greater than or equal to n_0. There is no difficulty in this—any integer greater than $1/\epsilon$ will do. For if

$n_0 > 1/\epsilon$ and $n \geqslant n_0$, then $n > 1/\epsilon$ and therefore $1/n < \epsilon$ for all values of $n \geqslant n_0$. For example,

if $\epsilon = 0{\cdot}001$ then $\phi_n < \epsilon$ for all $n \geqslant 1001$;
if $\epsilon = 10^{-6}$, then $\phi_n < \epsilon$ for all $n \geqslant 1{,}000{,}001$; and so on.

Example 2

The sequence $1, -\frac{1}{2}, \frac{1}{3}, -\frac{1}{4}$, tends to zero. Here $\phi_n = (-1)^{n-1}/n$; the alternating signs disappear when the modulus is taken and the argument of Example 1 applies.

Example 3

The sequence $2, \frac{1}{2}, \frac{4}{3}, \frac{3}{4}, \frac{6}{5}, \frac{5}{6}, \ldots \to 1$. Here $\phi_n = 1 - (-1)^n/n$ so that $|\phi_n - 1| = 1/n < \epsilon$ if $n > 1/\epsilon$.

The results of the examples above can be summarised in the form $a/\infty = 0$ where a is a finite number; it is quite legitimate to do this, provided one does not attempt to use the symbol ∞ as if it represented a number obeying the arithmetical rules.

2.44. *Non-convergent sequences*

Some sequences are not convergent. The possibilities are:

(1) ϕ_n diverges to $+\infty$; e.g. $\phi_n = n^2, n!, n^n, n^n - n^2$, etc.
(2) ϕ_n diverges to $-\infty$; e.g. $\phi_n = (n - n^2), (n! - n^n)$, etc.
(3) ϕ_n oscillates finitely; e.g. $\phi_n = \sin \frac{1}{2}n\pi, (-1)^n$, etc.
(4) ϕ_n oscillates infinitely; e.g. $\phi_n = n \sin \frac{1}{2}n\pi, n^2[1 + (-1)^n]$ etc.

The examples so far used have been straightforward, but in many cases it is not obvious what the limit of a sequence is, or even whether the limit exists: examples are the sequences $[1 + (1/n)]^n$ and $\sqrt[n]{n}$. To deal with more complicated functions of this kind we need one or two simple theorems.

2.45. *Combinations of functions*

If ϕ_n, ψ_n are two sequences with limits a and b, then it is readily established that the sequences $\phi_n + \psi_n$, $\phi_n - \psi_n$, $\phi_n\psi_n$ and ϕ_n/ψ_n have limits $a + b$, $a - b$, ab and a/b, (provided that, in the last case $b \neq 0$. If $b = 0$ and $a \neq 0$, then ϕ_n/ψ_n does not converge but diverges to $\pm\infty$ or oscillates infinitely). For formal proofs, see, for example, Hardy, *Pure Mathematics*, §63.

These theorems on the limits of $\phi_n \pm \psi_n$, $\phi_n\psi_n$ and ϕ_n/ψ_n can be extended to the general statement that if $\mathrm{R}\{\phi_n, \psi_n, \chi_n, \ldots\}$ is any function obtained by a *finite* number of arithmetical operations on the numbers $\phi_n, \psi_n, \chi_n, \ldots$ and if the limits of the sequences ϕ_n, ψ_n, χ_n are $a, b, c, \ldots$ then the limit of the sequence $\mathrm{R}(\phi_n, \psi_n, \chi_n, \ldots)$ is $\mathrm{R}(a, b, c, \ldots)$ provided that this exists. (It will not if the denominator, if any, in the function R happens to be zero for these values of the arguments.)

A useful way of expressing this theorem is that the 'operation' of finding the limit of an algebraic combination of functions commutes with the arithmetical operations. Two operations are said to commute if the order in which they are performed is immaterial. Thus it does not matter whether we evaluate $\lim (\phi_n + \psi_n)$ by operations in the order :

First. Adding ϕ_n to ψ_n (the operation $+$).

Second. Finding the limit of the sum (the operation $n \to \infty$).

or

First. Finding the limits of ϕ_n and ψ_n separately.

Second. Adding the two limiting values.

We have not stated, however, and it is not always true, that the operation $(\lim\limits_{n\to\infty})$ commutes with other *limiting* operations.

For example $$\lim_{m\to\infty} \lim_{n\to\infty} \frac{(-1)^m}{n} = 0$$

(the convention is that the extreme right-hand operation is performed first, followed by the others in the order stated from right to left). On the other hand

$$\lim_{n\to\infty} \lim_{m\to\infty} \frac{(-1)^m}{n}$$

does not exist.

Example

The sequence defined by $\phi_n = \dfrac{n+1}{n-1}$ i.e. by $\phi_n = \dfrac{1+(1/n)}{1-(1/n)}$ has the limit $\dfrac{1+0}{1-0}$ i.e. 1.

2.46. *Monotonic sequences*

A sequence of terms ϕ_n which increase or decrease steadily as n increases is called a monotonic sequence. We also include sequences whose terms have the same value for a number of successive values of n.

Monotonic sequences arise very frequently in numerical work, and it is important to be able to say whether they converge to a limit or diverge to infinity—they obviously cannot oscillate. We cannot usually use the definition of a limit directly since we do not know l; the decision must therefore be based either on internal evidence, that is on comparison of successive terms of the sequence, or else on experience, that is by comparison with standard sequences whose behaviour has already been determined. The following examples incorporate standard results of importance.

Example 1

To investigate the limit of the sequence $\phi_n = x^n$ where x is a constant independent of n. We see that $\phi_{n+1}/\phi_n = x$. First suppose that x is positive; then the sequence is monotonic; if $x > 1$ each term is greater than the previous; if $x < 1$ each term is less than the previous; in the intermediate case $(x = 1)$, $\phi_n = 1$ for all values of n and hence $\lim \phi_n = 1$. If $x > 1$, we can show that $\phi_n \to \infty$. (For, since the sequence is monotonic increasing it must tend either to a limit l or to $+\infty$. Now since each term is greater than the previous one, l, if it exists, must be at least greater than the first term of the sequence and therefore in particular $l \neq 0$; moreover if l exists

$$\lim \frac{\phi_{n+1}}{\phi_n} = \frac{\lim \phi_{n+1}}{\lim \phi_n} = \frac{l}{l} = 1,$$

whereas we know that $\phi_{n+1}/\phi_n = x > 1$. Thus the assumption $\phi_n \to l$ leads to a contradiction; hence $\phi_n \to \infty$.) Similarly if $0 < x < 1$, the sequence is monotonic decreasing and must tend either to a limit l or to $-\infty$. Negative values are manifestly impossible and hence the sequence tends to a limit l. But the contradiction obtained for $x > 1$ still occurs unless the limit l is zero. Having disproved all alternatives we must conclude that $\phi_n \to 0$ (and this is perfectly reasonable). For negative values of x, the sequence alternates in sign, but $|\phi_n| = |x|^n$ which is positive and hence the above arguments apply, i.e. $|\phi_n|$ tends to $+\infty$ for $|x| > 1$, to 1 for $|x| = 1$, and to 0 for $0 < |x| < 1$.

To complete the discussion there is the trivial case $x = 0$: clearly ϕ_n is then zero for all finite n and hence $\lim \phi_n = 0$ also. To summarise the results;

$$\begin{array}{lll} \phi_n \to +\infty & \text{if } 1 < x & \\ \phi_n \to \quad 1 & \text{if } x = 1 & \\ \phi_n \to \quad 0 & \text{if } -1 < x < 1 & \\ \phi_n & \text{oscillates finitely} & \text{if } x = -1 \\ \phi_n & \text{oscillates infinitely} & \text{if } x < -1 \end{array}$$

Notice the graphical convention used in the inequalities on the right. Instead of writing $x>1$, the smaller quantity is placed on the left, corresponding to the arrangement of the x-axis in a graph. The analogy is useful for recognising the meaning of expressions such as $x< -1$, for it emphasizes that x lies outside, not inside the range -1 to 0.

Since it is easy, in these formal investigations, to lose sight of the simple basis of the argument, let us state the method in everyday language. Let us imagine that the numerical values of a few consecutive terms are written out. The eye scans them, and quickly judges whether (*a*) the terms are getting steadily bigger and bigger, or (*b*) the terms are getting steadily smaller and smaller, or (*c*) the terms sometimes increase from one to the next, and sometimes decrease. In case (*a*) or case (*b*) the rapid assessment of the eye, an assessment which is based on a few terms only, can be checked for the sequence as a whole by verifying that ϕ_{n+1}/ϕ_n is always (*a*) greater or (*b*) less than one. If such is the case, the only further decision to be made is whether the increase (or decrease) is limited or unlimited, i.e. whether the sequence tends to a limit or to plus (or minus) infinity.

If in case (*c*) the unsteadiness is caused merely by alternating signs, the value of ϕ_{n+1}/ϕ_n will again give the necessary basis of fact for determining the behaviour of the sequence as $n\to\infty$, though the alternatives are now $\phi_n\to 0$, ϕ_n oscillates finitely or ϕ_n oscillates infinitely as in Example 1. In less straightforward cases the scanning eye may recognise that only disturbing sub-sequences (every third or fourth term, say) destroy a regular behaviour of type (*a*) or (*b*); the component sequences in such a case would be separately examined, and the original sequence ϕ_n described in terms of its sub-sequences—bearing in mind, however, that the way the sequences are embedded one in another may be as important as their individual properties.

Erratically varying sequences are of comparatively rare occurrence, and when they do occur observant common sense is a strong weapon of attack.

Example 2

In Example 1 the value of ϕ_{n+1}/ϕ_n is constant. If, however, ϕ_{n+1}/ϕ_n is not constant but tends to a constant value x, the results of 1 still apply except at $x=\pm 1$. If $\lim_{n\to\infty} (\phi_{n+1}/\phi_n)=\pm 1$ we can say nothing without further investigation about the behaviour of ϕ_n.

For example, the function $\phi_n = 1/n$ converges to a limit; $\phi_n = +n$ diverges to $+\infty$; $\phi_n = -n$ diverges to $-\infty$; $\phi_n = (-1)^n$ oscillates finitely; $\phi_n = (-1)^n n$ oscillates infinitely; and yet in each case $\lim\limits_{n\to\infty} (\phi_{n+1}/\phi_n)$ is either $+1$ or -1.

Example 3

The function $\phi_n = n^p x^n$ where p is a fixed positive integer and x is any real number. Here

$$\lim_{n\to\infty}\left(\frac{\phi_{n+1}}{\phi_n}\right) = \lim_{n\to\infty}\left(\frac{n+1}{n}\right)^p x = x$$

(except for $x=0$ in which case $\phi_n = 0$ for all n). Thus, as before, the only difficulty is for $x = \pm 1$; this can be resolved by going back to the definition of ϕ_n. The results are:

$\phi_n \to +\infty$ for $1 \leqslant x$

$\phi_n \to 0$ for $-1 < x < 1$

ϕ_n oscillates infinitely for $x \leqslant -1$

Example 4

The function $\phi_n = n^{-p} x^n$, where p is a fixed positive integer.

$\phi_n \to +\infty$ for $+1 < x$

$\phi_n \to 0$ for $-1 \leqslant x \leqslant +1$

ϕ_n oscillates infinitely for $x < -1$

By comparison of 2, 3 and 4 it can be seen that for large values of n the variation both of n^p and of n^{-p} is 'weaker' than that of x^n, in the sense that the behaviour of both $x^n n^p$ and of $x^n n^{-p}$ as $n\to\infty$ is similar to that of x^n, except in the special case when $|x| = 1$.

Example 5

If x is positive and $\phi_n = \sqrt[n]{x}$ (the positive root is implied), then $\phi_n \to 1$. We note that ϕ_n can be written as $x^{1/n}$, so the result states that as $n\to\infty$, $x^{1/n}\to 1$ (cf. $x^0 = 1$).

To prove it we should first establish that ϕ_n is monotonic; then it is easy to eliminate all possibilities other than $\phi_n \to 1$. The details will be left as an exercise. If $x=0$, then $\phi_n = 0$ and $\lim \phi_n = 0$. If x is negative there is no real positive value of ϕ_n. Hence $\lim \phi_n$ is not defined.

Example 6

$\phi_n = \dfrac{x^n}{n!} \to 0$ for all x. For $\dfrac{\phi_{n+1}}{\phi_n} = \dfrac{x}{n}$ and $\lim \dfrac{\phi_{n+1}}{\phi_n} = 0$. Hence, from

Example 2, $\lim \phi_n = 0$. We may say that $n!$ is 'stronger' than x^n, meaning that the behaviour as $n \to \infty$ of $\frac{x^n}{n!}$ is similar to that of $\frac{1}{n!}$.

Example 7

$\phi_n = \sqrt[n]{n!} \to \infty$, for $n!$ is eventually greater than x^n, for any value of x; therefore $\sqrt[n]{n!}$ is greater than any value of x.

Example 8

$$\phi_n = \frac{n!}{n^n} \to 0. \quad \text{For } \frac{n!}{n^n} = \frac{n}{n}\,\frac{n-1}{n}\,\frac{n-2}{n} \cdots \frac{3}{n} \cdot \frac{2}{n} \cdot \frac{1}{n}$$

and each factor is less than 1. Therefore

$$\frac{n!}{n^n} \leqslant \frac{1}{n} \to 0 \text{ (the equality holds for } n=1 \text{ only).}$$

Example 9

Now consider the more complicated example $\phi_n = \left(1 + \frac{1}{n}\right)^n$. The term in brackets tends to unity, but it would be quite wrong to suppose that the product of a large number of factors, each nearly equal to unity, tends to unity or even that a limit necessarily exists.

An expression for ϕ_{n+1}/ϕ_n can be written down, but its limit is not apparent. From the binomial theorem (proved for positive integers in 2.41), however,

$$\begin{aligned}\phi_n &= 1 + n\frac{1}{n} + \tfrac{1}{2}n(n-1)\frac{1}{n^2} + \dots + \binom{n}{r}\frac{1}{n^r} + \dots + \frac{1}{n^n}\\ &= 1 + 1 + \tfrac{1}{2}\left(1 - \frac{1}{n}\right) + \dots + \frac{1}{r!}\left(1 - \frac{1}{n}\right)\left(1 - \frac{2}{n}\right)\cdots\left(1 - \frac{r-1}{n}\right) + \dots\\ &\qquad + \frac{1}{n!}\left(1 - \frac{1}{n}\right)\left(1 - \frac{2}{n}\right)\cdots\left(1 - \frac{n-1}{n}\right).\end{aligned}$$

The terms in brackets are all positive, and increase monotonically with n.

Hence ϕ_n is certainly greater than 2, and must tend to a limit or to $+\infty$. But ϕ_n is certainly less than

$$1 + 1 + \frac{1}{2!} + \frac{1}{3!} + \dots + \frac{1}{n!}$$

which in turn is less than

$$1 + 1 + \frac{1}{2} + \frac{1}{2^2} + \dots + \frac{1}{2^n}$$

which, after the 1st term, is a geometric progression, with sum

$$1 + \frac{1 - (\frac{1}{2})^{n+1}}{1 - \frac{1}{2}} < 3$$

Hence ϕ_n lies between 2 and 3, and the limit of ϕ is a number e such that $2 < e \leqslant 3$. (Note that we cannot say with certainty that $e < 3$ from the above argument. Every ϕ_n is less than 3, but it is possible that ϕ_n might tend to the limit 3, as is true for $\phi_n = 3 - (1/n)$.)

It is instructive to try to find a numerical value for e from the definition. The reader should verify the following ;

n	$n \log_{10}\left(1+\frac{1}{n}\right)$	$\left(1+\frac{1}{n}\right)^n$
1	0·303	$2{\cdot}00_0$
10	0·414	$2{\cdot}59_5$
100	0·432	$2{\cdot}70_4$
1000	0·434	$2{\cdot}71_7$

To extrapolate to infinite values of n, one may plot a graph of ϕ_n against $1/n$. The result is $e \approx 2{\cdot}72$. This value may be verified by more closely controlled calculation in a later section (5.31).

Example 10

$$\phi_n = \frac{(n!)^p}{n^n} \to \infty \quad \text{if } p > 1$$

For

$$\frac{\phi_{n+1}}{\phi_n} = \frac{(n+1)^p n^n}{(n+1)^{n+1}} = \frac{(n+1)^{p-1}}{[1+(1/n)]^n}$$

The denominator tends to e, but for $p > 1$ the numerator $\to \infty$. For $p = 1$, $\phi_{n+1}/\phi_n \to 1/e$ which with the results of example 2 gives an independent verification of example 8.

The behaviour of almost all sequences in which the reader is likely to be interested can be deduced by comparing them with the standard cases 1–10 above, or by use of similar methods of examination.

2.5. Infinite sequences of functions

Some of the examples discussed above, $\phi_n = x^n$, $\phi_n = n^p x^n$, $\phi_n = \sqrt[n]{x}$ and so on, have already introduced the notion of sequences of functions. To emphasise the dependence on a continuous variable x as well as on the discrete variable n we use the notation $\phi_n(x)$.

It will be seen that the limit of a sequence of this kind will in general depend on the value of x ; i.e. the limit of $\phi_n(x)$, if it exists, is itself a function of x ; a convenient symbol is $\phi(x)$.

The reader will see the examples $\phi_n = x^n$ and $\phi_n = \sqrt[n]{x}$ in a much clearer light if he plots the graphs of x^n and $x^{1/n}$ on a single diagram for a few values of n, say, $n=1$, 2, 3, and 10 as in Fig. 2.6. Fig. 2.9 is the graph of $\lim_{n\to\infty} x^n$.

The function $\phi(x)=\lim_{n\to\infty} x^n$ cannot usefully be represented by a graph as $\phi(x)$ is infinite for $|x|>1$, zero for $|x|<1$, and a graph cannot accurately represent its behaviour at the critical points $x=\pm 1$.

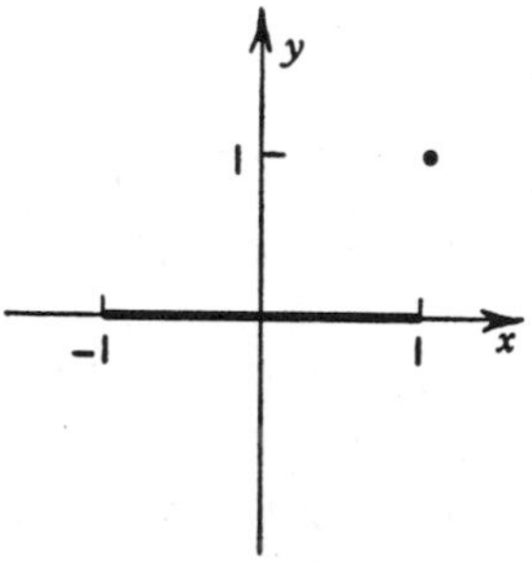

FIG. 2.9

We now give some further examples of functions defined as the limit of a sequence of functions. The limit is denoted by $\phi(x)$; i.e. $\phi(x)=\lim_{n\to\infty}\phi_n(x)$.

Example 1

$$\phi_n(x)=\frac{x^n}{x^n+1} \qquad \begin{aligned} \phi(x)&=1 && \text{for } |x|>1 \\ &=\tfrac{1}{2} && x=1 \\ &=0 && |x|<1 \end{aligned}$$

$\phi(x)$ undefined for $x=-1$

Example 2

$$\phi_n(x)=\frac{x^n\,\mathrm{f}(x)+\mathrm{g}(x)}{x^n+1} \qquad \begin{aligned} &\phi(x)=\mathrm{f}(x) && \text{for } |x|>1 \\ &\phi(x)=\tfrac{1}{2}[\mathrm{f}(1)+\mathrm{g}(1)] && \text{for } x=+1 \\ &\phi(x)=\mathrm{g}(x) && \text{for } |x|<1 \end{aligned}$$

$\phi(x)$ undefined at $x=-1$

Example 3

$\phi_n(x)=\cos^{2n}\pi x$. If x is a positive or negative integer or zero, $|\cos\pi x|=1$ and therefore $\cos^{2n}\pi x=1$. If x is not an integer $|\cos\pi x|<1$ and $\cos^{2n}\pi x\to 0$. Hence

$$\begin{aligned} \phi(x)&=1 && \text{for } |x|=0,\ 1,\ 2\ \ldots \\ \phi(x)&=0 && \text{elsewhere} \end{aligned}$$

2.6. Infinite series

The infinite series i.e. the sum of an infinite sequence of terms, is probably the most often used of all the mathematical weapons for dealing with scientific problems. Series, like sequences, may occur as the result of processes of successive approximation; but their importance in mathematical physics is much wider than this. For, with the exception of polynomials, rational functions (ratios of polynomials), and algebraic functions (i.e. functions y which satisfy an algebraic equation, of finite degree in y, whose coefficients are rational functions of x), the functions of mathematical physics can only be expressed in terms of the arithmetical operations by an infinite process of some kind, e.g., as the limit of a sequence, as an infinite series, as a definite integral, as the solution of a differential equation, and so on. The infinite series of ascending powers of x, $a_0+a_1x+a_2x^2+\dots$ and the infinite series of descending powers of x, $b_0+b_1/x+b_2/x^2+\dots$ are often convenient for computational purposes, the former for small values of x and the latter for large values. One of the first problems to be solved when a new function is introduced is therefore that of finding its representation as a power series. Having indicated the importance of infinite series we begin by considering series of numbers.

2.61. *Infinite series of numbers*

Let $u_1, u_2 \dots u_n$ be a sequence of numbers defined for all integral values of n. Then a new function of n, that is to say a new sequence, can be defined by taking the sum of 1, 2, 3, ... , n ... terms of the sequence. Denote the new function by S_n, so that $S_1=u_1$, $S_2=u_1+u_2$: and generally $S_n=u_1+u_2+\dots+u_n$. A shorter notation is obtained by the use of the symbol $\sum$ for the sum ; thus

$$S_n=\sum_{\nu=1}^{n} u_\nu$$

which in full means 'S_n is the sum from $\nu=1$ to $\nu=n$ inclusive of the terms u_ν'. Again we are interested mainly in the limit (if any) of the sequence S_n as $n\to\infty$. This is the 'sum to infinity' of the series and may be denoted by S ; we have the following equivalent forms for S :

$$S=\lim_{n\to\infty} s_n=\lim_{n\to\infty}\sum_{\nu=1}^{n} u_\nu=\sum_{\nu=1}^{\infty} u_\nu$$

The last form is the most convenient but it should be remembered that $\sum_1^\infty$ in fact represents a limiting operation.

The convergence of the series $\sum u_\nu$ is therefore dependent on the convergence of the sequence S_n ; if it does not converge its behaviour can be described with the same terminology as that used for sequences ; thus we say that a series diverges to $\pm\infty$, or else oscillates finitely or infinitely, according to the behaviour of the sequence S_n.

These possibilities are well illustrated by the *infinite geometric series*. For the finite series the sum of n terms, S_n, is given by

$$S_n = \sum_{\nu=1}^{n} r^{\nu-1} = 1 + r + r^2 + \ldots + r^{n-1} = \frac{1-r^n}{1-r}$$

for all values of r except $r=1$, when by inspection $S=n$. The sum to infinity is now obtained by considering the behaviour of S_n as $n\to\infty$. Thus

$$\begin{aligned} &S_n \to +\infty, \quad 1 \leqslant r \\ &S_n \to 1/(1-r), \quad -1<r<1 \\ &S_n \ \text{oscillates finitely}, \quad r=-1 \\ &S_n \ \text{oscillates infinitely}, \quad r<-1 \end{aligned}$$

When the limit exists at all it has the value $1/(1-r)$. Notice that the geometric series converges if the terms decrease to zero. This is not a sufficient condition in general; it is of course a necessary condition—a series cannot converge unless its terms do tend to zero ; an example of a series of terms which diminish to zero but whose sum does not converge is the harmonic series $1+\frac{1}{2}+\frac{1}{3}+\ldots+1/n+\ldots$.

A second point to notice is that one cannot always rely on the form of the expression for the limit to indicate the range for which it is valid. At $r=1$ there is clearly a discontinuity in the expression $1/(1-r)$; but at $r=-1$, $1/(1-r)$ is equal to $1/2$ and there is no indication that the formula ceases to apply at this point (see Fig. 2.10).

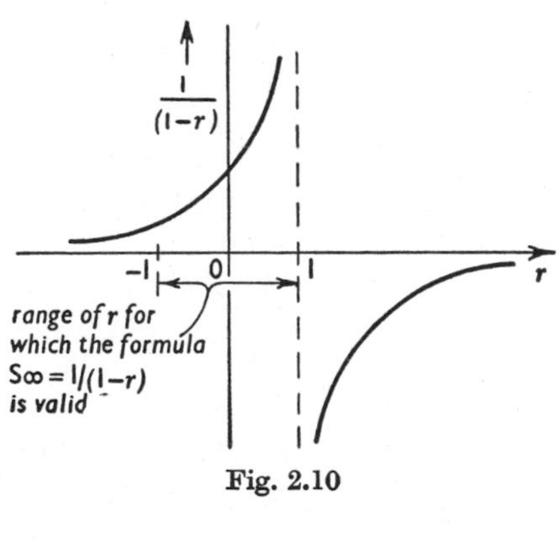

Fig. 2.10

We shall be able to throw fresh light on this rather peculiar circumstance when we consider the convergence of series of complex numbers.

2.62. *Decimals*

A familiar example of a convergent series is provided by the decimal notation for numbers. The decimal $0{\cdot}abcdef\ldots$ is of course the number

$$a\,.\,10^{-1}+b\,.\,10^{-2}+c\,.\,10^{-3}\ldots \tag{1}$$

If a, b, c are not restricted the series may diverge ; but since only the integers 0 to 9 are allowed, it is clear that

$$0<a\,.\,10^{-1}+b\,.\,10^{-2}+\ldots \leqslant 9\,.\,10^{-1}+9\,.\,10^{-2}+9\,.\,10^{-3}+\ldots$$

Since the last member is a geometric series with $r=1/10$, its limit $0{\cdot}9999\ldots$ is equal to 1. Hence a decimal of the form $0{\cdot}abc\ldots$ must either tend to a limit or else oscillate finitely in the range 0 to 1. The latter possibility is excluded since all the terms of (1) are of the same sign.

2.63. *The series* $\sum 1/n^s$

A full discussion of this series is somewhat long and will not be given in detail (see Hardy, *Pure Mathematics*, §181). If $s\leqslant 0$, the terms do not diminish in magnitude as n increases, and the series diverges. If $s>0$, they decrease, although, since the ratio $n/(n+1)\to 1$ they do so more and more slowly as n increases. The result, which is required for reference later, is that

$$\begin{aligned} 1/n^s \quad &\text{diverges for} \quad s\leqslant 1 \\ &\text{converges for } s>1 \end{aligned} \tag{1}$$

In particular the so-called ' harmonic series '

$$1+\tfrac{1}{2}+\tfrac{1}{3}+\tfrac{1}{4}+\ldots$$

diverges.

For completeness we state a general theorem on convergence of series which is useful for theoretical work.

A necessary and sufficient condition for convergence. The series $\sum u_\nu$ converges if and only if, for any $\epsilon>0$, there exists a number n_0 such that for all $n\geqslant n_0$, and every positive integer p,

$$\sum_{\nu=n+1}^{n+p} u_\nu<\epsilon.$$

2.64. *Alternating series*

A series of terms alternately positive and negative converges under the particularly simple condition that the terms diminish steadily to zero.

For let

$$s = u_1 - u_2 + u_3 \dots$$

be the series, and suppose that

$$u_1 > u_2 > u_3 > \dots > u_n \to 0.$$

Then the sequence S_n is less than u_1 and greater than $u_1 - u_2$ for all values of n.

For $$S_n = u_1 - (u_2 - u_3) - (u_4 - u_5) - \dots$$

and $$S_n = (u_1 - u_2) + (u_3 - u_4) + \dots$$

and the terms in brackets are always positive. For example

$$\begin{aligned} S_3 &= u_1 - (u_2 - u_3) < u_1 \\ &= (u_1 - u_2) + u_3 > u_1 - u_2 \\ S_4 &= u_1 - (u_2 - u_3) - u_4 < u_1 \\ &= (u_1 - u_2) + (u_3 - u_4) > u_1 - u_2 \end{aligned}$$

The sequence S_n must therefore tend to a limit or oscillate finitely. The latter possibility can be removed by extending the same argument thus

$$\begin{aligned} S_{2n+p} &= S_{2n} + (u_{2n+1} - u_{2n+2}) + \dots \\ &= (S_{2n} + u_{2n+1}) - (u_{2n+2} - u_{2n+3}) - \dots \end{aligned}$$

Hence S_{2n+p} lies between S_{2n} and $(S_{2n} + u_{2n+1})$, and $u_{2n+1} \to 0$. Hence the sequence must converge.

The theorem can obviously be extended to series whose terms u_n decrease in magnitude and alternate in sign only for n greater than some finite value, and also to series in which some successive terms are equal.

2.65. *Conditional and absolute convergence*

If a series of positive terms converges then it is clear that any series obtained by reversing the signs of some or all the terms must converge : but the converse is not true. If the terms of a convergent alternating series are taken with positive signs the new series may or may not converge. If the series of positive terms does not converge the original series of positive and negative terms is said to be conditionally convergent. If the series of positive terms does converge, then the original is said to be absolutely convergent.

An example of a conditionally convergent series is

$$\frac{(-1)^{n+1}}{n}=1-\frac{1}{2}+\frac{1}{3}-\frac{1}{4}+\ldots$$

which converges to a limit between $\frac{1}{2}$ and 1. If the signs are taken positive the series becomes the divergent harmonic series.

Conditionally convergent series necessarily converge very slowly; they are not so easy to handle as absolutely convergent series; for example the product of two conditionally convergent series does not necessarily converge.

These two disadvantages make conditionally convergent series less generally useful to the scientist than absolutely convergent ones. Special methods have to be devised to compute their sums and each case usually requires individual treatment. We shall therefore be more concerned with the absolutely convergent series in what follows.

2.66. *Tests for absolute convergence*

The convergence of a series of positive terms is not quite so easily recognised as that of an alternating series. The border line between absolute convergence and divergence cannot be fixed by answering a single question, such as 'Does $u_n \to 0$?' The following tests for absolute convergence are sufficient but not necessary; a series may converge without satisfying the conditions. However between them the tests cover almost all the series of mathematical physics.

The method used in the test about to be described is essentially a comparison of the given series against the standard series, $\sum x^n$. Thus if $u_n < Kx^n$ for all n, where K is independent of n and $x<1$, the series $\sum u_n$ converges. If $u_n > Kx^n$, where $x>1$ the series diverges.

The ratio test

If $u_n > 0$ (all n) and $u_n/u_{n-1} \to k$, then the series $\sum u_n$ converges if $k<1$ and diverges if $k>1$. The series also diverges if $u_n/u_{n-1} \to 1$ from above (i.e. if $u_n/u_{n-1} = 1+\delta_n$ where $\delta_n \geqslant 0$ but $\delta_n \to 0$ as $n \to \infty$.) If $u_n/u_{n-1} \to 1$ from below the test is inconclusive.

If we are given that $u_n/u_{n-1} \to k$, the higher terms of the series must be approximately of the form $u_N(1+k+k^2+\dots)$ which makes the results quoted appear reasonable, but this argument is not precise enough to be acceptable as a proof.

In our proof we want to show that if $k<1$, $\sum u_n$ is less than some finite quantity, and if $k>1$, $\sum u_n$ is greater than any finite quantity. From the given condition $u_n/u_{n-1}\to k$ we can adduce neither that $u_n \leqslant ku_{n-1}$ nor that $u_n \geqslant ku_{n-1}$, even for very large values of n. If, however, l is a number greater than k, it *is* true that for sufficiently large values of n, $u_n<lu_{n-1}$. Similarly if $l<k$, $u_n>lu_{n-1}$ when n is sufficiently large. This gives us the clue to the details of proof.

First consider the case $k<1$.

Then we can find a number l greater than k but less than 1. Since $u_n/u_{n-1}\to k$ which is less than l, we can certainly find a value of n, say $n=N$, such that $u_{n+1}/u_n<l$ whenever $n \geqslant N$. Hence

$$u_{N+1}<lu_N, \quad u_{N+2}<lu_{N+1}<l^2u_N$$

and in general $u_{N+P}<l^Pu_N$. Hence

$$\sum_{n=N}^{\infty} u_n<u_N(1+l+l^2+\dots),$$

and $l<1$. Therefore $\sum u_n$ converges.

If $k>1$, the proof follows similar lines; we choose l in the range $1<l<k$ and prove that the series $\sum u_n$ is eventually greater, term by term, than a divergent series.

The case $k=1$ cannot be decided by this test but must be examined by a more powerful test, described below. If however $u_n/u_{n-1} \geqslant 1$ for all finite n, but tends to 1 in the limit the series obviously diverges, since the terms do not diminish, which is a necessary condition for convergence.

Note 1. In the ratio test we may equally well use u_{n+1}/u_n or u_{n+2}/u_{n+1} instead of u_n/u_{n-1} since, by the definition of a limit, if u_{n+2}/u_{n+1} or $u_{n+1}/u_n\to k$ so also does u_n/u_{n-1}.

Note 2. A second, more powerful, ratio test can be obtained by a comparison of the given series against the standard series $\sum n^{-s}$. The result may be briefly stated: if $u_n/u_{n-1}\to 1-(s/n)$ as $n\to\infty$ (in the sense that $\lim_{n\to\infty} [n\{(u_n/u_{n-1})-1\}]=-s$), or, to write this in the accepted notation, if $u_n/u_{n-1}\approx 1-(s/n)$, then $\sum u_n$ converges if $s>1$ and diverges if $s<1$. The case $s=1$ is now borderline, but it can further be established that if the next term in u_n/u_{n-1} is $O(1/n^2)$, then the series $\sum u_n$ diverges for $s=1$. For more information about this and further tests, the reader is referred to Hardy, *Pure Mathematics*, 7th Edn., §§ 183, 218 and Ex. LXXXIX.

2.67. *Rearrangement of terms in a series*

If a *finite* number of terms in a series are reordered, none of the tests for convergence are affected in any essential way, for it is the behaviour as $n\to\infty$ which counts. The value of the sum of the series is also unchanged, since it may be evaluated in two parts, the first consisting of a finite number of terms including all the terms to be rearranged, and the remainder consisting of an infinite series which is left unaltered. Thus,

$$1-\tfrac{2}{3}+\tfrac{1}{2}-\tfrac{2}{5}+\tfrac{1}{3}-\tfrac{2}{7}+\tfrac{1}{4}-\tfrac{2}{9}+\tfrac{1}{5}-\tfrac{2}{11}+\tfrac{1}{6}-\dots$$
$$=(1+\tfrac{1}{2}+\tfrac{1}{3}+\tfrac{1}{4}+\tfrac{1}{5})-2(\tfrac{1}{3}+\tfrac{1}{5}+\tfrac{1}{7}+\tfrac{1}{9})-\tfrac{2}{11}+\tfrac{1}{6}-\dots$$

It would, however, be incorrect to conclude that the rearrangement of an *infinite* number of terms is necessarily permissible. That such rearrangement can give rise to wrong results may be seen from the following;

$$\begin{aligned}1-\tfrac{2}{3}+\tfrac{1}{2}-\tfrac{2}{5}+\dots &=(?)\ (1+\tfrac{1}{2}+\tfrac{1}{3}+\dots)-2(\tfrac{1}{3}+\tfrac{1}{5}+\tfrac{1}{7}+\dots)\\ &=(?)\ 1+\tfrac{1}{2}(1+\tfrac{1}{2}+\tfrac{1}{3}+\dots)+(\tfrac{1}{3}+\tfrac{1}{5}+\tfrac{1}{7}+\dots)\\ &\qquad -2(\tfrac{1}{3}+\tfrac{1}{5}+\tfrac{1}{7}+\dots)\\ &=(?)\ 1+\tfrac{1}{2}-\tfrac{1}{3}+\tfrac{1}{4}-\tfrac{1}{5}\dots\end{aligned}$$

The value of the conditionally convergent series on the left lies between $\frac{1}{3}$ and $\frac{5}{6}$ while the last series on the right converges to a value between $1\frac{1}{6}$ and $1\frac{1}{2}$. The source of the fallacy may be exposed by considering the remainder terms left outside the brackets when a finite number of terms in the series on the left-hand side is considered.

If the series originally taken had been absolutely convergent, on the other hand, $S=\sum u_n$ say, its value would have been unaltered by any rearrangement of its terms.

For example, let $\sum v_m$ be a rearrangement of $\sum u_n$. Then

$$|u_{n+1}|+|u_{n+1}|+\dots=\epsilon_n\to 0 \quad \text{as} \quad n\to\infty.$$

Each of the terms $u_1, u_2 \dots u_n$ occurs sooner or later in the series $\sum v_m$: let the last to appear be v_m. If $m\geqslant M$, then

$$v_1+v_2+\dots+v_m$$

includes *all* the terms u_1, $u_1 \dots u_n$ and *some* of the terms u_{n+1}, $u_{n+2} \dots$. Hence

$$|(v_1+v_2+ \dots +v_m)-(u_1+u_2+ \dots +u_n)| \leqslant \epsilon_n.$$

Since $\quad |S-(u_1+u_2+ \dots +u_n)| \leqslant \epsilon_n,$

$$|(v_1+v_2+ \dots +v_m)-S| \leqslant 2\epsilon_n$$

for all $m \geqslant M$, so that $\sum v_m$ converges to S, that is

$$\sum v_m = \sum u_n$$

i.e. the sum of an absolutely convergent series is unaltered by a rearrangement of its terms.

Example 1

Show that $\sum (x^n/n!)$ converges absolutely. We first note that $|x^n/n!| = |x|^n/n!$, so it is only necessary to establish the convergence of $\sum (x^n/n!)$ for positive values of x. The reader should now apply the ratio test to the series, and so establish the result.

We shall now prove the same result without reference to the ratio test in order to illustrate a valuable type of argument (it is in fact by this kind of argument that the truth of the ratio test may be established). We first note that $1/n_1 > 1/(n_1+1) > 1/(n_1+2) \dots$ so

$$\frac{x^{n_1}}{(n_1)!}+\frac{x^{n_1+1}}{(n_1+1)!}+\frac{x^{n_1+2}}{(n_1+2)!}+\dots=\frac{x^{n_1}}{(n_1)!}\left(1+\frac{x}{n_1+1}+\frac{x^2}{(n_1+1)(n_1+2)}+\dots\right)$$

$$<\frac{x^{n_1}}{(n_1)!}\left(1+\frac{x}{n_1}+\left(\frac{x}{n_1}\right)^2+\dots\right)$$

Now for any x we can choose $n_1 > x$, and then the series in brackets becomes a geometrical progression whose sum to infinity is $1/[1-(x/n_1)]$. Thus

$$\sum (x^n/n!) = \sum_{1}^{n_1-1} (x^n/n!) + \sum_{n_1}^{\infty} (x^n/n!)$$

$$< \sum_{1}^{n_1-1} (x^n/n!) + x^{n_1}/(n_1)!\,\{1-(x/n_1)\} \qquad (1)$$

When x is positive, the L.H.S. of (1) is a series of positive terms, so it either converges or tends to $+\infty$. But each of the terms on the R.H.S. is finite: it follows that $\sum (x^n/n!)$ converges when x is positive, and hence that for all values of x, $\sum (x^n/n!)$ is absolutely convergent.

Example 2

Determine the conditions under which the hypergeometric series converges. This is the series

$$1+\frac{\alpha\beta}{1\,.\,\gamma}x+\frac{\alpha(\alpha+1)\beta(\beta+1)}{1\,.\,2\,.\,\gamma(\gamma+1)}x^2+\frac{\alpha(\alpha+1)(\alpha+2)}{1\,.\,2\,.\,3}\cdot\frac{\beta(\beta+1)(\beta+2)}{\gamma(\gamma+1)(\gamma+2)}x^3+\dots$$

α, β, γ are real numbers not equal to 0, -1, -2 etc. : if such values were allowed for α and β the series would simply terminate as a polynomial, and if allowed for γ, all the terms after a certain point would involve division by zero.

The $(n+2)$th term in the series is

$$u_{n+2}=\frac{\alpha(\alpha+1)\dots(\alpha+n)}{1\,.\,2\quad\dots n(n+1)}\;\frac{\beta(\beta+1)\dots(\beta+n)}{\gamma(\gamma+1)\dots(\gamma+n)}x^{n+1}$$

so that
$$\frac{u_{n+2}}{u_{n+1}}=\frac{\alpha+n}{n+1}\cdot\frac{\beta+n}{\gamma+n}x$$

(One of the valuable features of ratio tests is that, as in this case, u_{n+2}/u_{n+1} is often much simpler in form than u_n itself.) As $n\to\infty$, we see that $u_{n+2}/u_{n+1}\to x$. Hence if $-1<x<1$ the series converges absolutely. Similarly if $|x|>1$ the series diverges. For the borderline case $x=1$ the more powerful tests referred to in Note 2.66 must be used. These show that if $x=1$ the series converges absolutely provided $\gamma>\alpha+\beta$ and diverges if $\gamma\leqslant\alpha+\beta$.

CHAPTER THREE

POLYNOMIAL,
RATIONAL FUNCTIONS, AND
ALGEBRAIC FUNCTIONS

3.1. Polynomial functions

The previous chapter has been concerned with some general ideas regarding functions in general. We now consider some particular classes of function, and begin with those termed polynomials.

The function $f(x)=a_0x^n+a_1x^{n-1}+\dots+a_n$ is called a 'polynomial' in x. The quantities $a_0, a_1, \dots, a_n$ are numerical constants, called the 'coefficients'; it may be supposed, without any loss of generality, that $a_0 \neq 0$. The integer n, the index of the highest power of x, is called the 'degree' of the polynomial.

For any given numerical value of x, the value of $f(x)$ can be calculated by a finite number of arithmetical operations of multiplication and addition. It follows that $f(x)$ has a unique, finite value at all finite values of x. Moreover, since x^n is continuous, it follows that $f(x)$ is a finite sum of continuous functions and is therefore itself continuous (see 2.21).

The graph of $f(x)$ is consequently an unbroken line extending over the whole range of x. Figs. 3.1–3.4 show the examples

$$f(x)=x^2-4, \quad -x^2+4x-6, \quad x^3+4x^2+x-6, \quad x^5-2x+1$$

respectively.

3.11. *Behaviour at infinity*

For very large values of x, the behaviour of a polynomial is determined by the term containing the highest power of x. For

$$\begin{aligned} f(x) &= a_0x^n+a_1x^{n-1}+\dots+a_n \\ &= a_0x^n[1+(a_1/a_0x)+\dots+(a_n/a_0x^n)] \end{aligned}$$

and the terms in square brackets tend to 1 as $|x| \to \infty$. Thus in the examples shown in Figs. 3.1–3.4 the curves tend towards $y=x^2$, $y=-x^2$, $y=x^3$ and $y=x^5$ respectively.

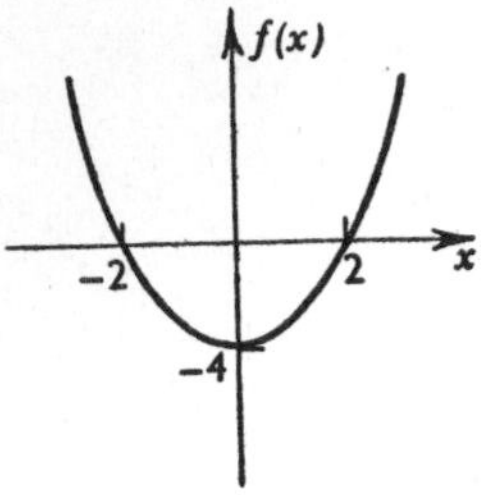

FIG. 3.1

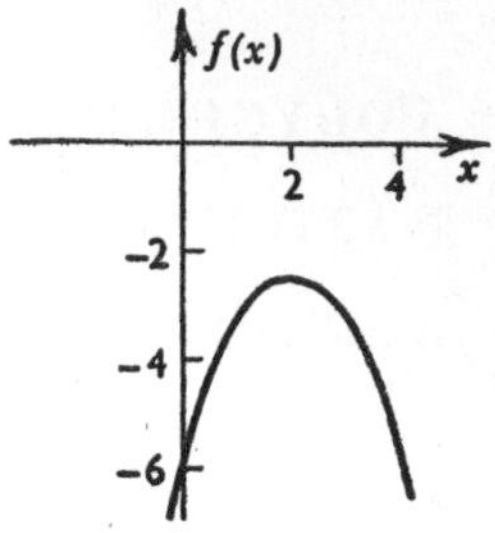

FIG. 3.2

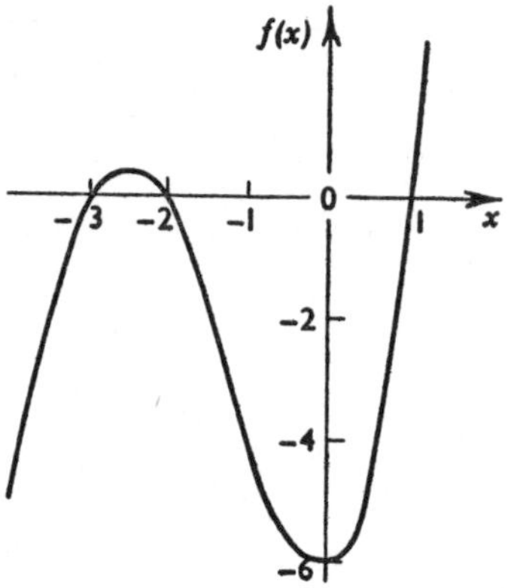

FIG. 3.3

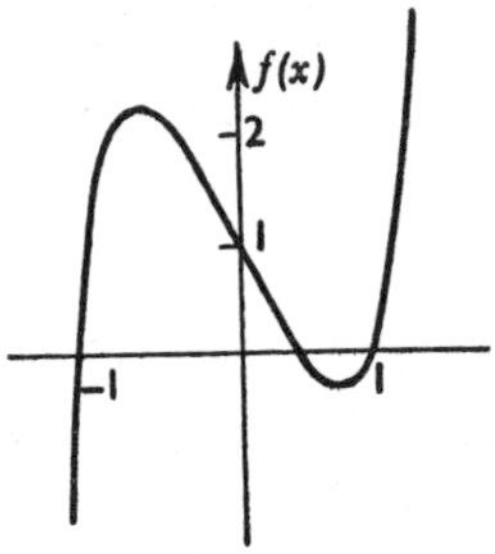

FIG. 3.4

These curves are curvilinear asymptotes of the graphs of the polynomials and we may write $f(x) \sim a_0 x^n$ to indicate that for large values of x, $f(x)$ 'behaves like' $a_0 x^n$. The difference $f(x) - a_0 x^n$ may of course be very large, since it is equal to $a_1 x^{n-1} + a_2 x^{n-2} + \dots + a_0$, so that the relation expressed by the symbol $\sim$ is by no means synonymous with equality. In fact $f(x) \sim g(x)$ means simply that $\lim_{x\to\infty} [f(x)/g(x)] = 1$; the difference $f(x) - g(x)$ is quite undetermined.

The only polynomial that does not tend to infinity with x is the one of zero order $f(x) \equiv a_0$ (a constant).

3.12. *The zeros of a polynomial*

The examples of Figs. 3.1–4 show that although $y=f(x)$ is single-valued, there may nevertheless be several different values of x, corresponding to a given value of y. For example there are two values of x which make $f(x)=0$ in Fig. 3.1, namely $x=-2$ and $x=+2$; these values of x are called the zeros of x^2-4. The function $-x^2+4x-6$ on the other hand has no zeros, for it can be written as $-(x-2)^2-2$ and is therefore always negative. In Fig. 3.3 is shown a third degree polynomial (a cubic) which has three zeros, and in Fig. 3.4 we see a fifth-degree polynomial which also has three zeros.

It is possible to consider similarly the values of x that make $f(x)=k$ where k is any constant, but this latter case can always be regarded as that of finding the zeros of a different polynomial $g(x)=f(x)-k$ and is not therefore an essentially different problem.

The determination of the zeros of $f(x)$ can also be looked at in a slightly different form as the determination of the 'roots' of the equation

$$f(x)\equiv a_0x^n+a_1x^{n-1}+\ldots+a_n=0$$

i.e. the values of x that satisfy the equation. Thus $x=\pm 2$ are the zeros of the polynomial $f(x)\equiv x^2-4$ and also the roots of the equation $x^2-4=0$.

A third problem, equivalent to these two, is that of factorising the expression $f(x)$. For if $f(x)$ can be recognised as the product of two factors, for example $f(x)=(x-\alpha)g(x)$ where $g(x)$ is a polynomial, then clearly $f(x)=0$ at $x=\alpha$ since $g(x)$ is finite for all finite x. Conversely if $f(x)=0$ at $x=\alpha$ then $(x-\alpha)$ is a factor of $f(x)$, for if $f(\alpha)=0$, then $f(x)=f(x)-f(\alpha)$. But $f(x)-f(\alpha)$ is the sum of a number of terms $a_{n-k}(x^k-\alpha^k)$ for $1\leqslant k\leqslant n$, and each of these has a factor $(x-\alpha)$, the other factor being a polynomial of degree $(k-1)$. Hence

$$f(x)=(x-\alpha)g(x)$$

where $g(x)$ is a polynomial of degree $(n-1)$.

It follows that if a polynomial $f(x)$ of degree n has n zeros, $x_1, x_2, x_3, \ldots, x_n$, all unequal, then

$$f(x)=A(x-x_1)(x-x_2)\ldots(x-x_n)$$

where A is a polynomial of degree zero, that is, a constant.

3.13. *Zeros of quadratic functions*

In the case of the quadratic $a_0x^2+a_1x+a_2$, the zeros, if any, can always be found by the elementary method of 'completing the square', and are

$$x=[-a_1\pm\sqrt{(a_1{}^2-4a_0a_2)}]/2a_0$$

If $a_1^2 < 4a_0a_2$, this formula involves the square root of a negative quantity and is therefore outside the realm of the real variable, to which we have so far restricted ourselves. In Chapter 6 we shall extend the idea of number so as to include such quantities, but for the moment we are content to say the quadratic has no zeros, or, what is equivalent, that it is ' irreducible ', meaning that it has no real factors. The quantity $a_1^2 - 4a_0a_2 = D$ is known as the ' discriminant ' of the quadratic ; if D is positive $a_0x^2 + a_1x + a_2$ has two distinct factors ; if $D = 0$ there are two equal factors ; if $D < 0$ the quadratic has no real factors.

It might now be expected that for some values of the coefficients, the quartic $a_0x^4 + a_1x^3 + a_2x^2 + a_3x + a_4$ would be irreducible, i.e. would have no real linear or quadratic factors. However, it can be shown that all polynomials of degree 3 or greater can be factorised into a product of linear factors and irreducible quadratic factors. For example $x^4 + a^4$ has no zeros (if x is confined to real values) but is not irreducible, for

$$x^4 + a^4 = (x^2 + a^2)^2 - 2a^2x^2 = (x^2 + \sqrt{2}ax + a^2)(x^2 - \sqrt{2}ax + a^2)$$

3.14. *Polynomial identities*

An identity $\mathrm{f}(x) \equiv \mathrm{g}(x)$ should be carefully distinguished from an equation $\mathrm{f}(x) = \mathrm{g}(x)$. The identity implies that the relationship of equality holds for *all* values of x (possibly in a restricted range) ; the equation on the other hand is a statement about the number x and defines a set of values of x, namely the roots of the equation. Thus the relation $x^2 - 1 = (x-1)(x+1)$ is an identity and is better written $x^2 - 1 \equiv (x-1)(x+1)$. It is a statement about the functions and not about x. The equation $x^2 + 3x + 2 = 0$ is a statement about x, namely that $x = -1$ or -2.

We shall now prove the important theorem that *if*

$$\mathrm{f}(x) = a_0x^n + a_1x^{n-1} + a_2x^{n-2} + \ldots + a_n$$

and
$$\mathrm{g}(x) = b_0x^n + b_1x^{n-1} + b_2x^{n-2} + \ldots + b_n$$

are two polynomials of degree n, *and* $\mathrm{f}(x) = \mathrm{g}(x)$ for $(n+1)$ *distinct values of* x, *then* $\mathrm{f}(x) \equiv \mathrm{g}(x)$ and

$$a_0 = b_0,\ a_1 = b_1,\ \ldots,\ a_n = b_n \tag{1}$$

This theorem justifies the process of ' equating coefficients.'

The same result is true if $f(x)=g(x)$ for all x in a continuous range, no matter how small.

Let $x_1, x_2, \dots, x_n$ be n distinct values of x for which $f(x)=g(x)$. Then $f(x)-g(x)$ is a polynomial of degree n, of which $x_1, x_2, \dots, x_n$ are n distinct zeros. So by the theorem at the end of 3.12.

$$f(x)-g(x)=A(x-x_1)(x-x_2)\dots(x-x_n) \tag{2}$$

where A is some constant. If $f(x)=g(x)$ for any other value of x, say $x=x_{n+1}$, then none of the linear factors in (2) are zero at $x=x_{n+1}$, so A must be 0, and $f(x)=g(x)$ for all x.

Now if $f(x)=g(x)$ for all x, then $f(0)=g(0)$, and hence $a_n=b_n$. The identity $f(x)\equiv g(x)$ can now be reduced to

$$a_0x^n+a_1x^{n-1}+\dots+a_{n-1}x\equiv b_0x^n+b_1x^{n-1}+\dots+b_{n-1}x$$

For values of x other than $x=0$ we can divide by x and obtain the relation

$$a_0x^{n-1}+a_1x^{n-2}+\dots+a_{n-1}=b_0x^{n-1}+b_1x^{n-2}+\dots+b_{n-1} \tag{3}$$

But since this is an equality between polynomials for all values of x except perhaps $x=0$, it is certainly true for $(n-1)+1$ distinct values and therefore also holds at $x=0$, and hence $a_{n-1}=b_{n-1}$, and so on.

Corollary. If $f(x)$, $g(x)$ are polynomials and it is known that $f(x)=g(x)$ for all values of x except at a finite number of discrete values, then $f(x)=g(x)$ at those discrete values also.

3.2. Division of polynomials

Let $f(x)$ and $g(x)$ be two polynomials of degrees m and n, $m>n$. Then by long division we can find a quotient $q(x)$ and a remainder $r(x)$, both polynomials, such that

$$\frac{f(x)}{g(x)}=q(x)+\frac{r(x)}{g(x)}$$

i.e.

$$f(x)=q(x)\,g(x)+r(x) \tag{1}$$

For example let $f(x)=5x^4-12x^3-10x^2+8x+7$ and $g(x)=x-3$. Then using an economical notation (that of ‘ detached coefficients ’) analogous to the decimal notation in arithmetic, in which the polynomial $1\times10^3+7\times10^2+8\times10+4$ is written simply as 1784 we can arrange the working as follows :

```
1  -3) 5  -12  -10  8  7  (5  3  -1  5
       5  -15
       -------
           3  -10
           3  - 9
           -------
              - 1  8
              - 1  3
              ------
                   5   7
                   5 -15
                   -----
                      22
```

Replacing the powers of x we obtain

$$\mathrm{q}(x)=5x^3+3x^2-x+5$$
$$\mathrm{r}(x)=22$$

The process is continued until the remainder is of lower degree than the divisor. When the divisor is linear, as here, the remainder is a constant.

3.21. *Synthetic division*

A method of building up the quotient $\mathrm{q}(x)$ known as Horner's method, or synthetic division, is much quicker. This method can be regarded as a compact way of writing down the working : thus the example in 3.2 could be arranged as follows

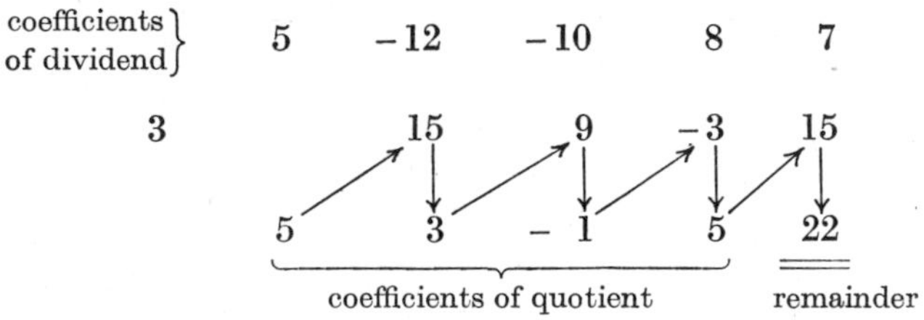

The last row contains the essence of the answer

$$\mathrm{q}(x)=5x^3+3x^2-x+5$$
$$\mathrm{r}(x)=22$$

The numbers of the second and third rows are written down alternately in the order shown by the arrows, the inclined arrows representing multiplications by 3, and the vertical arrows addition. The reader will see the significance of each step by a careful comparison with the longer method.

3.22. *Synthetic division by a quadratic*

Horner's method is easily extended to divisions by polynomials of higher degree. A study of the following example will make the principles of the extension clear.

Example

Divide $x^4 - 5x^3 + 9x^2 + 5$ by $x^2 - 3x + 5$

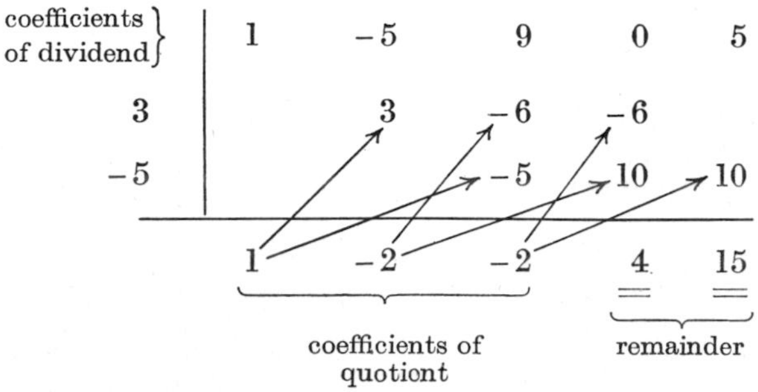

Hence the quotient is $x^2 - 2x - 2$ and the remainder $4x + 15$.

If the divisor polynomial is $x^2 + bx + c$, the values of $-b$ and $-c$ (here $+3$ and -5) are written on the left, in the second and third lines, and used in the calculation as multipliers of the entries in the fourth line, the products being placed as indicated by the arrows. Each of the entries in the fourth line is the sum of the corresponding entries in the first three lines. The blank last entry in the second line occurs because the 4 in the fourth line is a coefficient in the remainder, not a part of the quotient.

3.23. *The remainder theorem*

If $\mathrm{q}(x)$ is the quotient polynomial and r the remainder on division of $\mathrm{f}(x)$ by $(x - \alpha)$, the relation

$$\mathrm{f}(x) \equiv (x - \alpha)\mathrm{q}(x) + r \tag{1}$$

is an identity. For the value $x = \alpha$, it gives

$$\mathrm{f}(\alpha) = r$$

This provides a means of evaluating the remainder without carrying out the division.

It follows that if α is such that $\mathrm{f}(\alpha) = 0$, then

$$\mathrm{f}(x) \equiv (x - \alpha)\mathrm{q}(x) \tag{2}$$

that is, $(x - \alpha)$ is a factor of $\mathrm{f}(x)$.

Example

If $f(x) = x^3 + 4x^2 + x - 6$, $f(1) = 0$, so $(x-1)$ is a factor. Then by division $f(x) = (x-1)(x^2+5x+6) = (x-1)(x+2)(x+3)$ by factorising the quadratic.

Certain extensions are possible, for example if $f(x) = 0$ and also the quotient polynomial $q(x)$ in (2) is zero at $x = \alpha$, then $(x-\alpha)^2$ is a factor of $f(x)$.

3.3. The rational functions

By a rational function of x is meant the ratio of two polynomials $f(x)$ and $g(x)$. Thus the general rational function

$$R(x) = \frac{f(x)}{g(x)} = \frac{a_0x^n + a_1x^{n-1} + \ldots + a_n}{b_0x^m + b_1x^{m-1} + \ldots + b_m}$$

where the a's and b's are numerical coefficients. It will be supposed that the polynomials have no common linear or quadratic factor ; if they had a common linear factor $(x-\alpha)$, $R(x)$ would be undefined for $x = \alpha$, and for all other values of x the common factor could be cancelled out.

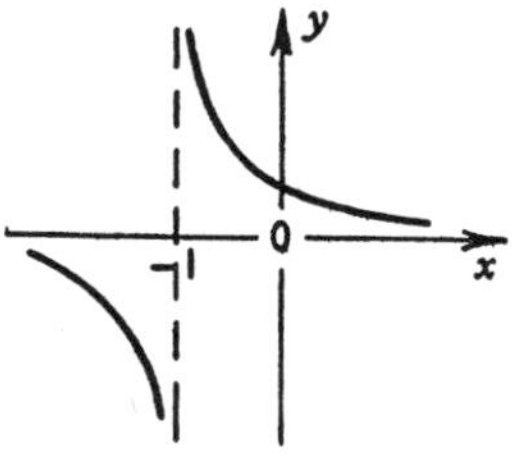

$y = 1/(x+1)$

FIG. 3.5

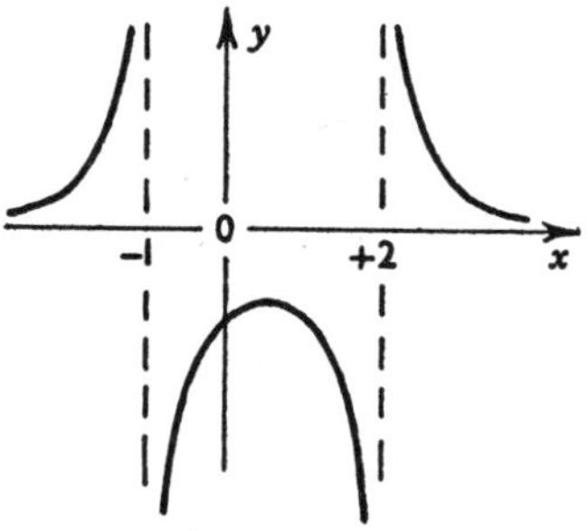

$y = 1/(x+1)(x-2)$

FIG. 3.6

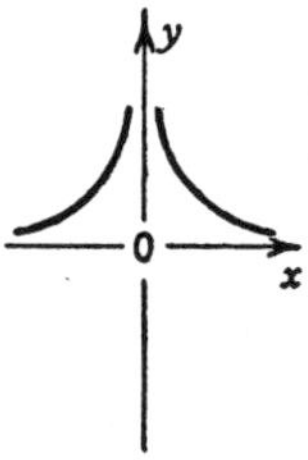

$y = 1/x^2$

FIG. 3.7

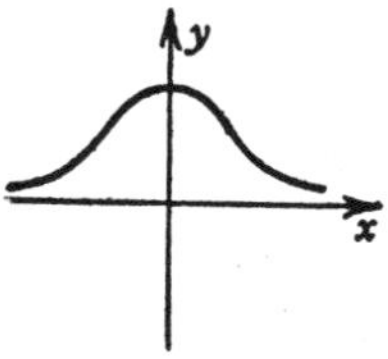

$y = 1/(1+x^2)$

FIG. 3.8

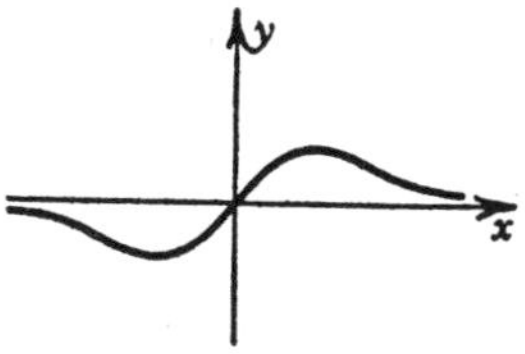

$y = x/(1+x^2)$

FIG 3.9

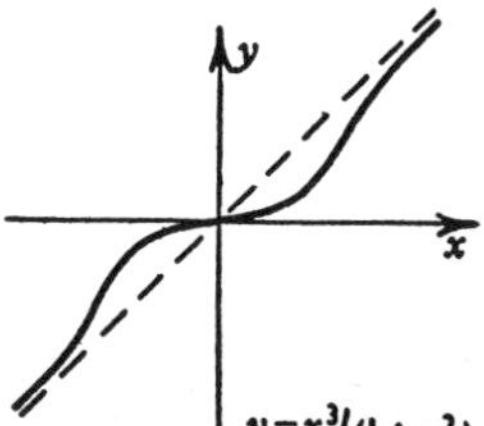

$y = x^3/(1+x^2)$

FIG. 3.10

It follows that R(x) is single-valued, and is continuous except at the zeros, if any, of g(x). At such a point, R(x) is of course undefined; in its neighbourhood, R(x) is unlimited, and a graph of the function would have a vertical asymptote, such as that at $x=-1$ in Fig. 3.5, for each simple factor of g(x); for a repeated factor such as $(x-\beta)^2$, there is an asymptote at $x=\beta$ near which the behaviour of R(x) is similar to that shown at $x=0$ in Fig. 3.7.

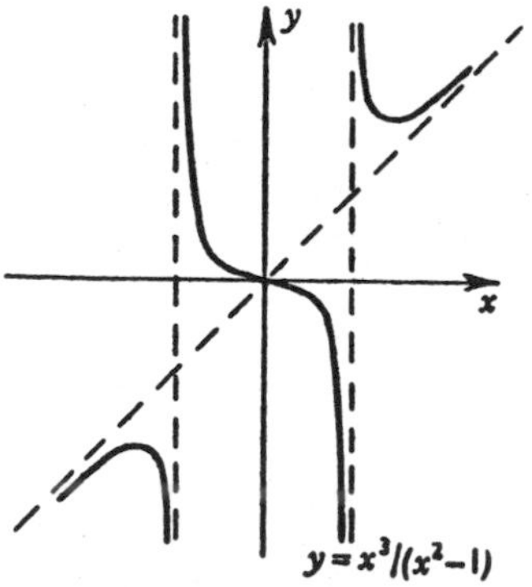

FIG. 3.11

Unlike a polynomial, R(x) does not necessarily tend to infinity as $x\to\infty$. It does tend to ∞ if $m<n$, but tends to 0 if $m>n$ and to a constant, a_0/b_0, if $m=n$ (see Figs 3·8–3·11).

3.31. *Partial fractions*

A rational function F$(x)/$g(x) can always be expressed in terms of its partial fractions, that is as the sum of rational functions whose denominators are the factors of g(x). A simple example is

$$\frac{x}{(x+1)(x+2)}=\frac{2}{x+2}-\frac{1}{x+1}$$

It will later be useful to have some general methods for splitting a rational function into its partial fractions.

The algebraic theory of this process is somewhat deeper than might be expected and will not be discussed. All practical requirements are adequately covered by the following rules of procedure.

(i) If F(x) is not already of lower degree than g(x) the rational function must be expressed (by dividing out) as the sum of a quotient polynomial q(x) and a rational fraction R$(x)=$f$(x)/$g(x) which can be called a proper fraction in the sense that the degree of f is less than that of g, thus F$(x)/$g$(x)=$q$(x)+$f$(x)/$g(x).

(ii) g(x) must now be factorised into irreducible factors; i.e. it is expressed as the product of linear factors $(x-\alpha)$, possibly repeated, and irreducible quadratic factors $(x^2+\beta x+\gamma)$, possibly repeated. In the result each factor will give rise to a partial fraction having a numerator of lower degree than the denominator.

(iii) The numerators are determined as in the following sections.

3.32. *Single linear factor*

Let $(x-\alpha)$ be the factor so that $g(x)=(x-\alpha)\,g_1(x)$. Since $(x-\alpha)$ is not repeated, $g_1(\alpha)\neq 0$ (cf. Remainder Theorem). Then (we quote it as a fact) it is always possible to write

$$\frac{f(x)}{(x-\alpha)g_1(x)} \equiv \frac{A}{x-\alpha}+\frac{f_1(x)}{g_1(x)} \tag{1}$$

where A is a constant. Strictly we must exclude $x=\alpha$ and the zeros of $g_1(x)$ from the range of validity of equation (1). The constant A can now be evaluated. Multiply both sides by $g(x)=(x-\alpha)\,g_1(x)$; then

$$f(x)\equiv A\,g_1(x)+(x-\alpha)f_1(x) \tag{2}$$

Now although both sides of identity (1) are indeterminate at $x=\alpha$ and of course at all other zeros of $g(x)$, (2) is a polynomial identity and therefore by the theorem at the end of 3.14 is valid for all x, in particular for $x=\alpha$. Putting $x=\alpha$ in (2) we now obtain

$$f(\alpha)=A\,g_1(\alpha) \quad \text{i.e. } A=f(\alpha)/g_1(\alpha)$$

Hence we have the simple rule for finding A in formula (1); delete the factor $(x-\alpha)$ on the left-hand side then put $x=\alpha$ in the remaining quotient. The result is A.

If all the factors of $g(x)$ are linear and not repeated, this rule enables all the partial fractions to be written down at sight.

Example

$$\frac{x^2-5x+2}{x^3-6x^2+11x-6} \equiv \frac{x^2-5x+2}{(x-1)(x-2)(x-3)}$$

$$\equiv \frac{1-5+2}{(x-1)(-1)(-2)}+\frac{4-10+2}{1(x-2)(-1)}+\frac{9-15+2}{1\,.\,2(x-3)}$$

$$\equiv \frac{-1}{x-1}+\frac{4}{x-2}-\frac{2}{x-3}$$

It is not, however, necessary for all the factors of $g(x)$ to be of this type before the rule can be applied. Thus

$$\frac{x^4+3x^2+1}{(x-1)(x^2+1)^2} \equiv \frac{1+3+1}{(x-1)4} + \text{other terms}$$

$$\equiv \frac{5}{4(x-1)} + \text{other terms}$$

3.33. *Repeated linear factor*

If $(x-\alpha)^s$ with $s \geqslant 2$ is a factor of $g(x)$ then the above rule is insufficient. The partial fraction with $(x-\alpha)^s$ as denominator cannot be taken simply as $A/(x-\alpha)^s$ but must be given either of the equivalent forms

$$\frac{A_1 x^{s-1} + A_2 x^{s-2} + \ldots + A_s}{(x-\alpha)^s} \quad \text{or} \quad \frac{B_1}{(x-\alpha)^s} + \frac{B_2}{(x-\alpha)^{s-1}} + \ldots + \frac{B_s}{(x-\alpha)}$$

where the A's or B's are to be determined.

Example

$$\frac{x^2}{(x-1)^2(x+1)} = \frac{A_1 x + A_2}{(x-1)^2} + \frac{1}{4(x+1)}$$

Multiplying by $(x-1)^2(x+1)$, we obtain

$$x^2 = (A_1 x + A_2)(x+1) + \tfrac{1}{4}(x-1)^2 \tag{3}$$

A_1 and A_2 can now be determined in a number of ways, e.g. : (*a*) First put $x=1$; this is a valid procedure, since we require (3) to be an identity in x ; it gives $2(A_1+A_2)=1$. A second relation is required, and is obtained, for example, by putting $x=0$, giving $A_2 = -\frac{1}{4}$. Hence $A_1 = \frac{3}{4}$ and

$$\frac{x^2}{(x-1)^2(x+1)} = \frac{3x-1}{4(x-1)^2} + \frac{1}{4(x+1)} \tag{4}$$

or (*b*) By comparison of coefficients : from the coefficients of x^2 $A_1 = \frac{3}{4}$, and from the constant terms, $A_2 = -\frac{1}{4}$ in agreement with (4).

3.34. *Single quadratic factor*

A quadratic factor $x^2+\alpha x+\beta$ gives rise to a partial fraction

$$\frac{A_1 x + A_0}{x^2+\alpha x+\beta}$$

Example

$$\frac{2(x^2+3x+1)}{(x-1)(x^2+1)} = \frac{5}{(x-1)} + \frac{A_1 x + A_0}{x^2+1}$$

Multiply by $(x-1)(x^2+1)$

$$2(x^2+3x+1) = 5(x^2+1) + (A_1 x + A_0)(x-1)$$

Comparing coefficients of x^2

$$2=5+A_1, \text{ giving } A_1=-3$$

and constant term

$$2=5-A_0, \quad \text{giving } A_0=+3$$

$$\therefore \frac{2(x^2+3x+1)}{(x-1)(x^2+1)} \equiv \frac{5}{(x-1)} - \frac{3(x-1)}{x^2+1}$$

An alternative is to expand x^2+1 into linear factors $(x+i)$ and $(x-i)$ where $i^2=-1$ (see Chapter 6) and use the method of 3.32. The imaginary terms thus introduced can always be regrouped so as to cancel leaving a purely real expression.

3.35. *Repeated quadratic factor*

The partial fraction corresponding to a repeated quadratic $(x^2+\alpha x+\beta)^s$ must be given a numerator of degree $2s-1$, thus

$$\frac{A_0x^{2s-1}+A_1x^{2s-2}+\ldots+A_{2s-1}}{(x^2+\alpha x+\beta)^s}$$

or alternately

$$\frac{B_0x+B_1}{(x^2+\alpha x+\beta)^s}+\frac{B_2x+B_3}{(x^2+\alpha x+\beta)^{s-1}}+\frac{B_{2s-2}x+B_{2s-1}}{(x^2+\alpha x+\beta)}$$

There are $2s$ coefficients to determine in either case. If $s>2$ the details become extremely tedious, but fortunately, such problems are academic only.

Example

$$\frac{2(x^2+2x+3)}{(x-1)(x^2+1)^2}=\frac{3}{(x-1)}+\frac{B_0x+B_1}{(x^2+1)^2}+\frac{B_2x+B_3}{x^2+1}$$

Multiplying by $(x-1)(x^2+1)^2$

$2(x^2+2x+3)$

$$=3(x^2+1)^2+(B_0x+B_1)(x-1)+(B_2x+B_3)(x-1)(x^2+1)$$

Comparing coefficients, we obtain

$x^4: \; 0=3+B_2$ i.e. $B_2=-3$

$x^3: \; 0=-B_2+B_3$ $B_3=B_2=-3$

$x^2: \; 2=6+B_0+B_2-B_3$ $B_0=-4-B_2+B_3=-4$

$x\;: \; 4=-B_0+B_1-B_2+B_3$ $B_1=+4+B_0+B_2-B_3=0$

As a check we note that the constant terms on the L.H.S. is 6 and on the R.H.S. $3-B_1-B_3$ which is also 6. The result is

$$2\frac{(x^2+2x+3)}{(x-1)(x^2+1)^2}\equiv\frac{3}{x-1}-\frac{4x}{(x^2+1)^2}-\frac{3(x+1)}{x^2+1}$$

3.4. Algebraic functions

If y is related to x by an algebraic equation of the form

$$P_0(x)y^n + P_1(x)y^{n-1} + \dots + P_n(x) = 0 \tag{1}$$

where the P's are polynomials in x, then y is said to be an algebraic function of x. Rational functions $y = R(x)$ are thus particular cases of algebraic functions, with $n=1$; thus: $P_0(x)R(x) + P_1(x) = 0$. Polynomials are a still more restricted class obtained by further putting $P_0(x) = \text{constant}$.

The simplest algebraic function that is not rational is obtained by putting $n=2$

$$P_0(x)y^2 + P_1(x)y + P_2(x) = 0 \tag{2}$$

By completing the square this can be re-arranged as

$$\{y + \tfrac{1}{2}P_1(x)/P_0(x)\}^2 - \{\tfrac{1}{2}P_1(x)/P_0(x)\}^2 + P_2(x)/P_0(x) = 0$$

i.e. $\{y + \frac{1}{2}P_1(x)/P_0(x)\}^2 \equiv f(x)$ where

$$f(x) \equiv \{\tfrac{1}{2}P_1(x)/P_0(x)\}^2 - P_2(x)/P_0(x) \tag{3}$$

and hence the solution of (1) differs from the solution of

$$y^2 = f(x) \tag{4}$$

by the rational function $\frac{1}{2}P_1(x)/P_0(x)$. Equation (4) has the simpler behaviour and the solution of (2) can always be recovered from that of (4) by subtracting, at each value of x, the rational function $\frac{1}{2}P_1(x)/P_0(x)$.

Two important properties of an algebraic function are apparent from equation (4). First, it may not be single-valued; in this case, for a given x there are two distinct values of y (provided $f(x) > 0$): these points may join up to give two distinct curves or, as we say, a curve with two branches as in Fig. 3.13; these branches meet at the zeros of $f(x)$. In a case like Fig. 3.12 the *function* has two branches, though the curve has only one branch. In the general case of an algebraic function defined by an equation of degree n, such as (1), there may be up to but not more than n values of y satisfying the equation for any x, so an algebraic function is never infinitely many-valued. Second, y is not necessarily real over the whole range of x, for if $f(x)$ is negative in an interval $a < x < b$ there is no corresponding real value of y in this interval and there is a corresponding gap in the curve.

Example 1

The simplest examples are those in which $f(x)$ is a simple power of x. Thus $y^2=x$, $y^2=x^2$, $y^2=x^3$ can be solved for y to give $y=\pm x^{1/2}$, $y=\pm x$, $y=\pm x^{3/2}$ respectively. The graphs of these functions are as shown in Figs. 3.12–3.14.

In Figs. 3.12 and 3.14, there are no real values of y for $x<0$, and the graph is confined to the right of the y-axis. In Fig. 3.13 we have the simplest example of a ‘ node ’, i.e. a point at which two branches of the graph intersect at an angle. In Fig. 3.14 we have a ‘ cusp ; i.e. a point at which two branches touch and terminate. Higher odd powers of x give cusps at the origin in a similar way. Higher even powers on the other hand give branches that touch at the origin but do not terminate (Fig. 3.15). Fig. 3.16 illustrates a graph consisting of an isolated point : the only real point on the graph of $y^2=-x^2$ is $x=0$, $y=0$.

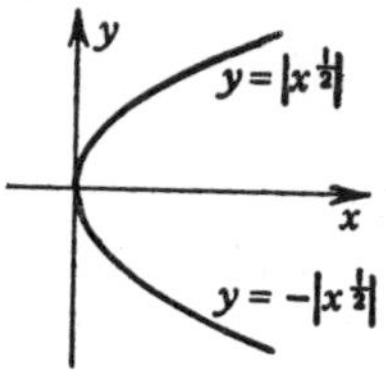

$y^2=x$

FIG. 3.12

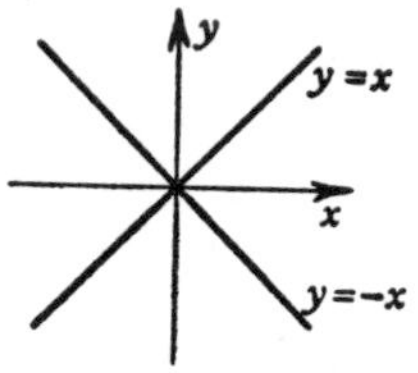

$y^2=x^2$

FIG. 3.13

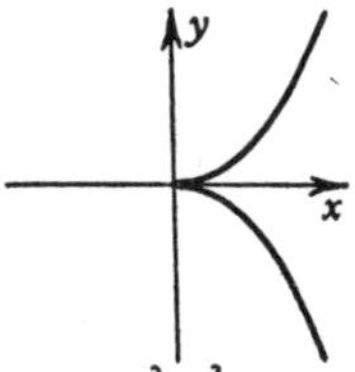

$y^2=x^3$

FIG. 3.14

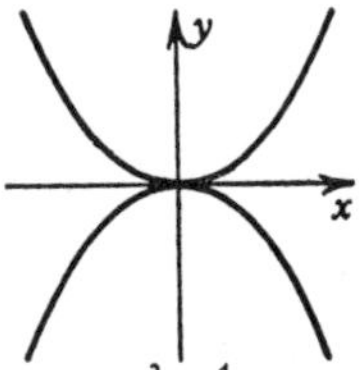

$y^2=x^4$

FIG 3.15

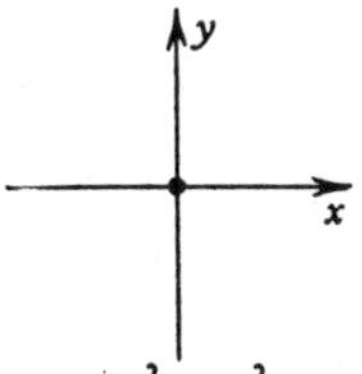

$y^2=-x^2$

FIG. 3.16

In more complicated examples of the form $y^2=f(x)$ it is often helpful to sketch the graph of $y=f(x)$ and thence to deduce the general shape of $y^2=f(x)$.

Example 2

With $n=2$, $P_0(x)=b$, $P_1(x)=2hx+2f$ and $P_2(x)=ax^2+2gx+c$ in equation (1) we obtain the general equation of a conic section :

$$ax^2+2hxy+by^2+2gx+2fy+c=0$$

Example 3

If $f(x)$ is a rational function $p(x)/q(x)$, the graph of

$$y^2 = f(x) = p(x)/q(x)$$

disappears in the intervals in which $f(x)$ is negative ; elsewhere it has zeros (nodes, cusps or contacts) at the zeros of $p(x)$ and discontinuities at the zeros of $q(x)$. A hypothetical case illustrating most of these possibilities is given in Fig. 3.17. The upper graph is of the rational function $y = R(x)$ and the lower one represents $y^2 = R(x)$.

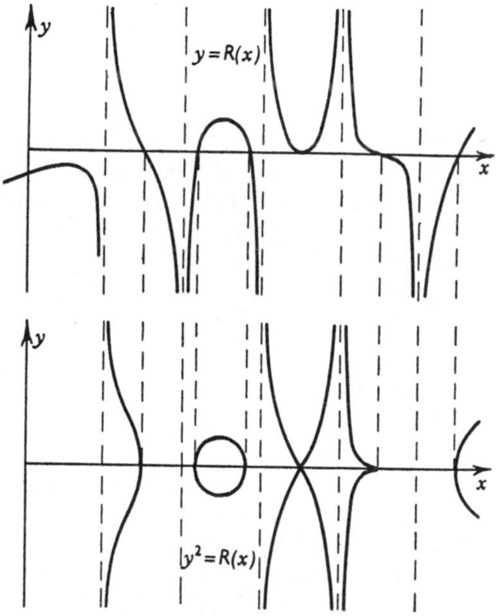

FIG. 3.17

Example 4

Graphs of functions defined by algebraic equations of higher degree become increasingly complicated because of the increasing number of branches that are possible. Equations of odd degree have at least one branch that is continuous (except perhaps at a finite number of points where infinite discontinuities occur) over the whole range of x. Fig. 3.18 illustrates the function defined by $y^3 - 3xy = 2x^2$.

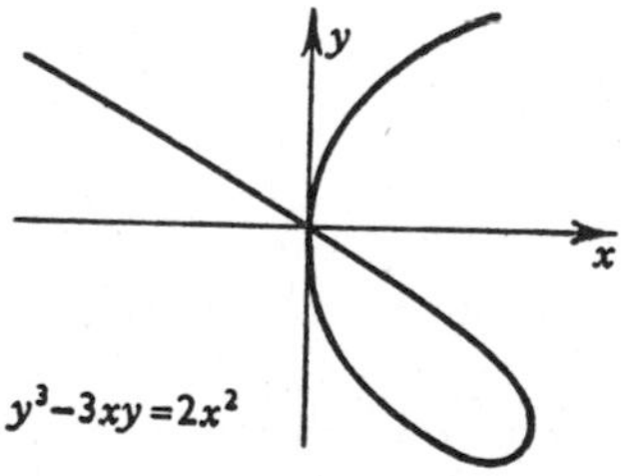

FIG. 3.18

Example 5

It can be shown that if the relation between x and y is given by a polynomial in y whose coefficients are algebraic functions, $A_n(x)$, of x.

$$A_0(x)y^n + A_1(x)y^{n-1} + \dots + A_n(x) = 0 \tag{1}$$

then y is still an algebraic function of x; equations like (1) do not define a new class of functions beyond those we have already considered.

The following result is of interest since it can be used to show that certain functions, for example the circular functions, are not algebraic functions.

The function inverse to an algebraic function is also algebraic.

Suppose $y = f(x)$ is algebraic of degree n say, i.e. it satisfies

$$P_0(x)y^n + \dots + P_n(x) = 0$$

Since $P_0(x)$, $P_1(x)$ etc. are polynomials, the left hand side is a sum of terms of the form ax^ry^s. Collect the terms in x^r and arrange as follows

$$Q_0(y)x^m + \dots + Q_m(y) = 0$$

The solution of this equation is $x = \phi(y)$ where ϕ is the function inverse to f. The equation is algebraic of degree m, where m is the highest power of x occurring in the polynomials $P_0(x), \dots, P_n(x)$.

3.5. Transcendental functions

A function which is not an algebraic function is called transcendental. Among the most important transcendental functions are functions defined geometrically e.g. $\sin x$, $\cos x$, those defined using the concepts of the calculus e.g.

$$\int \frac{\exp x}{x}\,dx$$

and those defined by infinite series. (Note that *algebraic* functions can be defined using only *finite* series of terms.) Not all functions defined by series, by calculus or by geometrical means are transcendental, neither are the classes of functions specified by these three methods mutually exclusive; the trigonometrical function $\sin x$ for example can be defined by each of the three.

Whatever method is used for the definition of a transcendental function, the investigation of its properties will almost always require the use of infinite series at some stage, and it is to a discussion of such series that we next turn.

CHAPTER FOUR

FUNCTIONS DEFINED BY SERIES

4.1. Functions defined by infinite series

If a function $f(x)$ is to be defined as the limit of an infinite series $\sum u_n$ the terms u_n must themselves be functions of x, $u_n = u_n(x)$ say ; we are thus concerned with a series of functions $\sum u_n(x)$. The value of the function $f(x)$ at any point $x=a$ is defined provided the series of numbers $\sum u_n(a)$ is convergent. We have already discussed the convergence of series of numbers in Chapter 2. In order to use a function in algebraical processes however, a detailed knowledge of its values is less relevant than general information about such matters as its continuity, its behaviour when subjected to limiting processes and the rules for combining it with other functions without evaluating all the functions at every point.

The question of the continuity of $f(x)$ at any point cannot be decided by anything we have said so far. It is an interesting, and at first sight a surprising fact that even if each of the functions $u_n(x)$ is continuous at $x=a$, and if $\sum u_n(a)$ is convergent, $f(x)=\sum u_n(x)$ is not necessarily continuous at $x=a$. An example of such a discontinuity is provided by the series

$$f(x)=(1+x)+x^2(1+x)+x^4(1+x)+\dots \tag{1}$$

For values of x in the range $-1<x<1$, we can sum the geometric series to infinity, the sum is $(1+x)/(1-x^2)=1/(1-x)$, so that very near to $x=-1$, $f(x)$ is very nearly equal to $\frac{1}{2}$. However at $x=-1$, each term in the series (1) is zero so the sum to infinity is zero; that is $f(-1)=0$.

We can gain insight into this apparently freakish kind of behaviour, as well as the ability to manipulate functions defined by series as confidently as any other kind of function, only by a thorough-going discussion of limits, continuity and, especially, convergence. Extensions of the work of 2.61–2.66 are needed because the previous discussion was mainly concerned with series of numbers rather than the more general properties of series of functions.

4.11. *The limit of a function of a continuous variable*

We discussed in 2.43 what is meant by the limit of a function of an integral variable n as $n \to \infty$. The limit of a function of a continuous variable x as $x \to a$ is not essentially different, but contains one extra step, viz. the selection of a sequence of values of x, and one extra proviso, viz. that the limit should be independent of this selection.

In order to define the limit of $f(x)$ as $x \to a$ we select a sequence of numbers x_n such that $x_n \to a$ as $n \to \infty$. If we now calculate $f(x_n)$ for each x_n we obtain a new sequence of numbers $f(x_n)$ which may itself have a limit. If the limit does exist, and is moreover the same no matter what particular sequence of values x_n tending to a is used, then the (uniquely defined) quantity $\lim_{n \to \infty} f(x_n)$ is called the limit of $f(x)$ as $x \to a$, or $\lim_{x \to a} f(x)$.

Theorem. If $f(x)$ *is continuous at* $x = a$, *then* $\lim_{x \to a} f(x) = f(a)$.

This is not a surprising statement, but it is not quite self-evident from the definition of continuity given in 2.21, and to prove it we must show that it is impossible to choose a sequence of x_n's such that $x_n \to a$ for which $f(x_n)$ fails to tend to $f(a)$. The proof runs as follows;

We are given (1) that $f(x)$ is continuous at $x = a$ and (2) that $x_n \to a$. We therefore know (1) that for any $\epsilon > 0$ there exists a $\delta > 0$ such that $|f(x) - f(a)| < \epsilon$ whenever $|x - a| < \delta$; and (2) that for every $\delta > 0$ there exists a number n_0 such that $|x_n - a| < \delta$ whenever $n \geqslant n_0$. Therefore for any $\epsilon > 0$ there exists a number n_0 such that $|f(x_n) - f(a)| < \epsilon$ when $n \geqslant n_0$. Hence $f(x_n) \to f(a)$, and the theorem is proved.

4.12. *Alternative definition of continuity, and definition of* $f(a \pm 0)$

Two important types of sequence x_n are those which increase and decrease monotonically respectively, to the limit a. Let $h_n \to 0$ be any monotonic sequence of positive numbers tending to zero. Then $x_n = a - h_n$ and $x_n = a + h_n$ are examples of the two types. A convenient definition of continuity easily seen to be equivalent to the first can now be given:

If for every monotonic sequence h_n of positive numbers tending to zero

$$\lim_{n \to \infty} f(a - h_n) = \lim_{n \to \infty} f(a + h_n) = f(a) \tag{1}$$

then the function $f(x)$ is continuous at $x=a$. A shorthand notation which is frequently used is

$$\lim_{n\to\infty} f(a-h_n) \equiv f(a-0) \quad \text{and} \quad \lim_{n\to\infty} f(a+h_n) \equiv f(a+0) \qquad (2)$$

This notation should only be used when the limits on the left-hand sides of (2) are independent of the sequence h_n. In terms of this notation the continuity of $f(x)$ at $x=a$ implies

$$f(a-0)=f(a+0)=f(a)$$

If the relations (1) do not hold the function is discontinuous.

If $f(a+0)=f(a-0)\neq f(a)$, as for the function $f(x)=1+x^2$ for $x\neq 0$, $f(0)=0$, the discontinuity is said to be 'removable'. This situation usually arises from an awkward or unsuitable definition of the function at the point $x=a$. Thus if $f(x)=1+x^2$ for $x\neq a$, and $f(x)=0$ for $x=a$, there is a removable discontinuity owing to the (rather perverse) definition of $f(x)$ at $x=a$. Similarly $f(x)=x/x$ has a removable discontinuity at $x=0$ owing to the fact that $0/0$ is indeterminate : the discontinuity can be removed by defining $f(x)=1$ at $x=0$.

If $f(a+0)$ and $f(a-0)$ exist but are not equal there is said to be a 'jump discontinuity', as for the function $f(x)=1-x$ for $x<0$, $-1+x$ for $x>0$. The value of $f(a)$ is immaterial.

If $f(a+0)=f(a)$ but $f(a-0)$ does not exist, the function is 'right hand continuous'. For example if $f(x)=\sqrt{x}$ (positive root), $f(x)$ is not defined for $x<0$, but $f(a+0)=f(0)=0$. A similar definition holds for 'left hand continuous'.

Finally both $f(a+0)$ and $f(a-0)$ may be undefined ; either of the sequences $f(a+h_n)$, $f(a-h_n)$ may tend to $\pm\infty$, oscillate finitely or oscillate infinitely. For example if $f(x)=\sin(1/x)$, the sequences $f(0\pm h_n)$ oscillate finitely; if $f(x)=\operatorname{cosec}(1/x)$, $f[(1/2n\pi)\pm h_n]$ tends to $\pm\infty$ and $f(0\pm h_n)$ oscillates infinitely.

4.2. Uniformity of convergence

Of all the aspects of infinite series of functions which can be investigated, 'uniformity of convergence' is probably the most difficult to grasp but the most important in its consequences. The essential point is closely connected with a phenomenon to which we have already called attention (namely that the function defined by an infinite series of functions is not necessarily continuous even though the individual functions are continuous) and which we now further examine. To avoid the purely technical difficulties of having to sum the terms of a series, we define the series, not by the general term u_n, but by the partial sums $S_n = \sum_{\nu=1}^{n} u_\nu(x)$. It is always possible to reconstruct the terms of a series so defined, for clearly,

$$u_1(x) = \mathrm{S}_1(x), \quad u_{n+1}(x) = \mathrm{S}_{n+1}(x) - \mathrm{S}_n(x)$$

Consider for example the series for which the partial sums are $\mathrm{S}_n(x) = (x^2)^{1/n}$. The corresponding series is

$$x^2 + [(x^2)^{1/2} - x^2] + [(x^2)^{1/3} - (x^2)^{1/2}] + \dots \tag{1}$$

and the limit $\mathrm{S}(x) \equiv \lim_{n\to\infty} \mathrm{S}_n(x) = 1$ for all values of x except $x=0$ where there is a discontinuity since $\mathrm{S}(0)=0$. (Notice incidentally that the terms of the series are the pairs of terms inside the square brackets : if the brackets are removed the result is an alternating series whose terms do not tend to zero ; so the new series without the restriction imposed by the brackets does not converge : in fact, removing the brackets converts (1) into a different series.) The partial sums $\mathrm{S}_n(x)$ are drawn for $n=1$, 2, 4, 6 and 20 in fig 2·6. It will be seen that $\mathrm{S}_n(x)$ is a good approximation to $\mathrm{S}(x)$ provided n is fairly large and x is not too small. If x is small, we can still make $\mathrm{S}_n(x)$ as close as we wish to $\mathrm{S}(x)$ but only by going to very high values of n. Thus although $\mathrm{S}_n(x)$ converges to $\mathrm{S}(x)$ for all values of x it does not do so equally rapidly for all x.

We can examine this quantitatively by considering how the number n of terms, required to obtain a specified degree of approximation to $\mathrm{S}(x)$, varies with x. We know that $\mathrm{S}_n(x) \to \mathrm{S}(x)$ and therefore for a given $\epsilon > 0$, there exists a number n_0 such that $|\mathrm{S}_n(x) - \mathrm{S}(x)| < \epsilon$ whenever $n \geqslant n_0$. The smaller we take ϵ, the larger in general must we take n_0. It is clear however that for values of x near $x=1$, quite a small value of n gives a very good approximation to the limit, whereas near $x=0$ the approximation is poor even for large values of n.

A numerical trial will make this very plain. Take $\epsilon = 0{\cdot}01$; then we require a value of n such that $|\mathrm{S}_n(x) - \mathrm{S}(x)| < 0{\cdot}01$. Since $\mathrm{S}_n(x) = (x^2)^{1/n}$, $\mathrm{S}(x) = 1$, the requirement is that

$$|1 - (x^2)^{1/n}| < 0{\cdot}01,$$

i.e. $(0{\cdot}99)^n < x^2 < (1{\cdot}01)^n$, that is,

$$n > 2 \mid \log x / \log 0{\cdot}99 \mid \tag{2}$$

It is clear from (2) that as $x \to 0$ the required value of n tends to ∞. Thus in order to obtain a given degree of approximation of $S_n(x)$ to $S(x)$, the value of n has to be increased *without limit* as $x \to 0$: there is no value of n which provides a specified degree of approximation for *all* non-zero values of x. This is expressed by calling the convergence of the series (1) 'non-uniform' over an interval including $x = 0$. Note that the function $S(x)$ is discontinuous at $x = 0$ where the convergence is non-uniform. On the other hand, the finite value $n = 1000$ is sufficient to ensure that $| S_n(x) - S(x) | < 0{\cdot}01$ for *all* values of x in the range $0{\cdot}01 \leqslant x \leqslant 1$, and similarly for any specified value of $\epsilon > 0$, and for any value of x_0 greater than 0, there is a definite value of n such that $| S_n(x) - S(x) | < \epsilon$ for all values of x in the range $x_0 \leqslant x \leqslant 1$: this is expressed by calling the convergence of the series 'uniform' over such a range. Note that the function $S(x)$ is continuous in all such ranges where the convergence is uniform.

Non-uniformity of convergence is typical of the behaviour of a discontinuous sum of an (infinite) series of continuous functions.

4.21. *Formal definition of uniform convergence*

A series $\sum_{\nu=1}^{\infty} u_\nu(x)$ is said to converge uniformly to a limit $S(x)$ in a range X of x provided that for any $\epsilon > 0$ there exists a number n_0 *independent of* x such that

$$\left| \sum_{\nu=1}^{n} u_\nu(x) - S(x) \right| < \epsilon$$

whenever $n \geqslant n_0$, and for x in the range X. Note: the range X may be either an open interval $a < x < b$ or a closed interval $a \leqslant x \leqslant b$.

Notice that uniformity of convergence is a property associated with the behaviour of a function over an interval whereas convergence is concerned with behaviour at a particular point $x = a$ or $x = b$ say. Note that the geometric series converges in the range $-1 < x < 1$, but does not converge uniformly in that range: for

$$\left| \sum_{\nu=1}^{n} x^\nu - \frac{x}{1-x} \right| = \left| \frac{x^{n+1}}{1-x} \right|$$

and if x approaches the value 1, indefinitely large values of n are required. The series does however converge uniformly in $a \leqslant x \leqslant b$ provided $-1 < a < b < +1$, since the greater of the values of n that suffice for the end points a, b for any particular ϵ, suffices for the whole interval.

Example

The series $\sum x^n/n!$ converges uniformly in any bounded range of x. We have shown (2.67, ex. 1) that the convergence is absolute for all finite values of x. A similar argument establishes that it is also uniform. Let the interval considered be $-a \leqslant x \leqslant a$; let $S_n(x) = \sum_{\nu=1}^{n} x^\nu/\nu!$ and let $S(x)$ be the limit; then

$$S_n(x) - S(x) = \frac{x^{n+1}}{(n+1)!} + \dots,$$

$$| S_n(x) - S(x) | < \frac{|x|^{n+1}}{(n+1)!} \frac{1}{1-(|x|/n)} \quad \text{if } n > |x|$$

$$< 2|x|^{n+1}/(n+1)! \quad \text{if } n > 2|x|$$

Hence in the whole range of x, we can make

$$| S_n(x) - S(x) | < \frac{2a^{n+1}}{(n+1)!} \quad \text{by taking } n > 2a.$$

Finally since (2.46 ex. 6) $2a^{n+1}/(n+1)! \to 0$ as $n \to \infty$ there is a number $n_0(\epsilon)$, independent of x, such that $| S_n(x) - S(x) | < \epsilon$ for all $n \geqslant n_0$. The series converges most slowly at the ends of the interval and what we have proved is that by taking the appropriate value of n_0 at the ends of the interval the remainder term $| S_n(x) - S(x) |$ is less than ϵ over the whole interval. The convergence becomes slower and slower as $x \to \pm\infty$ but is uniform over any finite interval of x.

We now prove the following theorem.

Theorem. If $\sum u_n(x)$ is a series of continuous functions which is uniformly convergent in an interval, then its limit is a continuous function in that interval.

Let $S_n(x) = \sum_{\nu=1}^{n} u_\nu(x)$. Then $S_n(x)$ is continuous for finite n, being the sum of a finite number of continuous functions. We have therefore the two facts that $S_n(x)$ varies continuously with x, and that $S_n(x)$ converges uniformly to $S(x)$ as $n \to \infty$. Let x_0 be any point in the interval.

From uniformity of convergence

$$| S_n(x) - S(x) | < \epsilon \text{ for } n \geqslant n_0, \text{ all } x.$$

In particular $| S_{n_0}(x) - S(x) | < \epsilon$ (all x) and $| S_{n_0}(x_0) - S(x_0) | < \epsilon$.

From continuity of the $u_n(x)$, $S_{n_0}(x)$ is continuous,

$$| S_{n_0}(x) - S_{n_0}(x_0) | < \epsilon \quad \text{for } | x - x_0 | < \delta.$$

Hence from the inequality $| A+B+C | \leqslant | A | + | B | + | C |$

$$\begin{aligned} | \mathrm{S}(x) - \mathrm{S}(x_0) | & \\ &= | \{\mathrm{S}(x) - \mathrm{S}_{n_0}(x)\} + \{\mathrm{S}_{n_0}(x) - \mathrm{S}_{n_0}(x_0)\} + \{\mathrm{S}_{n_0}(x_0) - \mathrm{S}(x_0)\} | \\ &\leqslant | \mathrm{S}(x) - \mathrm{S}_{n_0}(x) | + | \mathrm{S}_{n_0}(x) - \mathrm{S}_{n_0}(x_0) | + | \mathrm{S}_{n_0}(x_0) - \mathrm{S}(x_0) | \\ &< 3\epsilon \quad \text{if } | x - x_0 | < \delta. \end{aligned}$$

This is the required condition for the continuity of $\mathrm{S}(x)$, so the theorem is proved.

Corollary. It follows that the operations $\lim\limits_{x \to a}$ *and* $\sum\limits_{1}^{\infty}$ *commute (i.e. their order can be interchanged) provided the terms* $u_n(x)$ to *which they are applied form a uniformly convergent series, and* $\lim\limits_{x \to a} u_n(x)$ *exists.*

For if the nth partial sum is $\mathrm{S}_n(x) \to \mathrm{S}(x)$

$$\lim_{x \to a} \sum_{1}^{\infty} u_n(x) = \lim_{x \to a} \mathrm{S}(x) = \mathrm{S}(a)$$

and

$$\sum_{1}^{\infty} \lim_{x \to a} u_n(x) = \sum_{1}^{\infty} u_n(a) = \mathrm{S}(a)$$

The corresponding theorem for sequences is that the operations $\lim\limits_{x \to a}$ and $\lim\limits_{n \to \infty}$ commute provided the sequence $\phi_n(x)$ to which they are applied is uniformly convergent.

Uniformity of convergence of an infinite series is a very important property when the methods of the calculus (differentiation and integration) are applied to series. It is useful therefore to have tests for uniform convergence. The simplest is the M-test : more sensitive tests are not often necessary but two are given for completeness. It is perhaps necessary to add that the necessary and sufficient condition for convergence of an infinite sequence (2.43) becomes a necessary and sufficient condition for *uniform* convergence, if for any chosen value of ϵ the number n_0 is independent of x.

4.22. *Tests for uniform convergence*

The M-test. If $\sum u_n(x)$ *and* $\sum v_n$ *are a series of functions and a series of numbers respectively, and, if for all* x *in the range* $a \leqslant x \leqslant b$, $|u_n(x)| \leqslant |v_n|$: *if also* $\sum v_n$ *converges absolutely then* $\sum u_n(x)$ *converges uniformly.*

For if v_n converges absolutely then for all values of p

$$\sum_{n+1}^{n+p} |v_\nu| < \epsilon$$

provided $n \geqslant n_0$. Hence

$$\left|\sum_{n+1}^{n+p} u_\nu(x)\right| \leqslant \sum_{n+1}^{n+p} |u_\nu(x)| \leqslant \sum |v_\nu| < \epsilon$$

for $n \geqslant n_0$, for all x in the range and for all p. Since ϵ is obviously independent of x, $\sum u_n(x)$ is uniformly convergent in the interval.

The name of the test derives from a common notation $v_n 1 = M_n$. The following tests depend on splitting the general term $u_n(x)$ into factors one of which is monotonic in n.

Let $u_n(x) = \alpha_n v_n$ where α_n and v_n are both in general functions of x; in particular cases one of them may be a function of n only. We suppose that the functions α_n, v_n remain finite in the interval $a \leqslant x \leqslant b$ and that v_n is positive and monotonic decreasing as $n \to \infty$.

Abel's Test. If, in addition to the above conditions on α_n *and* v_n, *either* α_n *is independent of* x *and* $\sum \alpha_n$ *is convergent, or* $\alpha_n = \alpha_n(x)$ *and* $\sum \alpha_n(x)$ *is uniformly convergent, then* $\sum \alpha_n v_n$ *is uniformly convergent.*

Dirichlet's Test. If $\sum \alpha_n(x)$ *either converges or oscillates finitely, and if* $v_n(x)$ *converges uniformly as well as monotonically to zero as* $n \to \infty$ *(if* v_n *is independent of* x, $v_n \to 0$ *is sufficient) then* $\sum \alpha_n v_n$ *converges uniformly.* For the proofs of these results see Hardy, *Pure Mathematics*, Chap. VIII, §196.

Abel's Theorem. This is an important application of Abel's test; the theorem is: *If the series* $\sum \alpha_n$ *is convergent then the power series* $\sum \alpha_n x^n$ *is uniformly convergent in the range* $0 \leqslant x \leqslant 1$. *(If in addition* $\sum (-1)^n \alpha_n$ *converges, the power series is uniformly convergent throughout the range* $-1 \leqslant x \leqslant 1$.)

For x^n is monotonic decreasing as $n \to \infty$ (this is true even for $x = 1$, since x^n does not increase). The convergence of $\sum \alpha_n x^n$ is therefore uniform in the range $0 \leqslant x \leqslant 1$. It follows that if the power series converges to the sum $f(x)$, this function is left-hand continuous at $x = 1$ (cf. definition 4.12). In other words we may evaluate $\sum \alpha_n$, which is $f(1)$, as the limit of $f(x)$, viz. $f(1-0)$. Similarly if $\sum (-1)^n \alpha_n$ converges its sum is $f(-1+0)$.

Thus we can say at once from the theorem that

$$1 + \tfrac{1}{2}x + \tfrac{1}{4}x^2 + \tfrac{1}{8}x^3 + \dots$$

is uniformly convergent in the range $0 \leqslant x \leqslant 1$, since $1 + \frac{1}{2} + \frac{1}{4} + \dots$ is convergent; but that $1 - x + x^2 - x^3 + \dots$ may not be uniformly convergent throughout the range $0 \leqslant x \leqslant 1$ since $1 - 1 + 1 - 1 \dots$ is not convergent (in fact this series is certainly not uniformly convergent near $x = 1$).

Dirichlet's test is most often applied not to power series, but to oscillatory series of which the most important are trigonometric series $\sum v_n \sin nx$, $\sum v_n \cos nx$. For example the series

$$\cos\theta + \tfrac{1}{2}\cos 2\theta + \tfrac{1}{3}\cos 3\theta + \dots$$

is uniformly convergent except near $\theta = 0$, $\pm 2\pi$ ($v_n = 1/n$, $\alpha_n = \cos n\theta$). At these points the series becomes $1 + \frac{1}{2} + \frac{1}{3} + \dots$ which diverges.

Example

Show that the series $\sum n^{-s} \sin n\theta$ is convergent if $s > 0$, for all values of θ.

4.3. Functions defined by power series ; radius of convergence

We shall now consider some particular characteristics of functions defined by *power* series,

$$a_0 + a_1 x + a_2 x^2 + \dots = \sum_{n=0}^{\infty} a_n x^n$$

which converge in a range of values of x.

Let X be any value of x for which the series $\sum a_n x^n$ is absolutely convergent. Writing $a_n X^n = \alpha_n$ we see from Abel's theorem that $\sum \alpha_n y^n$ is uniformly convergent in the range $-1 \leqslant y \leqslant 1$: that is, $\sum a_n (Xy)^n$ is uniformly convergent in $-X \leqslant (Xy) \leqslant X$, i.e. $\sum a_n x^n$ is uniformly convergent throughout the range $-X \leqslant x \leqslant X$. This is worth stating as a theorem ;

If a power series is absolutely convergent for a certain value X of the argument, it is uniformly convergent in the range $-X \leqslant x \leqslant X$.

Although the idea of the radius of convergence of a power series cannot be fully developed until Chapter 13 it is convenient to introduce the idea here. The upper limit of the values of $|X|$ for which the series is absolutely convergent is known as the radius of convergence, R say, and the series is convergent for all $|x|<R$, and uniformly convergent in every range $-R+\epsilon<x<R-\epsilon$ $(\epsilon>0)$.

If a_n/a_{n-1} tends to a limit, $K>0$ say, as n tends to infinity, $(a_nX^n)/(a_{n-1}X^{n-1})$ tends to limit KX, so, from the Ratio test (2.66) the series $\sum a_nX^n$ converges if $|KX|<1$ i.e. if $|X|<1/K$, and diverges if $|X|>1/K$. It follows that in this case the radius of convergence $R=1/K$.

Example

Show that the radius of convergence of the binomial series $1+mx+m(m-1)x^2/2!+m(m-1)(m-2)x^3/3!\ldots$ is equal to 1 (unless m is an integer in which case the series reduces to a polynomial).

4.31. *Multiplication of series*

The product of two *finite* series is obtained in the same way as the product of two numbers, by long multiplication. Each term of one bracket is multiplied in turn by each term of the other and the results added. Thus

$$(a_0+a_1+a_2)(b_0+b_1+b_2)$$
$$=a_0b_0+a_0b_1+a_1b_0+a_0b_2+a_1b_1+a_2b_0+a_1b_2+a_2b_1+a_2b_2 \qquad (1)$$

A matter of notation needs care in this context. The product of two series $\sum_{n=0}^{M} a_n$ and $\sum_{n=0}^{N} b_n$ can be written

$$\left(\sum_{n=0}^{M} a_n\right)\left(\sum_{n=0}^{N} b_n\right) \text{ or as } \left(\sum_{m=0}^{M} a_m\right)\left(\sum_{n=0}^{N} b_n\right) \text{ or as } \sum_{m=0}^{M}\sum_{n=0}^{N} a_mb_n.$$

The product must *not* be written as $\sum_{n=0}^{M}\sum_{n=0}^{N} a_nb_n$ which is meaningless, nor, even if $M=N$, as $\sum_{n=0}^{N} a_nb_n$ which means something quite different, namely $a_0b_0+a_1b_1+a_2b_2+\ldots$. (The product contains numerous additional terms like a_0b_1, a_0b_2 etc.)

Since the relation

$$\left(\sum_{m=0}^{M} a_m\right)\left(\sum_{n=0}^{N} b_n\right)=\sum_{m=0}^{M}\sum_{n=0}^{N} a_mb_n \qquad (2)$$

holds without restriction for all finite values of M and N it would seem likely that, at least under some circumstances, the product of two convergent infinite series $\sum_{m=0}^{\infty} a_m$ and $\sum_{n=0}^{\infty} b_n$ should also be obtainable by long multiplication, as expressed by the formula

$$\left(\sum_{m=0}^{\infty} a_m\right)\left(\sum_{n=0}^{\infty} b_n\right) = \sum_{m=0}^{\infty} \sum_{n=0}^{\infty} a_m b_n \tag{3}$$

However, the expression on the right-hand side here is not a finite sum but a shorthand way of writing a complicated double limit, viz. the limit of the right-hand side of (2) as both $M \to \infty$ and $N \to \infty$. Since addition is a step-by-step process, the numbers to be added must first be arranged in sequence and there is now no unique rule for selecting the order in which they are to be taken. We have seen in 2.67 that the limit of the sum of terms of a conditionally convergent series may depend on the order in which the terms are taken, but that the terms of an absolutely convergent series may be rearranged. Using this result it can be shown that if the series $\sum_{m=0}^{\infty} a_m$ and $\sum_{n=0}^{\infty} b_n$ are *absolutely* convergent, and converge to A and B respectively, then the double sum $\sum_{m=0}^{\infty} \sum_{n=0}^{\infty} a_m b_n$ converges to a unique limit, and this limit is AB.

It is sometimes convenient to arrange the terms in the product in such a way that all the terms $a_m b_n$ for which $m+n$ has the same value are grouped together; that is

$$c_k = \sum_{m=0}^{k} a_m b_{k-m} \tag{4}$$

then the series is

$$\sum_{m=0}^{\infty} \sum_{n=0}^{\infty} a_m b_n = \sum_{k=0}^{\infty} c_k \tag{5}$$

The sequence (c_k) is called the ‘ convolution ’ of the sequences (a_m) and (b_n), and $\sum c_k$ is called the ‘ Cauchy expansion ’ of $\sum a_m \sum b_n$.

CHAPTER FIVE

THE ELEMENTARY TRANSCENDENTAL FUNCTIONS

The trigonometric functions and their inverses, and the exponential and its inverse the logarithmic function are called the ' elementary ' transcendental functions. As explained in 3.5 the term transcendental simply means 'non-algebraic'.

5.1. The trigonometric functions

The reader is assumed to be familiar with the definitions and elementary properties of the trigonometric or circular functions $\sin x$, $\cos x$, $\tan x$, and their reciprocals. The argument x is understood to be in radians unless other units are explicitly stated. The following properties are quoted for reference.

(i) A function $f(x)$ is said to have a period X if $f(x+X)=f(x)$ for *all* values of x : the graph of such a function is unaltered if it be displaced bodily by a distance X in the direction of the x-axis. The functions $\sin x$, $\cos x$, $\operatorname{cosec} x$ and $\sec x$ all have period 2π in x. The functions $\tan x$ and $\cot x$, on the other hand, have period π.

(ii) The functions $\sin x$, $\cos x$ and $\tan x$ have the ' addition formulae '

$$\sin(x+y)=\sin x\cos y+\cos x\sin y \tag{1}$$

$$\cos(x+y)=\cos x\cos y-\sin x\sin y \tag{2}$$

$$\tan(x+y)=(\tan x+\tan y)/(1-\tan x\tan y) \tag{3}$$

(iii) For all values of x, $\sin x$ and $\cos x$ can be represented by the following absolutely convergent series,

$$\sin x=x-x^3/3!+x^5/5!+\ldots(-1)^n x^{2n+1}/(2n+1)!+\ldots \tag{4}$$

$$\cos x=1-x^2/2!+x^4/4!+\ldots(-1)^n x^{2n}/(2n)!+\ldots \tag{5}$$

For small values of x

$$\sin x=x+O(x^3) : \cos x=1+O(x^2) : \tan x=x+O(x^2) \tag{6}$$

where $O(x^3)$ means 'of order x^3 ', see 5.5

(iv) The trigonometrical functions are transcendental. Since $\sin(x+2n\pi)=\sin x$ for any integer n, it follows that the function inverse to $\sin x$ is infinitely many-valued, and therefore is not an algebraic function (see 3.4); and since the inverse of an algebraic function is an algebraic function (see end of 3.4) it follows that $\sin x$ itself is not an algebraic function; similarly for the other trigonometrical functions. They are therefore transcendental functions.

Each of them has an 'addition theorem' of the type

$$\mathrm{f}(x+y)=\text{algebraic function of } \mathrm{f}(x) \text{ and } \mathrm{f}(y)$$

There is a remarkable theorem due to Weierstrass that the only transcendental functions possessing an addition theorem of this kind are the exponential function, the trigonometric functions, another group of functions called the 'elliptic functions', and algebraic functions of these (see Forsyth, *Functions of a Complex Variable*).

To exemplify the physical occurrence of trigonometric functions we may mention Lissajous figures and the cycloid.

5.11. *Lissajous figures*

These curves arise in the study of simple harmonic motion in two dimensions, in acoustics and in physical optics, and are easily demonstrated on a cathode ray tube.

The parametric representation of the curves is

$$x=a\cos(\omega t+\phi)$$
$$y=b\cos(\omega' t+\phi')$$

The parameter t in physical applications is invariably time; the constants, ω and ω' are then often called 'angular frequencies' (in radians per second) and $\omega/2\pi$, $\omega'/2\pi$ are the 'cyclic frequencies' (in cycles per second). The arguments $(\omega t+\phi)$ and $(\omega' t+\phi')$ are the 'phases' of the two motions. The motion of the point $P(x, y)$ is that of a particle subject to superposed simple-harmonic vibrations in two directions at right angles; its path is very easily sketched in this way.

Example 1

Let the frequencies of the two motions be the same, as in the case of polarisation in optics. By choice of the origin of t we can make $\phi'=0$ and $\phi=\delta$, say; δ is then the constant difference in the 'phases' of the two motions. We have then

$$x=a\cos(\omega t+\delta) \qquad y=b\cos\omega t$$

and the path of the point (x, y) can be constructed by considering the x and y components to be generated by the projections of uniform circular motions as in Fig. 5.1 which illustrates the cases $\delta = 0$ $\frac{1}{4}\pi$, $\frac{1}{2}\pi$, $\frac{3}{4}\pi$, π. By elimination of t, we see that these curves are the ellipses

$$x^2/a^2 - 2(xy/ab) \cos \delta + y^2/b^2 = \sin^2 \delta$$

The cases $\delta = 0$ and π give the degenerate ellipses

$$x/a = \pm y/b$$

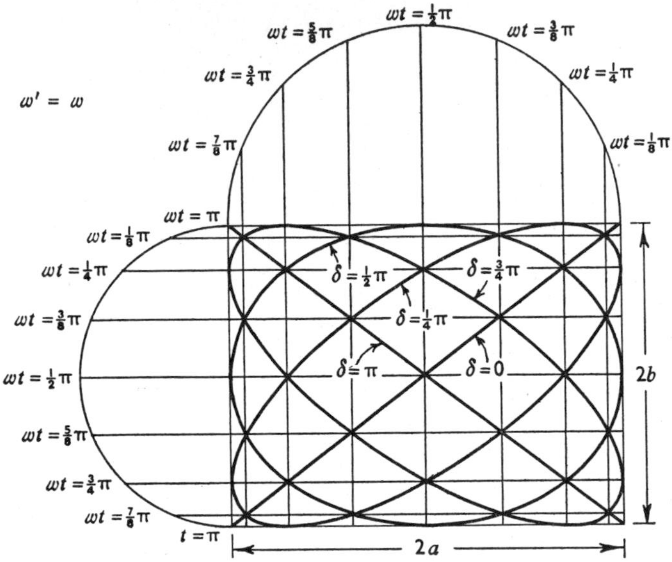

FIG. 5.1

Example 2

Construct curves corresponding to $\omega' = 2\omega$ and $\delta = 0$, $\frac{1}{8}\pi$, $\frac{1}{4}\pi$ and $\frac{1}{2}\pi$ (any convenient choice of a, b) : cf. Fig. 5.2.

Example 3

Show that if $\omega/\omega' = p/q$ where p and q are integers, then the Lissajous figure is a closed curve, but that if ω and ω' are incommensurable (i.e. their ratio is irrational) the curve never repeats itself.

5.12. *The cycloid*

The cycloid is the path of a point on the circumference of a circle rolling on a fixed straight line (Fig. 5.3).

Let the x-axis be taken as the straight line ; let the origin be taken where the point P on the circumference of the rolling circle

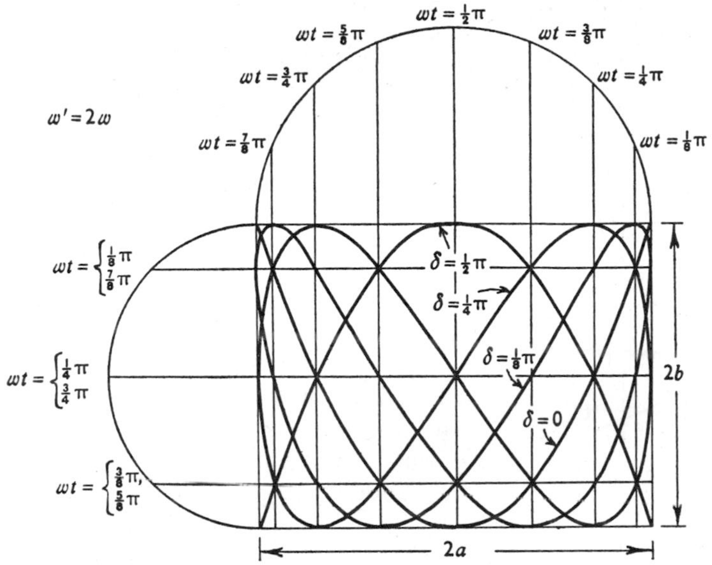

FIG. 5.2

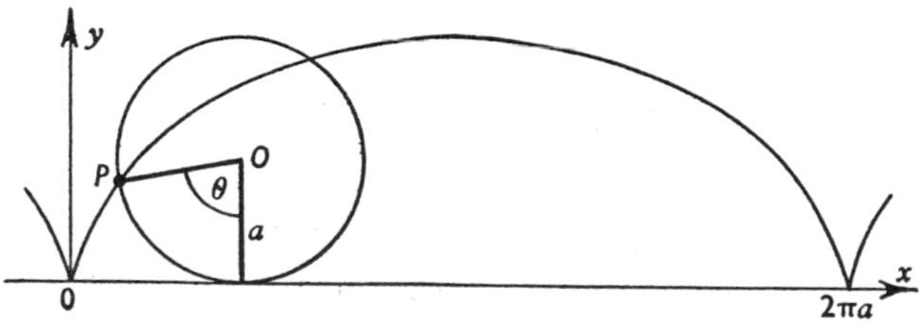

FIG. 5.3

touches the x-axis. Then if the circle, of radius a, rolls through an angle θ, the coordinates of its centre become $(a\theta, a)$ and hence the coordinates of P become

$$x = a\theta - a\sin\theta = a(\theta - \sin\theta)$$

$$y = a - a\cos\theta = a(1 - \cos\theta)$$

The curve consists of a number of segments or arches, repeated indefinitely in each direction.

5.2. The inverse circular functions

The function inverse to $\sin x$ is written $\sin^{-1} x$, and similarly for the inverses of the other circular functions. Thus if $y = \sin^{-1} x$, then $\sin y = x$, etc. Since $\sin(y + 2n\pi) = \sin y$ for any integral value of n, it follows that the function $\sin^{-1} x$ is infinitely many-valued, as already mentioned in 5.1.

The forms of the graphs of the functions $\sin^{-1} x$, $\cos^{-1} x$ and $\tan^{-1} x$ can be deduced directly from those of sin, cos and tan; for the graph of $y = \sin^{-1} x$ is identical with the graph of $x = \sin y$ and so on (cf. Fig. 5.4). Since $\cos y = \sin(y + \frac{1}{2}\pi)$, the graph of $\cos^{-1} x$ differs from that of $\sin^{-1} x$ only by a vertical displacement of $\frac{1}{2}\pi$ in the direction of the y-axis.

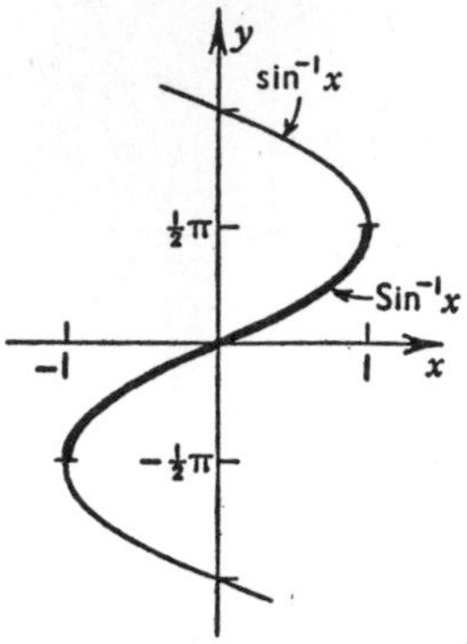

Fig. 5.4

It is sometimes convenient to restrict the range of y in such a way that the inverse circular functions are single-valued. For this purpose, $\mathrm{Sin}^{-1} x$ (with a capital S) may be used to denote the range of values of $\sin^{-1} x$ which lie between $-\frac{1}{2}\pi$ and $+\frac{1}{2}\pi$ (drawn with a heavy line in Fig. 5.4) and $\mathrm{Cos}^{-1} x$ that range of values of $\cos^{-1} x$ which lie between 0 and π. Then

(*a*) $\mathrm{Cos}^{-1} x + \mathrm{Sin}^{-1} x = \frac{1}{2}\pi$, and

(*b*) All values of $\sin^{-1} x$ and $\cos^{-1} x$ are given by

$$\sin^{-1} x = (-1)^n \,\mathrm{Sin}^{-1} x + n\pi$$
$$\cos^{-1} x = (-1)^n \,\mathrm{Cos}^{-1} x + n\pi$$

Similarly if $\mathrm{Tan}^{-1} x$ is used to denote the value of $\tan^{-1} x$ which lies in the range $-\frac{1}{2}\pi$ to $\frac{1}{2}\pi$, then

$$\tan^{-1} x = (-1)^n \,\mathrm{Tan}^{-1} x + n\pi$$

We shall see later (7.32) that the introduction of these functions $\mathrm{Sin}^{-1} x$ and $\mathrm{Cos}^{-1} x$ removes an ambiguity of sign in the expressions for the derivatives of $\sin^{-1} x$ and $\cos^{-1} x$.

5.3. The exponential function

A transcendental function can often be defined by means of an infinite series. The properties of the function must then be deduced from this series, and as an example of the way in which this can be done we now consider the function $\exp x$ defined by

$$\exp x = 1 + x + \frac{x^2}{2!} + \ldots + \frac{x^n}{n!} + \ldots = \sum_{n=0}^{\infty} \frac{x^n}{n!} \tag{1}$$

The series converges absolutely and uniformly in any bounded range of x by the ratio test (2.66 and 4.3), (the ratio of successive terms, u_{n+1}/u_n is equal to x/n which for all values of x tends to zero as $n \to \infty$). We deduce that (i) the function $\exp x$ exists for all values of x, (ii) that it is continuous for all x in any finite range (4.21), and (iii) since the series is absolutely convergent it can be manipulated algebraically as if it were a finite sum (4.31).

In particular

$$(\exp x) \,.\, (\exp y) = \sum_{m=0}^{\infty} (x^m/m!) \sum_{n=0}^{\infty} (y^n/n!)$$

If we write $a_m = x^m/m!$, $b_n = y^n/n!$, then formulae (4), (5) of 4.31 give

$$c_k = \sum_{m=0}^{k} a_m b_{k-m} = \sum_{m=0}^{k} x^m y^{k-m}/\{m!(k-m)!\} \tag{2}$$

$$\exp x \,.\, \exp y = \sum_{k=0}^{\infty} c_k \tag{3}$$

But by the binomial theorem

$$(x+y)^k = \sum_{m=0}^{k} \frac{k!}{m!\,(k-m)!} x^m y^{k-m}$$

so from (2) $c_k = (x+y)^k/k!$, and the series (3) is the series (1) with x replaced by $(x+y)$, and is therefore the function $\exp(x+y)$. Therefore

$$(\exp x) \,.\, (\exp y) = \exp(x+y) \tag{4}$$

In particular, putting $x = y$

$$(\exp x)^2 = \exp 2x$$

and by induction

$$(\exp x)^n = \exp nx \tag{5}$$

for any positive integral value of n. Also putting $y = -x$ in (4)

$$(\exp x) \,.\, (\exp(-x)) = \exp 0 = 1 \text{ from (1)}$$

so

$$\exp(-x) = 1/(\exp x) \tag{6}$$

and consequently (5) holds for negative integral values of n also.

The value of the function $\exp x$ at $x = 1$ is the number

$$1 + \frac{1}{1!} + \frac{1}{2!} + \frac{1}{3!} + \dots \tag{7}$$

which we shall shortly identify as the number e defined in 2.46. From (5) and (6) it follows that $\exp n = e^n$ for n integral (positive or negative).

From (5), it follows that if p and q are integers

$$[\exp (p/q)]^q = \exp p = e^p$$

Hence
$$\exp (p/q) = e^{p/q}$$

Thus for any rational value of x positive or negative $\exp x$ is equal to the xth power of the number e defined by equation (7), and hence we have the result

$$e^x = 1 + x + \frac{x^2}{2!} + \ldots$$

Thus, starting from the series definition of $\exp x$ (eqn. (1)), it has been deduced that $\exp x$ is the xth power of a number, that $\exp x = e^x$ in fact.

We now show that the numbers e defined by (7) and in (2.46, ex. 9) are the same, that is, that

$$\exp 1 = \lim_{n\to\infty} \left(1 + \frac{1}{n}\right)^n$$

Writing $x = 1/n$ in the defining series for $\exp x$, we have

$$\exp (1/n) = 1 + 1/n + 1/2!n^2 + 1/3!n^3 + \ldots$$
$$> 1 + 1/n \tag{8}$$

since all terms in the series are positive. But also

$$\exp (1/n) < 1 + 1/n + 1/n^2 + 1/n^3 + \ldots$$

i.e.
$$\exp (1/n) < 1/(1 - 1/n) = n/(n-1) = 1 + 1/(n-1) \tag{9}$$

Hence, from (5) and (8)

$$\exp 1 = [\exp (1/n)]^n > (1 + 1/n)^n$$

and from (5) and (9)

$$\exp 1 < [1 + 1/(n-1)]^n = [1 + 1/(n-1)]^{n-1}[n/(n-1)].$$

That is, for all n,

$$[1 + (1/n)]^n < \exp 1 < [1 + 1/(n-1)]^{n-1}[n/(n-1)] \tag{10}$$

Now
$$\lim_{n\to\infty} [1 + 1/(n-1)]^{n-1} = \lim_{n\to\infty} (1 + 1/n)^n$$

and $\lim_{n\to\infty} [n/(n-1)]=1$. Hence as $n\to\infty$ the two values between which exp 1 is sandwiched in (10) approach the same value, which must therefore be the value of exp 1, i.e.

$$\exp 1 = \lim_{n\to\infty} \left(1+\frac{1}{n}\right)^n,$$

which completes our proof.

Example

Prove that $\lim_{n\to\infty}\left[1+\frac{x}{n}\right]^n = e^x$

5.31. *Calculation of e*

The series (7) of 5.3 gives a much simpler method of calculating e than the limit of $(1+1/n)^n$ which was discussed in §2.46, Example 9. It can be shown for the series that the remainder after the term in $1/n!$ is less than $1/(n.n!)$; hence the sum taken to the term $1/5!$ gives an error of not more than 2 in the third decimal $(1/(5\,.\,5!)\approx 0{\cdot}0017)$ and the sum taken to the term $1/10!$ gives an error of not more than 3 in the eighth decimal. The calculation of e and other irrationals, including π, has been carried to prodigious lengths. The approximation $e\simeq 2{\cdot}718$ is often sufficient for practical purposes.

It may be added that e and π are examples of transcendental numbers, unlike $\sqrt{2}$ and $\sqrt[3]{10}$ for example which are 'algebraic' irrationals ; there is no polynomial $f(x)$, with rational coefficients, such that $f(e)=0$ or $f(\pi)=0$.

5.32. *Some properties of the exponential function*

From the defining series (1) of 5.3 we can deduce,

(i) For $x>0$, $e^x \equiv \exp x>0$, and $\exp x\to\infty$ as $x\to\infty$.

(ii) For $x>0$, $e^{-x}=1/e^x>0$, and $\exp(-x)\to 0$ as $x\to\infty$. Hence e^x is positive for all real values of x, positive and negative.

(iii) If $X>0$, $e^{x+X}-e^x=e^x(e^X-1)>0$, so $e^{x+X}>e^x$ i.e. e^x is a strictly increasing function of x for all x, and, since its increase is proportional to e^x, the rate of increase becomes more and more rapid as x increases.

(iv) The graphs of e^x and e^{-x} are of the forms shown in Fig. 5.6 (apart from the factor $\frac{1}{2}$ which is inserted to aid later comparisons with $\sinh x$ and $\cosh x$).

(v) $(\exp x-1)/x = 1+x/2!+x^2/3!+\ldots$ (1)

The radius of convergence of the series on the right is infinite, so the series is uniformly convergent, and its sum is therefore continuous for all finite values of x (cf. 4.21). In particular, the sum is continuous at $x=0$, so

$$\lim_{x\to 0} (\exp x - 1)/x = 1$$

(vi) $x^n e^{-x} \to 0$ as $x\to\infty$; and $e^x/x^n = 1/(x^n e^{-x}) \to \infty$ as $x\to\infty$; the latter result is often expressed in words by the statement that as $x\to\infty$, e^x increases more rapidly than any power of x. To show this, consider n given. Then since the terms in the exponential series are all positive, omission of any of them decreases the sum; let us omit all but those in x^{n+1}, x^{n+2}. Then it follows that

$$e^x > x^{n+1}/(n+1)! + x^{n+2}/(n+2)! = x^{n+1}\,[1 + x/(n+2)]/(n+1)!$$

This is greater than x^{n+1} for all sufficiently large values of x, say for all $x>X$. Hence

$$x^n/e^x < x^n/x^{n+1} \text{ for all } x > X \tag{2}$$
$$= 1/x \to 0 \text{ as } x\to\infty$$

and this result holds for any value of n (the value of X depends, of course, on n, but for any value of n there exists a finite value of X such that the inequality (2) is satisfied).

5.4. The logarithmic function

Since the exponential function is monotonic and continuous, we can define a new function by introducing its inverse. This is the logarithmic function.

If $y = \log_e x$, then $x = e^y$. The equivalent single statement that

$$e^{\log x} = x \tag{1}$$

is often handier in practice. The graph of $y = \log_e x$ follows immediately by reflection of the curve $y = e^x$ in the line $y = x$, since this gives the inverse curve $x = e^y$ (see fig. 5.5).

Some writers write $\log_e x$ as $\ln x$ in order to avoid confusion with logarithms to base 10 with which the reader will be already familiar, and which are merely multiples of logarithms to base e.

5.41. *Properties of the logarithmic function*

The most important property of the logarithmic function is derived from the property $e^{y_1} e^{y_2} = e^{y_1+y_2}$ of the exponential function.

$$e^{\log (x_1 x_2)} = x_1 x_2 \quad \text{by (1)}$$
$$= e^{\log x_1}\, e^{\log x_2} = e^{(\log x_1 + \log x_2)}$$

Now e^y is a strictly monotonic function of x, so $e^{y_1}=e^{y_2}$ implies $y_1=y_2$. Hence

$$\log(x_1x_2)=\log x_1+\log x_2 \tag{2}$$

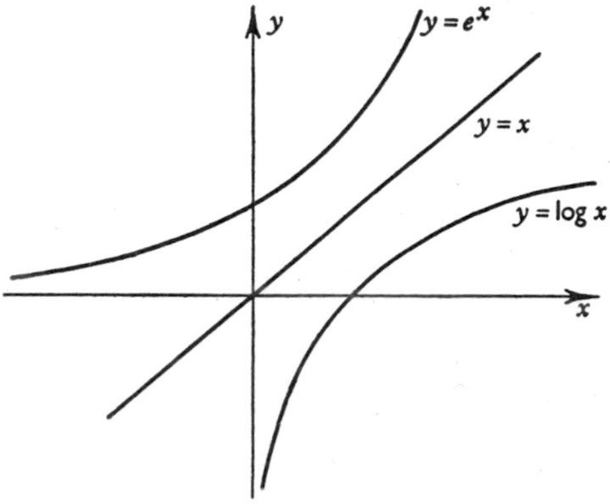

FIG. 5.5

Other properties are, if $y=\log x$

(i) At $x=1$, $y=0$.

(ii) For negative values of x, $\log x$ is not defined, since there is no (real) value of y such that e^y is negative. The graph of $y=\log x$ is therefore confined to the right of the y-axis.

(iii) For $x<1$, $\log x$ is negative. As $x\to 0$, $\log x\to -\infty$.

(iv) Near $x=1$, $y=x-1$. For $x=e^y$ and y is small; hence $x\approx 1+y$.

(v) y is monotonic and continuous in the range $0<x<\infty$.

(vi) $\log x\to\infty$ as $x\to\infty$, but it tends to infinity more slowly than any positive power of x. For replacing x by $\log x'$ in (2) of 5.32

$$(\log x')^n/x' \to 0 \quad \text{as} \quad x'\to\infty$$

so

$$\log x/x^{1/n}\to 0 \quad \text{as} \quad x\to\infty$$

for any value of n.

(vii) If $|x|<1$, $\log(1+x)=x-x^2/2+x^3/3-\dots+(-1)^{m-1}x^m/m+\dots$, a series which is most easily discussed by the methods of Chapter 7.

5.5. Orders of magnitude

We can say that e^x is 'of higher order' than x^n for large x in the sense that $e^x/x^n\to\infty$ as $x\to\infty$. But e^{x^2} is of higher order still, since $e^{x^2}/e^x=e^{x^2-x}\to\infty$ as $x\to\infty$, and e^{e^x} is of still higher order.

It is a convenience to have a notation for this concept of relative order of magnitude of functions as $x \to \infty$ (or as $x \to 0$).

We write
$$f(x) = o(g(x))$$
to signify that $f(x)/g(x)$ tends to 0 as $x \to \infty$ ($f(x)$ is ' of smaller order ' than $g(x)$), and
$$f(x) = O(g(x))$$
to mean that $f(x)/g(x)$ remains finite as $x \to \infty$ ($f(x)$ is ' of the same order ' as $g(x)$). The latter, $O(g(x))$ notation is of more common use than the former $o(g(x))$ notation. If $f(x)$ remains finite (whether it tends to a limit or not) we write
$$f(x) = O(1)$$

For example, as $x \to \infty$,
$$\sqrt{(x^2+1)} = O(x)\ ;\ e^{x^2+bx+c} = O(e^{x^2}) \text{ if } b \leqslant 0\ ;\ \sin(ax+b) = O(1)$$
$$\sin e^x = O(1)$$
An obvious and convenient, but not wholly orthodox extension of the notation is represented by the statement
$$O(x) < x \log x < O(x^2).$$

Notice incidentally that the gap between any two consecutive functions e.g. $y = x^{\frac{1}{2}}$ and $y = x$ cannot be completely filled in by inserting the functions x^r where r is a real number ($\frac{1}{2} < r < 1$). For $x^{\frac{1}{2}} \log x$ is of higher order than $x^{\frac{1}{2}}$ and of lower order than any function $x^{\frac{1}{2}+\epsilon}$ no matter how small a value of $\epsilon > 0$ is chosen.

5.51. *Behaviour of log x as $x \to 0$*

As $x \to 0$, $\log x \to -\infty$: the behaviour of $x^n \log x$ is given by putting $x = e^{-y}$. Then
$$x^n \log x = -ye^{-ny} \to 0 \text{ as } x \to 0, \text{ that is as } y \to \infty$$

5.6. The hyperbolic functions

The function e^x is neither even nor odd but, like any other function that is defined for negative values of x, it can be regarded as the sum of odd and even parts. Thus
$$e^x = \tfrac{1}{2}(e^x + e^{-x}) + \tfrac{1}{2}(e^x - e^{-x})$$
These two parts are given the names cosh x and sinh x, so that
$$e^x = \cosh x + \sinh x$$
where
$$\cosh x = \tfrac{1}{2}(e^x + e^{-x})$$
and
$$\sinh x = \tfrac{1}{2}(e^x - e^{-x})$$

It follows that cosh x and sinh x both tend to $\frac{1}{2}e^x$ as $x \to \infty$ (see Fig. 5.6), and that

$$\sinh x < \tfrac{1}{2}e^x < \cosh x$$

and also that

$$\cosh x - \sinh x = e^{-x}$$

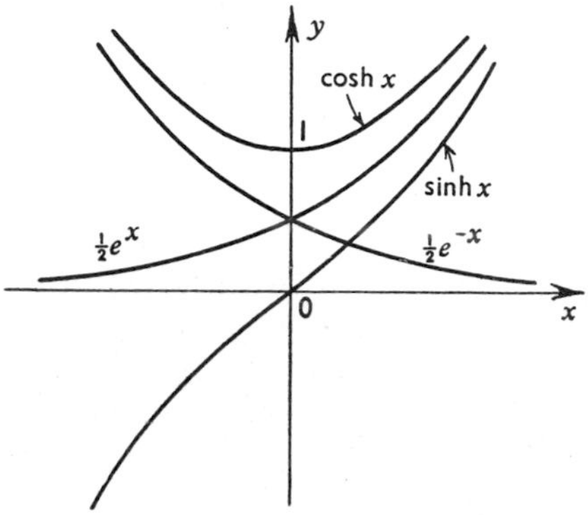

FIG. 5.6

The following functions are now defined, in close analogy with the trigonometric functions :

$$\begin{aligned}
\tanh x &= \sinh x/\cosh x = (e^x - e^{-x})/(e^x + e^{-x}) \\
\operatorname{cosech} x &= 1/\sinh x \qquad\quad = 2/(e^x - e^{-x}) \\
\operatorname{sech} x &= 1/\cosh x \qquad\quad = 2/(e^x + e^{-x}) \\
\coth x &= \cosh x/\sinh x = (e^x + e^{-x})/(e^x - e^{-x})
\end{aligned}$$

Graphs of the functions tanh x and sech x are plotted in Figs. 5.7 and 5.8. They behave quite differently from their trigonometric

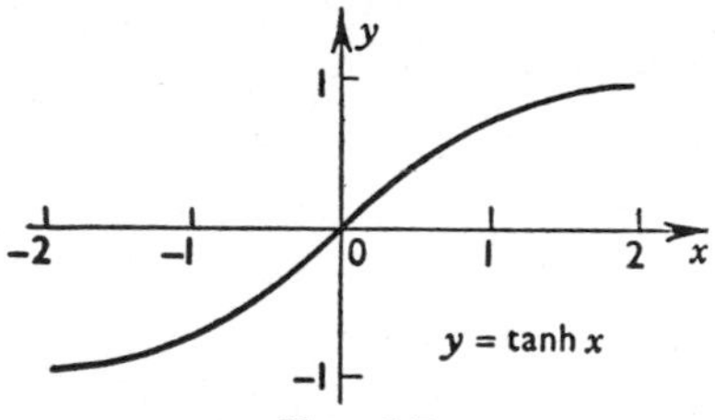

FIG. 5.7

counterparts ; compare for example the well-behaved graph of tanh x with that of tan x. The relations between the hyperbolic functions are however closely similar to those between the trigonometric functions. The important relations, which can be verified from the definitions, are

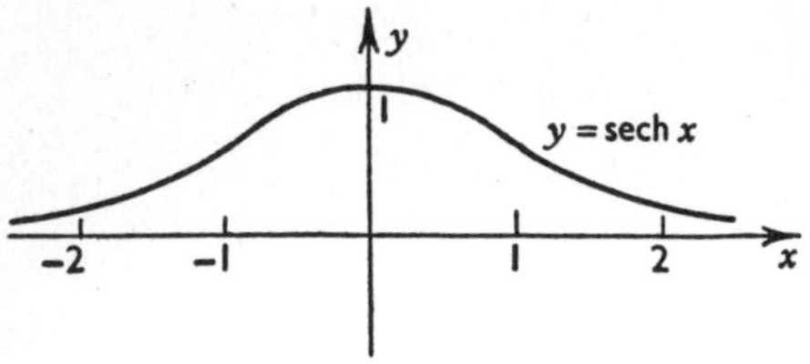

FIG. 5.8

$$\begin{aligned}
\cosh^2 x - \sinh^2 x &= 1 \\
\operatorname{sech}^2 x &= 1 - \tanh^2 x \\
\coth^2 x &= 1 + \operatorname{cosech}^2 x \\
\sinh (u \pm v) &= \sinh u \cosh v \pm \cosh u \sinh v \\
\cosh (u \pm v) &= \cosh u \cosh v \pm \sinh u \sinh v \\
\tanh (u \pm v) &= \frac{\tanh u \pm \tanh v}{1 \pm \tanh u \tanh v} \\
\sinh 2u &= 2 \sinh u \cosh u \\
\cosh 2u &= \cosh^2 u + \sinh^2 u = 2 \cosh^2 u - 1 \\
&= 2 \sinh^2 u + 1 \\
\tanh 2u &= \frac{2 \tanh u}{1 + \tanh^2 u}
\end{aligned}$$

The term ' hyperbolic ' is applied to these functions because if the relation between two variables x and y is determined by the parametric equations

$$x = a \cosh u, \quad y = a \sinh u$$

the graph of x against y is the rectangular hyperbola $x^2 - y^2 = a^2$: correspondingly the functions $\cos \theta$, $\sin \theta$ are called ' circular functions ' because the graph of the function expressed in parametric form by

$$x = a \cos \theta, \quad y = a \sin \theta$$

is the circle $x^2 + y^2 = a^2$.

It may be noted however that if $x = a \tanh u$, $y = a \operatorname{sech} u$ then $x^2 + y^2 = a^2$; and if $x = a \sec \theta$, $y = a \tan \theta$ then $x^2 - y^2 = a^2$.

5.7. The inverse hyperbolic functions

The functions $\sinh^{-1} x$, $\cosh^{-1} x$ are defined as the inverse functions to $\sinh x$ and $\cosh x$. Thus if $y = \sinh^{-1} x$, $\sinh y = x$

etc. The inverse hyperbolic functions are related to the inverse of the exponential, for if

$$y = \sinh^{-1} x$$

then $$\sinh y = x$$

and $$\cosh y = \sqrt{(1 + x^2)}$$

Adding we obtain

$$e^y = x + \sqrt{(1 + x^2)}$$

and hence $y = \sinh^{-1} x = \log [x + \sqrt{(1 + x^2)}]$

Similarly $\cosh^{-1} x = \log [x + \sqrt{(x^2 - 1)}]$, $(x \geqslant 1)$

Also if $y = \tanh^{-1} x$

$$x = \tanh y = \frac{e^y - e^{-y}}{e^y + e^{-y}} = \frac{e^{2y} - 1}{e^{2y} + 1}$$

Hence $e^{2y} = (1 + x)/(1 - x)$

so that for $x < 1$, $y = \tanh^{-1} x = \frac{1}{2} \log \left(\frac{1 + x}{1 - x}\right)$.

Similarly $\coth^{-1} x = \frac{1}{2} \log \left(\frac{x + 1}{x - 1}\right)$, $(x > 1)$.

5.8. The Gudermannian

The function $y = \tan^{-1} (\sinh x)$ is called the Gudermannian function and written gd x.

The inverse Gudermannian function, $y = \text{gd}^{-1} x = \tanh^{-1} (\sin x)$ arises naturally in the integral calculus since $\int_0^x \sec \xi \, d\xi = \text{gd}^{-1} x$.

If $\phi = \text{gd}\ x$, then $\tan \phi = \sinh x$, and also $\sec \phi = \cosh x$, $\sin \phi = \tanh x$, $\cot \phi = \text{cosech}\ x$, $\cos \phi = \text{sech}\ x$, $\text{cosec}\ \phi = \coth x$. Hence a table of values of the Gudermannian enables the hyperbolic functions to be determined from tables of the trigonometric functions. Thus to find $\sinh x$ for a given value of y, we find ϕ from $\phi = \text{gd}\ x$ and then $\sinh x = \tan \phi$. However now that adequate tables of the hyperbolic functions are available, the Gudermannian has lost its importance and the student requires a knowledge of it only occasionally, for the understanding of mathematical writings of the past.

5.9. Obscurities in notation

The reader has probably by now acquired sufficient familiarity with notation to avoid being confused by the following digression. The symbols x and y are conventionally used in graphical work to refer to lengths measured in two specified directions.

A particular point in the plane can be specified by two coordinates, e.g. the point P in Fig. 5.9 is the point $x=3$, $y=2$, or simply the point (3, 2). A general point in the plane can be specified similarly by (x, y), but this already requires a change in the interpretation of the symbols x and y. In the notation (x, y), x and y stand simply for two numbers, whereas in the statement $y=2$, the symbol y means 'the distance measured in the y-direction'. The bracket notation, not the symbol, specifies the order in which the pair of numbers is to be taken, and the further association of direction with the symbols themselves in notations such as (x, x) or (y, x) would be either redundant or, worse, conflicting.

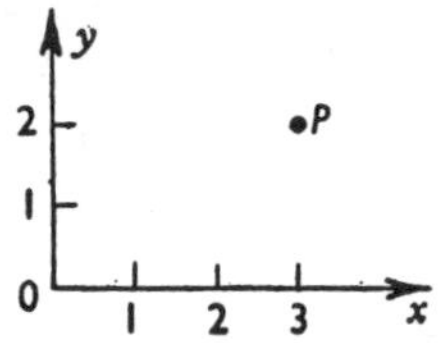

FIG. 5.9

Finally we may use y to denote a function of x, $y=y(x)$. It is clear that the symbol y is being overworked if we proceed to inquire, for example, What is the value of the function $y(x)$ when x has the particular numerical value $x=y$?, and further, For a given function $y(x)$ is there a value of y such that $y(y)=y$?

We have in fact introduced three interpretations of the symbol y:

(1) simply as an arbitrary number on the same footing as x;

(2) specifically as a coordinate measured in the south-north direction as distinct from x, e.g. in the statement $y=\mathrm{f}(x)$;

(3) as a symbol for a functional relationship as in $y=y(x)$, analogous to $y=\mathrm{f}(x)$. This notation is particularly useful when the locus of a point moving in space is to be discussed. For example if the coordinates of a point in three dimensions viz. (x, y, z) are functions of the time, then we can introduce the parametric equations $x=\mathrm{f}(t)$, $y=\mathrm{g}(t)$, $z=\mathrm{h}(t)$, but a more economical notation is $x=x(t)$, $y=y(t)$, $z=z(t)$.

The best plan is to use only one interpretation in any given problem, but this is not always very convenient.

It is scarcely possible to combine (1) successfully with either (2) or (3) and there are plenty of pitfalls even in using (2) and (3) together.

For example, if $x=x(t)\equiv 4t$ and $y=y(t)\equiv 16t^2$ then y may be expressed as a function of x, viz. $y=x^2$. We notice that it would be tempting but quite wrong to write $y=y(x)$ since $y(x)=16x^2$ (cf. the *definition* of the function y viz. $y(t)=16t^2$).

Finally we mention that similar ambiguities of notation often occur in the integral calculus, for example expressions such as $\int_0^x \sin x \, dx$ are encountered quite frequently. It is usually best to change the notation at once, writing the expression as, say $\int_0^x \sin u \, du$. A variable like u in the last expression, whose name (whether u or v or t or ξ, etc.) is immaterial because the value of the expression defined—in this case the integral—is independent of the name of the variable in question, is often called a *dummy variable.*

CHAPTER SIX

THE COMPLEX VARIABLE

6.1. Introduction

The system of real numbers described in Chapter 1 is composed of the integers, the rational fractions and the irrationals. Of these the positive integers were invented in antiquity to deal with the process of counting. The rational fractions were introduced to make possible the division of any integer by any other (except zero); negative integers and negative rationals were then brought in to make the subtraction of any two integers or rationals possible; finally it was found that purely algebraic operations on rational numbers and integers could lead to quantities that were not themselves rational or integral, for example the quantity $\sqrt{2}$. To deal with these the abstract notion of an irrational number was introduced; with this addition the system of real numbers is complete. It is found in particular that any finite number of arithmetical operations $(+, -, \times, \div)$ on real numbers leads always to a real number, and not to a quantity of still greater generality. This is still true, with due precautions to ensure convergence, even if the number of operations is allowed to become infinite; for example if a sequence of real numbers a_n converges at all, it converges to a real number.

However there are algebraic equations which are not satisfied by any real number. For example, the real number system does not contain a number x that will satisfy the equation

$$x^2+1=0 \tag{1}$$

Similarly no real numbers satisfy

$$x^2+2\xi ax+a^2=0, \quad -1<\xi<1 \tag{2}$$

or

$$x^4+1=0 \tag{3}$$

The reader will be prepared, by the completely artificial nature of even the real number system, to recognise the inevitable development : the mathematician does not accept the deficiency, but circumvents it by introducing further numbers into the system. For example he can now introduce an abstract entity, symbolised by i, for the sole purpose of satisfying equation (1). Whether it is a ‘ number ’ or not is a matter of terminology ; the term ‘ number ’ is usually regarded as extended to include i and other entities constructed from it. The basic property of this number is then

$$i^2+1=0$$

In all other respects the arithmetical behaviour of i is defined to be that of an ordinary real number ; thus if a is any real number

$$a+i=i+a \tag{4}$$

$$ai=ia \tag{5}$$

$$\begin{aligned}(a+bi)(c+di)&=a(c+di)+bi(c+di)\\&=ac-bd+i(ad+bc)\end{aligned} \tag{6}$$

and so on. The totality of numbers of the form $a+ib$ where a and b are real is then called the system of complex numbers. It is a complete system in the sense that the result of arithmetical operations on any two complex numbers is itself a complex number, and not something more elaborate ; see for example equation (6) above. In contrast to the ‘ real number ’ a, a number ib is called ‘ pure imaginary ’.

This venture might of course have turned out to be unprofitable. If for example every algebraic equation that had no real roots required the ad hoc introduction of new imaginary numbers j, k ... etc. then the scheme would be obviously unsatisfactory.

This however is not the case. The introduction of the single number i is sufficient to provide roots not only of equation (1) but, in the form $a+ib$, of every algebraic equation. It remains to explain however how this abstract notion has been of value to the scientist, not only indirectly by its contributions to mathematics, but also directly for the representation of physical quantities.

In its original use the complex number is a single abstract number which can take values denied to real numbers, and therefore denied to physical variables (for the measurement of a physical quantity gives an ordinary, real number). In applying complex numbers to physical problems, the scientist is therefore not concerned with the original usage. To him the complex number $z=x+iy$ does not represent a single physical variable. It represents two separate variables. It carries in one symbol, the two distinct variables x and y or, as we shall see later, r and θ, and it is in this sense only that the complex number is used in physical problems.

The reader should notice the analogy between the scientist's use of complex numbers and his use of negative numbers. The idea of a negative number, a number less than nothing, is originally a purely artificial mathematical concept introduced to make subtraction of any two numbers possible. The scientist takes it over and uses it not in this sense, but as part of a code. The number -5 is not to the scientist a mysterious quantity less than zero but simply the familiar number 5 with a prefix $-$ instead of $+$; these prefixes $-$ and $+$ are regarded as pure symbols containing an extra piece of information about the variable ; since there are only two possibilities the information can refer only to some property which has one or other of two values. The usual application is that of specifying direction along a given line ; according to the code employed, -1 may mean to the left and $+1$ to the right or vice versa. There are however other possible uses, for example in geometrical optics, objects and images may be either real or virtual and it is possible to arrange for this information to be carried by the signs of the object and image distances.

The number i is also in the first place an abstract concept, invented by the mathematician to simplify theorems about the roots of algebraic equations. The scientist again takes it over and uses it as part of a code. The simplest is the coding of direction in a plane ; thus if $+1$ means displacement to the East, $+i$ can mean displacement to the North, -1 to the West, $-i$ to the South ; and all four directions are specified by single numbers from the complex number system.

This application of the complex variable is perhaps the simplest, but an equally important one is to the theory of vibrations, which actually includes much of physical theory ; for example simple harmonic motion, alternating currents, physical optics, acoustics, electromagnetic theory and wave mechanics. In these applications the essential step is to encode both the amplitude of the vibration and its phase into a single complex number.

It is not of course self-evident at this stage that either of these applications can be carried out successfully. Before discussing them in detail, we revert to the mathematical concept and set down a few formal definitions and theorems, for reference. As the reader will have gathered, the algebra of complex numbers is, by design, as close as possible to the algebra of real numbers ; the principal additions are in fact to terminology.

6.2. Algebra of complex numbers

Definition. If a and b are real numbers and i satisfies the equation

$$i^2 = -1 \tag{1}$$

then the quantity $c = a + ib$ is a complex number ; a is said to be the real part and b the imaginary part of c. Either of the following shorthand notations may be used ; $a = \text{R.P.}(c)$, $b = \text{I.P.}(c)$: or $a = \mathscr{R}(c)$, $b = \mathscr{I}(c)$.

Complex conjugate. The number $c^* = a - ib$ is called the complex conjugate of $c = a + ib$.

Equality of complex numbers. If $c_1 = a_1 + ib_1$ and $c_2 = a_2 + ib_2$ are two complex numbers then $c_1 = c_2$ if and only if both $a_1 = a_2$ and $b_1 = b_2$.

Sum of complex numbers. If c_1 and c_2 are two complex numbers then the sum $c_1 + c_2$ is defined as

$$c_1 + c_2 = (a_1 + a_2) + i(b_1 + b_2) \tag{2}$$

Product of complex numbers. The product c_1c_2 is defined by

$$c_1c_2 = (a_1 + ib_1)(a_2 + ib_2) = (a_1a_2 - b_1b_2) + i(a_1b_2 + a_2b_1) \tag{3}$$

Commutative and Associative Laws of addition. It follows from equation (2) that $c_1 + c_2 = c_2 + c_1$ and

$$c_1 + (c_2 + c_3) = (c_1 + c_2) + c_3$$

These are respectively the commutative and associative laws of addition.

Commutative and Associative laws of multiplication. It follows from (3), by writing out the products in full, that $c_1c_2 = c_2c_1$ and that $c_1(c_2c_3) = (c_1c_2)c_3$.

These are the commutative and the associative laws of multiplication. Further from (2) and (3)

$c_1(c_2+c_3)=c_1c_2+c_1c_3$ which is the distributive law.

Since the whole of the algebra of real numbers can be deduced from the commutative, associative and distributive laws together with the property that for any non-zero number a, $1/a$ exists and $ab=0$ implies $b=0$, the algebra of complex numbers is identical with the algebra of real numbers. The order of terms in a sum and the order of factors in a product can be rearranged, and brackets can be removed in the usual way.

Division. The quotient of two complex numbers a/b can be found by a process analogous to that of 'rationalising' the denominator in elementary algebra. Thus by multiplying numerator and denominator by the complex conjugate of b, we find

$$\frac{a}{b}=\frac{a_1+ia_2}{b_1+ib_2}=\frac{(a_1+ia_2)(b_1-ib_2)}{b_1^2+b_2^2}=\frac{a_1b_1+a_2b_2}{b_1^2+b_2^2}+i\frac{a_2b_1-a_1b_2}{b_1^2+b_2^2}$$

Notice in particular that $1/i=-i$.

6.3. The Argand diagram

We now come to the simplest application of the complex variable, namely that of representing the position of a point in a plane.

In Fig. 6.1 let a pair of rectangular axes Ox, Oy be drawn so that any point P in the plane can be specified by its cartesian coordinates (x, y). Now consider the complex number $z=x+iy$. It is evident that to each complex number z there corresponds one and only one point P in the plane ; also to each point P there corresponds one and only one value of z. Therefore as an alternative to writing 'P is the point (x, y)' we can convey the same information equally well by writing 'P is the point $z=x+iy$'.

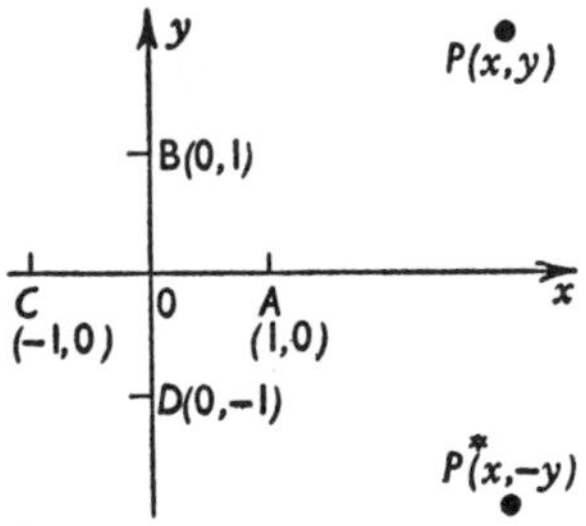

FIG. 6.1

Let us locate the points corresponding to some special complex numbers. First the real numbers (i.e. complex numbers whose imaginary parts are zero) lie along the x-axis. In particular A and C with coordinates (1, 0) and (−1, 0) respectively correspond to $z=1$ and $z=-1$. The complex numbers with real parts zero (the pure imaginaries) correspond to points lying along the y-axis. This axis is sometimes referred to as the ' imaginary axis ', which may suggest that there is something mysterious about it. However, the word ' imaginary ' here is used purely in its technical sense. The line itself, and the whole Argand diagram, is perfectly real in the everyday use of the word ; but points in the y-axis represent ' imaginary ' numbers in the technical sense ; that is, multiples of i. In particular the points $B(0, 1)$ and $D(0, -1)$ represent the complex numbers $z=i$ and $z=-i$. The origin O of course represents $z=0$.

Notice the relative position of ' conjugate points ' i.e. points corresponding to a conjugate pair of complex numbers. P is the point representing $3+2i$, and P^* is the point representing $3-2i$; these are mirror images in the x-axis, a general result for conjugate points.

6.31. *The vector law of addition and the Argand diagram*

Suppose that Fig. 6.2 is a force diagram in which the forces acting on a point in some mechanical system are represented in magnitude and direction by the lines OA and OB. The resultant force at the point is found by drawing AC equal and parallel to OB ; then by the parallelogram of forces the diagonal OC represents the resultant force in magnitude and direction. If the coordinates of A and B are (a_1, a_2) and (b_1, b_2) respectively, the construction implies that the coordinates of C are (c_1, c_2) where

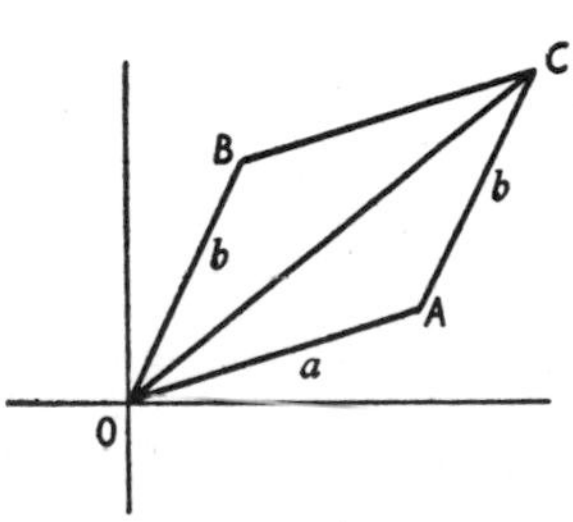

FIG. 6.2

$$c_1=a_1+b_1$$

$$c_2=a_2+b_2$$

Now A is represented by the complex number $a=a_1+ia_2$, B by $b=b_1+ib_2$ and C by $c=c_1+ic_2$

$$=(a_1+b_1)+i(a_2+b_2)$$

$$=(a_1+ia_2)+(b_1+ib_2)$$

$$=a+b$$

Hence the law of addition of complex numbers corresponds exactly to the parallelogram law of addition of displacement vectors ; however the multiplication of two complex numbers does not follow either of the laws of multiplication of vectors.

6.32. *Geometrical representation of multiplication*

Let a and b be two complex numbers and c their product ; let the corresponding points in the Argand diagram be A, B and C. We wish to find the geometrical relation between these points, i.e. the geometrical significance of multiplication of complex numbers.

First consider the cartesian coordinates of C. If

$$a = a_1 + ia_2, \; b = b_1 + ib_2$$

then

$$c = ab$$

$$= a_1 b_1 - a_2 b_2 + i(a_1 b_2 + a_2 b_1) \tag{1}$$

and thus C is the point $(a_1b_1 - a_2b_2, a_1b_2 + a_2b_1)$. This is not suggestive of any simple relation of C to A and B. If however we go to polar coordinates, the implication becomes plainer. Let the polar coordinates of A, B and C be (A, α) (B, β) and (C, γ) ; then

$$a_1 = A \cos \alpha, \; b_1 = B \cos \beta, \; c_1 = C \cos \gamma$$

$$a_2 = A \sin \alpha, \; b_2 = B \sin \beta, \; c_2 = C \sin \gamma$$

and equation (1) becomes

$$c = AB\{\cos \alpha \cos \beta - \sin \alpha \sin \beta + i(\cos \alpha \sin \beta + \sin \alpha \cos \beta)\}$$

$$= AB\{\cos(\alpha + \beta) + i \sin(\alpha + \beta)\} \tag{2}$$

Now comparing this with $c = c_1 + ic_2 = C(\cos \gamma + i \sin \gamma)$, we have

$$C(\cos \gamma + i \sin \gamma) = AB\{\cos(\alpha + \beta) + i \sin(\alpha + \beta)\} \tag{3}$$

so

$$C = AB$$

$$\gamma = \alpha + \beta$$

In other words the displacement vector OC is the result of rotating OB through an angle α and then increasing it in length by the factor A (or equally well by rotating OA through an angle β and increasing it by a factor B) (Fig. 6.3).

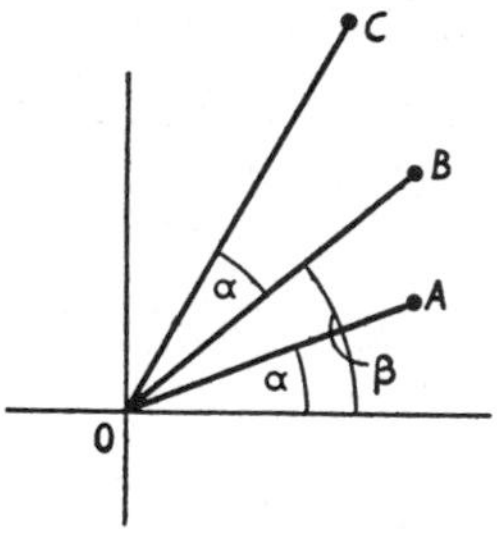

FIG. 6.3

6.33. *Geometrical representation of division*

To find the point Q corresponding to the complex number $q=a/b$, we notice that we must have

$$bq=a \quad (1)$$

so Q must have polar coordinates (r, θ) such that

$$rB=A$$
$$\theta+\beta=\alpha$$

Hence the point Q corresponding to (a/b) has the polar coordinates $(A/B, \alpha-\beta)$; if I is the point (1, 0), the triangles OAB and OQI are similar (Fig. 6.4).

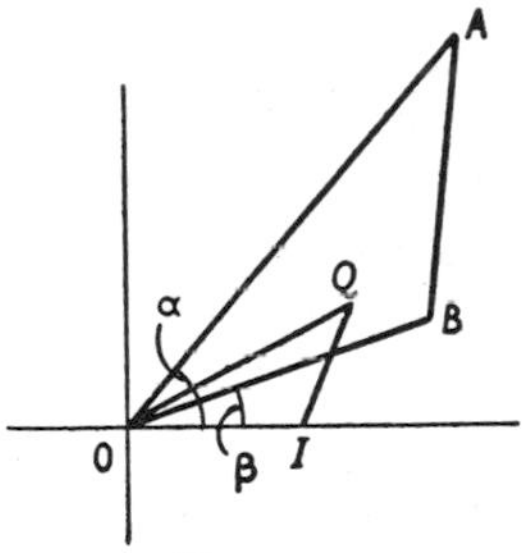

FIG. 6.4

6.4. De Moivre's theorem

If in formula (2) of 6.32 we put $A=B=1, \alpha=\theta_1, \beta=\theta_2$, bearing in mind that $c=ab=AB(\cos\alpha+i\sin\alpha)(\cos\beta+i\sin\beta)$, the result is

$$(\cos\theta_1+i\sin\theta_1)(\cos\theta_2+i\sin\theta_2)=\cos(\theta_1+\theta_2)+i\sin(\theta_1+\theta_2) \quad (1)$$

and this can evidently be extended to any finite number of factors; in particular if we take $\theta_1=\theta_2=\ldots=\theta_n=\theta/n$, we get

$$[\cos(\theta/n)+i\sin(\theta/n)]^n=\cos\theta+i\sin\theta \quad (2)$$

A very important formula is obtained by allowing n to become large without limit. Since (2) holds for every finite value of n it holds in the limit, that is

$$\lim_{n\to\infty}[\cos(\theta/n)+i\sin(\theta/n)]^n=\cos\theta+i\sin\theta \quad (3)$$

The limit on the left can however be evaluated in a different form. For from eqn. (6) of §5.1,

$$\cos(\theta/n) = 1 + O(1/n^2)$$
$$\sin(\theta/n) = (\theta/n) + O(1/n^3)$$

Hence $\quad [\cos(\theta/n) + i\sin(\theta/n)]^n = (1 + i(\theta/n) + O(1/n^2))^n$

Now the symbol i obeys the laws of algebra and therefore this quantity can be expanded by the binomial theorem and indeed the inductive proof of the binomial theorem for real numbers (2.41) can be applied to complex numbers without alteration. Hence we can write

$$\lim_{n\to\infty} [\cos(\theta/n) + i\sin(\theta/n)]^n = \lim_{n\to\infty} [1 + i(\theta/n)]^n$$

so that from (3)

$$\lim_{n\to\infty} [1 + i\theta/n]^n = \cos\theta + i\sin\theta \tag{4}$$

Now for real values of x

$$\lim_{n\to\infty} [1 + (x/n)]^n = e^x \tag{5}$$

(see 5.3), and the formal similarity of the left-hand sides of (4) and (5) suggests that we should *define* $e^{i\theta}$ for real values of θ by

$$e^{i\theta} = \lim_{n\to\infty} [1 + i\theta/n]^n$$
$$= \cos\theta + i\sin\theta \tag{6}$$

Many properties of $e^{i\theta}$ would follow from algebra parallel to that of 5.3, but it is rather simpler to verify the main properties independently.

In terms of the function $e^{i\theta}$ defined by (6), (1) can be written

$$e^{i\theta_1}e^{i\theta_2} = e^{i(\theta_1+\theta_2)} \tag{7}$$

Also if in (2), (θ/n) is replaced by θ and the result expressed in terms of the function $e^{i\theta}$, it is

$$(e^{i\theta})^n = e^{in\theta} \tag{8}$$

whereas taking the nth root of (2) gives

$$(e^{i\theta})^{1/n} = e^{i\theta/n} \tag{9}$$

and, using (8) to take the mth power of both sides of (9)

$$(e^{i\theta})^{m/n} = e^{im\theta/n} \tag{10}$$

Thus if $e^{i\theta}$ is defined by (6), the imaginary exponent satisfies all the index laws of the algebra of real numbers.

Furthermore $\frac{\mathrm{d}}{\mathrm{d}\theta}(e^{i\theta})=\frac{\mathrm{d}}{\mathrm{d}\theta}(\cos\theta+i\sin\theta)=-\sin\theta+i\cos\theta$

$$=i(\cos\theta+i\sin\theta)$$

$$=ie^{i\theta} \qquad (11)$$

Relations (8), (9). (10) can all be written

$$(\cos\theta+i\sin\theta)^p=(\cos p\theta+i\sin p\theta)$$

and this is called de Moivre's theorem. We have shown that it holds for rational values of p ; its extension to irrational values of p depends on the meaning of an irrational power of a complex number, and is postponed for the present.

Replacing θ by $-\theta$ in (6) gives

$$e^{-i\theta}=\cos\theta-i\sin\theta$$

which, combined with (6) gives

$$\left.\begin{aligned}\cos\theta&=\tfrac{1}{2}(e^{i\theta}+e^{-i\theta})\\ \sin\theta&=\frac{1}{2i}(e^{i\theta}-e^{-i\theta})\end{aligned}\right\} \qquad (12)$$

Also from the series for $\cos\theta$, $\sin\theta$ it follows that

$$e^{i\theta}=\left(1-\frac{1}{2!}\theta^2+\frac{1}{4!}\theta^4-\ldots\right)+i\left(\theta-\frac{1}{3!}\theta^3+\frac{1}{5!}\theta^5-\ldots\right)$$

$$=1+i\theta+\frac{1}{2!}(i\theta)^2+\frac{1}{3!}(i\theta)^3+\ldots$$

so that the expansion of $e^{i\theta}$ in powers of $i\theta$ is the same as that of e^x in powers of x.

6.41. *The representation of polar coordinates by complex numbers*

From equation (6) of 6.4 we now have

$$z=x+iy=r(\cos\theta+i\sin\theta)=re^{i\theta} \qquad (1)$$

Hence if the position of a point in a plane is given by its polar coordinates (r, θ) the corresponding complex number can be written down immediately ; it is not necessary to calculate the cartesian coordinates first.

Notice that multiplication of two complex numbers is particularly simple when they are in this form. Thus if

$z_1 = r_1 e^{i\theta_1}$ and $z_2 = r_2 e^{i\theta_2}$ then $z_1 z_2 = r_1 r_2 e^{i(\theta_1+\theta_2)}$ in accordance with the result of 6.32.

It is very useful to be able to translate from the cartesian to the polar representation or vice versa with facility; stated explicitly the rule of translation is

$$x + iy = re^{i\theta} \qquad \text{where } \left.\begin{aligned} r &= (x^2+y^2)^{1/2} \\ \theta &= \tan^{-1}(y/x) \end{aligned}\right\} \tag{2}$$

$$\text{i.e.} \qquad \left.\begin{aligned} x &= r\cos\theta \\ y &= r\sin\theta \end{aligned}\right\} \tag{3}$$

where equations (2) are used when x, y are given, while equations (3) are used when r, θ are the known quantities. The quantity $(x^2+y^2)^{1/2}$ is known as the modulus of the complex number $x+iy$ and can be written in the alternative form $|x+iy|$. The quantity $\tan^{-1}(y/x)$, lying in the quadrant consistent with (3), is known as the argument of $x+iy$ and can be written $\arg(x+iy)$.

Examples

(1) Show that $|z_1 z_2| = |z_1| \, |z_2|$, and that $|z_1/z_2| = |z_1|/|z_2|$.

(2) Let A, B, C and D be the points $(1, 0)$ $(0, 1)$ $(-1, 0)$ and $(0, -1)$. The corresponding complex numbers are $z = 1$, i -1, $-i$. In polar form these numbers are 1, $e^{i\pi/2}$, $e^{i\pi}$ and $e^{i3\pi/2}$

The equations $e^{i\pi/2} = i$ (4)

$$e^{i\pi} = -1 \tag{5}$$

$$e^{i2\pi} = +1 \tag{6}$$

and their geometrical significance should be particularly noted.

In scientific applications it is more often a pair of quantities resembling r, θ which is represented by a complex number than a pair like x, y. This is largely owing to the close association between motion in a circle ($r = A$, $\theta = \omega t +$ constant) and simple harmonic motion (see also next paragraph).

6.5. The phase-amplitude diagram

The second main application of the complex variable is to the theory of vibrations. This application is made by means of a diagram analogous to the vector diagram of 6.31. Consider for example an oscillation specified by the equation

$$y = Y\cos(\omega t + \phi).$$

The quantity Y, one half of the peak-to-peak swing in the oscillation is called the amplitude, and $\omega t+\phi$ the phase of the oscillation. (As we shall see later, amplitude and phase can often be conveniently represented by the modulus and argument respectively of a complex number.) Now suppose that a number of vibrations are superimposed; for example that the lines labelled 1, 2, 3 in Fig. 6.5 represent wires carrying alternating currents y_1, y_2, y_3 of the same frequency $\omega/2\pi$ joined into a common conductor, and that we require an expression for the resultant current.

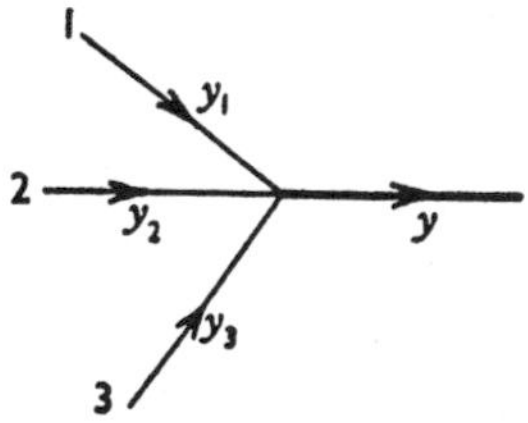

FIG. 6.5

We suppose that there is a law giving the resultant vibration y in the form $y=y_1+y_2+y_3$. In the electric circuit this is supplied by Kirchhoff's laws; in physical optics by the principle of superposition. (There are fields in which this law for the resultant is not valid; for example water and sound waves of large amplitude; the following discussion does not then apply).

We can use one of three methods, straight-forward trigonometry, the phase-amplitude diagram or the complex variable. The equivalence of the three methods may be regarded as a consequence of the close association of all three with the vector i.e. parallelogram law of addition—the trigonometrical formulae for cos $A+$ cos B etc. are embodiments of the vector law, the phase-amplitude diagram is a vector diagram, and, as we have seen, there is a close association between the vector law of addition and the algebra of complex numbers.

Let us compare the three methods in detail for two vibrations only,

$$y_1=Y_1\cos(\omega t+\phi_1)$$

$$y_2=Y_2\cos(\omega t+\phi_2)$$

Then the resultant is

$$y=y_1+y_2=Y_1\cos(\omega t+\phi_1)+Y_2\cos(\omega t+\phi_2) \qquad (1)$$

This has to be put into a form in which both phase and amplitude can be easily identified, i.e. into the form

$$y=Y\cos(\omega t+\phi) \qquad (2)$$

If we use straightforward trigonometry, we can first put

$$\phi_2 - \phi_1 = \theta_2 \tag{3}$$

write $\cos(\omega t + \phi_2) = \cos[(\omega t + \phi_1) + \theta_2]$, expand, substitute in (1) and collect terms in $\cos(\omega t + \phi_1)$, $\sin(\omega t + \phi_1)$. This gives

$$y = (Y_1 + Y_2 \cos\theta_2)\cos(\omega t + \phi_1) - (Y_2 \sin\theta_2)\sin(\omega t + \phi_1) \tag{4}$$

Now put

$$\left.\begin{aligned} Y_1 + Y_2 \cos\theta_2 &= Y \cos\theta \\ Y_2 \sin\theta_2 &= Y \sin\theta \end{aligned}\right\} \tag{5}$$

Then (4) becomes

$$y = Y \cos(\omega t + \phi_1 + \theta)$$

which is of the form (2) with $\phi = \phi_1 + \theta$. Also, solving the two relations (5) for Y and θ,

$$\begin{aligned} Y^2 &= (Y_1 + Y_2 \cos\theta_2)^2 + (Y_2 \sin\theta_2)^2 \\ &= Y_1^2 + Y_2^2 + 2Y_1 Y_2 \cos\theta_2 \end{aligned} \tag{6}$$

$$\tan\theta = Y_2 \sin\theta_2 / (Y_1 + Y_2 \cos\theta_2) \tag{7}$$

where θ_2, is given by (3). The calculation shows that the sum of two simple harmonic vibrations of the same frequency is itself simple harmonic and of the same frequency.

The phase-amplitude diagram shortens this calculation considerably by cutting out some of the trigonometric details. The vibration is represented purely formally by means of a straight line or displacement vector whose length is proportional to the amplitude and whose inclination to a given axis is equal to the phase of the vibration. In practice one avoids the time dependent term ωt by taking some vibration as a standard of reference and using the phase differences of the other vibrations in the problem relative to this standard. For example if we take $y_1 = Y_1 \cos(\omega t + \phi_1)$ as the standard and represent it by the line OA in Fig. 6.6 then the second vibration

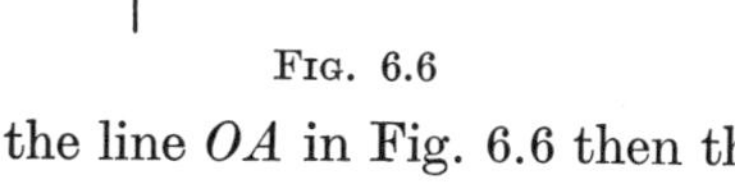

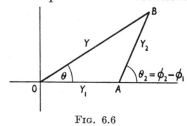

FIG. 6.6

$$y_2 = Y_2 \cos(\omega t + \phi_2)$$

is represented in amplitude and in phase by the line AB. If these displacements are added vectorially the result is the displacement vector OB whose length is given by

$$OB^2 = Y_1^2 + Y_2^2 + 2Y_1 Y_2 \cos\theta_2 \tag{8}$$

and whose phase differs from the standard by the angle θ, where

$$\tan\theta = \frac{Y_2 \sin\theta_2}{Y_1 + Y_2 \cos\theta_2} \tag{9}$$

Comparing these equations with (6) and (7) we see that OB correctly represents the resultant of y_1 and y_2 both in phase and amplitude. We have therefore shown that simple harmonic vibrations of the same frequency can be added on the phase-amplitude diagram by the parallelogram rule, a result of wide application especially in physical optics and a.c. theory.

Now if a vibration can be represented by a line in a plane, then it can also be represented by a complex number. This leads to the third and most generally useful method of dealing with vibrations. The complex number representing OA in the phase-amplitude diagram is Y_1 and is real because y_1 was chosen as the standard of reference. On this basis the complex number representing y_2 is $Y_2 e^{i(\phi_2-\phi_1)}$ or $Y_2 e^{i\theta_2}$ and hence the number representing the resultant is

$$Y_1 + Y_2 e^{i\theta_2} \tag{10}$$

since the parallelogram rule of vector addition is represented by simple addition of the corresponding complex numbers. It will be noticed however that the phases can equally well be left in their original form ; thus the complex numbers representing y_1, y_2 can be taken as $Y_1 e^{i(\omega t+\phi_1)}$ and $Y_2 e^{i(\omega t+\phi_2)}$. In this case the resultant is

$$Y_1 e^{i(\omega t+\phi_1)} + Y_2 e^{i(\omega t+\phi_2)} = (Y_1 + Y_2 e^{i\theta_2}) e^{i(\omega t+\phi_1)}$$

There is evidently no difference in practice whichever convention is adopted. This possibility of removing common factors such as $e^{i\omega t}$ from a sum is not the least of the advantages of the complex representation.

There is little to choose between the phase-amplitude diagram and the complex number in this simple case. To put (10) into the required form we have to separate the real and imaginary parts of $e^{i\theta_2}$ and write

$$\begin{aligned} Y_1 + Y_2 e^{i\theta_2} &= (Y_1 + Y_2\cos\theta_2) + iY_2\sin\theta_2 \\ &= Ye^{i\theta} \end{aligned}$$

where $\quad Y^2 = (Y_1 + Y_2\cos\theta_2)^2 + (Y_2\sin\theta_2)^2$

and $\quad \tan\theta = Y_2\sin\theta_2/(Y_1 + Y_2\cos\theta_2)$

as previously.

However in anything more elaborate the superiority of algebraic (complex number) over geometrical techniques becomes evident.

6.51. *Application to the linear A.C. circuit*

An a.c. circuit is a combination of generators, resistors, condensers and inductance coils, connected in any way. The following physical properties of these circuit elements are required.

(i) When a current $I = I_0 \cos \omega t$ passes through a resistor a back e.m.f. equal to $V_R = RI = RI_0 \cos \omega t$ is developed. By back e.m.f. is meant a voltage difference in a direction opposite to that of the current. This is Ohm's Law ; the constant R is called the resistance of the element. In certain types of conductor R is not constant but depends on the current ; circuits containing such elements are called non-linear and require radically different treatment.

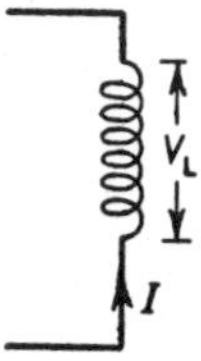

FIG. 6.7

(ii) When a current I passes through an inductance coil (fig. 6.7) the back e.m.f. developed is given by $V_L = L\, \mathrm{d}I/\mathrm{d}t$ and in particular if $I = I_0 \cos \omega t$

$$V_L = -\omega L I_0 \sin \omega t$$
$$= \omega L I_0 \cos (\omega t + \tfrac{1}{2}\pi)$$

The back e.m.f. is not in phase with the current but leads by 90° ; alternatively the current lags 90° behind the e.m.f. The constant L is called the self-inductance of the coil.

(iii) When a current $I = I_0 \cos \omega t$ is passed through the primary one of two coils, for example through a transformer, an e.m.f.

$$V_M = M\, \mathrm{d}I/\mathrm{d}t$$
$$= \omega M I_0 \cos (\omega t + \tfrac{1}{2}\pi)$$

is developed in the other coil (fig. 6.8). M is the mutual inductance of the two coils. Similarly if the current is passed through the second coil an equal e.m.f. is developed in the other. The direction of the induced e.m.f. in the secondary coil is always such as to oppose the inducing current in the primary but unlike L which is always positive, M may be positive or negative, depending on the relative presentation of the two coils.

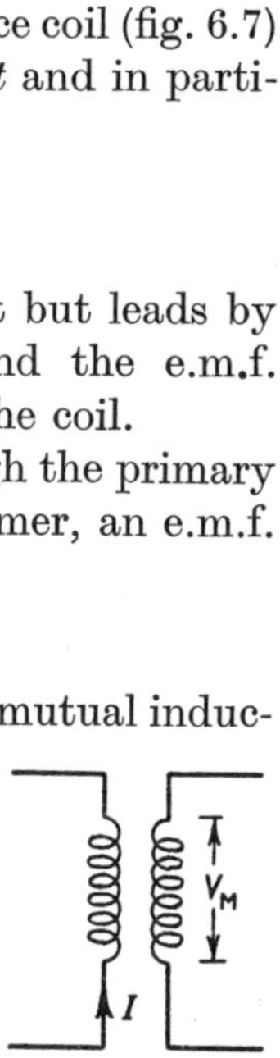

FIG. 6.8

(iv) When the current $I = I_0 \cos \omega t$ is passed into a condenser the back e.m.f. due to the accumulation of charge is

$$V_C = (1/C) \int I \, \mathrm{d}t = (1/\omega C) I_0 \sin \omega t$$

The arbitrary constant in the integral corresponds to an additional steady potential difference across the condenser, which is irrelevant when we are concerned only with currents and potential differences varying simple-harmonically with time.

(v) We need also the two addition laws for e.m.f.s and currents ;

(*a*) the total back e.m.f. developed across a number of elements in series and therefore carrying the same current is the sum of the back e.m.f.s developed across the separate elements ; and the total back e.m.f. in a closed circuit is equal to the total forward e.m.f.

(*b*) the total current taken by elements in parallel and therefore having the same e.m.f. across them, is the sum of the currents in the individual elements.

Example 1

The series resonant circuit (Fig. 6.9)

Let the generator develop an alternating e.m.f. $E = E_0 \cos \omega t$. Then after possible transients have died down (see Chapter 11 for the fuller implications of this innocent statement) we can suppose that an alternating current $I = I_0 \cos (\omega t + \phi)$ is set up. The results can be obtained most directly however by employing complex representation. To emphasise the logical difference between the real variable $I = I_0 \cos (\omega t + \phi)$ and the complex variable $I_0 e^{i(\omega t+\phi)}$ which represents it, we shall denote the latter by a different symbol. Also in accordance with the usual practice in this application we shall in dealing with electrical problems denote the imaginary unit by j, leaving i to represent a current. That i stands for 'current' rather than for the imaginary unit is an established convention in electrical engineering.

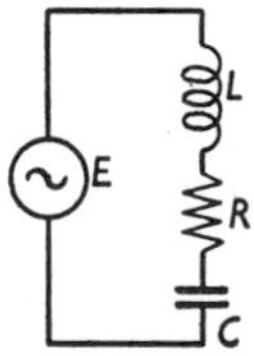

FIG. 6.9

Let E, V_L, V_R, V_C and I denote the real variables, and e, v_L, v_R, v_C and i the corresponding complex variables ; then we note that $E = R.P.\,(\mathrm{e})$; $I = R.P.\,(i)$ etc. The back e.m.f. developed in a coil carrying current $I = I_0 \cos \omega t$ is (see 6.51, ii)

$$V_L = \omega L I_0 \cos (\omega t + \tfrac{1}{2}\pi) \tag{1}$$

and therefore is represented in complex form by

$$v_L = \omega L I_0 \, e^{j(\omega t + \frac{1}{2}\pi)} \tag{2}$$

But since the current $I = I_0 \cos \omega t$ is itself represented by

$$i = I_0 \, e^{j\omega t}$$

the relation (2) can be written simply

$$v_L = e^{j\pi/2}\omega Li = j\omega Li$$

We have in this equation, a most economical statement of the essential features of the back e.m.f. in a coil, namely that it is equal to the magnitude of the current multiplied by L and its phase is ahead of the current by 90°. Similarly

$$v_M = j\omega Mi$$
$$v_R = Ri$$
$$v_C = (1/j\omega C)i$$

The quantities ωL and $1/\omega C$ are called the reactances of the coil and condenser; they play the same part in the complex representation of a.c. circuits as resistance plays in the d.c. case. The quantity $j\omega M$ is of a slightly different character since the back e.m.f. developed by mutual inductance is developed in another circuit.

The addition law for e.m.f.s can be written

$$\begin{aligned} \mathrm{e} &= v_L + v_R + v_C \\ &= [j\omega L + R + (1/j\omega C)]i \end{aligned}$$

Hence $$\mathrm{e}/i = j\omega L + R + (1/j\omega C)$$

The quantity on the right is called the complex impedance of the circuit and is denoted by the symbol z; it will be noticed that it is simply the sum of the impedances of the individual elements. Combining the terms we have

$$\mathrm{e}/i = R + j(\omega L - 1/\omega C) \tag{3}$$
$$= [R^2 + (\omega L - 1/\omega C)^2]^{\frac{1}{2}} \, e^{-j\phi} \quad \text{(cf. eqn. (2) of §6.41)}$$

where $$\tan \phi = [(1/\omega C) - \omega L]/R = (1 - \omega^2 LC)/R\omega C$$

Transforming back to real variables we have

$$\begin{aligned} I &= R.P.(i) = R.P.\{E_0 e^{j\omega t} e^{j\phi}/[R^2 + (\omega L - 1/\omega C)^2]^{\frac{1}{2}}\} \\ &= E_0 \cos(\omega t + \phi)/[R^2 + (\omega L - 1/\omega C)^2]^{\frac{1}{2}} \end{aligned}$$

In view of the algebraical complication of the last two steps we may remind the reader that equation (3) contains the essentials of the solution, the purpose of the final operations being to express the result in real form.

It will also be well if the reader will at this stage remind himself of the steps which led to the definition of the complex impedance z. These were (i) the experimental data giving the amplitude and phase shift of the back e.m.f. in a resistance, capacity or inductance,

(ii) the observation that each of these experimental laws could be expressed by a complex equation of the form e = (complex no.) i, (iii) the further deduction, using the experimental law (v(a) above) that a similar law, e = (complex no.) i held for the circuit as a whole, and (iv) the final stage of giving a name, the complex impedance z to the factor multiplying i, so that e $= zi$ is the equation for the circuit. It is only in the context of these steps that the 'meaning' of complex impedance and the laws for its manipulation can be appreciated.

Example 2

The parallel resonant circuit (Fig. 6.10)

If I_1 and I_2 are the currents taken by the two separate arms, the current I supplied by the generator is

$$I = I_1 + I_2 \qquad (1)$$

But for the inductive arm

$$E = L\,\mathrm{d}I_1/\mathrm{d}t + RI \qquad (2)$$

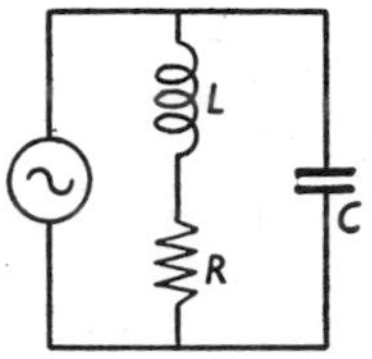

FIG. 6.10

and for the capacitative arm

$$E = (1/C)\int I_2\,\mathrm{d}t \qquad (3)$$

Hence going over to the complex representation we have the equations

$$\left.\begin{aligned} \mathrm{e} &= (R + j\omega L)i_1 \\ \mathrm{e} &= (1/j\omega C)i_2 \end{aligned}\right\} \qquad (4)$$

and therefore

$$i/\mathrm{e} = (i_1 + i_2)/e = 1/(R + j\omega L) + j\omega C \qquad (5)$$

The quantity on the right is the reciprocal of the complex impedance and is called the complex admittance, $1/z$, of the circuit ; it appears that the admittance of two arms in parallel is the sum of the admittances of the separate arms. This is a direct consequence of equation (1) ; and is analogous to the similar relation holding for resistances in parallel in the d.c. case.

From (5) it now follows that

$$\begin{aligned} i/\mathrm{e} &= [1 - \omega^2 LC) + j\omega CR]/(R + j\omega L) \\ &= \left[\frac{(1 - \omega^2 LC)^2 + \omega^2 C^2 R^2}{R^2 + \omega^2 L^2}\right]^{\frac{1}{2}} e^{j(\phi_1 - \phi_2)} \end{aligned}$$

where $\tan\phi_1 = \omega CR/(1 - \omega^2 LC)$

$\tan\phi_2 = \omega L/R$

In real form

$$I = E_0\left[\frac{(1 - \omega^2 LC)^2 + \omega^2 C^2 R^2}{R^2 + \omega^2 L^2}\right]^{\frac{1}{2}} \cos(\omega t + \phi_1 - \phi_2)$$

6.52. *Applications to wave theory*

A complete account of the physical basis of wave theory would be out of place here and we shall consider only the simple case of simple-harmonic plane waves of a single frequency, i.e. space and time variations of a physical quantity measured by a variable U, the variations being such that

$$U(x, t) = U_0 \cos(\omega t - kx + \phi) \tag{1}$$

where the direction of the x-axis is the direction of propagation of the wave. The significance of ω, as in the alternating current example, can be appreciated by noting that for a given point x

$$U(x, t + 2\pi/\omega) = U(x, t)$$

in other words $2\pi/\omega$ is the periodic time of the oscillation. Similarly, at a given instant

$$U(x + 2\pi/k, t) = U(x, t)$$

so that $2\pi/k$ is the wave-length of the waves. Notice incidentally that ω/k is the velocity of the wave, for U is constant if $\omega t - kx$ is constant i.e. if $k(x_2 - x_1) = \omega(t_2 - t_1)$. If there is a law of superposition for the physical quantity U, the real variable $U(x, t)$ can usefully be represented by the complex variable

$$u = U_0 e^{i(\omega t - kx + \phi)} \tag{2}$$

and the law of superposition can be written

$$u = u_1 + u_2 + \dots$$

where u represents the resultant and $u_1, u_2 \dots$ the separate vibrations.

Example 1

Diffraction of plane waves at a slit. Take the optical case for definiteness ; let S be a point source at the focal point of a lens L_1 and let the ensuing plane waves pass through a long rectangular slit of width AB in an otherwise opaque screen D (Fig. 6.11). The

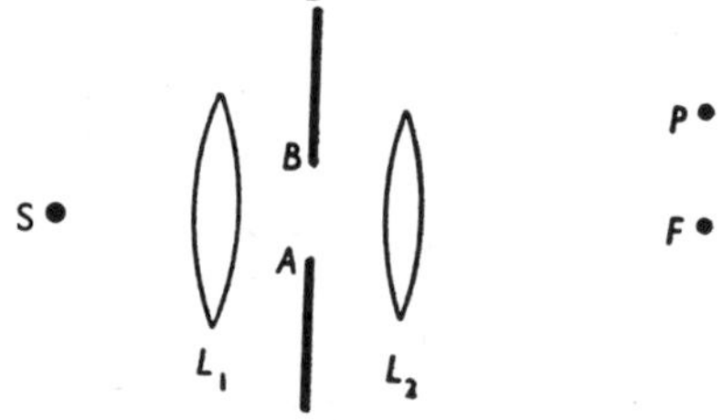

FIG. 6.11

waves pass through to the second lens L_2. In the absence of the screen a sharp image of S would be formed at the focal point F and no other point in the focal plane through F would be illuminated. To see what happens when D is inserted we use Huygens' Principle, a semi-quantitative rule very useful in approximate treatments of wave propagation. According to this principle any point on a surface can be regarded as a source of secondary waves and the disturbance at any other point in space can be calculated as the resultant of contributions from these secondary waves summed over the whole surface.

In the present example we consider these secondary sources to be uniformly distributed over the aperture AB. To find the resultant disturbance due to waves diffracted through an angle θ by the slit and therefore focused by L_2 on to a non-axial point P we have to sum the contributions of the secondary waves from each element of

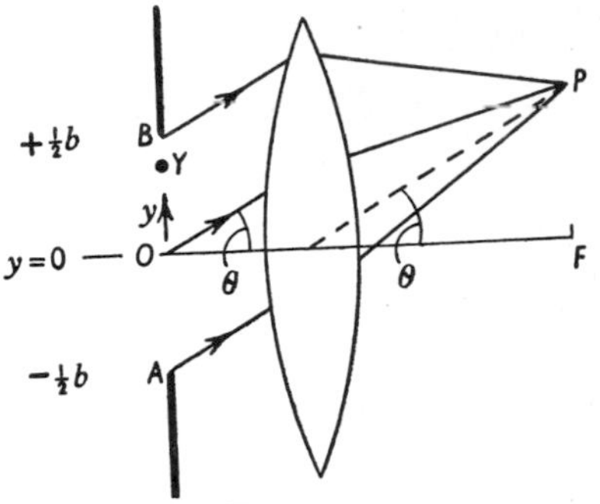

FIG. 6.12

area in the wavefront AB. Let y be a coordinate as shown (Fig. 6.12) with $y = -\frac{1}{2}b$ at A and $y = +\frac{1}{2}b$ at B; and let the contribution from a small element dy near O be

$$dU = K\,dy \cos \omega t$$

Then the contribution from the secondary sources in the element dy at the point Y will be

$$dU = K\,dy \cos (\omega t - ky \sin \theta) \qquad (3)$$

The amplitude is the same; the difference in phase arises because the point Y is optically closer to P than is the point O; the y-axis makes an angle $(\frac{1}{2}\pi - \theta)$ with the parallel beam which we are considering as it leaves the slit, so the difference in the length of the optical path from O and Y is $y \sin \theta$. Thus (3) may be compared with (1) in which $U_0 = K\,dy$, $\phi = 0$ and $x = y \sin \theta$.

In terms of the complex variable (2), equation (3) is replaced by

$$du = K\,dy\, e^{i(\omega t - ky \sin \theta)}$$

Integration over the width of the slit, that is from

$$y = -\tfrac{1}{2}b \text{ to } y = +\tfrac{1}{2}b, \text{ gives}$$

$$u = K\left[\int_{-\frac{1}{2}b}^{+\frac{1}{2}b} e^{-iky \sin \theta}\, dy\right] e^{i\omega t} \tag{4}$$

(note, the integration is with respect to y, for constant K and a constant value of θ). Now,

$$\int_{-\frac{1}{2}b}^{+\frac{1}{2}b} e^{-i\lambda y}\, dy = (-1/i\lambda)\Big[e^{-i\lambda y}\Big]_{-\frac{1}{2}b}^{+\frac{1}{2}b} \quad \text{(cf. eqn. (11) of 6.4)}$$

$$= -(1/i\lambda)[e^{-\frac{1}{2}i\lambda b} - e^{+\frac{1}{2}i\lambda b}]$$

$$= (2/\lambda) \sin \tfrac{1}{2}\lambda b \quad \text{by (12) of 6.4} \tag{5}$$

and the integral in (4) is this integral with $\lambda = k \sin \theta$.

Hence from (4) and (5)

$$u = 2K \sin (\tfrac{1}{2}kb \sin \theta) e^{i\omega t}/(k \sin \theta)$$

or, if we make the substitution $\beta = \frac{1}{2}kb \sin \theta$

$$u = [(Kb \sin \beta)/\beta] e^{i\omega t} \tag{6}$$

Example 2

The diffraction grating

Instead of a single slit of width b consider now N slits each of width b separated by opaque strips of width a (Fig. 6.13).

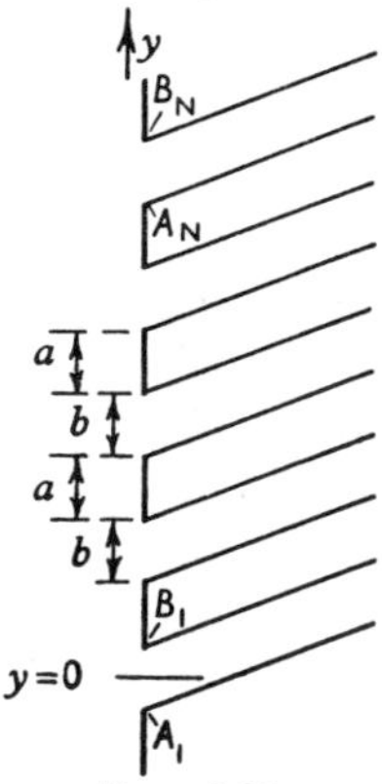

FIG. 6.13

The contribution from sources in the element dy at distance y from the origin can, as before, be written $K\, dy \cos (\omega t - kx \sin \theta)$, and the contribution to u from the first slit A_1B_1 to the disturbance at P is as in the previous example

$$u_1 = Ae^{i\omega t}$$

where

$$A = (Kb \sin \beta)/\beta$$

The contribution from the second slit is the same in amplitude but retarded by an amount $k(a+b) \sin \theta$ in phase; if we write

$$2\gamma = k(a+b) \sin \theta = 2\pi[(a+b)/\lambda] \sin \theta$$

this contribution to u is

$$u_2 = Ae^{i(\omega t - 2\gamma)}$$

Similarly

$$u_3 = Ae^{i(\omega t - 4\gamma)}$$

and for N slits

$$u = Ae^{i\omega t}(1 + e^{-2i\gamma} + e^{-4i\gamma} + \ldots + e^{-2(N-1)i\gamma})$$

The series is a finite geometrical progression with common ratio $e^{-2i\gamma}$ and can be summed by the usual formula. Hence

$$u = Ae^{i\omega t}[1 - e^{-2Ni\gamma}]/[1 - e^{-2i\gamma}]$$
$$= Ae^{i\omega t}\, e^{-Ni\gamma}(e^{Ni\gamma} - e^{-Ni\gamma})/e^{-i\gamma}(e^{i\gamma} - e^{-i\gamma})$$
$$= Ae^{i\omega t}\, e^{-(N-1)i\gamma}(\sin N\gamma)/(\sin\gamma) \quad \text{by (12) of 6.4.}$$

Hence the amplitude at P is $A\ (\sin N\gamma)/(\sin\gamma)$ and the intensity, which is the square of this, is

$$I(\theta) = K^2b^2[(\sin^2\beta)/\beta^2][(\sin^2 N\gamma)/\sin^2\gamma] \qquad (7)$$

where $\beta = \frac{1}{2}kb\sin\theta$. Fig. 6.14 shows the variation of $I(\theta)$ graphically.

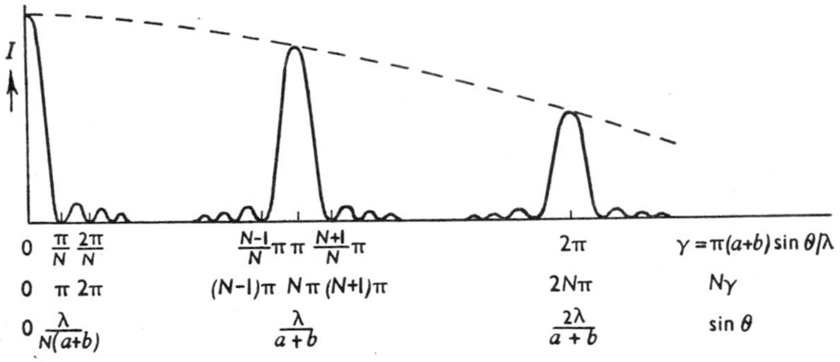

FIG. 6.14

The peaks at $\gamma = n\pi$ are called the principal maxima ; in between are $N-2$ subsidiary or second maxima. In a 6-inch grating, with 15,000 lines to the inch as used in spectroscopic work, N is of the order 100,000 and hence the principal maxima are the only ones observed. These occur at

$$\gamma = n\pi$$

i.e. $$(a+b)\sin\theta = n\lambda \qquad (8)$$

which is the elementary formula for the diffraction grating. The present method gives not only the *positions* of the maxima (8), but the intensity everywhere (7).

CHAPTER SEVEN

CALCULUS

7.1. Differentiation and integration

The simplest examples of differentiation are based on the problems of calculating gradients and rates of change. However the student should realise that these two problems are not in themselves the principal applications of the calculus. The calculus was developed by Isaac Newton for the purpose of solving much more general physical problems, and the tremendous advances of the physical sciences since Newton's day could not conceivably have been made without it.

The student will not be able to appreciate the full value of the technique until he has used it widely, but the essence of its power is simple enough. Consider the example, representative of a very large part of mathematical physics, of the vibrating string. Let an elastic string be stretched between two fixed points A and B, Fig. 7.1, so that its tension has the value T. The string is then slightly displaced in some specified way and released. What is the subsequent motion? This problem may appear at first sight too complicated for a solution to be attainable, but as a first step towards formulating it in a shape in which we may attempt to solve it, consider a snapshot of the string at a particular instant. We look at this instantaneous picture (Fig. 7.2) a little more hopefully, but reflect that a

FIG. 7.1

FIG. 7.2

string (in tension) cannot remain in such a shape, and as soon as we begin to consider how it will move there are so many moving points to consider, the motion of each affecting and being affected by its neighbours, that any detailed solution of the problem seems out of the question.

The clue to its solution is to analyse the string into small parts, and to discuss the motion, not of the whole, but of one part. For example take a small element PQ of the string (Fig. 7.3). This element interacts with its neighbours but these interactions can be specified by the forces T acting along the *tangents* at its two ends. The motion of PQ can be expressed in terms of these forces by Newton's second law of motion which relates the acceleration of a particle to the force acting on it. Now acceleration is a *rate of change* of velocity and velocity is a *rate of change* of position. The equation of motion of the element PQ therefore involves precisely those concepts, tangent and rate of change, which are dealt with by the differential calculus.

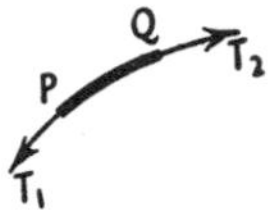

FIG. 7.3

The differential calculus is thus the perfect medium for analysing the motion of a continuous system. It does not of course solve the problem of calculating the motion ; it simply enables us to formulate it. The process of finding the motion of the whole string from the equations so formulated is called the integration of the equations ; the integral calculus is the appropriate mathematical tool.

The differential calculus and the integral calculus are inversely related. The first analyses, the second synthesizes. Together they form the calculus, the core of mathematical physics. The reader is presumed to be acquainted with the elementary ideas and techniques of the calculus ; these are summarised shortly here as a reminder and for reference.

7.2. Differentiation

Suppose we have a function $y = \mathrm{f}(x)$. From this function of a single variable x we may construct a function of two variables (x, h).

$$\mathrm{F}(x, h) = [\mathrm{f}(x+h) - \mathrm{f}(x)]/h$$

and enquire whether, for a fixed value of x, this tends to a limit as $h \to 0$. This limit may exist for all values of x, for some values only or for no value of x. Where the limit exists a new function of the single variable x can be defined, namely,

$$\mathrm{f}'(x) = \lim_{h \to 0} \mathrm{F}(x, h)$$

This function $f'(x)$ is called the *derivative* of the original function $f(x)$.

An alternative notation sometimes offers certain advantages. We may write δx for the increment h in x, δy for the increment in y, and dy/dx for the derivative $f'(x)$, thus ;

$$\frac{dy}{dx} = f'(x) = \lim_{\delta x \to 0} \frac{\delta y}{\delta x} = \lim_{\delta x \to 0} \frac{f(x+\delta x) - f(x)}{\delta x}$$

The process of calculating dy/dx or $f'(x)$ is called differentiation, and alternative names for the derivative $f'(x)$ are 'derived function' or 'differential coefficient' of $f(x)$.

7.21. *The existence of the derivative and continuity*

The criterion for the existence of the derivative of $f(x)$ is the existence of the limit, $\lim_{h \to 0} [f(x+h) - f(x)]/h$. The denominator $h \to 0$, so the limit can only exist if $f(x+h) - f(x) \to 0$ also. The continuity of the function (at a point or within a range) is thus a necessary condition for the existence of the derivative (at the point or within the range). The continuity of $f(x)$ is not however sufficient for the existence of $f'(x)$. Consider for example the function $f(x) = | x - a |$, whose graph is shown in Fig. 7.4: it consists of two linear segments. When $x < a$, $f'(x) = -1$ and when $x > a$, $f'(x) = +1$. At $x = a$, this function is continuous, but the limit of $[f(a+h) - f(a)]/h$ does not exist ; for this ratio has the value -1 or $+1$ according as h is positive or negative, and for a general sequence h_n of values of h, these values of $| f(a+h) - f(a) |/h$ do not tend to a limit. For this function there is a jump discontinuity in $f'(x)$ at $x = a$, as shown in the graph, and $f'(a)$ is not defined. Differentiation always emphasises the unsmoothness of a curve.

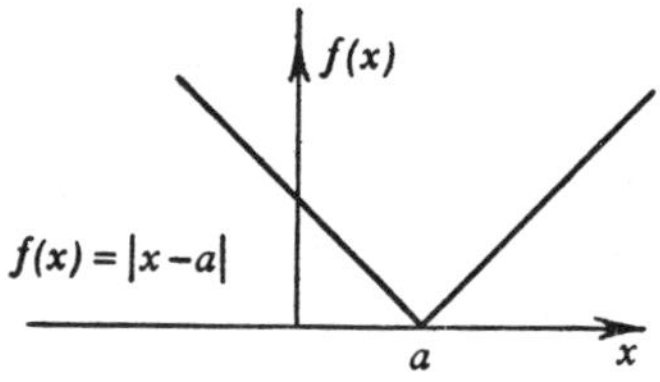

FIG. 7.4

7.22. *Differentials*

It will be noted that although the notation dy/dx for a derivative appears to express it as the ratio of two quantities dy and dx, no definition of such quantities has yet been given.

However it is occasionally convenient to use formulae such as $\mathrm{d}y = \mathrm{f}'(x)\,\mathrm{d}x$ in which they are separate and it is therefore useful to attribute some meaning to these quantities, which are called 'differentials'. The most obvious interpretation is that they are analogous to the finite quantities δx and δy but with the proviso that they are infinitesimally small; but this is unsatisfactory in many ways and the following interpretation should also be noticed. Let P and Q be two points on the curve and let the coordinates be (x, y) and $(x+\delta x, y+\delta y)$ respectively. Then provided δx and δy are not too large we have the approximation $\delta y \simeq \mathrm{f}'(x)\,\delta x$. Now take a point T on the tangent with coordinates $(x+\mathrm{d}x, y+\mathrm{d}y)$, where $\mathrm{d}x$, $\mathrm{d}y$ are not infinitesimal but ordinary finite quantities. Then we have the exact equation $\mathrm{d}y = \mathrm{f}'(x)\,\mathrm{d}x$.

An equation between differentials can therefore always be interpreted as an exact equation referring not to points on the curve $y = \mathrm{f}(x)$ but to points on its tangent at the point (x, y). This interpretation removes the necessity of regarding differentials as being vanishingly small.

7.23. *Derivatives of elementary functions*

We could, whenever the derivative of a function is required calculate it from the basic definition. For example to obtain the derivative of e^{ax}, (using the definition and properties stated in section 5.3 ff.), let $y = e^{ax}$, then

$$\delta y = e^{a(x+\delta x)} - e^{ax} = e^{ax}(e^{a\,\delta x} - 1)$$

$$\delta y/\delta x = e^{ax}(e^{a\,\delta x} - 1)/\delta x = ae^{ax}[(e^{a\,\delta x} - 1)/a\,\delta x]$$

But we know from 5.32 that $[(e^{u} - 1)/u] \to 1$ as $u \to 0$

Hence
$$\frac{\mathrm{d}y}{\mathrm{d}x} = \lim_{\delta x \to 0} \frac{\delta y}{\delta x} = ae^{ax}$$

For reasons of efficiency it is best to evaluate the derivatives of a number of commonly occurring functions once and for all, and to memorise the resulting standard forms. The range of applicability of the standard forms can then be extended by the use of the relations for the derivatives of combinations of functions. The following is a minimum working list of standard forms.

	f(x)	f′(x)
*	x^n	$n\,x^{n-1}$
	$\sin x$	$\cos x$
	$\cos x$	$-\sin x$
	$\tan x$	$\sec^2 x$
†	$\sin^{-1} x$	$\pm 1/\surd(1-x^2)$
†	$\cos^{-1} x$	$\pm 1/\surd(1-x^2)$
†	$\tan^{-1} x$	$1/(1+x^2)$
	e^x	e^x
	$\log_e x$	$1/x$
	$\sinh x$	$\cosh x$
	$\cosh x$	$\sinh x$
	$\tanh x$	$\operatorname{sech}^2 x$

7.3. Derivatives of combinations of functions

The important results for derivatives of combinations of functions are

y	dy/dx	
(i) $f(x)+g(x)$	$f'(x)+g'(x)$	
(ii) $f(x)\,g(x)$	$f'(x)\,g(x)+f(x)\,g'(x)$	
(iii) $f(x)/g(x)$	$[f'(x)\,g(x)-f(x)\,g'(x)]/[g(x)]^2$	
(iv) $f(u)$, where $u=g(x)$	$\dfrac{dy}{dx}=\dfrac{dy}{du}\cdot\dfrac{du}{dx}$	(1)
(v) $\phi^{-1}(x)$ [that is, $x=\phi(y)$]	$1/\phi'(y)$	(2)

The general form of the relation (1) should be noted. If the derivatives are regarded as ratios of differentials (see 7.22), the relation (1) can be regarded as the result of cancelling the differential du on the right-hand side. But the reader must not regard this as a *proof* of the relation (1); it is no more than a convenient mnemonic.

* If n is not integral this result must be used with care unless x is positive.
† See 7.32 for further discussion of the derivatives of these functions.

Example

If $y = e^{x^2}$, put $y = e^u$, $u = x^2$

then $dy/du = e^u = e^{x^2}$, $du/dx = 2x$, $dy/dx = 2xe^{x^2}$

If we put $y = x$ in (1), we obtain

$$1 = (dx/du) \,.\, (du/dx)$$

Hence $dx/du = 1/(du/dx)$.

This is another form of the relation (2).

7.31. *A note on notation*

The notation $f'(x)$ for the derivative is compact and often convenient, but it must be used with care in any context in which it might be at all ambiguous. In particular, in application of formula (1) of 7.3, either dy/dx or dy/du might be denoted by y'. Often when a derivative is expressed by a dash the argument is also expressed explicitly (as in $y'(x)$ or $y'(u)$); then a dash means a derivative with respect to this argument: for example $f'(ax^2+b)$ means the derivative of f with respect to the argument $u = ax^2 + b$, that is df/du, *not* df/dx. In this case

$$\frac{d}{dx} f(ax^2+b) = \left[\frac{d}{du} f(u)\right] . \frac{du}{dx} = f'(u) \,.\, 2ax = 2ax\, f'(ax^2+b) \qquad (1)$$

7.32. *Examples of differentiation*

The following are some examples of the application of the general results of the previous sections.

(i) $y = a_n x^n + a_{n-1} x^{n-1} + \ldots + a_0$

$$\frac{dy}{dx} = n a_n x^{n-1} + (n-1) a_{n-1} x^{n-2} + \ldots + a_1$$

The derivative of a polynomial of degree n is also a polynomial, but of degree $(n-1)$.

(ii) $y = \sin^{-1} x$. We have $x = \sin y$, $\dfrac{dx}{dy} = \cos y$

Hence

$$\frac{dy}{dx} = 1/\cos y = \pm 1/(1-x^2)^{1/2}.$$

The ambiguous sign can be understood most easily from a diagram (Fig. 7.5); A and B are points on the graph of $y = \sin^{-1} x$

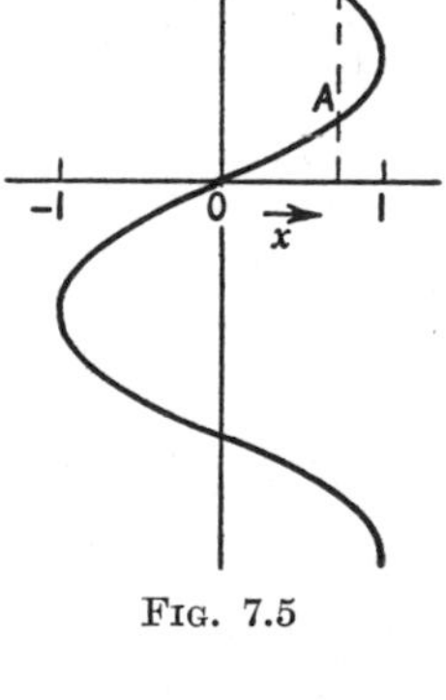

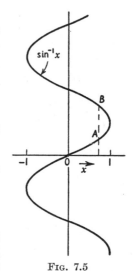

FIG. 7.5

at the same value of x, but dy/dx is positive at A, negative at B. For a given x in the range $-1<x<1$, there is an infinite number of values of $\sin^{-1} x$, but only two values of its derivative. It is possible to remove this ambiguity by a convention; for example let $\operatorname{Sin}^{-1} x$ denote the particular branch of the multivalued function $\sin^{-1} x$ that lies between $-\frac{1}{2}\pi$ and $+\frac{1}{2}\pi$ (see §5.2). Then $\frac{d}{dx}\operatorname{Sin}^{-1} x$ is always positive (except at the ends of this range) and its value is therefore $+1/\sqrt{(1-x^2)}$.

(iii) $y=\cos^{-1} x$. Here $\cos y=x$, and $-\sin y\,(dy/dx)=1$. Hence

$$dy/dx = \pm 1/(1-x^2)^{1/2}$$

as before.

For a given value of x the two functions $\sin^{-1} x$ and $\cos^{-1} x$ have the same gradients; as pointed out in 5.2, the graphs of these functions differ only by a vertical displacement of amount $\frac{1}{2}\pi$. The ambiguity in sign of dy/dx is removed if we consider the function $\operatorname{Cos}^{-1} x$ (see 5.2), for which the derivative is $-1/\sqrt{(1-x^2)}$.

(iv) $y=\tan^{-1} x$. Here $\tan y=x$, $\sec^2 y\,\frac{dy}{dx}=1$ and therefore

$$\frac{dy}{dx}=\frac{1}{\sec^2 y}=\frac{1}{1+x^2}$$

The derivative is therefore single-valued; the branches of the many-valued function $\tan^{-1} x$ differ only by vertical displacements of amount π.

Using the standard forms of 7.23 and results of 7.31 we are able to differentiate any function which can be expressed as a finite number of elementary functions (including their inverses). There are still the problems of differentiating infinite series and results of other limiting processes, and also of differentiating functions of two or more variables. Discussions of these points are postponed until 7.6 ff. and Chapters 8 and 9.

7.4. Repeated differentiation

Just as $f(x)$ can be differentiated to give $f'(x)$, so $f'(x)$ can be differentiated to give $f''(x)$, and so on. The first, second, third, fourth, nth derivatives of $f(x)$ are denoted by $f'(x)$, $f''(x)$, $f'''(x)$, $f^{iv}(x)$, $f^{(n)}(x)$ respectively; the differential notation is dy/dx, d^2y/dx^2, d^3y/dx^3, d^ny/dx^n: other notations are Dy, D^2y, D^3y, etc., and $\dot{y}$, $\ddot{y}$, $\dddot{y}$. The last notation (using dots) is usually restricted to functions of a variable which is a measure of time, and is hardly ever used beyond the second derivative, and never beyond the third.

If $f(x)$ is itself a complicated expression the evaluation of its second and third derivatives becomes very tedious, and a general expression for the nth derivative is usually out of the question. In the following cases which are of subsequent importance a simple result is possible : in each case the general result can be proved by induction

1. $y=x^m$. $\mathrm{d}^n y/\mathrm{d}x^n = m(m-1)\ldots(m+1-n)x^{m-n}$. In particular if m is an integer and we differentiate x^m m times, the result is $m!$

2. $y=e^{ax}$. $\mathrm{d}^n y/\mathrm{d}x^n = a^n e^{ax}$

3. $y=\sin bx$. Here

$$\mathrm{d}y/\mathrm{d}x = b\cos bx = b\sin(bx+\tfrac{1}{2}\pi)$$
$$\mathrm{d}^2y/\mathrm{d}x^2 = -b^2\sin bx = b^2\sin(bx+\pi)$$

and for any positive n

$$\mathrm{d}^n y/\mathrm{d}x^n = b^n\sin(bx+\tfrac{1}{2}n\pi)$$

4. $y=\cos bx$. $\qquad \mathrm{d}^n y/\mathrm{d}x^n = b^n\cos(bx+\tfrac{1}{2}n\pi)$.

5. $y=e^{ax}\sin bx$. Here

$$\mathrm{d}y/\mathrm{d}x = e^{ax}(a\sin bx + b\cos bx) = (a^2+b^2)^{1/2}\,e^{ax}\sin(bx+\phi),$$

where $\phi = \mathrm{Tan}^{-1}(b/a)$ (see § 5.2) and

$$\mathrm{d}^n y/\mathrm{d}x^n = (a^2+b^2)^{\frac{1}{2}n}\,e^{ax}\sin(bx+n\phi)$$

6. $y=e^{ax}\cos bx$ $\quad \mathrm{d}^n y/\mathrm{d}x^n = (a^2+b^2)^{\frac{1}{2}n}\,e^{ax}\cos(bx+n\phi)$.

7.41. *Leibnitz's theorem*

If $y=uv$ where u and v have known differential coefficients, then by the product formula $y'=uv'+u'v$. Differentiating again, and using the product formula on each term,

$$\begin{aligned} y'' &= (uv''+u'v')+(v'u'+u''v) \\ &= uv''+2u'v'+u''v \end{aligned}$$

Leibnitz's theorem is a generalisation to the nth derivative of uv, namely

$$\begin{aligned} y^{(n)} &= uv^{(n)} + nu'\,.\,v^{(n-1)} + \tfrac{1}{2}n(n-1)u''\,.\,v^{(n-2)} + \ldots \\ &\quad + \binom{n}{r}u^{(r)}\,.\,v^{(n-r)} + \ldots + u^{(n)}\,.\,v \end{aligned} \tag{1}$$

where $\binom{n}{r}$ is the binomial coefficient $n!/(n-r)!\,r!$

Again the simplest proof is the indirect one provided by the method of induction, and is algebraically similar to the inductive proof of the binomial theorem.

7.42. *Logarithmic differentiation*

A useful preliminary to the differentiation of a complicated product is to take the logarithm of the function first. For example :

$$y = e^{-x^2} x^x, \qquad \log y = -x^2 + x \log x$$

$$\frac{1}{y}\frac{dy}{dx} = -2x + (\log x + 1)$$

so that

$$dy/dx = (1 - 2x + \log x)y$$

$$= (1 - 2x + \log x)e^{-x^2} x^x$$

7.5. Integration

Integration is the inverse of differentiation. In saying that the integral of $f(x)$ is $F(x)$, we mean that the derivative of $F(x)$ is $f(x)$. It is essential however to grasp the direct significance of the integral, rather than rely on the inversion of differentiation.

If we put $y = F(x)$ then y satisfies $\dfrac{dy}{dx} = f(x)$, and for a small increment δx in x the corresponding increment δy is given approximately by $\delta y = f(x)\,\delta x$. Now consider a succession of values of x, namely x_0, $x_1 = x_0 + \delta x_0$, $x_2 = x_1 + \delta x_1$, ... the increments δx_0, δx_1 ... being supposed small : the corresponding increments in y are given approximately by $\delta y_0 = f(x_0)\,\delta x_0$, $\delta y_1 = f(x_1)\,\delta x_1$ ... and the total increase in y is $\sum f(x_n)\,\delta x_n$ approximately, that is

$$y \simeq \sum f(x_n)\,\delta x_n + \text{constant}$$

the constant being the value of y at $x = x_0$. The idea suggests itself that the errors involved in the approximation might disappear if we evaluated $\lim\limits_{\delta x \to 0} \sum f(x)\,\delta x$ instead of the sum for finite increments, but such a hypothesis obviously demands careful consideration and we shall return to it in Chapter 8.

In the foregoing paragraph y is the integral of $f(x)$. Although we have not proved that $y = \lim\limits_{\delta x \to 0} \sum f(x)\,\delta x + \text{constant}$, we are at liberty to introduce a notation for the integral, namely $y = \int f(x)\, dx + \text{constant}$, which, historically, was suggested by such an equation.

As a matter of convenience, the arbitrary constant is usually suppressed. The quantity $\int f(x)\, dx$ is called the indefinite integral of $f(x)$ and the arbitrary additive constant is to be regarded as implied by the notation.

From the considerations outlined above, it would appear that almost any function $f(x)$ can be integrated, and we shall see that this is in fact substantially true, in the sense that the existence of an integral can be proved for all continuous functions, and for a great many discontinuous ones as well, and the value of the integral at any value of x can be estimated numerically to any desired accuracy. However, it is seldom possible to recognise the algebraic formula of the function so obtained. In fact the integral of an elementary function is not necessarily itself elementary. In this respect integration is different from differentiation. Integration is in fact a prolific source of transcendental functions.

Although the step-by-step process of construction of an integral gives the most useful mental picture of what integration is, the first step towards the integration of functions in general, is to use the original definition that integration is the inverse of differentiation. Every successful differentiation gives by inversion one more function whose integral is known.

Example 1

$$y = \int x^n\, dx, \quad \frac{dy}{dx} = x^n = \frac{1}{n+1}\{(n+1)x^n\} \qquad \text{provided } n+1 \neq 0$$

$$= \frac{1}{n+1}\frac{d}{dx}(x^{n+1}) = \frac{d}{dx}\left\{\frac{x^{n+1}}{n+1}\right\}$$

Thus $y = \dfrac{x^{n+1}}{n+1} + C$, provided $n+1 \neq 0$, i.e. $n \neq -1$.

Example 2

$y = \int (1/x)\, dx$. This is the exceptional case $n = -1$ of the previous example. There is no difficulty in finding the function whose derivative is $1/x$; it is $\log x$ and hence $y = \log_e x + c$. The example shows incidentally that the integral of a rational function may be transcendental.

It may be surprising that the formal expression for the integral of $1/x$ is different from that for the integral of, say, $1/x^{0.9}$ which is $10x^{0.1}$, or of $1/x^{1.1}$ which is $-10/x^{0.1}$. However the graphs of all three functions are very similar. They are shown in Fig. 7.6 with the arbitrary constant adjusted so that each passes through the point (1, 0).

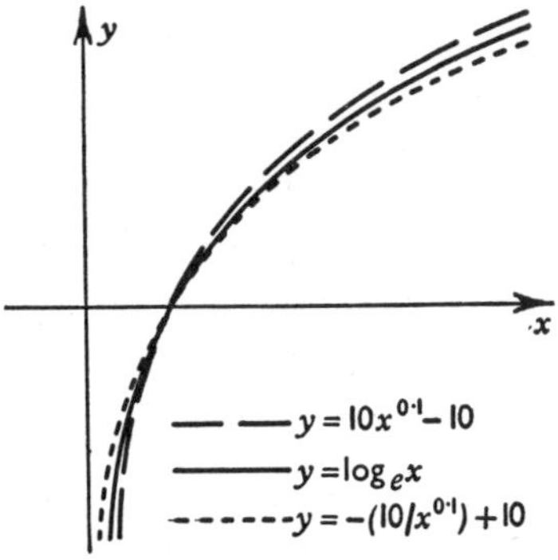

FIG. 7.6

A feature of the logarithmic function should be noticed: $\log f(x) + c$ can be written $\log [a\, f(x)]$, where $a = e^c$; this way of expressing the constant of integration may sometimes be convenient. This is the case for example when $f(x)$ is negative. Formally we should expect $\int [f'(x)/f(x)]\, dx = \log f(x) + C$, as can be seen if we make the substitution $f(x) = X$, whence $f'(x)\, dx = dX$. The interpretation of $\log f(x)$ when $f(x)$ is negative requires the introduction of complex numbers as shown below, but this complication can be avoided by using the constant a, thus,

$$\begin{aligned} \log f(x) + C &= \log\{a\, f(x)\} \\ &= \log |f(x)| + \log(-a) \quad \text{when } f(x) \text{ is negative} \\ &= \log |f(x)| + \text{constant} \end{aligned}$$

In normal applications the integral will be real, i.e. the constant $\log(-a)$ will be real i.e. the constant a will itself be negative so that $-a$ is positive.

Without the use of the constant a the proof would run as follows

If $\qquad f(x) = -F(x) = e^{i\pi}F(x) \qquad$ (cf. eqn. 5 of 6.41)

then
$$\begin{aligned} \log f(x) + C &= \log(e^{i\pi}) + \log F(x) + C \\ &= \log F(x) + i\pi + C \\ &= \log |f(x)| + \text{constant} \end{aligned}$$

In normal applications the constant $(C + i\pi)$ will be real rather than C itself.

In view of what we have said it is clear that the most convenient form in which to remember the standard integral $\int (1/x)\, dx$ is

$\log|x|+C$, this form being both valid and convenient for x positive or negative.

Example 3. $y=\int e^{ax}\,dx$. The function whose derivative is e^{ax} is obviously e^{ax}/a. Hence $y=(1/a)e^{ax}+C$.

In this way we can build up a stock of integrals as in Table I. Each entry is obtained by recasting the result of a differentiation.

Table I

$$F(x)=\int f(x)\,dx, \text{ i.e. } F'(x)=f(x)$$

f(x)	F(x)	f(x)	F(x)
1. $x^n\ (n\neq -1)$	$\dfrac{x^{n+1}}{n+1}$	8. $1/(1+x^2)$	$\tan^{-1} x$
2. $1/x$	$\log_e\|x\|$	9. $\sinh x$	$\cosh x$
3. e^x	e^x	10. $\operatorname{sech}^2 x$	$\tanh x$
4. $\sin x$	$-\cos x$	11. $1/\surd(1+x^2)$	$\sinh^{-1} x$
5. $\cos x$	$+\sin x$	12. $1/\surd(x^2-1)$	$\cosh^{-1} x$
6. $\sec^2 x$	$\tan x$	13. $1/(1-x^2)$	$\tanh^{-1} x$ $(\|x\|<1)$
7. $1/\surd(1-x^2)$	$\sin^{-1} x$	14. $1/(x^2-1)$	$\coth^{-1} x$ $(\|x\|>1)$

We now require some general methods by which this rather meagre list can be extended to compound functions such as e^{ax+b}, $1/(x\log x)$, $x^2\sin x$, etc. There are unfortunately no generally applicable formal methods for finding a function F(x) of which a given function f(x) is the derivative. One can only try a variety of artifices in turn ; as we have said there is no guarantee even that the integral can be expressed as an elementary function.

The following are some simple relations, which can be verified by differentiation.

Integral of a sum

If
$$w(x)=u(x)+v(x)$$

then
$$\int w(x)\,dx=\int u(x)\,dx+\int v(x)\,dx$$

Integral of $k\,\mathrm{f}(x)$ (k constant)

$$\int k\,\mathrm{f}(x)\,\mathrm{d}x = k\int \mathrm{f}(x)\,\mathrm{d}x$$

Integral of $\mathrm{f}(ax+b)$

If $\int \mathrm{f}(x)\,\mathrm{d}x = \mathrm{F}(x)$, then $\int \mathrm{f}(ax+b)\,\mathrm{d}x = (1/a)\,\mathrm{F}(ax+b)$

For example

$$\int \cos 2x\,\mathrm{d}x = \frac{1}{2}\sin 2x. \left(\text{compare } \frac{\mathrm{d}}{\mathrm{d}x}\sin 2x = 2\cos 2x\right).$$

7.51. *The integral of a product*

The integral of a product of two functions of x can sometimes (though not always) be obtained or simplified by a process known as integration by parts, viz.

Let the product whose integral is required be uv where $u = u(x)$, and v is a function which can be integrated formally, its integral being $V(x)$; that is $V'(x) = v(x)$. Then by the product formula in differentiation (7.3, (ii))

$$\frac{\mathrm{d}}{\mathrm{d}x}(uV) = u\frac{\mathrm{d}V}{\mathrm{d}x} + \frac{\mathrm{d}u}{\mathrm{d}x}V = uv + u'V$$

and hence $uv = \dfrac{\mathrm{d}}{\mathrm{d}x}(uV) - u'V$

Now integrate both sides of the equation. Since integration and differentiation are inverse operations, the integral of the first term on the right is simply uV; and thus

$$\int uv\,\mathrm{d}x = uV - \int u'V\,\mathrm{d}x \tag{1}$$

The problem of integrating uv is therefore transformed into that of integrating $u'V$, and this may be more tractable than the original. It can be verified that it is immaterial whether we include the arbitrary constant in V or not.

Example 1

$$\int x^2e^x\,\mathrm{d}x = x^2e^x - \int 2x\,e^x\,\mathrm{d}x = x^2e^x - 2\left[xe^x - \int e^x\,\mathrm{d}x\right]$$

$$= (x^2 - 2x + 2)e^x + C$$

For the first integration by parts $u(x) = x^2$; $v(x) = e^x$. This simplifies the integral but a second integration by parts is required to complete the solution.

Example 2

It is occasionally convenient to take $v=1$, $V=x$, particularly when the function to be integrated has a simple derivative. For example

$$\int \log x \, dx = \int \log x \,.\, 1 \,.\, dx = (\log x) \,.\, x - \int (1/x) \,.\, x \,.\, dx$$
$$= (\log x) \,.\, x - x + C$$
$$= x(\log x - 1) + C$$

Example 3

$$\int e^x \cos x \, dx = e^x \sin x - \int e^x \sin x \, dx$$
$$= e^x \sin x - \left[e^x(-\cos x) - \int e^x(-\cos x) \, dx \right]$$
$$= e^x \sin x + e^x \cos x - \int e^x \cos x \, dx$$

In this example the result of two integrations by parts is to produce another integral of the original form. This however does not mean the procedure has failed; for the sign has been reversed in the process and hence $2\int e^x \cos x \, dx = e^x(\sin x + \cos x)$ so that

$$\int e^x \cos x \, dx = \tfrac{1}{2} e^x (\sin x + \cos x)$$

7.52. *Integration by substitution*

This is a most important technique in integration. Let $y = \int f(x) \, dx$ be the required integral, so that

$$dy/dx = f(x) \tag{1}$$

The aim of the method is to make a change of the variable of integration such that the integrand $\phi(u)$ in terms of the new variable u has a known integral.

Let u be a function of x, differentiable and monotonic over the range of x concerned, so that du/dx exists and also a value of u defines a unique value of x. Then

$$\frac{dy}{dx} = \frac{dy}{du} \cdot \frac{du}{dx} \tag{2}$$

Now let the integrand $f(x)$ of the required integral be written as the product of du/dx and a function of u, thus:

$$f(x) = \phi(u) \frac{du}{dx} \tag{3}$$

Substitution of (2) and (3) in (1) gives

$$\frac{dy}{du} = \phi(u)$$

so that
$$y = \int \phi(u)\,du \tag{4}$$

By suitable choice of the function u, it may in this way be possible to reduce $\int f(x)\,dx$ to a known integral in terms of u.

It may be noted that integration of (3) with respect to x gives

$$y = \int \phi(u)\,(du/dx)\,dx \tag{5}$$

and the form (4) for the integral with respect to u is given formally by ' cancelling ' the two dx's in (5). This provides a convenient way of remembering and using the method of substitution, but must not be regarded as a *proof*.

Example 1

$$y = \int \cos x \sin^2 x\,dx$$

put $u = \sin x$; then $du/dx = \cos x$, and $\sin^2 x = u^2$; the integrand $\sin^2 x \cos x$ is therefore $u^2(du/dx)$. Hence

$$y = \int u^2 (du/dx)\,dx = \int u^2\,du = \tfrac{1}{3}u^3 + C = \tfrac{1}{3}\sin^3 x + C$$

This is needlessly pedestrian, of course; with a little practice one can simply combine the terms $\cos x\,dx$ mentally into $d(\sin x)$. The integral then becomes

$$\int \sin^2 x\,d(\sin x) = \tfrac{1}{3}\sin^3 x + C$$

Example 2

$y = \int e^{-x^2} x\,dx$. The substitution is $u = x^2$ but again the full detail is unnecessary. The following steps can be formed mentally.

$$y = \tfrac{1}{2}\int e^{-x^2}\,2x\,dx = \tfrac{1}{2}\int e^{-x^2}\,d(x^2) = -\tfrac{1}{2}e^{-x^2} + C$$

Example 3

$$y = \int x^2 \cos(x^3)\,dx = \tfrac{1}{3}\int (\cos x^3)\,d(x^3) = \tfrac{1}{3}\sin x^3 + C$$

Example 4

$$y = \int \tan x\,dx = \int \frac{\sin x}{\cos x}\,dx = -\int \frac{d(\cos x)}{\cos x} = -\log \cos x + C$$

7.53. *Trial substitutions*

In more elaborate cases there may not be an obvious substitution which reduces the integrand immediately to the required form $\phi(u)\dfrac{du}{dx}$; whereas there may be a substitution that simplifies the algebraic appearance of the integrand. In such cases it may be necessary to write down the details of the transformation: its success or failure can only be assessed after it has been tried out.

Example 1

$y=\int dx/(1+x^{\frac{1}{2}})$. Put $x=u^2$, so that $x^{\frac{1}{2}}=u$ and $dx=2u\,du$.

Hence
$$y=\int\frac{2u\,du}{1+u}=2\int\left[1-\frac{1}{1+u}\right]du$$
$$=2u-2\log(1+u)+C=2x^{\frac{1}{2}}-2\log(1+x^{\frac{1}{2}})+C$$

Example 2

$y=\int dx/\cos x$. There are a number of possible substitutions, which give various different forms for the integral. We shall see later that any rational function of sin x and cos x can be integrated by the substitution $\tan\frac{1}{2}x=t$. With this substitution

$$\sin x=2\sin\tfrac{1}{2}x\cos\tfrac{1}{2}x=2\tan\tfrac{1}{2}x/\sec^2\tfrac{1}{2}x=2t/(1+t^2)$$
$$\cos x=2\cos^2\tfrac{1}{2}x-1=[2/(1+t^2)]-1=(1-t^2)/(1+t^2)$$
$$dt=\tfrac{1}{2}\sec^2\tfrac{1}{2}x\,dx,\quad\text{whence}\quad dx=2dt/(1+t^2)$$

so
$$\int dx/\cos x=2\int dt/(1-t^2) \tag{1}$$
$$=2\tanh^{-1}(\tan\tfrac{1}{2}x)+C\quad\text{for}\quad x<\tfrac{1}{2}\pi$$

Alternatively, by use of partial fractions in (1)

$$\int dt/(1-t^2)=\int\left(\frac{1}{1+t}+\frac{1}{1-t}\right)dt=\log\left(\frac{1+t}{1-t}\right)$$
$$=\log[(1+\tan\tfrac{1}{2}x)/(1-\tan\tfrac{1}{2}x)]+C$$

The following are other alternatives:

(*a*) put $x+\frac{1}{2}\pi=u$, and then $\tan\frac{1}{2}u=t$. This gives

$$y=\log\tan(\tfrac{1}{2}x+\tfrac{1}{4}\pi)+C$$

(*b*) put $\tan x=z$, which gives

$$y=\sinh^{-1}(\tan x)+C$$

or, with the logarithmic form for the inverse sinh

$$y=\log(\tan x+\sec x)+C$$

The student should not suppose that great skill in integration is required in scientific work. Elaborate integrals are confined mainly to the examination hall, and elsewhere one can save considerable time and labour by using the tables of integrals compiled by Dwight (Macmillan) or Peirce (Ginn, New York).

It is much more useful to bear in mind the graphical forms of the integrand and its integral, especially any discontinuities or changes of sign, than to aspire to a detailed knowledge of, for example, the reduction formulae for $\int dx/(x^2+px+q)^5$.

It is also useful to be able to recognise whether a function can be integrated in finite terms. It is possible for example to waste a lot of time trying to find suitable substitutions for the integration of, say, $1/\surd(1-x^3)$, $\surd[(a-x^2)/(b-x^2)]$, or e^x/x, none of which possesses an integral in terms of elementary functions. There are no general rules that enable one to decide whether any given function has an elementary integral ; an answer can however be given for certain restricted types of function, some of which we now discuss.

7.54. *Integration of polynomials*

The integration can always be done term by term and therefore involves only the integration of x^n where n is a positive integer.

7.55. *Integration of rational functions*

The integrals of one or two rational functions have already been given ; thus

$$\int dx/x \qquad = \log|x| \tag{1}$$

$$\int dx/(a^2+x^2) = (1/a)\tan^{-1}(x/a) \tag{2}$$

$$\int dx/(a^2-x^2) = (1/a)\tanh^{-1}(x/a), \quad x<a \tag{3}$$

$$\int dx/(x^2-a^2) = (1/a)\coth^{-1}(x/a), \quad a<x \tag{4}$$

It was shown in 3.31 that any rational function can be

expanded into a polynomial plus a sum of partial fractions such as

$$\frac{A}{x-a}, \; \frac{Ax+B}{x^2+2px+q}, \; \frac{A}{(x-a)^s}, \; \frac{Ax+B}{(x^2+2px+q)^s} \tag{5}$$

These four rational functions can be integrated, as shown below, hence the integral of any rational function can be found explicitly.

Consider the functions (5) in turn :

(i) $\int A \, \mathrm{d}x/(x-a) = A \log |(x-a)|$

(ii) $\int [(Ax+B)/(x^2+2px+q)] \, \mathrm{d}x.$

The denominator is $(x+p)^2+(q-p^2)$, $(q-p^2)$ being positive (otherwise it would have real linear factors). Put

$$x+p=(q-p^2)^{\frac{1}{2}} u \tag{6}$$

then the integrand has the form $(2\alpha u+\beta)/(u^2+1)$ of which the integral is $\alpha \log (u^2+1)+\beta \tan^{-1} u$.

(iii) $\int A \, \mathrm{d}x/(x-a)^s = -[A/(s-1)]/(x-a)^{s-1}$

(iv) $\int [(Ax+B)/(x^2+2px+q)^s] \, \mathrm{d}x.$ The substitution (6) reduces this integral to the form $\int (2\alpha u+\beta)/(u^2+1)^s \, \mathrm{d}u$. Now

$$\int 2u \, \mathrm{d}u/(u^2+1)^s = -1/(s-1)(u^2+1)^{s-1}$$

also

$$\frac{\mathrm{d}}{\mathrm{d}u}\left\{\frac{u}{(u^2+1)^{s-1}}\right\} = \frac{1-2(s-1)}{(u^2+1)^{s-1}} + \frac{2(s-1)}{(u^2+1)^s}$$

Hence

$$2(s-1)\int \mathrm{d}u/(u^2+1)^s = u/(u^2+1)^{s-1} + (2s-3)\int \mathrm{d}u/(u^2+1)^{s-1}$$

This is a reduction formula for the integral $I_s = \int \mathrm{d}u/(u^2+1)^s$; it gives I_s in terms of I_{s-1}, which in turn can be expressed in terms of I_{s-2} and so on down to I_1 which is $\int \mathrm{d}u/(u^2+1)$ which is $\tan^{-1} u$. Thus any function $(Ax+B)/(x^2+2px+q)^s$ (s integral) can be integrated, although for large values of s the work involved may become very considerable ; however, values of s larger than 2 seldom occur in applications.

This completes the integration of partial fractions of the forms specified in (5) above.

The integration of rational functions can therefore always be accomplished and does not require the introduction of new transcendental functions.

7.56. *Integration of algebraic functions*

The following integrals of algebraic functions can be found readily from results already stated ;

$$\int dx/\surd(ax+b) = (2/a)\surd(ax+b) \tag{1}$$

$$\int dx/\surd(a^2-x^2) = \sin^{-1}(x/a) \tag{2}$$

$$\int dx/\surd(a^2+x^2) = \sinh^{-1}(x/a) \tag{3}$$

$$\int dx/\surd(x^2-a^2) = \cosh^{-1}(x/a) \tag{4}$$

In attempting to integrate other algebraic functions one must try to convert them into one of these forms or else into integrals of rational functions. There is no general guarantee that an algebraic function will be integrable in terms of elementary functions.

The simplest algebraic functions are those in which the irrational part is confined to a single term $\surd(ax+b)$; integrands of this kind are rationalised by the substitution $ax+b=t^2$. Any rational function of x and $\surd(ax^2+bx+c)$ can also be integrated, see Dwight or Pierce for special cases.

7.57. *Integration of* R[x, $\surd$P(x)]

If P(x) is a polynomial of higher degree than 2, the integral of a rational function, R, of x and $\surd$P(x) cannot generally be expressed as a finite combination of elementary functions. If P(x) is cubic or quartic, the integral can be expressed in terms of the functions termed elliptic functions. Integrals of this kind occur in quite elementary problems, for example the simple pendulum, and it is quite easy to waste time looking for a substitution that will rationalise, say

$$y = \int [\surd(2-x^2)/\surd(1-x^2)]\,dx$$

The student should therefore be able to recognise that such an integral does not yield to the methods so far used.

The commonest elliptic integrals are:—

$$\int_0^X \frac{dx}{\sqrt{[(1-x^2)(1-k^2x^2)]}}; \quad \int_0^X \sqrt{\frac{1-k^2x^2}{1-x^2}}\, dx;$$

$$\int_0^X \frac{dx}{(1+n^2x^2)\sqrt{[(1-x^2)(1-k^2x^2)]}}$$

or, on putting $x = \sin\phi$,

$$\int_0^\Phi \frac{d\phi}{\sqrt{(1-k^2\sin^2\phi)}}; \quad \int_0^\Phi \sqrt{(1-k^2\sin^2\phi)}\, d\phi;$$

$$\int_0^\Phi \frac{d\phi}{(1+n^2\sin^2\phi)\sqrt{(1-k^2\sin^2\phi)}}$$

none of which can be evaluated explicitly in terms of elementary functions.

There is, however, nothing bizarre about the functions of X defined by these integrals: for any value of X the value of any of these functions can be looked up in tables of Elliptic Integrals in the same way that the value of $\sin X$ or $\log X$ can be looked up in appropriate tables.

7.58. *Integration of rational function of* $\sin x$ *and* $\cos x$

A rational function of $\sin x$ and $\cos x$, $R(\sin x, \cos x)$ can always be integrated in terms of elementary functions. The substitution $t = \tan \frac{1}{2}x$ gives

$$\sin x = 2t/(1+t^2), \quad \cos x = (1-t^2)/(1+t^2)$$

$$dx = 2\, dt/(1+t^2)$$

(compare 7.53, ex. 2), so

$$\int R(\sin x, \cos x)\, dx = \int R\left(\frac{2t}{1+t^2}, \frac{1-t^2}{1+t^2}\right)\frac{2dt}{1+t^2}$$

The integrand is a rational function of t and its integral can therefore be expressed in terms of elementary functions. In particular cases, of course, automatic substitution for $\tan \frac{1}{2}x$ may be less wise than a suitably chosen alternative, such as $\cos x$ or $\tan x$.

7.6. Differentiation and integration of series

The rules for differentiating and integrating the sum of a *finite* number of functions are simple, viz.

$$\frac{d}{dx}[f_1(x)+f_2(x)+\ldots+f_n(x)]=\frac{df_1}{dx}+\frac{df_2}{dx}+\ldots+\frac{df_n}{dx}$$

$$\int[f_1(x)+f_2(x)+\ldots+f_n(x)]\,dx$$

$$=\int f_1(x)\,dx+\int f_2(x)\,dx+\ldots+\int f_n(x)\,dx$$

and are easily established from the definitions of differentiation and integration. We express this by saying that a (finite) sum can be differentiated or integrated 'term by term'.

For an *infinite* series of terms on the other hand, certain requirements about convergence must be satisfied before we are justified in saying that the series can be differentiated or integrated term by term. The statement of these conditions in a precise form needs the concept of the definite integral $\int_a^b f(x)\,dx$ which is dealt with in the next chapter. The reader who is not already reasonably familiar with the use of integrals between limits will do well to delay the reading of this section until he has read Chapter 8.

We deal first with integration of a series term by term, for which the requirements are less stringent than those for differentiation term by term.

Theorem 1. If the infinite series $f_1(x)+f_2(x)+\ldots$ is *uniformly* convergent in the interval $a<x<b$, the sum being $g(x)$, then the series

$$\int_c^X f_1(x)\,dx+\int_c^X f_2(x)\,dx+\ldots$$

where $a\leqslant c<X\leqslant b$ is also convergent and its sum is equal to $\int_c^X g(x)\,dx$; that is, the series for $g(x)$ can be integrated term by term.

Proof: Let $S_n(x)=f_1(x)+f_2(x)+\ldots+f_n(x)$

$$R_n(x)=f_{n+1}(x)+f_{n+2}(x)+\ldots$$

Since $S_n(x)$ is the sum of a finite number of terms, it follows that

$$\int_c^X S_n(x)\,dx = \int_c^X f_1(x)\,dx + \int_c^X f_2(x)\,dx + \ldots + \int_c^X f_n(x)\,dx$$

Then

$$\int_c^X g(x)\,dx = \int_c^X [S_n(x) + R_n(x)]\,dx$$

$$= \int_c^X S_n(x)\,dx + \int_c^X R_n(x)\,dx$$

Now, since the series for $g(x)$ is uniformly convergent, we can, for any $\epsilon > 0$, choose m so that if $n \geqslant m$, the remainder $R_n(x)$ will be less in magnitude than ϵ for every x in the range $a \leqslant x \leqslant b$.

Therefore $\left| \int_c^X R_n(x)\,dx \right| \leqslant \int_c^X \epsilon\,dx = \epsilon(X - c)$, so, for all $n \geqslant m$

$$\left| \int_c^X g(x)\,dx - \int_c^X S_n(x)\,dx \right| \leqslant \epsilon(X - c)$$

Hence $\int_c^X g(x)\,dx = \lim_{n\to\infty} \left[\int_c^X f_1(x)\,dx + \ldots + \int_c^X f_n(x)\,dx \right]$

$$= \int_c^X f_1(x)\,dx + \int_c^X f_2(x)\,dx + \ldots \text{ to infinity.} \quad (1)$$

The *uniformity* of the convergence is essential to the argument here; it ensures that the *same* value of n will serve to make $|R_n(x)| < \epsilon$ over the *whole* range of x.

The result (1) can now be used to establish the theorem on differentiation of series, viz.

Theorem 2. If the series $f_1(x) + f_2(x) + \ldots$ is convergent when $a \leqslant x \leqslant b$, its sum being $g(x)$, then

$$g'(x) = f_1'(x) + f_2'(x) + \ldots$$

provided the series $f_1'(x) + f_2'(x) + \ldots$ is *uniformly* convergent in the interval $a < x < b$.

Proof: Let $u(x) = f_1'(x) + f_2'(x) + \ldots$ then from Theorem 1, since $f_1'(x) + f_2'(x) \ldots$ is uniformly convergent,

$$\int_c^X u(x)\,dx = \int_c^X f_1'(x)\,dx + \int_c^X f_2'(x)\,dx + \ldots$$

$$= [f_1(X) + f_2(X) + \ldots] - [f_1(c) + f_2(c) + \ldots]$$

$$= g(X) - \text{constant} \quad (2)$$

where both $a \leqslant X \leqslant b$ and $a \leqslant c \leqslant b$, so both $f_1(X)+f_2(X)+\ldots$ and $f_1(c)+f_2(c)+\ldots$ are convergent. From (2),

$$u(X)=\frac{d}{dX}\int_c^X u(x)\,dx \qquad \text{(cf. eqn. (3) of 8.6)}$$

$$=\frac{d}{dX}g(X),$$

which may equally well be written

$$u(x)=g'(x)$$

whence $g'(x)=f_1'(x)+f_2'(x)+\ldots$ as required. The condition that the differentiated series should be *uniformly* convergent should be noted.

Example 1

The series $1+x+x^2+\ldots$ is uniformly convergent in the interval $-k<x<k$ where $0<k<1$, because the remainder after n terms $\leqslant k^n/(1-k)$ for all x in the interval, and this can be made less than any chosen ϵ by taking n sufficiently large. Hence from Theorem 1,

$$\int_0^X \frac{dx}{1-x}=X+\tfrac{1}{2}X^2+\tfrac{1}{3}X^3+\ldots$$

$$\text{i.e.}\quad -\log(1-X)=X+\tfrac{1}{2}X^2+\tfrac{1}{3}X^3+\ldots$$

provided $|X|\leqslant k<1$.

Using Theorem 2 with the same series, we find

$$\frac{1}{(1-x)^2}=\frac{d}{dx}\left(\frac{1}{1-x}\right)$$

$$=1+2x+3x^2+\ldots$$

provided that this latter series is uniformly convergent in an appropriate interval. Now the remainder after n terms is

$$R_n(x)=x^n[(n+1)+(n+2)x+(n+3)x^2+\ldots]$$

so that $$(1-x)R_n(x)=x^n[(n+1)+x+x^2+\ldots]$$

$$=x^n[n+1/(1-x)]$$

hence $(1-x)\,|R_n(x)|\leqslant k^n[n+1/(1-k)]$, since $|x|<k<1$

so $$|R_n(x)|\leqslant k^n[n+1/(1-k)]/(1-k)$$

Thus if $|k|<1$, $R_n(x)$ can be made as small as we wish for all $|x|\leqslant k$ by taking n sufficiently large, and therefore, for any chosen ϵ, there is an n such that $R_n(x)<\epsilon$ for all x in the interval $-k<x<k$. The series $1+2x+3x^2+\ldots$ is thus uniformly convergent in the interval $-k<x<k$ and therefore, by Theorem 2

$$\frac{1}{(1-x)^2}=1+2x+3x^2+\ldots \text{ for } |x|<k$$

Example 2

Find a series for $\tan^{-1} x$ by integrating

$$(1+x^2)^{-1} = 1 - x^2 + x^4 - x^6 + \dots$$

Example 3

Find by integration, a series for $\sin^{-1} x$ and show, by means of p. 66 and note 2 of p. 39, that the series is uniformly convergent in $|x| \leqslant 1$ and ce represents $\sin^{-1} x$ in that range.

Example 4

Given that for $-\pi \leqslant x \leqslant \pi$

$$x^2 = \frac{\pi^2}{3} - 4\left(\frac{\cos x}{1^2} - \frac{\cos 2x}{2^2} + \frac{\cos 3x}{3^2} - \frac{\cos 4x}{4^2} + \dots\right)$$

find a series for x in terms of sine functions and discuss its range of validity.

7.61. *Radius of convergence of power series obtained by differentiating or integrating term by term*

Consider two series of which either can be obtained from the other by differentiating or integrating term by term, e.g.

$$f(x) \equiv a_0 + a_1 x + a_2 x^2 + \dots + a_n x^n + \dots \quad (1)$$

$$g(x) \equiv a_1 + 2a_2 x + \dots + n a_n x^{n-1} + \dots \quad (2)$$

and suppose the radii of convergence of the series are R_1 and R_2 respectively. We shall show that $R_1 = R_2$.

If $\lim (a_n/a_{n+1})$ exists, $R_1 = \lim (a_n/a_{n+1})$ (cf. 4.3). But if $\lim (a_n/a_{n+1})$ exists, so also does $\lim [na_n/(n+1)a_{n+1}]$ and in fact the two are equal, so $R_2 = R_1 = R$ say. If $\lim (a_n/a_{n+1})$ does not exist the same result can be proved with a little more trouble. For if $|x| < k_1 < R_1$, series (1) can be compared with

$$\sum M \,|\,(x/k_1)\,|^n$$

where $M > a_n x^n$ for all n, and series (2) with

$$\sum Mn \,|\,(x/k)\,|^{n-1}.$$

The argument can be filled out to show that both series are convergent (and in fact absolutely and uniformly convergent) for $|x| < k_1 < R_1$ and divergent for $|x| > R_1$. Hence $R_2 = R_1 = R$ say. We note that the special case $|x| = R$ is not dealt with by the above argument.

Concerning the special case $|x| = R$ we note only that since $(n+1)a_{n+1}/na_n = (1+1/n)a_{n+1}/a_n$, i.e. since the ratio of coefficients of the derived series is greater than the ratio of coefficients of the original series, a power series obtained by differentiation of another is less likely to converge at the critical radius, while one obtained by integration is more likely to be convergent at $|x| = R$.

7.62. *Taylor's Series*

Consider the function $f(x) \equiv f(a+y)$ which is defined by the power series

$$f(a+y) = b_0 + b_1 y + b_2 y^2 + \dots$$

Let the radius of convergence of the power series be R, so the function $f(x)$ is defined for $|y| < R$, and both the series and its term by term derivatives are from 7.61 uniformly convergent in $-R < y < R$. Therefore, the equations

$$f'(a+y) = b_1 + 2b_2 y + 3b_3 y^2 + \dots$$
$$f''(a+y) = \qquad 2b_2 + 6b_3 y + \dots$$

and so on, are all valid for $|y| < R$. In particular, putting $y = 0$, we find

$$b_0 = f(a)\ ;\ b_1 = f'(a)\ ;\ b_2 = f''(a)/2!\ ;\ \dots ;\ b_n = f^{(n)}(a)/n!\ ;\ \dots$$

Hence

$$f(a+y) = f(a) + yf'(a) + y^2 f''(a)/2! + \dots + y^n f^n(a)/n! + \dots \quad (1)$$

This is Taylor's series for $f(a+y)$; it gives the values of the function $f(x)$ as a power series in $y = x - a$, the coefficients of the powers of y being the values of the function and its derivatives at the point $x = a$.

Example

Suppose it is known that $\sin x$ can be represented by a power series in x (i.e. $a = 0$), thus

$$\sin x = b_0 + b_1 x + b_2 x^2 + \dots$$

Then $b_0 = \sin 0 = 0$; $b_1 = \cos 0 = 1$; $b_2 = -\sin 0/2! = 0$; $b_{2n} = (-1)^n \dfrac{\sin 0}{(2n)!}$ $= 0$; $b_{2n+1} = (-1)^n \cos 0/(2n+1)! = (-1)^n/(2n+1)!$ i.e.

$$\sin x = x - x^3/3! + x^5/5! - \dots (-1)^{n+1} x^{2n}/(2n+1)! \dots \quad (2)$$

Having found the series (2), it is fairly easy to show that it is convergent for all finite x, and, indeed, uniformly convergent in every finite range and so represents (i.e. its value converges to) a continuous function. That this function is $\sin x$ however has not been fully proved, since a hypothesis, namely that $\sin x$ is capable of a power series representation, had to be made. Such difficulties in the application of Taylor's theorem can be side-stepped by using an alternative form of the theorem, which will be developed in the following sections.

7.63. *Preliminaries to the proof of Taylor's theorem with remainder*

The following theorem is almost obvious, but is very useful. *Rolle's Theorem.* If a function $f(x)$ and its derivative $f'(x)$ are both continuous for $a \leqslant x \leqslant b$, and if $f(x)=0$ at $x=a$ and at $x=b$, then $f'(x)$ is zero for at least one value of x between a and b.

For if $f'(x)$ were nowhere zero in the range, it could nowhere change sign in the range (for $f'(x)$ is, by postulate, continuous), and hence $f(x)$ would either steadily increase in which case $f(b)>f(a)$ or steadily decrease, i.e. $f(b)<f(a)$. Neither of these inequalities is compatible with the condition $f(a)=f(b)=0$; so there must be at least one point in $a<x<b$ at which $f'(x)=0$.

The next theorem is a simple particular case of Taylor's theorem with remainder. *First Mean Value Theorem.* If $f(x)$ and $f'(x)$ are continuous for $a<x<b$, then there is a number, ξ_1 say, between a and b such that

$$f(b)=f(a)+(b-a)f'(\xi_1)$$

To prove this theorem we proceed as follows. Let

$$R=[f(b)-f(a)]/(b-a)$$

Therefore
$$-f(b)+f(a)+(b-a)\,.\,R=0 \tag{1}$$

Let
$$F(x)=-f(b)+f(x)+(b-x)\,.\,R \tag{2}$$

Then $F(a)=0$ by (1), and $F(b)=0$ directly from (2). Moreover from (2) and the fact that $f(x)$, $f'(x)$ are continuous it follows that $F(x)$, $F'(x)$ are continuous, so by Rolle's theorem there exists at least one value of x, ($x=\xi_1$ say) lying between a and b for which $F'(x)$ is zero, i.e.

$$f'(\xi_1)-R=0 \quad \text{i.e.} \quad R=f'(\xi_1)$$

So from equation (1)

$$f(b)=f(a)+(b-a)f'(\xi_1)$$

as required.

7.64. *Taylor's theorem with remainder*

Theorem. If $f(x)$ and its first n derivatives are continuous for $a \leqslant x \leqslant b$, then there is a number, ξ say, between a and b such that

$$f(b)=f(a)+(b-a)f'(a)+\tfrac{1}{2}(b-a)^2f''(a)+\dots$$
$$+\frac{(b-a)^{n-1}}{(n-1)!}f^{(n-1)}(a)+\frac{(b-a)^n}{n!}f^n(\xi)$$

We proceed as in the proof of the first mean value theorem.

Let $R = \left[f(b) - \left\{ f(a) + (b-a)f'(a) + \ldots + \frac{(b-a)^{n-1}}{(n-1)!} f^{(n-1)}(a) \right\} \right] \Big/ \frac{(b-a)^n}{n!}$

We note that

$$-f(b) + f(a) + (b-a)f'(a) + \ldots + \frac{(b-a)^{n-1}}{(n-1)!} f^{(n-1)}(a) + \frac{(b-a)^n}{n!} R = 0 \quad (1)$$

Now put $F(x) = -f(b) + f(x) + (b-x)f'(x) + \frac{1}{2}(b-x)^2 f''(x) + \ldots$

$$+ \frac{(b-x)^{n-1}}{(n-1)!} f^{(n-1)}(x) + \frac{(b-x)^n}{n!} . R \quad (2)$$

Then $F(a) = 0$ by (1), and $F(b) = 0$ directly from (2). Moreover from (2) and the fact that the first n derivatives of f are continuous it follows that $F(x)$, $F'(x)$ are continuous, so by Rolle's theorem there exists at least one value of x ($x = \xi$ say) lying between a and b for which $F'(x)$ is zero

Now differentiation of (2) gives

$$F'(x) = \frac{(b-x)^{n-1}}{(n-1)!} f^n(x) - \frac{(b-x)^{n-1}}{(n-1)!} . R$$

Hence $$\frac{(b-\xi)^{n-1}}{(n-1)!} f^{(n)}(\xi) - \frac{(b-\xi)^{n-1}}{(n-1)!} R = 0$$

i.e. $R = f^{(n)}(\xi)$. So from equation (1)

$$f(b) = f(a) + (b-a)f'(a) + \ldots + \frac{(b-a)^{n-1}}{(n-1)!} f^{(n-1)}(a) + \frac{(b-a)^n}{n!} f^{(n)}(\xi) \quad (3)$$

as required.

Putting $b = a + y$, i.e. $b - a = y$ and $\xi = a + \theta y$ (where $0 < \theta < 1$), we get the rather more convenient form

$$f(a+y) = f(a) + yf'(a) + \ldots + \frac{y^{n-1}}{(n-1)!} f^{(n-1)}(a) + \frac{y^n}{n!} f^{(n)}(a + \theta y) \quad (4)$$

The use of the symbol θ to stand for a variable whose value lies between 0 and 1 is fairly common in mathematical work.

When $a = 0$, Taylor's theorem takes the form

$$f(y) = f(0) + yf'(0) + \ldots + y^{n-1} f^{(n-1)}(0)/(n-1)! + y^n f^{(n)}(\theta y)/n! \quad (5)$$

and this special form is called Maclaurin's theorem. There is, of course, no need to remember it separately.

Example

Show that $\sin x = x - x^3/3! + x^5/5! - \ldots + (-1)^n x^{2n+1}/(2n+1)! + \ldots$

We know that $\sin x$ and its derivatives of all orders are continuous. In particular writing $f(x) = \sin x$, we have

$$f^{(2r+1)}(x) = (-1)^r \cos x \; ; \; f^{(2r+2)}(x) = (-1)^{r+1} \sin x.$$

From equation (5) with x substituted for y, we therefore find that

$$\sin x = x - x^3/3! + x^5/5! - \dots + (-1)^r x^{2r+1}/(2r+1)! + (-1)^{r+1} x^{2r+2}[\sin(\theta x)]/(2r+2)!$$

where $0 < \theta < 1$.

As $r \to \infty$, $x^{2r+2}/(2r+2)! \to 0$ (cf. 2.46 ex. 6). It follows that the difference between $\sin x$ and $[x - x^3/3! + \dots (-1)^r x^{2r+1}/(2r+1)!]$ tends to zero as $r \to \infty$, i.e. the infinite series

$$x - x^3/3! + x^5/5! - \dots \text{ converges to the value } \sin x.$$

The reader should note, by comparing this proof with the example of 7.62, that use of Taylor's theorem *with remainder* often succeeds in proving the validity of series expansions, where the earlier form, without remainder, fails.

CHAPTER EIGHT

THE DEFINITE INTEGRAL

8.1. The definite integral

The previous chapter dealt with the indefinite integral of a function f(x), defined as a function F(x) whose derivative is equal to f(x). It is 'indefinite' only to the extent that an arbitrary constant may be added.

In some contexts the information required is the change in F(x) between two given values of x. Let f(x) be a given function (Fig. 8.1) and let $F_1(x)$ be any particular function such that $F_1' = f(x)$. Then the indefinite integral of f(x) is

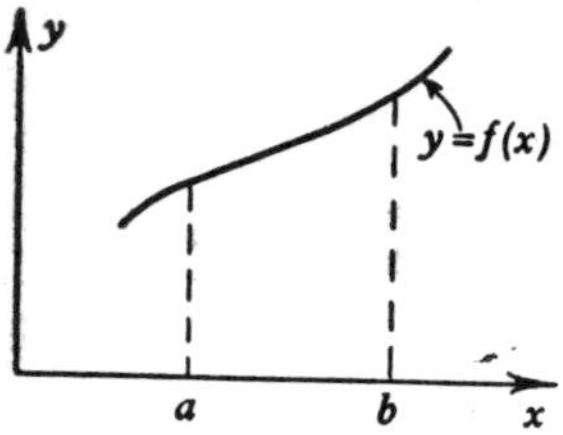

FIG. 8.1

$$F(x) = F_1(x) + C$$

The difference in F(x) between $x=a$ and $x=b$ is $F(b) - F(a)$ or equally well $F_1(b) - F_1(a)$, since the arbitrary constant C disappears from the difference. This quantity $F(b) - F(a)$, is called the definite integral of f(x) between $x=a$ and $x=b$.

If the indefinite integral is known it follows that there is no difficulty in calculating the definite integral.

Notation

The notation used for the definite integral of f(x) between $x=a$ and $x=b$ is $\int_a^b f(x)\,dx$. If F(x) is the indefinite integral of f(x), the definite integral is written $\Big[F(x)\Big]_a^b$; or occasionally $F(x)\Big|_a^b$. Thus we have

$$\int_a^b f(x)\,dx \equiv \Big[F(x)\Big]_a^b \equiv F(b) - F(a)$$

Example 1

Calculate the definite integral $\int_0^1 x^n \, dx$. We have

$$\int_0^1 x^n \, dx = \left[x^{n+1}/(n+1) \right]_0^1 = 1/(n+1)$$

Example 2

The motion of a body falling freely under gravity is one of constant acceleration g. If the velocity of such a body at $t=0$ is u, calculate the velocity v and the distance s travelled in a time t.

The velocity $v = \frac{ds}{dt}$, and the acceleration $g = \frac{dv}{dt}$. Therefore, taking the definite integral of both sides

$$\int_0^t \frac{dv}{dt} \, dt = \int_0^t g \, dt \quad \text{i.e.} \left[v \right]_0^t = \left[gt \right]_0^t$$

Thus $$v - u = gt \quad \text{i.e. } v = u + gt$$

Similarly, we have

$$\frac{ds}{dt} = v = u + gt \quad \text{whence} \left[s \right]_0^t = \left[ut + \tfrac{1}{2}gt^2 \right]_0^t$$

$\left[s \right]_0^t$ is the required distance travelled in a time t, and hence we have obtained the elementary kinematic formulae

$$v = u + ft \, ; \quad s = ut + \tfrac{1}{2}ft^2$$

with $f = g$ in this particular case.

8.11. *Addition of the ranges of a definite integral*

Let $f(x)$ be finite with the indefinite integral $F(x)$ in the range $a < x < c$ and let b be an intermediate point in this range; then

$$\int_a^c f(x) \, dx = \int_a^b f(x) \, dx + \int_b^c f(x) \, dx \qquad (1)$$

for $$\int_a^c f(x) \, dx = \left[F(x) \right]_a^c = F(c) - F(a)$$

and similarly $$\int_a^b f(x) \, dx = F(b) - F(a)$$

$$\int_b^c f(x) \, dx = F(c) - F(b)$$

The result quoted therefore follows immediately.

The same argument shows more generally that

$$\int_a^{b_1} f(x)\, dx + \int_{b_1}^{b_2} f(x)\, dx + \ldots + \int_{b_n}^{c} f(x)\, dx = \int_a^c f(x)\, dx$$

and also that

$$\int_a^b f(x)\, dx = -\int_b^a f(x)\, dx$$

8.12. *Definite integral over a small range*

Let $f(x)$ be a given function with an indefinite integral $F(x)$. Then by definition

$$F'(x) = f(x)$$

or if we write $y = F(x)$

$$\frac{dy}{dx} = f(x)$$

Now take a given value of x, say $x = a$ and consider the equation

$$\frac{\delta y}{\delta x} = f(a)$$

This may be interpreted either as an exact equation applying not to the curve $y = F(x)$ but to its tangent at $x = a$, or as an

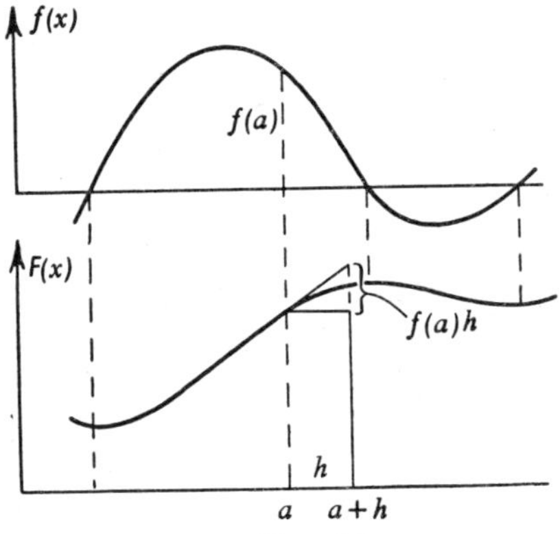

FIG. 8.2

approximate equation valid when δx is sufficiently small (see Fig. 8.2). Take $\delta x = h$; then as x increases from a to $a+h$, y increases by the amount δy given approximately by

$$\delta y \simeq f(a)h$$

and exactly by

$$\delta y = \int_a^{a+h} f(x)\, dx$$

Hence we have as an approximate value for the definite integral over a small range

$$\int_a^{a+h} \mathrm{f}(x)\,\mathrm{d}x \simeq \mathrm{f}(a)h$$

The amount of the error is clearly determined by the extent to which the curve $y = \mathrm{F}(x)$ departs from its tangent in the interval $a < x < a + h$

8.2. Definite integrals and areas

A geometrical interpretation of the definite integral can now be given, which considerably extends the application of the integral calculus. The interpretation is concerned not with the inversion of differentiation, but with the at first sight unrelated process of finding the limit of a sum.

Let $y = \mathrm{f}(x)$ be a given function, which we suppose for the present to be finite and continuous in the range $a < x < b$. Let $z = \int_a^b y\,\mathrm{d}x$ be its definite integral in this range.

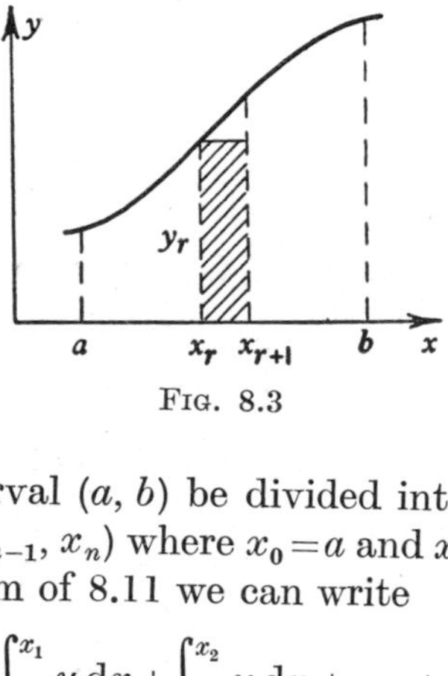

FIG. 8.3

Now let the interval (a, b) be divided into smaller intervals (x_0, x_1) (x_1, x_2) ... (x_{n-1}, x_n) where $x_0 = a$ and $x_n = b$ (see Fig. 8.3). Then by the theorem of 8.11 we can write

$$z = \int_a^b y\,\mathrm{d}x = \int_a^{x_1} y\,\mathrm{d}x + \int_{x_1}^{x_2} y\,\mathrm{d}x + \ldots + \int_{x_{n-1}}^{b} y\,\mathrm{d}x$$

$$= \sum_{r=0}^{n-1} \int_{x_r}^{x_{r+1}} y\,\mathrm{d}x$$

so far without approximation. Now let the number of intervals n become very large in such a way that each interval is eventually arbitrarily small.

Then for each interval we can write, approximately,

$$\int_{x_r}^{x_{r+1}} y\,\mathrm{d}x \simeq y_r(x_{r+1}-x_r) \tag{1}$$

using the result of 6.11, and therefore

$$z \simeq \sum y_r(x_{r+1}-x_r) \tag{2}$$

Geometrically, the quantity $y_r(x_{r+1}-x_r)$ is equal to the area of the small rectangle shown in Fig. 6.1 and the sum (2) is equal to the sum of the areas of all these rectangles.

It is now intuitively obvious that if n is allowed to tend to infinity, in such a way that each interval (x_r, x_{r+1}) tends to zero, the sum of these rectangular areas tends to the area bounded by the curve $y = \mathrm{f}(x)$, the ordinates at a and b and the x-axis.

This tentative result gives us a new interpretation of the definite integral, and also indicates more clearly how the symbol $\int_a^b \mathrm{d}x$ arises. For if $x_{r+1}-x_r$ is written as δx_r the equation

$$z \simeq \sum_{r=0}^{n-1} y_r(x_{r+1}-x_r)$$

can be written as

$$z \simeq \sum_{r=0}^{n-1} y_r\,\delta x_r$$

In the limiting case as $n \to \infty$, the summation sign $\sum$ is replaced by $\int$, and δx_r by $\mathrm{d}x_r$ (as in differentiation), giving

$$z = \int_{r=0}^{\infty} y_r\,\mathrm{d}x_r$$

Finally r is suppressed, and the limits of the summation are given in terms of x,

$$z = \int_{x=a}^{b} y\,\mathrm{d}x = \int_a^b \mathrm{f}(x)\,\mathrm{d}x$$

Example 1

Let $y = mx + c$ (Fig. 8.4); then $\int_a^b y\,\mathrm{d}x = \int_a^b (mx+c)\,\mathrm{d}x$

$$= \Big[\tfrac{1}{2}mx^2\Big]_a^b + \Big[cx\Big]_a^b$$
$$= \tfrac{1}{2}m(b^2-a^2) + c(b-a)$$
$$= (b-a)\tfrac{1}{2}[m(b+a)+2c]$$

which is in agreement with the known rule for the area of a trapezium, viz : the distance between the parallel edges multiplied by their mean length.

Example 2

Let $y=\surd(a^2-x^2)$ (Fig. 8.5) ; then the curve is the upper half of the circle

$$x^2+y^2=a^2$$

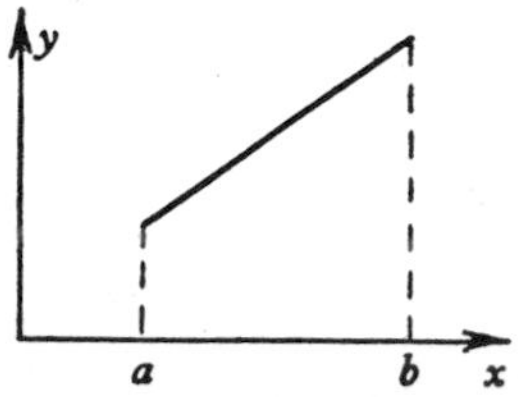

FIG. 8.4

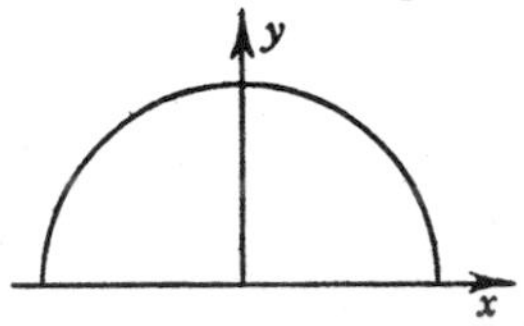

FIG. 8.5

the lower half being of course the branch $y=-\surd(a^2-x^2)$. The area of the curve between the ordinates $x=0$ to $x=a$ is

$$\int_0^a \surd(a^2-x^2)\,dx$$

The indefinite integral can be found by the substitutions $x=a\sin\theta$; $\surd(a^2-x^2)=a\cos\theta$; $dx=a\cos\theta\,d\theta$, whence

$$\int \surd(a^2-x^2)\,dx=\tfrac{1}{2}a^2\sin^{-1}(x/a)+\tfrac{1}{2}x\surd(a^2-x^2)$$

Inserting the limits

$$\int_0^a \surd(a^2-x^2)\,dx=\tfrac{1}{2}a^2\Big[\sin^{-1}(x/a)\Big]_0^a+\Big[\tfrac{1}{2}x\surd(a^2-x^2)\Big]_0^a$$

$$=\tfrac{1}{2}a^2[\tfrac{1}{2}\pi-0]+[0-0]$$

$$=\frac{\pi}{4}a^2$$

and the area of the whole circle is thus πa^2.

The inversion of differentiation and the calculation of areas are not apparently similar problems but we now see that they are interlinked in this most remarkable way : on the one hand the equation $\frac{dy}{dx}=f(x)$ can be regarded as defining a function y whose derivative at all points is equal to $f(x)$: on the other hand from the approximate form $\delta y=f(x)\,\delta x$ it appears that δy can also be interpreted as the area of a small strip of height $f(x)$ and of width δx, and that y is therefore the total area of a number of these strips.

There are obvious weaknesses in the argument. The most important is that we have used an approximate equality (1), subject to an unspecified error, and have then summed a large number of these errors ; results obtained in this way may well be invalid. From the graphical point of view it is clear that the process is valid in the case of, for example, continuous, monotonic functions ; for the errors so introduced are simply the small irregular shapes shown in Fig. 8.6. The sum of their areas clearly becomes negligible when the values of δx tend to zero. However, one cannot be quite so confident about functions such as $\sin^2(1/x)$ or $1/x^2$ (Figs. 8.7 and 8.8) where in each case intuition is silent on the area to be associated with the curve in an interval that includes $x=0$.

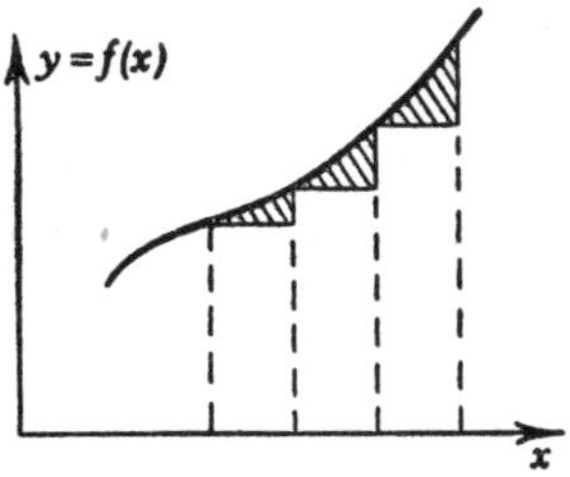

Fig. 8.6

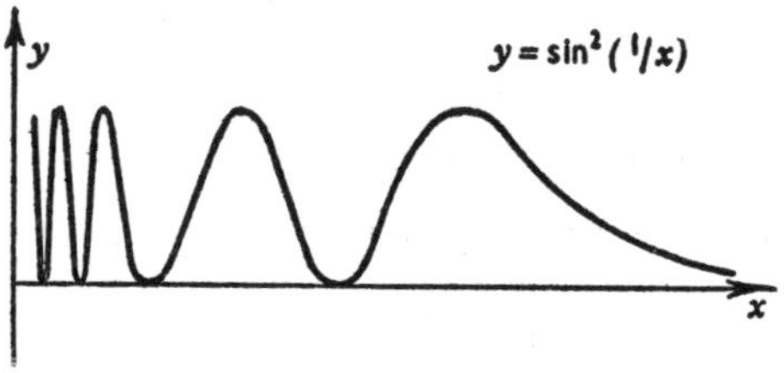

Fig. 8.7

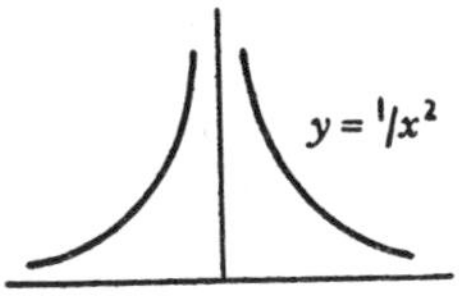

Fig. 8.8

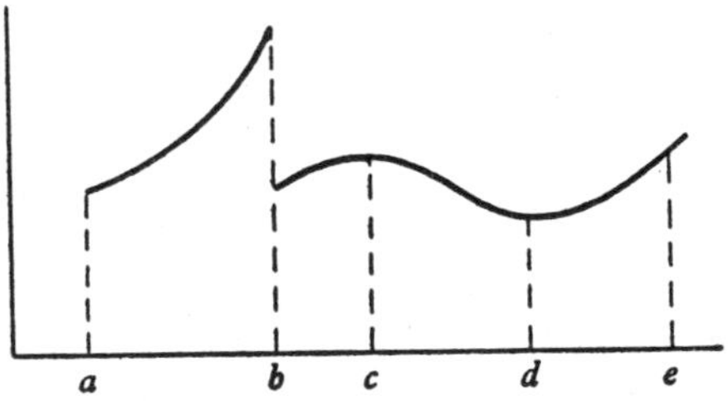

Fig. 8.9

Our argument therefore merely shows that the areas of some curves are given by the definite integral. Without as yet a detailed verification we can expect that the curves to which the result applies are those of monotonic continuous finite functions ; but with the aid of the addition formula (1) of 8.11, curves with a finite number of jump discontinuities can also be included, and also curves with a finite number of maxima and minima. For the interval of integration can then be divided into sub-intervals in each of which the curve is monotonic and continuous (Fig. 8.9), and the definite integral for the whole interval can be obtained as the sum of contributions from the sub-intervals.

The next sections contain a more precise account of the area of a curve between given ordinates. The plan we shall adopt requires some explanation.

Instead of defining the definite integral indirectly by means of

$$\int_a^b f(x)\,dx = F(b) - F(a)$$

where $F(x)$ is an indefinite integral, we shall formulate a direct analytical definition (the limit of a sum) of $\int_a^b f(x)\,dx$ in terms of the values of $f(x)$ in the range $a<x<b$. This definition will be chosen in accordance with the intuitive concept of area. We shall then prove (8.6) that, for a continuous function $f(x)$ possessing an indefinite integral $F(x)$, the definite integral $\int_a^b f(x)\,dx$ defined as a limit is equal in value to $F(b) - F(a)$. Indeed, although the direct definition is not rigorously deducible from the indirect, the equivalence of the two for all functions possessing an indefinite integral can be established.

The direct definition has three valuable characteristics. It (i) lends itself more readily than the indirect to rigorous analysis (ii) is equivalent to the definition $F(b) - F(a)$ whenever $F(x)$ is determinable (iii) can often be defined when $F(x)$ is unknown or even non-existent.

There are several slightly different ways of specifying the limit (associated with the names of Riemann, Cauchy, Stieltjes, Lebesgue etc.), the multiplicity having arisen from a desire to make the definition applicable to wider and wider classes of functions. The Riemann integral may be regarded as sufficiently general for most scientific work but we shall also give a brief description of the Stieltjes and Lebesgue integrals as these are sometimes referred to in scientific literature. The Cauchy integral is merely a particular version of the Riemann integral.

8.3. The Riemann integral

Let $f(x)$ be the integrand and let the range of integration be $a<x<b$. Select $(n-1)$ distinct points $x_1, x_2, \ldots, x_{n-1}$ in ascending order within this range, and for convenience let $x_0=a$ and $x_n=b$. The range (a, b) is now subdivided into n smaller intervals of lengths $\delta x_0, \delta x_1, \delta x_2, \ldots, \delta x_{n-1}$ say. For each subinterval δx_r let m_r and M_r, be the least and greatest values of $f(x)$ in the interval. Let

$$L_n = \sum_{r=0}^{n} m_r\, \delta x_r$$

and

$$U_n = \sum_{r=0}^{n} M_r\, \delta x_r$$

be two finite sums, which we shall call the lower and upper Riemann sums respectively. Their geometrical significance will be apparent from Fig. 8.10.

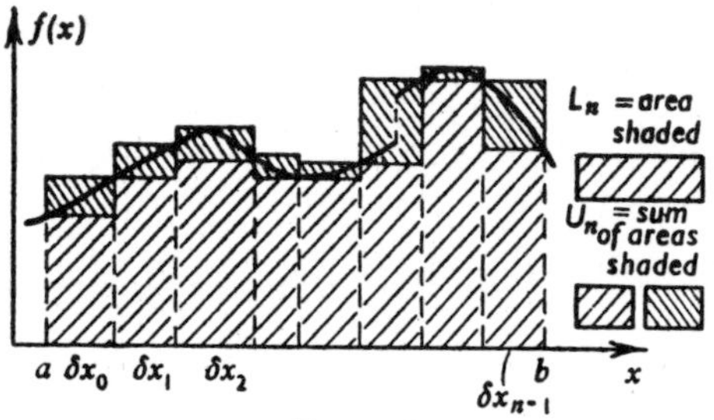

FIG. 8.10

Now let n tend to infinity in such a way that the greatest of the δx's tends to zero. If the sums L_n and U_n tend to a common and unique limit S, independent of the mode of subdivision, then this limit is defined as the Riemann integral $\int_a^b f(x)\, dx$.

The Cauchy integral is specified as follows: let the value of $f(x)$ at the points of subdivision, $a, x_1, x_2, \ldots$ be $y_0, y_1, y_2, \ldots$; form the sum $\sum_{r=0}^{n} y_r\, \delta x_r$; if the limit of this sum as n tends to infinity exists and is independent of the mode of subdivision, it is called the Cauchy integral. We note that $m_r \leqslant y_r \leqslant M_r$, so $L_n \leqslant \sum_{r=0}^{n} y_r\, \delta x_r \leqslant U_n$. It follows that if as $n \to \infty$,

$$\lim L_n = \lim U_n = I \text{ (the Riemann integral)},$$

then also $\sum_{r=0}^{n} y_r\, \delta x_r = I$, i.e. the Cauchy integral is equal to the Riemann integral.

The Cauchy definition of the integral is often used in elementary introductions to the calculus, but for most analytical purposes is less convenient than the Riemann definition.

8.31. *Addition theorem*

If c is a point within the range of integration i.e. $a<c<b$, we may choose it as one of our points of subdivision, $x_p = c$ say. The corresponding lower Riemann sum for $\int_a^b \mathrm{f}(x)\, \mathrm{d}x$ can then be written

$$\sum_{r=0}^{n} m_r\, \delta x_r = \sum_{r=0}^{p} m_r\, \delta x_r + \sum_{r=p+1}^{n} m_r\, \delta x_r$$

Thus if $\int_a^b \mathrm{f}(x)\, \mathrm{d}x$ exists, on letting p and $(n-p) \to \infty$ we find

$$\int_a^b \mathrm{f}(x)\, \mathrm{d}x = \int_a^c \mathrm{f}(x)\, \mathrm{d}x + \int_c^b \mathrm{f}(x)\, \mathrm{d}x$$

i.e. the same addition theorem holds for the Riemann integral as for the definite integral originally defined as $\mathrm{F}(b) - \mathrm{F}(a)$.

8.32. *The Riemann integral of a continuous function*

It is clear that the Riemann integral does not necessarily exist; for example the function defined by $\mathrm{f}(x) = 1$ (x rational), $\mathrm{f}(x) = 0$ otherwise has a lowest value of zero and a highest value of unity in every interval δ; hence the sums L_n and U_n are zero and $(b-a)$ respectively.

However it can be shown that if $\mathrm{f}(x)$ is continuous the Riemann integral exists. (See Hardy, *Pure Mathematics*, §161.)

8.33. *The Riemann integral of a discontinuous function*

Although continuity of the integrand is certainly sufficient to establish the existence of the Riemann integral it is not necessary. A necessary and sufficient condition, known as du Bois Reymond's condition, can be given: this shows clearly that the integrand is permitted a finite number of jump discontinuities in the interval. The condition can be formulated as follows: let $\mathrm{f}(x)$ be finite, less than M say, in the interval $a<x<b$

and let $x_1, x_2, \dots, x_{n-1}$ be intermediate points dividing the interval (a, b) into n sub-intervals $\delta_1, \dots, \delta_n$; let these sub-intervals be divided into two groups according as $M_r - m_r > \epsilon$ or $\leqslant \epsilon$. The Riemann integral exists provided that the sum of the lengths of the first group of intervals can be reduced to less than δ say, by taking n sufficiently large. ϵ and δ are arbitrarily small quantities.

Over the first group the upper and lower Riemann sums cannot differ by more than $M\delta$; over the second they cannot differ by more than $\epsilon(b-a)$. Hence if ϵ and δ can be made indefinitely small the Riemann integral exists. If, however, for a given value of ϵ, greater than zero, the first group cannot be reduced to a total length of less than δ, then the Riemann sums must differ by at least $\epsilon\delta$, and the integral is therefore not defined.

The condition is therefore necessary and also sufficient. As a particular case of functions satisfying du Bois Reymond's condition we mention sectionally continuous functions: all piecewise or sectionally continuous functions (see 2.21) possess a Riemann integral in any finite range.

Example 1

$$\int_0^1 \mathrm{f}(x)\,\mathrm{d}x \quad \text{where} \quad \mathrm{f}(x) = \sin(1/x^2) \quad x>0$$
$$= 0 \qquad x = 0$$

Since $\mathrm{f}(x)$ oscillates finitely as $x \to 0$, the function is discontinuous at this point but continuous elsewhere in the range $0 < x \leqslant 1$. On dividing the interval (0, 1) into sub-intervals it is clear that the first sub-interval, $(0, x_1)$ say, is the only one that can give rise to any uncertainty. But the contribution from this sub-interval is certainly less than x_1 (since $|\sin(1/x^2)| \leqslant 1$) and therefore tends to zero as $x_1 \to 0$. The Riemann integral of this function therefore exists.

Example 2

$$\int_0^2 \mathrm{f}(x)\,\mathrm{d}x \quad \text{where} \quad \left.\begin{aligned}\mathrm{f}(x) &= 1 \text{ for } 0<x<1\\ &= 2 \text{ for } x>1\end{aligned}\right\} \quad \text{(see Fig. 8.11)}$$

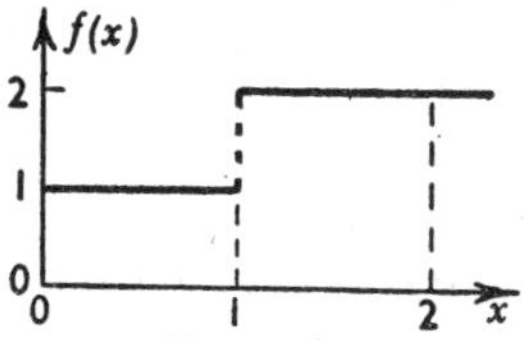

FIG. 8.11

The Riemann integral clearly exists in this case since the function has only one finite discontinuity in the range under consideration.

8.4. Functions of bounded variation

Let f(x) be defined in a range $a \leqslant x \leqslant b$ and let a number n of sub-intervals covering this range be introduced ; if M_r and m_r are the upper and lower bounds of f(x) in the interval $x_r \leqslant x \leqslant x_{r+1}$, then the difference $M_r - m_r$ is called the variation of f(x) in the sub-interval. The function f(x) is said to be of bounded variation if, when the number of intervals is increased without limit, the quantity $V = \sum_{r=0}^{n-1} (M_r - m_r)$ remains finite, whatever the mode of subdivision.

A monotonic function is obviously of bounded variation. If f(x) is monotonic increasing $M_r = \mathrm{f}(x_{r+1})$ and $m_r = \mathrm{f}(x_r)$ and hence

$$V = \sum_{r=0}^{n-1} (M_r - m_r) = \mathrm{f}(b) - \mathrm{f}(a)$$

which is finite and independent of n.

Similarly a function, not necessarily continuous, which is piecewise monotonic, is of bounded variation, as is also any continuous function with only a finite number of maxima and minima.

Any such function has a Riemann integral between the limits $x = a$ and b : for the upper and lower Riemann sums

$$U_m = \sum M_r \, \delta x_r$$
$$L_m = \sum m_r \, \delta x_r$$

differ by $\sum (M_r - m_r) \, \delta x_r$ and hence when the largest of the δx_r has been reduced to less than δ this difference is certainly less than $V\delta$ which can be reduced indefinitely by increase of n.

Example

Sin $(1/x)$ is clearly not of bounded variation, in any interval containing $x = 0$. The existence of a Riemann integral such as $\int_0^1 \sin (1/x) \, \mathrm{d}x$ can nevertheless be established by direct application of du Bois Reymond's condition.

8.41. *The Stieltjes integral*

If f(x) is a differentiable function of x, then in an integral like $\int \mathrm{g}(x)\mathrm{f}'(x) \, \mathrm{d}x$, $\mathrm{f}'(x) \, \mathrm{d}x$ can be replaced by $\mathrm{df}(x)$ (compare (5) and (4) of 7.52). A Stieltjes integral is an integral defined in such a way that this replacement can be made even when $f(x)$ is not differentiable, or even continuous.

The principal application of the Stieltjes integral is to the method of integration by parts. Let $f(x)$ and $g(x)$ be two functions of x; if $f(x)$ and $g(x)$ are both differentiable, then it was shown in 7.51 (by inversion and rearrangement of the product formula of differentiation) that

$$\int f(x)g'(x)\,dx = f(x)g(x) - \int g(x)f'(x)\,dx$$

If $f'(x)\,dx$ and $g'(x)\,dx$ can be replaced by $df(x)$ and $dg(x)$ respectively this becomes

$$\int f(x)\,dg(x) = f(x)g(x) - \int g(x)\,df(x)$$

By use of the Stieltjes integral the application of this second form of the formula for integration by parts can now be extended to functions $f(x)$ and $g(x)$ that are not differentiable, and therefore obviously outside any argument based on the indefinite integral.

Let $f(x)$ and $g(x)$ be two functions defined in the interval $a \leqslant x \leqslant b$ and let $x_1, x_2, \dots, x_{n-1}$ be any values of x in ascending order within the interval; for convenience let $x_0 = a$ and $x_n = b$. We thus obtain n intervals in x. In the interval $x_r < x < x_{r+1}$ let the greatest and least values of $g(x)$ be M_r and m_r and let $f(x_{r+1}) - f(x_r)$ be denoted by δf_r. Then in close analogy to the Riemann definitions we form the following sums, called the upper and lower Stieltjes sums:

$$U_n = \sum_{r=0}^{n-1} M_r\,\delta f_r = \sum_{r=0}^{n-1} M_r\{f(x_{r+1}) - f(x_r)\}$$

$$L_n = \sum_{r=0}^{n-1} m_r\,\delta f_r = \sum_{r=0}^{n-1} m_r\{f(x_{r+1}) - f(x_r)\}$$

Let n now tend to infinity in such a way that the largest sub-interval in x tends to zero. If both U_n and L_n tend to the same limit S, then the Stieltjes integral of $g(x)$ with respect to $f(x)$ is defined by

$$\int_{x=a}^{b} g(x)\,df(x) = S$$

A precisely similar definition can be given for

$$\int_{x=a}^{b} \mathrm{f}(x)\, \mathrm{dg}(x)$$

It may not at first seem obvious in what way the Stieltjes integral $\int_{x=a}^{b} \mathrm{g}(x)\, \mathrm{df}(x)$ differs from

(i) the Riemann integral $\int_{x=a}^{b} \mathrm{g}(x)\mathrm{f}'(x)\, \mathrm{d}x$

(ii) from the Riemann integral $\int_{f=\mathrm{f}(a)}^{\mathrm{f}(b)} g\, \mathrm{d}f$ where f, g are two variables related through the parametric equations

$$f=\mathrm{f}(x)$$
$$g=\mathrm{g}(x)$$

The distinction lies in this : for the evaluation of the Riemann integral in case (i) $\mathrm{df}/\mathrm{d}x$ must be defined in the range $a \leqslant x \leqslant b$ and in case (ii) g must be expressible as a function of f in the range $\mathrm{f}(a) \leqslant f \leqslant \mathrm{f}(b)$; but the Stieltjes integral may exist when neither of these conditions is satisfied. An example illustrating this greater generality of the Stieltjes integral occurs when the function $\mathrm{f}(x)$ has a simple discontinuity at $x=c$ say, the function $\mathrm{g}(x)$ being continuous (Fig. 8.12).

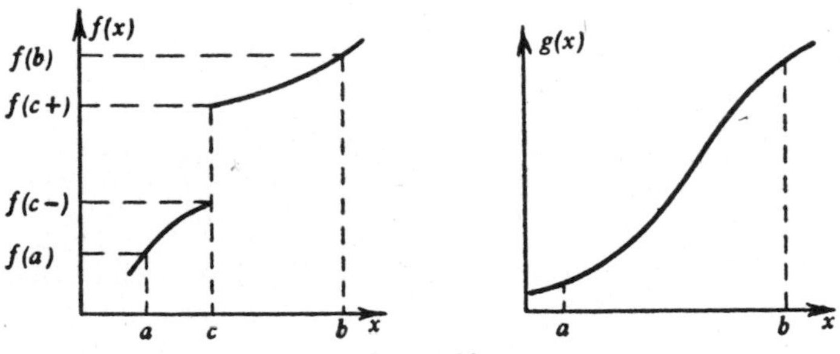

FIG. 8.12

We first note that no difficulty arises in forming the Stieltjes upper and lower sums

$$U_n = \sum_{r=0}^{n-1} M_r\{\mathrm{f}(x_{r+1}) - \mathrm{f}(x_r)\}$$
$$L_n = \sum m_r\{\mathrm{f}(x_{r+1}) - \mathrm{f}(x_r)\}$$

where M_r and m_r are the greatest and least values of $\mathrm{g}(x)$ in the interval $x_r < x < x_{r+1}$, and as $n \to \infty$ these sums tend to the same limit, so the Stieltjes integral exists.

The Riemann definition for case (i) fails because $\mathrm{d}f/\mathrm{d}x$ does not exist at $x=c$. That the Riemann definition for case (ii) also fails can be appreciated at once if we draw the graph of g against f (Fig. 8.13). The quantity g is undefined between $f = \mathrm{f}(c-)$ and $\mathrm{f}(c+)$ so the integral $\int_{\mathrm{f}(a)}^{\mathrm{f}(b)} g\,\mathrm{d}f$ is undefined.

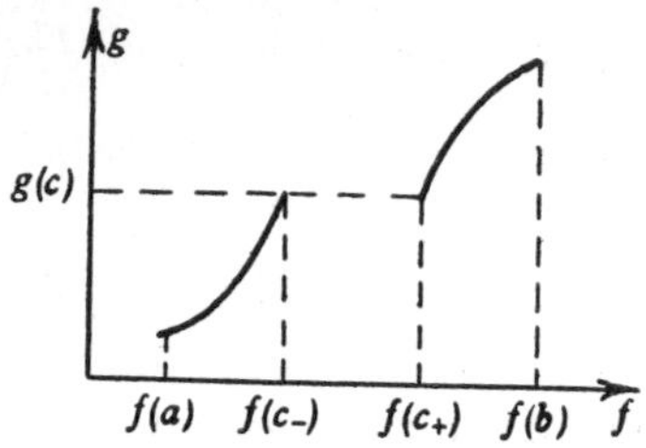

FIG. 8.13

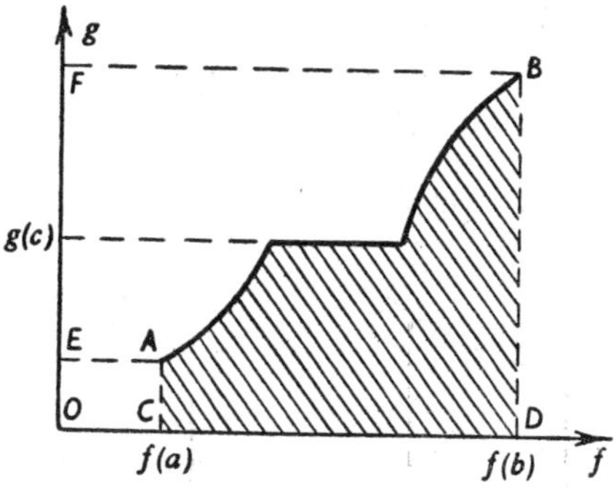

FIG. 8.14

There is a simple geometrical interpretation of the Stieltjes integral in this example: the contribution to U_n (or L_n) corresponding to the element δx_r containing $x=c$ is $M_r\,\delta f_r$ (or $m_r\,\delta f_r$) where, as $\delta x \to 0$

$$\left.\begin{matrix} M_r\,\delta f_r \\ m_r\,\delta f_r \end{matrix}\right\} \to \mathrm{g}(c)\{\mathrm{f}(c+) - \mathrm{f}(c-)\}$$

The Stieltjes integral thus measures the shaded area in Fig. 8.14. The same figure illustrates the integration by parts formula

$$\int_{x=a}^{x=b} g\,\mathrm{d}f = \Big[gf\Big]_{x=a}^{x=b} - \int_{x=a}^{x=b} f\,\mathrm{d}g = \mathrm{g}(b)\mathrm{f}(b) - \mathrm{g}(a)\mathrm{f}(a) - \int f\,\mathrm{d}g$$

which interpreted in terms of areas is

$$\text{Area } ACDB = ODBF - OCAE - \text{area } EABF$$

8.5. The Lebesgue integral

In the upper and lower Riemann sums $U_n = \sum M_r\ \delta x_r$ $L_n = \sum m_r\ \delta x_r$ the intervals δx_r were first specified, the quantities M_r, m_r then being defined as the greatest and least values of the integrand in the interval δx_r. In Lebesgue's definition of an integral $\int_a^b \mathrm{f}(x)\,dx$ $(b > a)$ the quantities m_r and M_r are first chosen, $m_r = f_r$, $M_r = f_{r+1}$ say, and the entity replacing δx_r is subsequently defined. Thus if $\mathrm{f}(x)$ is a continuous function in the range $a \leqslant x \leqslant b$, as shown in Fig. 8.15, the quantity replacing

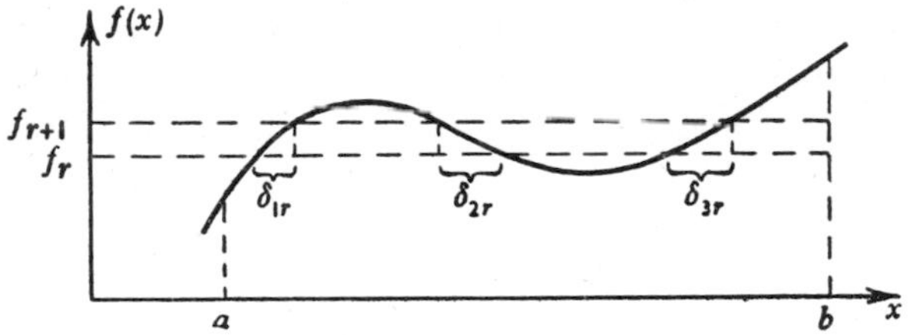

FIG. 8.15

δx_r is $\delta_{1r} + \delta_{2r} + \delta_{3r}$ i.e. the sum of the lengths of the intervals in which the value of $\mathrm{f}(x)$ lies between f_r and f_{r+1}. This sum is called the 'measure' of the set of values of x for which $f_r < \mathrm{f}(x) \leqslant f_{r+1}$, and we shall denote it by the symbol μ, thus

$$\delta_{1r} + \delta_{2r} + \delta_{3r} = \mu\{f_r < \mathrm{f}(x) \leqslant f_{r+1}\}$$

Let $f_0 < f_1 < \ldots < f_n$ be a sequence of numbers such that $f_0 < f(x) < f_n$ for all $a \leqslant x \leqslant b$, then

$$u_n = \sum_{r=0}^{n} f_{r+1}\mu\{f_r < \mathrm{f}(x) \leqslant f_{r+1}\}$$

$$l_n = \sum_{r=0}^{n} f_r\mu\{f_r < \mathrm{f}(x) \leqslant f_{r+1}\}$$

are the corresponding upper and lower Lebesgue sums, and if as $n \to \infty$ in such a way that $f_{r+1} - f_r \to 0$ for each r, u_n and l_n both tend to the same limit S independent of the mode of choosing $f_0, f_1, \ldots$ this limit S is called the Lebesgue integral $\int_a^b \mathrm{f}(x)\,dx$. It is intuitively obvious (and formal proof presents no difficulty) that for continuous functions the Riemann and Lebesgue integrals are wholly equivalent.

8.51. *Lebesgue integral for a discontinuous function*

If the function $f(x)$ is discontinuous, in particular if it has an infinite number of jump discontinuities or of oscillations, an extension of the foregoing definition of the Lebesgue integral is necessary, and it is this extension, appropriate to these difficult cases, which constitutes the power of the Lebesgue method.

Provided $f(x)$ is bounded (i.e. not infinite) in the range $a \leqslant x \leqslant b$ the choice of sequences $f_0, f_1, \ldots$ causes no difficulty. The definition of the measure $\mu\{f_r < f(x) \leqslant f_{r+1}\}$ as the sum of the lengths of intervals in which $f_r < f(x) \leqslant f_{r+1}$ is on the other hand no longer adequate, as the points for which $f_r < f(x) \leqslant f_{r+1}$ no longer form a finite set of intervals. The appropriate extension is again named the measure (of the set of points in which $f_r < f(x) \leqslant f_{r+1}$), but must now be defined by means of upper and lower sums.

Let $d_{1r}, d_{2r}, d_{3r}, \ldots, d_{nr}, \ldots$ be the lengths of any sequence of finite intervals such that every x for which $f_r < f(x) \leqslant f_{r+1}$ is contained in at least one of these intervals. Put

$$\mu_r = \text{lower bound of } (d_{1r} + d_{2r} + \ldots + d_{nr} + \ldots)$$

for all possible choices of the sequence of intervals $\{d_{nr}\}$. Similarly let $\Delta_{1r}, \Delta_{2r}, \ldots, \Delta_{nr}, \ldots$ be lengths such that every x in $a \leqslant x \leqslant b$ for which $f(x) \leqslant f_r$ or $f_{r+1} < f(x)$ is contained in at least one of the corresponding intervals ; and put

$$\mu_{ab-r} = \text{lower bound of } (\Delta_{1r} + \Delta_{2r} + \ldots + \Delta_{nr} + \ldots)$$

We note that $\mu_r + \mu_{ab-r} \geqslant b - a$ since every point of the range is covered at least once.

If $\mu_r + \mu_{ab-r} = b - a$ the set of points for which $f_r < f(x) \leqslant f_{r+1}$ is said to be measurable and its measure is μ_r, i.e.

$$\mu\{f_r < f(x) \leqslant f_{r+1}\} = \mu_r = b - a - \mu_{ab-r}$$

With this definition of measure the Lebesgue integral of a discontinuous function can be described in exactly the same terms as were given on 8.5 for a continuous function.

Any function which has a Riemann integral has a Lebesgue integral and the two are equal (ref. Titchmarsh : *Theory of Functions* §10.6). The Riemann separation into upper and lower sums is however coarser than the Lebesgue process, and the former may fail to converge to a definite answer when the Lebesgue integral is well-defined.

Example

$$\int_a^b \mathrm{f}(x)\,\mathrm{d}x \quad \text{where } \mathrm{f}(x)=1 \quad x \text{ rational}$$
$$=0 \quad \text{otherwise}$$

We have shown (8.33) that the Riemann integral $\int_a^b \mathrm{f}(x)\,\mathrm{d}x$ does not exist: we shall now prove that the Lebesgue integral has a well-defined value.

As there are no points for which f(x) has a value other than 0 or 1, $\mu\{f_r<f(x)\leqslant f_{r+1}\}$ is zero except for those values of r for which $f_r<0\leqslant f_{r+1}$ or $f_r<1\leqslant \mathrm{f}_{r+1}$. Call these values s and t so that $f_s<0\leqslant f_{s+1}$ and $f_t<1\leqslant f_{t+1}$; then

$$u_n=f_{s+1}\mu\{f_s<\mathrm{f}(x)\leqslant f_{s+1}\}+f_{t+1}\mu\{f_t<\mathrm{f}(x)\leqslant f_{t+1}\}$$
$$l_n=f_s\mu\{f_s<\mathrm{f}(x)\leqslant f_{s+1}\}+f_t\mu\{f_t<\mathrm{f}(x)\leqslant f_{t+1}\}$$

As $n\to\infty$, $f_s\to 0$, $f_{s+1}\to 0$, $f_t\to 1$, $f_{t+1}\to 1$ and, if the quantities μ and their limits exist,

$$u_n=\mathrm{Lim}\ \mu\{f_t<\mathrm{f}(x)\leqslant f_{t+1}\}$$
$$l_n=\mathrm{Lim}\ \mu\{f_t<\mathrm{f}(x)\leqslant f_{t+1}\}$$

Hence $\int_a^b \mathrm{f}(x)\,\mathrm{d}x=\mathrm{Lim}\ \mu\{f_t<\mathrm{f}(x)\leqslant f_{t+1}\}$ provided this limit exists.

Now only the points for which x is rational contribute to $\mu\{f_t<\mathrm{f}(x)\leqslant f_{t+1}\}$ (we may assume the subdivisions small enough to ensure $f_t>0$). The rational numbers in the interval $a<x\leqslant b$ can be arranged in a sequence, e.g. if $a=0$ and $b=1$ we can take the sequence $1, \frac{1}{2}, \frac{1}{3}, \frac{2}{3}, \frac{1}{4}, \frac{3}{4}, \frac{1}{5}, \frac{2}{5}, \frac{3}{5}, \frac{4}{5}, \ldots$. Then for any $\epsilon>0$ we may cover these points by a sequence of intervals whose lengths are $\frac{1}{2}\epsilon, \frac{1}{4}\epsilon, \frac{1}{8}\epsilon, \ldots, (1/2^n)\,\epsilon, \ldots$. Hence

$$\mu_r\leqslant\epsilon\left(\tfrac{1}{2}+\tfrac{1}{4}+\tfrac{1}{8}+\ldots\right)=\epsilon$$

The quantity ϵ can be made arbitrarily small, so the lower bound of such sums is zero. No different kind of sequence could give rise to a negative lower bound, hence $\mu_r=0$.

Further $$\mu_{ab-r}+\mu_r\geqslant b-a$$

Hence $$\mu_{ab-r}\geqslant b-a$$

But the whole interval certainly includes all the points where $\mathrm{f}(x)\neq 1$, so

$$\mu_{ab-r}=b-a$$

Hence $\mu\{f_t < f(x) \leqslant f_{t+1}\} = \mu_r = b - a - \mu_{ab-r}$
$$= 0$$

$$\therefore \ \operatorname{Lim} \mu\{f_t < f(x) \leqslant f_{t+1}\} = 0 \quad \text{and} \quad \int_a^b f(x)\, dx = 0$$

8.52. *Lebesgue-Stieltjes integral*

An integral of the type $\int g(x)\, df(x)$ may be defined using the Stieltjes definition of $df(x)$ in conjunction with the Lebesgue interpretation in terms of measure.

8.6. The definite integral and differentiation

We have given two independent types of definition of the definite integral of a function, viz. by summation and by means of the inverse of differentiation, and it is necessary to verify that, for functions to which both definitions can be applied, they are equivalent.

Let $f(x)$ be a given function which for the moment we shall suppose continuous and let it possess the indefinite integral $F(x)$; then by definition $F(x)$ and $f(x)$ are related by

$$\frac{d}{dx} F(x) = f(x)$$

As x increases from a to b, $F(x)$ increases by $F(b) - F(a)$; this was our first definition of the definite integral, through the indefinite integral $F(x)$. The definite integral of $f(x)$ was then defined separately by means of a limiting operation; for example the Riemann integral $\int_a^b f(x)\, dx$ is defined as the common limit of the sums

$$U_n = \sum_{r=0}^{n-1} M_r\, \delta x_r \quad \text{and} \quad L_n = \sum_{r=0}^{n-1} m_r\, \delta x_r$$

If $f(x)$ is continuous then both sums are in fact known to converge to a common limit (see 8.32), which we shall denote by $S(a, b)$.

What we have to show is that the results obtained by either definition are the same; in other words that

$$F(b) - F(a) = S(a, b)$$

We shall in fact show that $F(x) - F(a) \equiv S(a, x)$. This change of notation is not significant; the argument holds without modification if b replaces x throughout, for b can take any numerical value that x can; the change is made to avoid infringing the useful convention that letters at the beginning of the alphabet are reserved for numbers that, although arbitrary, do not vary during the course of the problem.

Consider then the quantity

$$y = S(a, x) - \{F(x) - F(a)\}$$

At $x = a$, $S(a, x)$ is zero, and hence $y = 0$.

Also
$$\frac{dy}{dx} = \frac{d}{dx} S(a, x) - F'(x)$$
$$= \frac{d}{dx} S(a, x) - f(x) \qquad (1)$$

Now by definition

$$\frac{d}{dx} S(a, x) = \operatorname*{Lt}_{h \to 0} \left\{ \frac{S(a, x+h) - S(a, x)}{h} \right\}$$

To evaluate this limit, we use the addition theorem (§8.31) from which

$$S(a, x+h) - S(a, x) = S(x, x+h)$$

Now suppose that the greatest and least values of $f(x)$ in the interval $(x, x+h)$ are M and m. Then

$$mh < S(x, x+h) < Mh$$

and therefore
$$m < [S(x, x+h)]/h < M$$

As h tends to zero both M and m tend to the value $f(x)$, because of the assumed continuity of $f(x)$. Hence

$$\frac{d}{dx} S(a, x) = \operatorname*{Lt}_{h \to 0} \frac{S(x, x+h)}{h} = f(x) \qquad (2)$$

and hence from (1) $\dfrac{dy}{dx} = 0$ for all values of x. It follows from this that y is constant; and from the fact that $y = 0$ at $x = a$ this constant must be zero. Hence $y \equiv 0$ and

$$S(a, x) \equiv F(x) - F(a)$$

In particular, of course, $S(a, b) = F(b) - F(a)$

Equation (2) may be written in the important form

$$\frac{d}{dx} \int_a^x f(u)\, du = f(x) \qquad (3)$$

It is also useful to note that $\frac{d}{dx}\int_x^b f(u)\,du = -\frac{d}{dx}\int_b^x f(u)\,du$

$$= -f(x) \qquad (4$$

The above argument can be extended to functions f(x having a simple discontinuity at $x=c$ within the range o integration. At such a point F(x) has a discontinuity in gradien and F′(c) does not exist (see Fig. 8.16). However the argumen

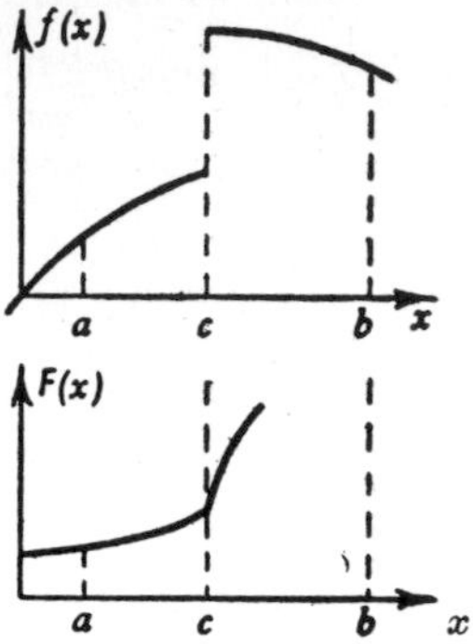

FIG. 8.16

applies to each of the intervals $(a, c-\eta)$ and $(c+\epsilon, b)$ separately where η, ϵ are positive numbers and it is not difficult to prove that the contribution from the interval $(c-\eta, c+\epsilon)$ to y can be made arbitrarily small by taking η and ϵ sufficiently small. This follows from the continuity of F(x) and S(a, x) at $x=c$.

A further extension can now be made to functions f(x) having a finite number of discontinuities.

8.61. *Sign conventions*

In defining the definite integral as the limit of a sum, we have supposed that $a<b$. If $a \geqslant b$ the following supplementary rules are required to complete the definition of the definite integral (in a way consistent with the earlier definition by indefinite integrals),

$$\int_a^b f(x)\,dx = -\int_b^a f(x)\,dx\,; \quad \int_a^a f(x)\,dx = 0$$

If f(x) is negative over a part of the range, then the contribution to the sum from this part is also negative. The area given by the definite integral is therefore the difference between he areas above the axis and those below (see Fig. 8.17). If the rea of a curve without regard to sign is required, the positive nd negative parts must be evaluated separately.

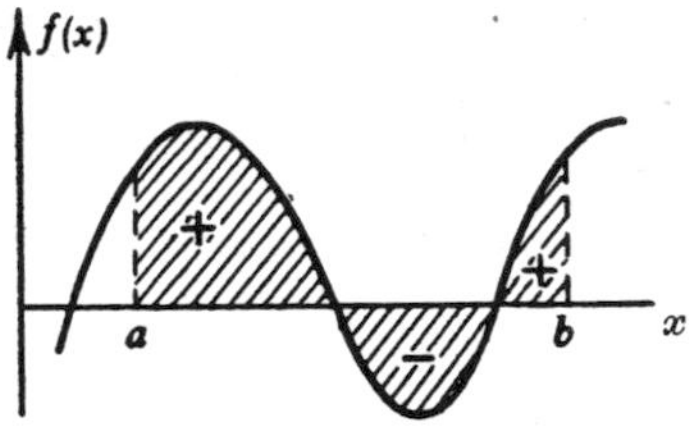

FIG. 8.17

.7. Infinite and improper integrals

If either the range of integration or the integrand itself is nfinite the Riemann definition is no longer immediately pplicable. An integral over an infinite range is called an nfinite integral; one containing an infinite discontinuity in he integrand is called an improper integral. Both types occur ery frequently in physical problems.

To deal with the infinite integral, for example $\int_a^\infty f(x)\,dx$, ve must remember that, as always, the symbol ∞ is simply an bbreviation for a limiting process. Thus $\int_a^\infty f(x)\,dx$, if it means anything at all, means

$$\operatorname*{Lt}_{X\to\infty} \int_a^X f(x)\,dx$$

A few examples will illustrate the application of this process.

Example 1

$\int_0^\infty e^{-ax}\,dx$. The indefinite integral is $-e^{-ax}/a$. Hence

$$\int_0^X e^{-ax}\,dx = \Big[-(1/a)e^{-ax}\Big]_0^X = (1-e^{-aX})/a$$

As X tends to infinity this tends to $1/a$ and hence

$$\int_0^\infty e^{-ax}\,dx = 1/a$$

Example 2

$\int_{-\infty}^{\infty} dx/(1+x^2)$. This has to be interpreted as the double limit of $\int_{-X_1}^{X_2} dx/(1+x^2)$ when X_1 and X_2 separately tend to infinity. Here the indefinite integral is $\tan^{-1} x$ and hence

$$\int_{-X_1}^{X_2} dx/(1+x^2) = \Big[\tan^{-1} x\Big]_{-X_1}^{X_2} = \tan^{-1} X_2 - \tan^{-1}(-X_1)$$

and this tends to $\frac{1}{2}\pi - (-\frac{1}{2}\pi) = \pi$ as $X_1 \to \infty$, $X_2 \to \infty$.

Example 3

$\int_1^{\infty} (1/x^n)\, dx$, $n > 1$. The indefinite integral is $-1/\{(n-1)x^{n-1}\}$ and hence $\displaystyle\int_1^X \frac{dx}{x^n} = \frac{1}{n-1}\Big[-\frac{1}{x^{n-1}}\Big]_1^X = \frac{1}{n-1}\Big[1 - \frac{1}{X^{n-1}}\Big]$

As X tends to infinity, $\dfrac{1}{X^{n-1}} \to 0$ and hence $\int_1^{\infty} (1/x^n)\, dx = 1/(n-1)$.

Example 4

If $n=1$ in Example 3, the infinite integral does not exist. For the indefinite integral is now $\log x$ and hence

$$\int_1^X (1/x)\, dx = \Big[\log x\Big]_1^X = \log X$$

which tends to infinity with X.

Example 5

$\int_0^{\infty} \sin mx\, dx$. This again does not exist, for

$$\int_0^X \sin mx\, dx = \Big[-\frac{\cos mx}{m}\Big]_0^X = \frac{1}{m}[1 - \cos mX]$$

which oscillates finitely as X tends to infinity.

8.71. *Improper Integrals*

A similar device is used in the integration of a function which is infinitely discontinuous at some point in the range. The simplest case is the one in which the discontinuity is at one end of the range. Let $\int_a^b f(x)\, dx$ be the required integral where $f(x) \to \infty$ as $x \to a$ but is integrable elsewhere. We define

$$\int_a^b f(x)\, dx = \underset{X\to a}{\mathrm{Lt}} \int_X^b f(x)\, dx$$

provided that this limit exists.

If the discontinuity is within the range of integration, we may proceed as follows. Let the range be (a, b) and let the discontinuity be at $x=c$. Then the integral over the whole range can be put equal to the sum of the separate integrals

$$\int_a^c f(x)\,dx + \int_c^b f(x)\,dx,$$

in each of which the discontinuity occurs at an end of the range, thus

$$\int_a^b f(x)\,dx = \lim_{\epsilon\to 0}\int_a^{c-\epsilon} f(x)\,dx + \lim_{\eta\to 0}\int_{c+\eta}^b f(x)\,dx \qquad (1)$$

Example

$$I = \int_0^1 x^{-n}\,dx$$

If $n>0$ this is an improper integral, the integrand being infinite at $x=0$. We consider

$$\int_X^1 \frac{1}{x^n}\,dx = \left[\frac{x^{-n+1}}{-n+1}\right]_X^1 = \frac{1}{1-n}(1-X^{1-n}),\quad n\neq 1$$

Now as $X\to 0$, $\qquad X^{1-n}\to 0 \quad \text{if } n<1$

$$X^{1-n} = \frac{1}{X^{n-1}} \to \infty \text{ if } n>1$$

Thus if $n<1$ the integral is equal to $\dfrac{1}{1-n}$, while if $n>1$ the integral does not exist. The case $n=1$ diverges also since $\log X\to -\infty$ as $X\to 0$.

8.72. *The Cauchy principal value*

If the function $f(x)$ changes sign at $x=c$, say from $-\infty$ to $+\infty$, we shall also expect $\int_a^{c-\epsilon} f(x)\,dx$ to be strongly negative and $\int_{c+\eta}^b f(x)\,dx$ to be large and positive. Then, even when neither

$$\lim_{\epsilon\to 0}\int_a^{c-\epsilon} f(x)\,dx \quad \text{nor} \quad \lim_{\eta\to 0}\int_{c+\eta}^b f(x)\,dx$$

separately exists it may be possible to pair off positive and negative portions in such a way that a convergent limit can be constructed. An obvious way of doing this is to pair the points $c-\epsilon$ and $c+\epsilon$, the corresponding 'integral' being defined as

$$\lim_{\epsilon\to 0}\left\{\int_a^{c-\epsilon} f(x)\,dx + \int_{c+\epsilon}^b f(x)\,dx\right\} \tag{2}$$

In (2) we have restricted the mode of subdivision of the range by the condition $\eta=\epsilon$; had we specified $\eta=2\epsilon$ a quite different value would in general be obtained. It must not be forgotten however that the definition of the definite integral requires the subdivision of the range to be arbitrary, so that strictly speaking the integral in cases such as we are now discussing cannot be said to exist. The particular quantity defined by equation (2) is nevertheless sometimes of interest, and is usually referred to as the Cauchy principal value of $\int_a^b f(x)\,dx$ and written $P\int_a^b f(x)\,dx$.

Example. As an example we take the integrand $1/x$ (Fig. 8.18).

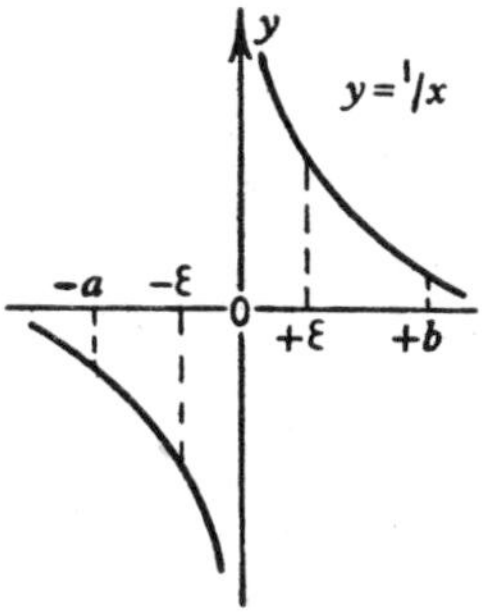

FIG. 8.18

If a and b are positive the range $(-a, b)$ includes the origin. We can evaluate $P\int_{-a}^b f(x)\,dx$, in spite of the fact that neither $\int_{-a}^0 dx/x$ nor $\int_0^b dx/x$ exists. By definition

$$\begin{aligned} P\int_{-a}^b dx/x &= \lim_{\epsilon\to 0}\left[\int_{-a}^{-\epsilon} dx/x + \int_{+\epsilon}^b dx/x\right] \\ &= \lim_{\epsilon\to 0}\{\log(\epsilon/a)+\log(b/\epsilon)\} \\ &= \lim_{\epsilon\to 0}\{\log(b/a)\}=\log(b/a) \end{aligned}$$

It will be noticed that this result is the same as that obtained by a purely formal insertion of the limits b and $-a$ into the indefinite integral ; thus

$$\Big[\log|x|\Big]_{-a}^{b}=\log|b|-\log|-a|=\log(b/a)$$

Only by careful reference to the context of its occurrence can one decide whether it is in any way meaningful to represent an undefined integral like $\int_a^b \frac{dx}{x}$ by its Cauchy principal value.

8.73. *The convergence of infinite and improper integrals*

If $\int_0^X f(x)\,dx$ tends to a limit as X tends to infinity the infinite integral $\int_0^\infty f(x)\,dx$ is said to converge. Similarly if $\int_0^X f(x)\,dx$ oscillates or diverges, the infinite integral is also said to oscillate or diverge. If $\int_0^\infty |f(x)|\,dx$ converges, then $\int_0^\infty f(x)\,dx$ is absolutely convergent. If however $\int_0^\infty f(x)\,dx$ converges and $\int_0^\infty |f(x)|\,dx$ does not, the convergence is conditional.

An exactly similar terminology is used for improper integrals.

The question of the convergence of an integral is easily settled if the indefinite integral is known. However, this is not usually the case and it is desirable to have some independent means of deciding the point.

The most useful test is that of comparison with a known integral. Thus if $|f(x)|\leqslant K|g(x)|$ where K is any positive number, then $\int_0^\infty |f(x)|\,dx$ converges if $\int_0^\infty |g(x)|\,dx$ converges.

Example 1

$\int_0^\infty e^{-x^2}\,dx$. For $x<1$ the contribution is certainly finite and for $x>1$, $x^2>x$ so $e^{-x^2}<e^{-x}$. Now $\int_0^\infty e^{-x}\,dx$ converges, hence

$\int_0^\infty e^{-x^2}\,dx$ converges. Its evaluation is of course a different matter and will be considered in 9.47.

Example 2

$\int_0^\infty dx/\sqrt{(1+x^3)}$. $\sqrt{(1+x^3)}>x^{3/2}$ for all $x>0$ and therefore the convergence of the integral over the whole range follows from that of $\int_1^\infty x^{-3/2}\,dx$.

Example 3

$\int_0^\infty [(\sin^2 x)/x^2]\,dx$. For small values of x the integrand is finite. For large values $(\sin^2 x)/x^2<1/x^2$. Hence the convergence of the integral follows from that of $\int_a^\infty (1/x^2)\,dx=1/a$.

The same sort of argument can be applied to improper integrals. For example, the divergence of $\int_0^a x^{-2}\sec^2 x\,dx$ follows from that of $\int_0^a x^{-2}\,dx$.

CHAPTER NINE

DIFFERENTIATION AND INTEGRATION OF FUNCTIONS OF TWO OR MORE VARIABLES

9.1. Differential properties

9.11. *Partial derivatives*

The change in a function $f(x, y)$ of two variables due to increments δx, δy in x, y is

$$\delta f = f(x+\delta x, y+\delta y) - f(x, y)$$

We note that in general $\delta f \to 0$ as $\delta x \to 0$ only if δy is either identically equal to zero during the limiting process or $\delta y \to 0$ as $\delta x \to 0$. If x, y are independent variables there is no reason why δy should $\to 0$ as $\delta x \to 0$: the most acceptable definition of a derivative of f with respect to x in such a case is that obtained by postulating that y = constant i.e. $\delta y = 0$ during the limiting process. Since of the two variables only one is varied, the limit so obtained is called the partial derivative of $f(x, y)$ with respect to x, and is denoted $\partial f/\partial x$, thus

$$\frac{\partial f}{\partial x} = \lim_{\delta x \to 0} \frac{f(x+\delta x, y) - f(x, y)}{\delta x} \tag{1}$$

In a similar way the partial derivative with respect to y,

$$\frac{\partial f}{\partial y} = \lim_{\delta y \to 0} \frac{f(x, y+\delta y) - f(x, y)}{\delta y} \tag{2}$$

The evaluation of partial derivatives presents no new problems for, as far as the limiting process is concerned there is only a single variable. We note that $\partial f/\partial x$ exists at the point (x_0, y_0) if the ordinary derivative $d\{f(x, y_0)\}/dx$ exists at $x = x_0$, for the definitions of $\partial f/\partial x$ and this latter quantity are identical at (x_0, y_0). The value of partial derivatives can therefore be immediately written down by using the standard rules of differentiation. For example if $f(x, y)$ is equal to (i) x^2y^3 (ii) $x+y$ (iii) $\sin(2x+y)$, $\partial f/\partial x$ is equal to (i) $2xy^3$ (ii) 1 (iii)

$2\cos(2x+y)$ and $\partial f/\partial y$ is equal to (i) $3x^2y^2$ (ii) 1 (iii) $\cos(2x+y)$.

The symbol $\partial f/\partial x$ fails to keep before our eyes the fact that f is a function of y as well as x; and when dealing with functions of more than one variable mistakes can easily creep in if there is any mental vagueness about what the independent variables are. For this reason the notation

$$\left(\frac{\partial f}{\partial x}\right)_y = \lim_{\delta x\to 0} \frac{f(x+\delta x, y) - f(x, y)}{\delta x} \tag{3}$$

is recommended.

The foregoing ideas and conventions can easily be extended to functions of several variables. Thus the notation $\left(\frac{\partial F}{\partial x}\right)_{y,z,u,v,}$ implies that F is a function of five variables, $F(x, y, z, u, v)$, and the value of the partial derivative with respect to x is

$$\left(\frac{\partial F}{\partial x}\right)_{y,z,u,v,} = \lim_{\delta x\to 0} \frac{F(x+\delta x, y, z, u, v) - F(x, y, z, u, v)}{\delta x} \tag{4}$$

We may also define higher derivatives. If f is a function of x, y and F is a function of x, y, z, u, v as above we may write

$$\frac{\partial^2 f}{\partial x^2} = \frac{\partial}{\partial x}\left(\frac{\partial f}{\partial x}\right); \quad \frac{\partial^2 f}{\partial x\,\partial y} = \frac{\partial}{\partial x}\left(\frac{\partial f}{\partial y}\right)$$

$$\frac{\partial^3 F}{\partial y\,\partial z^2} = \frac{\partial}{\partial y}\left(\frac{\partial^2 F}{\partial z^2}\right) = \frac{\partial}{\partial y}\left\{\frac{\partial}{\partial z}\left(\frac{\partial F}{\partial z}\right)\right\} \text{ etc.}$$

or, in the more explicit form,

$$\left(\frac{\partial^2 f}{\partial x^2}\right)_y = \left[\frac{\partial}{\partial x}\left(\frac{\partial f}{\partial x}\right)_y\right]_y; \quad \frac{\partial^2 f}{\partial x\,\partial y} = \left[\frac{\partial}{\partial x}\left(\frac{\partial f}{\partial y}\right)_x\right]_y$$

and $$\left(\frac{\partial^3 F}{\partial y\,\partial z^2}\right)_{x,u,v} = \left[\frac{\partial}{\partial y}\left\{\frac{\partial}{\partial z}\left(\frac{\partial F}{\partial z}\right)_{x,y,u,v}\right\}_{x,y,u,v}\right]_{x,z,u,v}$$

The notation on the left-hand side, not that on the right, of course, is recommended!

9.12. *Total differentials and total derivatives*

Although the partial derivatives recommend themselves by their ease of evaluation, it is to be expected that in practical problems interest will centre on the total increment

$$\delta f = f(x+\delta x, y+\delta y) - f(x, y).$$

We may write

$$\delta f=\frac{f(x+\delta x,\ y+\delta y)-f(x,\ y+\delta y)}{\delta x}\delta x+\frac{f(x,\ y+\delta y)-f(x,\ y)}{\delta y}\delta y \tag{1}$$

Now if the partial derivatives of $f(x, y)$ with respect to x and y exist at the points $(x, y+\delta y)$ and (x, y) respectively, on letting $\delta x \to 0$ we have

$$\frac{f(x+\delta x,\ y+\delta y)-f(x,\ y+\delta y)}{\delta x}\to \partial f(x,\ y+\delta y)/\partial x$$

while if $\delta y \to 0$

$$\frac{f(x,\ y+\delta y)-f(x,\ y)}{\delta y}\to \partial f(x,\ y)/\partial y$$

The brackets $(x, y+\delta y)$ and (x, y) on the right-hand side serve to indicate the points at which the partial derivatives are to be evaluated. If $\partial f/\partial x$ is a continuous function of y,

$$\partial f(x,\ y+\delta y)/\partial x \to \partial f(x,\ y)/\partial x$$

as $\delta y \to 0$, and, using the differential notation we write the limiting form of (1)

$$df=\frac{\partial f}{\partial x}dx+\frac{\partial f}{\partial y}dy \tag{2}$$

which may be interpreted as meaning that for small values of δx, δy

$$\delta f=\frac{\partial f}{\partial x}\delta x+\frac{\partial f}{\partial y}\delta y+\text{terms of higher order} \tag{3}$$

The loose phrase ‘ terms of higher order ’ may more strictly be replaced by $O(\delta x^2+\delta y^2)$.

The useful entity defined by (2) is known as the *total differential of* f. In (2) the quantities dx, dy can be put equal to δx, δy respectively, but of course df is not exactly equal to δf, except for special functions f for which the terms of higher order in (3) are zero.

It is necessary to know each of the quantities δx, δy before δf can be evaluated, so, when we are interested in the variations of $f(x, y)$ in all directions in the (x, y) plane, i.e. when no particular relation is specified between δx and δy, the general equations (2) and (3) are the appropriate forms to use. If, on the other hand, we are interested in the variations of $f(x, y)$

only along some specified curve C in the (x, y) plane, so that some relation between x and y and hence between δx and δy is prescribed, more convenient expressions for df and δf can be discovered.

If the curve C is specified by the parametric equations $x=x(t)$, $y=y(t)$ then, on the curve C, $\mathrm{d}x=\frac{\mathrm{d}x}{\mathrm{d}t}\,\mathrm{d}t$ and $\mathrm{d}y=\frac{\mathrm{d}y}{\mathrm{d}t}\,\mathrm{d}t$, these expressions having meaning only if $x(t)$ and $y(t)$ are differentiable functions. Hence on the curve C

$$\mathrm{df}=\left\{\frac{\partial \mathrm{f}}{\partial x}\frac{\mathrm{d}x}{\mathrm{d}t}+\frac{\partial \mathrm{f}}{\partial y}\frac{\mathrm{d}y}{\mathrm{d}t}\right\}\mathrm{d}t \tag{4}$$

To avoid the necessity of the qualifying phrase 'on the curve C' as well as the explanation that f is a function of x and y expressible in terms of t on curve C, we write

$$\left(\frac{\mathrm{df}}{\mathrm{d}t}\right)_C=\left(\frac{\partial \mathrm{f}}{\partial x}\right)_y\left(\frac{\mathrm{d}x}{\mathrm{d}t}\right)_C+\left(\frac{\partial \mathrm{f}}{\partial y}\right)_x\left(\frac{\mathrm{d}y}{\mathrm{d}t}\right)_C \tag{5}$$

When there is no danger of confusion this can be written

$$\frac{\mathrm{df}}{\mathrm{d}t}=\frac{\partial \mathrm{f}}{\partial x}\frac{\mathrm{d}x}{\mathrm{d}t}+\frac{\partial \mathrm{f}}{\partial y}\frac{\mathrm{d}y}{\mathrm{d}t}$$

The quantity $\left(\frac{\mathrm{df}}{\mathrm{d}t}\right)_C$ is called the total derivative of f with respect to t on the given path C.

The parameter t may itself be either of the variables x or y. The corresponding total derivatives would then take the forms

$$\left(\frac{\mathrm{df}}{\mathrm{d}x}\right)_C=\frac{\partial \mathrm{f}}{\partial x}+\frac{\partial \mathrm{f}}{\partial y}\left(\frac{\mathrm{d}y}{\mathrm{d}x}\right)_C$$

$$\left(\frac{\mathrm{df}}{\mathrm{d}y}\right)_C=\frac{\partial \mathrm{f}}{\partial y}+\frac{\partial \mathrm{f}}{\partial x}\left(\frac{\mathrm{d}x}{\mathrm{d}y}\right)_C$$

A function of two variables, $\mathrm{f}(x, y)$ is said to be differentiable if, for all δx, δy

$$\delta \mathrm{f}=\frac{\partial \mathrm{f}}{\partial x}\,\delta x+\frac{\partial \mathrm{f}}{\partial y}\,\delta y+\text{higher order terms}$$

This is a rather stronger condition than the mere existence of $\frac{\partial \mathrm{f}}{\partial x}$ and $\frac{\partial \mathrm{f}}{\partial y}$.

For example, the function

$$\begin{aligned} f &= x & |y| &< |x| \\ &= y & |y| &> |x| \\ &= 0 & |y| &= |x| \end{aligned}$$

has partial derivatives $\partial f/\partial x = 1$, $\partial f/\partial y = 1$ at the origin, so that

$$\frac{\partial f}{\partial x}\,\delta x + \frac{\partial f}{\partial y}\,\delta y = \delta x + \delta y.$$

But this is not in general the value of δf, for if $|\delta y| < |\delta x|$, $\delta f = \delta x$, while if $|\delta y| > |\delta x|$, $\delta f = \delta y$.

Example 1

If $x = r\cos\theta$, $y = r\sin\theta$ and x, y, r, θ are functions of t, prove that $\dot{x}\cos\theta + \dot{y}\sin\theta = \dot{r}$ where the dots denote total derivatives with respect to t.

$$\dot{x} = \left(\frac{\partial x}{\partial r}\right)_\theta \dot{r} + \left(\frac{\partial x}{\partial \theta}\right)_r \dot{\theta} = \cos\theta\,.\,\dot{r} - r\sin\theta\,.\,\dot{\theta}$$

$$\dot{y} = \sin\theta\,.\,\dot{r} + r\cos\theta\,.\,\dot{\theta}$$

Hence $$\dot{x}\cos\theta + \dot{y}\sin\theta = \dot{r}$$

Example 2

If $f(x, y) = \text{constant}$, then $\dfrac{dy}{dx} = -\left(\dfrac{\partial f}{\partial x}\right)_y \Big/ \left(\dfrac{\partial f}{\partial y}\right)_x$

For $$\frac{df}{dx} = \left(\frac{\partial f}{\partial x}\right)_y + \left(\frac{\partial f}{\partial y}\right)_x \frac{dy}{dx}$$

and on a curve on which $f(x, y)$ is a constant, $df/dx = 0$.

Hence $$\frac{dy}{dx} = -\left(\frac{\partial f}{\partial x}\right)_y \Big/ \left(\frac{\partial f}{\partial y}\right)_x \tag{6}$$

Example 3

If three variables, v, p and θ, are related in such a way that $f(v, p, \theta) = 0$, where $f(v, p, \theta)$ is some function of v, p and θ, prove that

$$\left(\frac{\partial v}{\partial \theta}\right)_p \left(\frac{\partial \theta}{\partial p}\right)_v \left(\frac{\partial p}{\partial v}\right)_\theta = -1$$

If θ is held constant, the equation $f(v, p, \theta) = 0$ assumes the same form as the equation of the previous example, $f(x, y) = 0$. The quantity corresponding to dy/dx is $(\partial p/\partial v)_\theta$, that corresponding to $(\partial f/\partial x)_y$ is $(\partial f/\partial v)_{p,\theta}$ and that corresponding to $(\partial f/\partial y)_x$ is $(\partial f/\partial p)_{v,\theta}$. Hence the result (6) becomes

$$\left(\frac{\partial p}{\partial v}\right)_\theta = -\left(\frac{\partial f}{\partial v}\right)_{p,\theta} \Big/ \left(\frac{\partial f}{\partial p}\right)_{v,\theta}$$

similarly

$$\left(\frac{\partial \theta}{\partial p}\right)_v = -\left(\frac{\partial f}{\partial p}\right)_{v,\theta} \Big/ \left(\frac{\partial f}{\partial \theta}\right)_{p,v}$$

$$\left(\frac{\partial v}{\partial \theta}\right)_p = -\left(\frac{\partial f}{\partial \theta}\right)_{p,v} \Big/ \left(\frac{\partial f}{\partial v}\right)_{p,\theta}$$

on multiplying together these three relations, the required result follows.

9.13. *Change of variable*

Let a quantity f be expressible either as a function of x and y, or as a function of two other variables s, t. It will be supposed that x and y are expressible in terms of s and t, and that the expressions are differentiable so that

$$\left(\frac{\partial x}{\partial t}\right)_s, \quad \left(\frac{\partial x}{\partial s}\right)_t, \quad \left(\frac{\partial y}{\partial t}\right)_s, \quad \text{and} \quad \left(\frac{\partial y}{\partial s}\right)_t$$

are known functions.

We can now apply formula (5) of 9.12 taking as our 'curve C' the path s=constant. With this choice of C we note that

$$\left(\frac{df}{dt}\right)_C = \left(\frac{\partial f}{\partial t}\right)_s,$$

and similarly

$$\left(\frac{dx}{dt}\right)_C = \left(\frac{\partial x}{\partial t}\right)_s; \quad \left(\frac{dy}{dt}\right)_C = \left(\frac{\partial y}{\partial t}\right)_s.$$

Thus equation (5) of 9.12 takes the form

$$\left(\frac{\partial f}{\partial t}\right)_s = \left(\frac{\partial f}{\partial x}\right)_y \left(\frac{\partial x}{\partial t}\right)_s + \left(\frac{\partial f}{\partial y}\right)_x \left(\frac{\partial y}{\partial t}\right)_s \tag{1}$$

Similarly, interchanging the roles of s and t,

$$\left(\frac{\partial f}{\partial s}\right)_t = \left(\frac{\partial f}{\partial x}\right)_y \left(\frac{\partial x}{\partial s}\right)_t + \left(\frac{\partial f}{\partial y}\right)_x \left(\frac{\partial y}{\partial s}\right)_t \tag{2}$$

Higher derivatives of f with respect to s and t can be similarly expanded by repeated application of relations (1) and (2).

The importance of specifying the variables which are held

constant as well as the variable of differentiation in a partial derivative is well illustrated by particular applications of (1) or (2). Suppose, for example, that f can be expressed either as a function of x and y, or as a function of x and t. We use equation (2) with $s=x$ and find

$$\left(\frac{\partial f}{\partial x}\right)_t = \left(\frac{\partial f}{\partial x}\right)_y + \left(\frac{\partial f}{\partial y}\right)_x \left(\frac{\partial y}{\partial x}\right)_t$$

which shows clearly that in general

$$\left(\frac{\partial f}{\partial x}\right)_t \neq \left(\frac{\partial f}{\partial x}\right)_y$$

Example 1

The function $\dfrac{\partial^2 V}{\partial x^2}+\dfrac{\partial^2 V}{\partial y^2}+\dfrac{\partial^2 V}{\partial z^2}$ where V is a function of x, y, z, is of great importance in many physical problems, and is usually denoted by the symbol $\nabla^2 V$. It frequently happens that other coordinates, e.g. cylindrical polars (r, θ, z) or spherical polars are better suited to the solution of the problem than cartesian coordinates x, y, z, and in such cases $\nabla^2 V$ must first be expressed in terms of partial derivatives with respect to the chosen system of coordinates.

The question of notation again rears its head. We may either write $V=f_1(x, y, z)=f_2(r, \theta, z)$, which clearly indicates that the form of the function for V depends on the coordinate system which is chosen; or we may write $V=V(x, y, z)=V(r, \theta, z)$ which obscures the distinction of functional forms (and so must be used with special care), but which keeps in view the physical quantity V in a way that the f_1, f_2, notation does not.

Consider cylindrical polar coordinates $r=(x^2+y^2)^{\frac{1}{2}}$, $\theta=\tan^{-1}(y/x)$, z, and suppose that $V(x, y, z)=V(r, \theta, z)$; z-derivatives are unaffected by the change of coordinates in the (x, y) plane, so we need only consider the transformation of the x- and y-derivatives. Then

$$\frac{\partial r}{\partial x} \equiv \left(\frac{\partial r}{\partial x}\right)_{y, z} = \frac{1}{2\sqrt{(x^2+y^2)}} \cdot 2x = \frac{x}{r} = \cos\theta$$

$$\frac{\partial r}{\partial y} \equiv \left(\frac{\partial r}{\partial y}\right)_{z, x} = \frac{1}{2\sqrt{(x^2+y^2)}} \cdot 2y = \frac{y}{r} = \sin\theta$$

$$\frac{\partial \theta}{\partial x} \equiv \left(\frac{\partial \theta}{\partial x}\right)_{y, z} = \frac{x^2}{x^2+y^2} \cdot \frac{-y}{x^2} = \frac{-r\sin\theta}{r^2} = -\frac{1}{r}\sin\theta$$

$$\frac{\partial \theta}{\partial y} \equiv \left(\frac{\partial \theta}{\partial y}\right)_{z, x} = \frac{x^2}{x^2+y^2} \cdot \frac{1}{x} = \frac{1}{r}\cos\theta$$

(There are neater derivations of the above results, but we will not distract the reader from the main line of argument by introducing them here.)

$$\left.\begin{aligned}\frac{\partial V}{\partial x}&=\frac{\partial V}{\partial r}\frac{\partial r}{\partial x}+\frac{\partial V}{\partial \theta}\frac{\partial \theta}{\partial x}=\cos\theta\frac{\partial V}{\partial r}-\frac{1}{r}\sin\theta\frac{\partial V}{\partial \theta}\\ \frac{\partial V}{\partial y}&=\frac{\partial V}{\partial r}\frac{\partial r}{\partial y}+\frac{\partial V}{\partial \theta}\frac{\partial \theta}{\partial y}=\sin\theta\frac{\partial V}{\partial r}+\frac{1}{r}\cos\theta\frac{\partial V}{\partial \theta}\end{aligned}\right\} \quad (1)$$

To form $\partial^2 V/\partial x^2$ we replace V by $\partial V/\partial x$ on the left-hand side of (1), and correspondingly replace V by $\left(\cos\theta\frac{\partial V}{\partial r}-\frac{1}{r}\sin\theta\frac{\partial V}{\partial \theta}\right)$ on the right-hand side :

$$\begin{aligned}\frac{\partial^2 V}{\partial x^2}&=\cos\theta\frac{\partial}{\partial r}\left[\cos\theta\frac{\partial V}{\partial r}-\frac{1}{r}\sin\theta\frac{\partial V}{\partial \theta}\right]\\ &\qquad -\frac{1}{r}\sin\theta\frac{\partial}{\partial \theta}\left[\cos\theta\frac{\partial V}{\partial r}-\frac{1}{r}\sin\theta\frac{\partial V}{\partial \theta}\right]\\ &=\cos^2\theta\frac{\partial^2 V}{\partial r^2}+\sin^2\theta\left[\frac{1}{r}\frac{\partial V}{\partial r}+\frac{1}{r^2}\frac{\partial^2 V}{\partial \theta^2}\right]\\ &\qquad +2\sin\theta\cos\theta\left[\frac{1}{r^2}\frac{\partial V}{\partial \theta}-\frac{1}{r}\frac{\partial^2 V}{\partial r\partial \theta}\right]\end{aligned}$$

In $\partial^2 V/\partial y^2$, $\cos\theta$ is replaced by $\sin\theta$ and $\sin\theta$ by $-\cos\theta$ and altogether

$$\frac{\partial^2 V}{\partial x^2}+\frac{\partial^2 V}{\partial y^2}=\frac{\partial^2 V}{\partial r^2}+\frac{1}{r}\frac{\partial V}{\partial r}+\frac{1}{r^2}\frac{\partial^2 V}{\partial \theta^2}$$

and, on adding $\partial^2 V/\partial z^2=\partial^2 V/\partial z^2$ to each side

$$\nabla^2 V=\frac{\partial^2 V}{\partial r^2}+\frac{1}{r}\frac{\partial V}{\partial r}+\frac{1}{r^2}\frac{\partial^2 V}{\partial \theta^2}+\frac{\partial^2 V}{\partial z^2}$$

Example 2

As a somewhat lengthy exercise in manipulation, the reader may like to establish the corresponding expression in terms of spherical polar coordinates, namely

$$\nabla^2 V=\frac{\partial^2 V}{\partial r^2}+\frac{2}{r}\frac{\partial V}{\partial r}+\frac{1}{r^2\sin\theta}\frac{\partial}{\partial \theta}\left(\sin\theta\frac{\partial V}{\partial \theta}\right)+\frac{1}{r^2\sin^2\theta}\frac{\partial^2 V}{\partial \phi^2}$$

where $r^2=x^2+y^2+z^2$, $\tan\theta=(x^2+y^2)^{\frac{1}{2}}/z$, $\tan\phi=y/x$

This result is obtained by a different method in Chapter 18.

9.14. *Order of differentiation*

Since $\dfrac{\partial f}{\partial x} = \lim\limits_{\delta x \to 0} \dfrac{f(x+\delta x, y) - f(x, y)}{\delta x}$

$$\frac{\partial^2 f}{\partial y\,\partial x} = \frac{\partial}{\partial y}\left(\frac{\partial f}{\partial x}\right) = \lim_{\delta y \to 0}\left\{\lim_{\delta x \to 0} \frac{f(x+\delta x, y+\delta y) - f(x, y+\delta y)}{\delta x} - \lim_{\delta x \to 0} \frac{f(x+\delta x, y) - f(x, y)}{\delta x}\right\}\Big/ \delta y$$

$$= \lim_{\delta y \to 0}\ \lim_{\delta x \to 0} \frac{f(x+\delta x, y+\delta y) - f(x, y+\delta y) - f(x+\delta x, y) + f(x, y)}{\delta x\,\delta y} \tag{1}$$

Similarly $\dfrac{\partial^2 f}{\partial x\,\partial y} =$

$$\lim_{\delta x \to 0}\ \lim_{\delta y \to 0} \frac{f(x+\delta x, y+\delta y) - f(x, y+\delta y) - f(x+\delta x, y) + f(x, y)}{\delta x\,\delta y} \tag{2}$$

Although the limits (1) and (2) are frequently equal, they are not necessarily so unless the function $f(x, y)$ satisfies certain conditions. Either one of two sets of conditions, corresponding to the two following theorems, is sufficient. (*a*) (*Young's theorem*). If $\dfrac{\partial f}{\partial x}$ and $\dfrac{\partial f}{\partial y}$ are differentiable at (x_0, y_0) then $\dfrac{\partial^2 f}{\partial x\,\partial y} = \dfrac{\partial^2 f}{\partial y\,\partial x}$ at (x_0, y_0).

or (*b*) (*Schwarz's theorem*). If $\dfrac{\partial f}{\partial y}$ and $\dfrac{\partial}{\partial y}\left(\dfrac{\partial f}{\partial x}\right)$ exist in a region containing (x_0, y_0) and the latter is continuous at this point then at (x_0, y_0) $\dfrac{\partial^2 f}{\partial x\,\partial y}$ exists and is equal to $\dfrac{\partial^2 f}{\partial y\,\partial x}$. We shall not write out the details of the proofs.

The result that if $\partial^2 f/\partial y\,\partial x$ is continuous at (x_0, y_0) then

$$\frac{\partial^2 f}{\partial x\,\partial y} = \frac{\partial^2 f}{\partial y\,\partial x} \tag{1}$$

has consequences that are far less obvious-seeming than the relation itself. For example if we know that a function $F(x, y)$ exists such that

$$dF = f_1(x, y)\,dx + f_2(x, y)\,dy \tag{2}$$

then $$\left(\frac{\partial \mathrm{F}}{\partial x}\right)_y = \mathrm{f}_1(x, y)\,; \quad \left(\frac{\partial \mathrm{F}}{\partial y}\right)_x = \mathrm{f}_2(x, y)$$

$$\frac{\partial^2 \mathrm{F}}{\partial y\, \partial x} \equiv \left(\frac{\partial \mathrm{f}_1}{\partial y}\right)_x; \quad \frac{\partial^2 \mathrm{F}}{\partial x\, \partial y} = \left(\frac{\partial \mathrm{f}_2}{\partial x}\right)_y$$

and we may deduce that, subject to the continuity of the functions,

$$\left(\frac{\partial \mathrm{f}_1}{\partial y}\right)_x = \left(\frac{\partial \mathrm{f}_2}{\partial x}\right)_y \tag{3}$$

a result far from obvious from our original premises.

The fact that a relation of type (2) implies equation (3) is of great use in thermodynamics. Thus Maxwell's four thermodynamic relations

$$\left.\begin{aligned} (\partial T/\partial v)_S &= -(\partial p/\partial S)_v \\ (\partial S/\partial v)_T &= (\partial p/\partial T)_v \\ (\partial T/\partial p)_S &= (\partial v/\partial S)_p \\ (\partial S/\partial p)_T &= -(\partial v/\partial T)_p \end{aligned}\right\} \tag{4}$$

where T, p, v, S are the temperature, pressure, volume and entropy of a quantity of some substance, are most readily proved in this way. Any two of the four inter-related quantities T, p, v, S are ordinarily sufficient to define the ' state ' of the substance and, if the ' state ' is known so also is the internal energy E. Now it can be shown that

$$\mathrm{d}E = T\,\mathrm{d}S - p\,\mathrm{d}v$$

and from this it follows that also

$$\left.\begin{aligned} \mathrm{d}(E+pv) &= T\,\mathrm{d}S + v\,\mathrm{d}p \\ \mathrm{d}(E-TS) &= -S\,\mathrm{d}T - p\,\mathrm{d}v \\ \mathrm{d}(E+pv-TS) &= -S\,\mathrm{d}T + v\,\mathrm{d}p \end{aligned}\right\} \tag{5}$$

(the quantity $E+pv$ is known as the ' total heat ' or ' enthalpy ', and $E-TS$ and $E+pv-TS$ as the ' thermodynamic potentials ' at constant volume and constant pressure respectively).

Since the ' state ' of the substance is determined completely by v and S, and E depends on the ' state ' only, it follows that E is expressible as a function of S and v only. Then formula (3), applied to the first of the relations (5), enables us to deduce

$$(\partial T/\partial v)_S = -(\partial p/\partial S)_v$$

which is the first of the relations (4).

The other three equations (4) follow in like manner from the corresponding equations of set (5) since $(E-TS)$ is known when the state is given, i.e. $(E-TS)$ is expressible as a function of v, T; $(E+pv)$ as a function of S, p; $(E+pv-TS)$ as a function of p, T: where we have in each case picked out the *appropriate* pair of variables so that equation (3) may be applied.

9.21. *Taylor's theorem for functions of two or more variables*

Suppose we want to find an expansion of $f(x+h, y+k)$ in ascending powers of h and k. First consider the function of t defined by $F(t) = f(x+ht, y+kt)$

$$F(t) = f(X, Y) \text{ say where } X = x+ht$$
$$Y = y+kt$$

$$\therefore \qquad F'(t) = \frac{\partial f}{\partial X}\frac{\partial X}{\partial t} + \frac{\partial f}{\partial Y}\frac{\partial Y}{\partial t}$$
$$= h\frac{\partial f}{\partial X} + k\frac{\partial f}{\partial Y}$$

$$\text{But} \qquad \frac{\partial f}{\partial x} = \frac{\partial f}{\partial X}\frac{\partial X}{\partial x} + \frac{\partial f}{\partial Y}\frac{\partial Y}{\partial x} = \frac{\partial f}{\partial X}$$

$$\text{and} \qquad \frac{\partial f}{\partial y} = \frac{\partial f}{\partial X}\frac{\partial X}{\partial y} + \frac{\partial f}{\partial Y}\frac{\partial Y}{\partial y} = \frac{\partial f}{\partial Y}$$

$$\therefore \qquad F'(t) = h\frac{\partial f}{\partial x} + k\frac{\partial f}{\partial y}$$

Proceeding in the same way, or by induction, we can show that

$$F''(t) = h^2\frac{\partial^2 f}{\partial x^2} + 2hk\frac{\partial^2 f}{\partial x\,\partial y} + k^2\frac{\partial^2 f}{\partial y^2}$$
$$F'''(t) = h^3\frac{\partial^3 f}{\partial x^3} + 3h^2k\frac{\partial^3 f}{\partial x^2\,\partial y} + 3hk^2\frac{\partial^3 f}{\partial x\,\partial y^2} + k^3\frac{\partial^3 f}{\partial y^3}$$

etc., the terms having binomial coefficients. Symbolically we can write

$$F'(t) = \left(h\frac{\partial}{\partial x} + k\frac{\partial}{\partial y}\right)f$$
$$F''(t) = \left(h\frac{\partial}{\partial x} + k\frac{\partial}{\partial y}\right)^2 f$$
$$F'''(t) = \left(h\frac{\partial}{\partial x} + k\frac{\partial}{\partial y}\right)^3 f$$

etc.

Now $$F(t) = F(0) + tF'(0) + \frac{t^2}{2!}F''(0) + \dots$$

(provided the series converges)

Hence $$f(x+ht, y+kt) = f(x, y) + t\left(h\frac{\partial}{\partial x} + k\frac{\partial}{\partial y}\right)f(x, y) + \frac{t^2}{2!}\left(h\frac{\partial}{\partial x} + k\frac{\partial}{\partial y}\right)^2 f(x, y) + \dots$$

so, putting $t=1$,

$$f(x+h, y+k) = f(x, y) + h\frac{\partial f}{\partial x} + k\frac{\partial f}{\partial y} + \frac{1}{2!}\left\{h^2\frac{\partial^2 f}{\partial x^2} + 2hk\frac{\partial^2 f}{\partial x\,\partial y} + k^2\frac{\partial^2 f}{\partial y^2}\right\} + \dots \quad (1)$$

This is the required result.

Corresponding formulae for three or more variables can be found in the same way.

9.22. *Maxima and minima*

The function f is said to have a stationary value at (x, y) if for all sufficiently small h, k

$$f(x+h, y+k) = f(x, y) + O(h^2 + k^2)$$

So for a stationary value we must have (cf. (1) of 9.21 above)

$$\frac{\partial f}{\partial x} = 0 \quad \text{and} \quad \frac{\partial f}{\partial y} = 0 \quad (1)$$

For a maximum at (x, y) the second order terms must be negative, for a minimum the second order terms must be positive, for all h, k.

Now $$h^2\frac{\partial^2 f}{\partial x^2} + 2hk\frac{\partial^2 f}{\partial x\,\partial y} + k^2\frac{\partial^2 f}{\partial y^2} > 0$$

for all h, k requires :

$$\text{(i)} \; \frac{\partial^2 f}{\partial x^2} \text{ and } \frac{\partial^2 f}{\partial y^2} > 0 \quad \text{and} \quad \text{(ii)} \left(\frac{\partial^2 f}{\partial x\,\partial y}\right)^2 < \frac{\partial^2 f}{\partial x^2}\cdot\frac{\partial^2 f}{\partial y^2} \quad (2)$$

(1) and (2) are therefore the conditions for a minimum of f at (x, y).

$$h^2\frac{\partial^2 f}{\partial x^2} + 2hk\frac{\partial^2 f}{\partial x\,\partial y} + k^2\frac{\partial^2 f}{\partial y^2} < 0$$

for all h, k requires

$$\text{(i)}\quad \frac{\partial^2 f}{\partial x^2} \quad\text{and}\quad \frac{\partial^2 f}{\partial y^2} < 0 \qquad \text{(ii)}\quad \left(\frac{\partial^2 f}{\partial x\,\partial y}\right)^2 < \frac{\partial^2 f}{\partial x^2}\cdot\frac{\partial^2 f}{\partial y^2} \tag{3}$$

(1) and (3) are therefore the conditions for a maximum of f at (x, y).

If
$$\left(\frac{\partial^2 f}{\partial x\,\partial y}\right)^2 > \frac{\partial^2 f}{\partial x^2}\cdot\frac{\partial^2 f}{\partial y^2}$$

(as, for example, is necessarily true if one of $\frac{\partial^2 f}{\partial x^2}$, $\frac{\partial^2 f}{\partial y^2}$ is positive and the other negative) $f(x+h, y+k)$ will be greater than $f(x, y)$ for some values of h, k, less for others. The stationary point (x, y) is then known as a saddle point.

If $\left(\frac{\partial^2 f}{\partial x\,\partial y}\right)^2 = \frac{\partial^2 f}{\partial x^2}\frac{\partial^2 f}{\partial y^2}$ the second order terms vanish for some ratios of $h : k$, and the higher order terms must be examined.

9.3. Integral properties

We shall now consider in turn various ways in which a function of several variables can be integrated. A quantity which varies from point to point in three dimensional space can be summed over any selection of points lying along a linear path, or it can be summed over any selection of points spread over a surface, or in a volume. By taking suitable limits of such sums, we can define integrals which are known as line integrals, surface integrals and volume integrals respectively.

Functions of several variables which are not space variables, however, also occur in scientific problems, and we shall first investigate in what sense an integral with respect to one of the variables can be said to have meaning.

9.31. *Integration of functions of more than one variable*

If $f(x)$ is a continuous function of a single variable x, the contribution to $\int f(x)\,dx$ from the interval between x_0 and $x_0 + \delta x$ is unambiguous : its value is in fact very nearly equal to $f(x_0)\,\delta x$. Now let us consider a continuous function $f(x, y)$ of two variables, and try to form an integral in the same way as for the single variable case. The contribution to $\int f(x, y)\,dx$ from the interval between x_0 and $x_0 + \delta x$ is very nearly equal to

$f(x_0, y)\,\delta x$, a quantity whose value depends not only on the interval of x which is being considered, but also on y. A meaning can therefore be given to the definite integral $\int_a^b f(x, y)\,dx$ in the same way as in our previous work only if a value of y is specified for each value of x between a and b.

It would, for example, be possible to specify $y=$constant for all x; the value of the integral would then be completely determinate when the (constant) value of y was specified, i.e. the integral would define a function of y. This interpretation is implied when equations of the form $g(y)=\int_{x=a}^{b} f(x, y)\,dx$ are written, but, except in this case, the more general interpretation of the notation $\int f(x, y)\,dx$ must be used, and the integral is in fact better written $\int_C f(x, y)\,dx$ where C denotes the 'path of integration' i.e. the given dependence of y on x.

The above paragraph indicates the nature of the situation which arises when integrating functions of several variables, and to obtain rigorous definitions nothing new is required. For if y is a known function of x the Riemann (or Cauchy or Lebesgue) definition of integration can be applied directly to evaluate $\int_C f(x, y)\,dx$.

In the same way if x and y are both known functions of a third variable u, $x=g_1(u)$, $y=g_2(u)$ say, the integral

$$\int_{u_0}^{u_1} f(x, y)\,du$$

can be evaluated by finding x and y, and hence $f(x, y)$, for each value of u, $f(x, y)=F(u)$ say, and forming

$$\int f(x, y)\,du=\int F(u)\,du$$

by the standard methods.

The variables in terms of which the function f is expressed need not, of course, originally occur as coordinates in physical space: an integral $\int_{u_0}^{u_1} f(p, v)\,du$ (where $p=g_1(u)=$the pressure and $v = g_2(u)$ = the volume of a given system, say) would be evaluated in exactly the same way, the integral now being associated with a ' path ' in the (p, v) ' plane ' defined by the parametric equations $p = g_1(u)$, $v = g_2(u)$.

9.32. *Line integrals*

When the function to be integrated is a function of position (whether in a two- or three-dimensional space), such as $f_1(x, y, z)$ or $f_2(r, \theta)$, the path length s of the curve of integration is often the variable of integration : i.e. we want $\int_{s_0}^{s_1} f(x, y, z)\, ds$ where $x = g_1(s)$, $y = g_2(s)$, $z = g_3(s)$ or $\int_{s_0}^{s_1} f_2(r, \theta)\, ds$ along the curve whose parametric equations are $r = h_1(s)$, $\theta = h_2(s)$.

If the curve is a closed circuit, the initial and final points in space coinciding, the integral is often written $\oint f_1(x, y, z)\, ds$ or $\oint f_2(r, \theta)\, ds$. Here, as in all the preceding forms, the notation is incomplete, the equations of the path of integration being necessary before the integral is adequately defined.

Expressions such as $\int f_1(x, y, z)\, ds$ and $\int f_2(r, \theta)\, ds$ are called line integrals of the scalar functions f_1 and f_2. If on the other hand the function under consideration is a vector (cf. chap. 17) i.e. if for each point (x, y, z) there is a specified direction as well as a magnitude $F(x, y, z)$, the expression ' line integral ' means an integral of the form $\int F(x, y, z) \cos \chi\, ds$ where χ is the angle between the element ds and the special direction associated with the function F at the point x, y, z.

Example 1

Find $\int_{x=2}^{x=3} x^2 y\, dx$ along each of the following paths :
(i) $y = 0$, (ii) $y = x$, (iii) $y = 1/x^3$. The results are (i) 0, (ii) 65/4, (iii) $\log_e (3/2)$ respectively.

Example 2

Evaluate $\int xe^y\, dx$ between the limits $x = 0$, $y = 0$ and $x = 1$, $y = 1$

(i) along the curve $y=x$, (ii) along the curve $y=x^2$. Answers (i) 1, (ii) $\frac{1}{2}(e-1)$.

Example 3

Evaluate $\int (1/r^2)\,\mathrm{d}s$ between the points $r=1$, $\theta=-\frac{1}{4}\pi$ and $r=1$, $\theta=\frac{1}{4}\pi$, (i) along the minor arc of the circle $r=1$, (ii) along the straight line joining the two points, i.e. the line $r\cos\theta=1/\sqrt{2}$. (Note : in case (ii) the integral may be evaluated either by changing to cartesian coordinates, or by noting that $r\,\mathrm{d}\theta/\mathrm{d}s=\cos\theta$ and expressing entirely in terms of θ.) Answers : (i) $\pi/2$, (ii) $\pi\sqrt{2}/2$.

Example 4

Evaluate $\oint (k/r)\,\mathrm{d}s$ where k is constant and the path of integration is a circle of any radius with centre at $r=0$. The result is $2\pi k$ independent of the radius of the circle.

9.33. *Integrals which are independent of the path : exact differential*

It is clear from the foregoing paragraphs that the value of an integral of a function of two or more variables is in general dependent not only on the initial and final values of the variables, but on the form of the intervening path. In some special cases, however, combinations of integrals of functions of several variables can be shown to be equivalent to the integral of a function of a single variable, and therefore dependent only on the initial and final values of the variables, *not* on the path of integration. Thus, suppose that u is a quantity expressible as a function of two variables x, y. Then

$$\int \mathrm{f}(u)\,\mathrm{d}u=\int \mathrm{f}(u)\left(\frac{\partial u}{\partial x}\,\mathrm{d}x+\frac{\partial u}{\partial y}\,\mathrm{d}y\right)$$

$$=\int \{\mathrm{g}_1(x, y)\,\mathrm{d}x+\mathrm{g}_2(x, y)\,\mathrm{d}y\} \qquad (1)$$

where $\mathrm{g}_1(x, y)=\mathrm{f}(u)\dfrac{\partial u}{\partial x}$

$$\mathrm{g}_2(x, y)=\mathrm{f}(u)\frac{\partial u}{\partial y}$$

If the initial and final values of x and y are given, the initial and final values of u are known, and hence the value of either side of equation (1) is determined by the initial and final values of x, y irrespective of the path of integration.

If the line integral of a vector function is independent of path taken between the end-points, the function is said to be *conservative*, or, if the vector is a force, to define a *conservative field of force*.

Example

The vector function of magnitude $1/r^2$ (where $r^2 = x^2 + y^2 + z^2$) associated with the positive direction of r defines a conservative field, i.e. inverse square law forces are conservative. For the line integral of the vector function between any two points P, Q is $\int_P^Q \frac{1}{r^2} \cos \chi \, ds$ where $\cos \chi = \frac{dr}{ds}$, i.e. the integral $= \int_P^Q \frac{1}{r^2} dr$ which depends only on the values of r at the end-points P and Q.

We now ask, under what circumstances is

$$\int \{g_1(x, y)\, dx + g_2(x, y)\, dy\}$$

a function of the limits of integration only, independent of path?

If $\int_{x_0, y_0}^{x, y} (g_1\, dx + g_2\, dy)$ is independent of the path between the limits (for all (x, y)), it defines a function of (x, y), say $\phi(x, y)$. Moreover

$$\left(\frac{\partial \phi}{\partial x}\right)_y = \frac{\partial}{\partial x} \int_{x_0}^{x} g_1 (y = \text{const})\, dx = g_1(x, y)$$

Similarly
$$\frac{\partial \phi}{\partial y} = g_2(x, y)$$

Moreover if g_1 and g_2 are differentiable we must have

$$\frac{\partial^2 \phi}{\partial x\, \partial y} = \frac{\partial^2 \phi}{\partial y\, \partial x}$$

that is
$$\frac{\partial g_2}{\partial x} = \frac{\partial g_1}{\partial y} \tag{2}$$

Equation (2) expresses a necessary condition that

$$\int \{g_1\, dx + g_2\, dy\}$$

shall be independent of path and that $(g_1\, dx + g_2\, dy)$ shall be an exact differential, $d\phi$. It can also be shown that equation (2) is also a sufficient condition.

9.34. *Differentiation and integration under the integral sign*

The equation $$\mathrm{g}(y) = \int_a^b \mathrm{f}(x, y)\,\mathrm{d}x \tag{1}$$
is somewhat analogous to the equation
$$\mathrm{g}(y) = \sum_{i=1}^{n} \mathrm{f}_i(y) \tag{2}$$
the most conspicuous difference being that the discrete variable i with increment $\Delta i = 1$ in (2) is replaced by the continuous variable x with increment $\mathrm{d}x$ in (1). The analogy between the two forms is so close that the following theorems and definitions for integrals can be stated with little comment other than a reference to the corresponding theorems for series (especially 4.21, 7.6). A full treatment, with proofs, may be found in Titchmarsh, *Theory of Functions*, chap. 1.

The reader is not advised to try to memorise these theorems as forms of words, but to recognise theorems 1–4 as quite natural consequences of the fact that integration is a smoothing process (and differentiation the reverse). In the course of time, or at a second reading of the book, he will probably see theorems 5, 6 in the same light: in the meantime the important thing is that he should know that differentiation or integration under the integral sign is admissible only under certain conditions, which he can look up when required.

Theorem 1. Continuity Property.

If $\mathrm{f}(x, y)$ is a continuous function of x, y in the rectangle $a \leqslant x \leqslant b$, $a' \leqslant y \leqslant b'$, then the function defined by the integral $\mathrm{g}(y) = \int_a^b \mathrm{f}(x, y)\,\mathrm{d}x$ is a continuous function of y.

(To prove this we note that
$$\mathrm{g}(y+h) - \mathrm{g}(y) = \int_a^b \{\mathrm{f}(x, y+h) - \mathrm{f}(x, y\}\,\mathrm{d}x$$
and the right-hand side can, by suitable choice of h be made less than $(b-a)\delta$ i.e. less than any desired ϵ.)

Theorem 2. Differentiation under the integral sign.

If $\mathrm{f}(x, y)$ and $\partial\mathrm{f}/\partial y$ are continuous functions of x, y in the rectangle $a \leqslant x \leqslant b$, $y_1 \leqslant y \leqslant y_2$, then for $y_1 < y < y_2$,
$$\frac{\mathrm{d}}{\mathrm{d}y}\,\mathrm{g}(y) \equiv \frac{\mathrm{d}}{\mathrm{d}y}\left\{\int_a^b \mathrm{f}(x, y)\,\mathrm{d}x\right\} = \int_a^b \frac{\partial \mathrm{f}}{\partial y}\,\mathrm{d}x$$

Theorem 3. Integration under the integral sign.

If $f(x, y)$ is a continuous function of (x, y) in the rectangle $a \leqslant x \leqslant b$, $y_1 \leqslant y \leqslant y_2$, then

$$\int_a^b \left\{ \int_{y_1}^{y_2} f(x, y)\, dy \right\} dx = \int_{y_1}^{y_2} \left\{ \int_a^b f(x, y\, dx) \right\} dy$$

When one or both of the limits of integration is infinite, e.g.

$$g(y) = \int_a^{\infty} f(x, y)\, dx \qquad (3)$$

the series analogue is

$$g(y) = \sum_{i=1}^{\infty} f_i(y)$$

and the discussions of continuity, of differentiation and of integration under the integral sign (cf. summation sign) require the concept of uniformity of convergence.

Definition. The integral $\int_a^{\infty} f(x, y)\, dx\ [= g(y)]$ is said to converge uniformly in the range $y_1 < y < y_2$ if, for any ϵ, there exists a number M, independent of y, such that for all $N > M$, $\left| \int_N^{\infty} f(x, y)\, dx \right| < \epsilon$.

In the following theorems 4–6 we assume that the conditions of theorems 1–3 are fulfilled.

Theorem 4. Continuity property of infinite integrals.

If the integral $g(y) = \int_a^{\infty} f(x, y)\, dx$ converges uniformly in $y_1 < y < y_2$, then $g(y)$ is a continuous function of y in that range.

Theorem 5. Differentiation of an infinite integral.

If $g(y) = \int_a^{\infty} f(x, y)\, dx$, and if $\int_a^{\infty} \frac{\partial f}{\partial y}\, dx$ converges uniformly in the range $y_1 - \delta < y < y_2 + \delta$ $(\delta > 0)$, then

$$\frac{dg}{dy} = \int_a^{\infty} \frac{\partial f}{\partial y}\, dx$$

for $y_1 \leqslant y \leqslant y_2$.

Theorem 6. Integration of an infinite integral.

If $g(y) = \int_a^{\infty} f(x, y)\, dx$ converges uniformly in the range $y_1 - \delta < y < y_2 + \delta$ $(\delta > 0)$ then

$$\int_{y_1}^{y_2} g(y)\, dy \equiv \int_{y_1}^{y_2} \left\{ \int_a^{\infty} f(x, y)\, dx \right\} dy = \int_a^{\infty} \left\{ \int_{y_1}^{y_2} f(x, y)\, dy \right\} dx$$

In Theorems 2 and 5 on the differentiation of integrals the limits of integration a, b, $+\infty$ were assumed to be constants. When the limits are themselves functions of x we make use of two results from §8.6, viz.

$$\frac{\mathrm{d}}{\mathrm{d}x}\int_a^x \mathrm{f}(u)\,\mathrm{d}u=\mathrm{f}(x)$$

and

$$\frac{\mathrm{d}}{\mathrm{d}x}\int_x^b \mathrm{f}(u)\,\mathrm{d}u=-\mathrm{f}(x)$$

If a and b are variables, the corresponding results in the notation of the present paragraph are

$$\frac{\partial}{\partial b}\int_a^b \mathrm{f}(x,y)\,\mathrm{d}x=\mathrm{f}(b,y)$$

$$\frac{\partial}{\partial a}\int_a^b \mathrm{f}(x,y)\,\mathrm{d}x=-\mathrm{f}(a,y)$$

These results allow us to complete the discussion of the differentiation of an integral $\int_a^b \mathrm{f}(x,y)\,\mathrm{d}x$, which is a function of y, a, b; for we have shown how each of its partial derivatives may be found, and can therefore deduce its total derivative with respect to any variable. Thus, if

$$I(y,a,b)=\int_a^b \mathrm{f}(x,y)\,\mathrm{d}x$$

$$\frac{\mathrm{d}I}{\mathrm{d}z}=\frac{\partial I}{\partial y}\cdot\frac{\mathrm{d}y}{\mathrm{d}z}+\frac{\partial I}{\partial a}\frac{\mathrm{d}a}{\mathrm{d}z}+\frac{\partial I}{\partial b}\frac{\mathrm{d}b}{\mathrm{d}z}$$

$$=\frac{\mathrm{d}y}{\mathrm{d}z}\int_a^b \frac{\partial \mathrm{f}}{\partial y}\,\mathrm{d}x-\mathrm{f}(a,y)\frac{\mathrm{d}a}{\mathrm{d}z}+\mathrm{f}(b,y)\frac{\mathrm{d}b}{\mathrm{d}z}$$

Example 1

Discuss the validity of evaluating $\frac{\mathrm{d}}{\mathrm{d}y}\int_0^\infty \exp(-xy)\,\mathrm{d}x$ as $\int_0^\infty \frac{\partial}{\partial y}\exp(-xy)\,\mathrm{d}x$. We note that

$$\int_N^\infty \frac{\partial}{\partial y}\exp(-xy)\,\mathrm{d}x=\left[\frac{xy+1}{y^2}\exp(-xy)\right]_N^\infty=-\frac{Ny+1}{y^2}\exp(-Ny)$$

Now if $0<y_1<y$, $(Ny+1)\exp(-Ny)/y^2<(Ny+1)\exp(-Ny_1)/y_1^2$ and this $<\epsilon$ if $N>M$ where M is the positive number for which

$$(My+1)\exp(-My_1)=\epsilon y_1^2.$$

Hence $\int_0^\infty \frac{\partial}{\partial y} \exp(-xy)\,dx$ is uniformly convergent for all y in the range $0<y_1<y<y_2$ where y_1 and y_2 are any positive numbers. So for $y>y_1>0$,

$$\frac{d}{dy}\int_0^\infty \exp(-xy)\,dx = \int_0^\infty \frac{\partial}{\partial y}\exp(-xy)\,dx$$

This result may of course be proved directly in this case by actual evaluation of the integrals, each of which gives $-1/y^2$ $(y \neq 0)$.

Example 2

Show that

$$\int_0^1 \left\{ \int_1^\infty (ae^{-axy} - be^{-bxy})\,dy \right\} dx \neq \int_1^\infty \left\{ \int_0^1 ae^{-axy} - be^{-bxy})\,dx \right\} dy$$

Hint: the sign of $(e^{-ax} - e^{-bx})/x$ is the same for all $x>0$. It follows that $\int_0^\infty \frac{1}{x}(e^{-ax}-e^{-bx})\,dx \neq 0$.

Example 3

Show that $y = \int_0^\infty \exp(-xt - \frac{1}{3}t^3)\,dt$ satisfies the equation

$$d^2y/dx^2 = -xy + 1.$$

[Hint: first establish $d^2y/dx^2 = \int_0^\infty t^2 \exp(-xt - \frac{1}{3}t^3)\,dt$, and then note that $t^2 = \frac{d}{dt}(xt + \frac{1}{3}t^3) - x$.]

9.4 Multiple integrals

9.41. *Area and volume integrals*

Suppose that we are given a function of position in two dimensions, e.g. $f(x, y)$ [or $F(r, \theta)$], and suppose that it is required to 'integrate the function over a given area A' of the two-dimensional space. By this we mean that the area A is subdivided into small areas $\delta A_1, \delta A_2, \ldots, \delta A_i, \ldots, \delta A_n$, and within each area a point is chosen; let us call these points (x_1, y_1), $(x_2, y_2), \ldots, (x_i, y_i), \ldots$ respectively (or $(r_1, \theta_1), \ldots, (r_i, \theta_i), \ldots$). The sum $\sum_{i=1}^{n} f(x_i, y_i)\,\delta A_i$ (or $\sum F(r_i, \theta_i)\,\delta A_i$) is now formed, and similar sums for a sequence of other subdivisions with increasing values of n, the sequence being such that as $n \to \infty$ all the linear dimensions of each of the δA_i tend to zero.

Then, if $\lim_{n\to\infty} \sum f(x_i, y_i)\,\delta A_i$ exists and is independent (i) of the method of choosing the points x_i, y_i within the area elements, (ii) of the way in which the dimensions of the δA_i tend to zero, $\lim_{n\to\infty} \sum f(x_i, y_i)\, \delta A_i$ in all cases $= I$, say, then the area integral of f over the given region exists and is equal to I. We write $\int_A f\, dA = I$.

The area A under consideration need not be a plane area; the integral I can be found in just the same way if A is an area of curved surface provided that the value of the function to be integrated is known on this surface.

When dealing with vectors, a particular type of surface integral called the 'flux' of the vector across the surface is often important. If dA is an elementary area on the surface at (x, y, z), if the magnitude of the vector is $F(x, y, z)$ and if χ is the angle between the direction of the vector at (x, y, z) and the normal to the element dA, the flux of the vector across the surface S is

$$\int_S F(x, y, z) \cos \chi \, dA \tag{1}$$

which may also be written $\int_S F_n \, dA$ where F_n is equal to $F \cos \chi$ i.e. F_n is the normal component of the vector.

A volume integral is defined in a corresponding way, e.g. in terms of r, θ, ϕ.

$$\int_V F(r, \theta, \phi) d\tau = \lim_{n\to\infty} \sum_{i=1}^{n} F(r_i, \theta_i, \phi_i)\, \delta\tau_i$$

provided that the limit on the R.H.S. is independent of the shapes and order of summation of the $\delta\tau_i$ and of the choice of the points r_i, θ_i, ϕ_i within each small volume $\delta\tau_i$.

9.42. *Evaluation of area and volume integrals*

If an area integral is known to exist, either because the expression has a clear practical meaning (though it is possible to be misled into a false confidence in the matter of 'clear practical meanings') or on theoretical grounds (cf. 9.45, 9.46), it may be evaluated by two successive ordinary integrations. For, if two coordinates u, v are used to specify position in the area A, the area element δA can in general be expressed in the form $g(u, v)\, du\, dv$ where $g(u, v)$ is an appropriate function. Since we may group together all terms with the same value of v before taking limits we may write,

$$\int \mathrm{f}\,\mathrm{d}A = \lim_{m,\,n\to\infty} \sum_{i=1,\,j=1}^{i=m,\,j=n} \mathrm{f}(u_i, v_j)\,\mathrm{g}(u_i, v_j)\,\delta u_i\,\delta v_j$$

$$= \lim_{m,\,n\to\infty} \sum_{j=1}^{n} \left(\sum_{i=1}^{m} \mathrm{f}(u_i, v_j)\,\mathrm{g}(u_i, v_j)\,\delta u_i\right) \delta v_j$$

$$= \lim_{n\to\infty} \sum_{j=1}^{n} \left\{\int \mathrm{f}(u, v_j)\,\mathrm{g}(u, v_j)\,\mathrm{d}u\right\} \delta v_j \qquad (1)$$

$$= \int \left\{\int \mathrm{f}(u, v)\,\mathrm{g}(u, v)\,\mathrm{d}u\right\} \mathrm{d}v \qquad (2)$$

Similarly, since the area integral has been assumed to be uniquely defined, it may be evaluated

$$= \int \left\{\int \mathrm{f}(u, v)\mathrm{g}(u, v)\,\mathrm{d}v\right\} \mathrm{d}u \qquad (3)$$

and either form may be written as

$$\iint \mathrm{f}(u, v)\mathrm{g}(u, v)\,\mathrm{d}u\,\mathrm{d}v \qquad (4)$$

which is called a double integral. The forms (2) and (3) above, in which the order of integration is made clear by the notation, are called repeated integrals. As we shall see later, not all repeated integrals can be regarded as double integrals.

In evaluating the inner bracket { } in (2) above, v is treated as a constant, cf. (1) ; similarly in (3) the quantity u is treated as a constant in the first, inner integration. An alternative way of writing (2) is

$$\int \mathrm{d}v \int \mathrm{f}(u, v)\mathrm{g}(u, v)\,\mathrm{d}u$$

which has obvious advantages of neatness over (2), and yet is explicit about the intended order of integration in a way that (4) is not.

The insertion of the upper and lower limits of the integrals is best done from a diagram. In the inner integral of (2), the limits are the values of u at the ends of the strip with the chosen value of v, i.e. the limits are in general functions of v; while the limits of v are the values of v on the extreme strips, i.e. ordinary numbers (cf. example below).

In evaluating a volume integral we first write it in the form

$$\int \mathrm{d}u \int \mathrm{d}v \int \mathrm{f}(u, v, w)\, \mathrm{g}(u, v, w)\, \mathrm{d}w$$

in which the limits of the w integration are functions of u and v, the limits of the v integration are functions of u, and the limits of the u integration are numbers.

By definition of area and volume integrals, the choice of coordinate system or order of integration is immaterial. The two methods of evaluating the integral in the following example give an illustration of this property, as well as illustrating (especially Method 1) the mode of putting in the limits of integration.

9.43. *Example of surface integration*

Moment of inertia of a uniform circular disc about its axis.

We have to evaluate $\int \sigma r^2\, \mathrm{d}A$ where σ is the mass per unit area of the disc (σ = constant), and r is the distance of the area element $\mathrm{d}A$ from the centre.

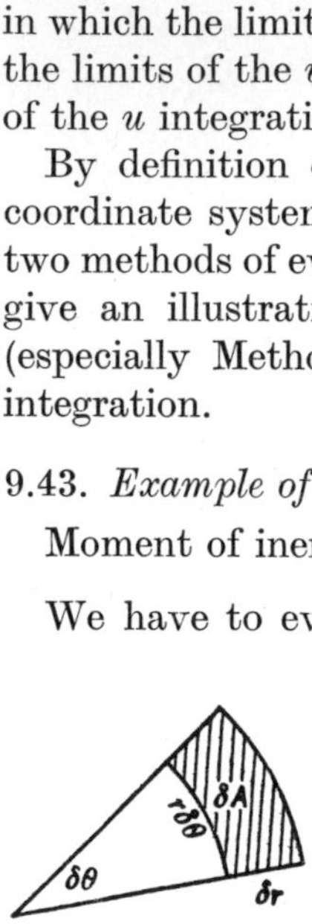

FIG. 9.1

In method 1 we subdivide the disc in rectangular elements $\delta A = \delta x\ \delta y$, in method 2 into polar elements $\delta A = r\ \delta\theta\ \delta r$ (Fig. 9.1).

Method 1 (see Fig. 9.2)

$$\int \sigma r^2\, \mathrm{d}A = \iint_{\text{circle}} \sigma\, (x^2 + y^2)\, \mathrm{d}x\, \mathrm{d}y$$

$$= \int_{y \text{ at } C}^{y \text{ at } B} \left\{ \int_{x \text{ at } P}^{x \text{ at } Q} \sigma\, (x^2 + y^2)\, \mathrm{d}x \right\} \mathrm{d}y$$

$$= \int_{y=-a}^{a} \mathrm{d}y \int_{x=-\sqrt{(a^2-y^2)}}^{\sqrt{(a^2-y^2)}} \sigma\, (x^2 + y^2)\, \mathrm{d}x$$

$$= \int_{y=-a}^{a} \sigma\ \{\tfrac{2}{3}(a^2 - y^2)^{3/2} + 2y^2\sqrt{(a^2 - y^2)}\}\, \mathrm{d}y$$

This can be integrated most easily by the substitution $y = a \sin \theta$, and gives

$$\int \sigma r^2 \, \mathrm{d}A = \tfrac{1}{2}\pi\sigma a^4$$

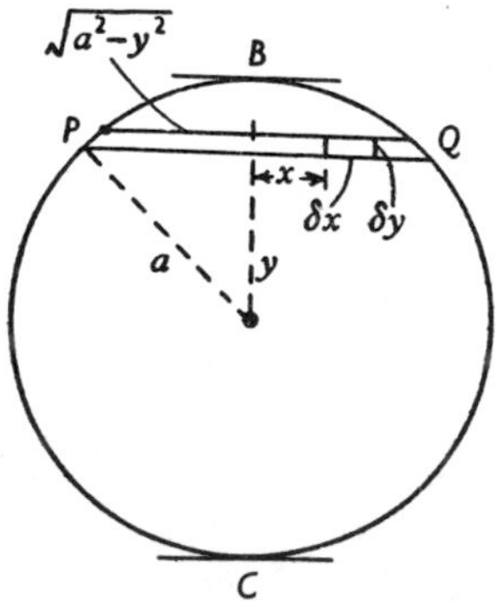

FIG. 9.2

Method 2

With polar coordinates the circle itself corresponds to a line on which one variable, r, is held constant. This results in much simpler inner limits, and consequently a simple second integration.

$$\int \sigma r^2 \, \mathrm{d}A = \iint \sigma r^2 \, . \, r \, \mathrm{d}\theta \, \mathrm{d}r$$

The integrations in r and θ separate, and give

$$\int \sigma r^2 \, \mathrm{d}A = \int_{r=0}^{a} \sigma r^3 \, \mathrm{d}r \int_{\theta=0}^{2\pi} \mathrm{d}\theta$$

$$= \tfrac{1}{4}\sigma a^4 \, . \, 2\pi = \tfrac{1}{2}\pi\sigma a^4$$

as before.

9.44. *Separable integrals*

If in an area integral $\iint \mathrm{f}(u, v) \, \mathrm{d}u \, \mathrm{d}v$ the integrand $\mathrm{f}(u, v)$ is the product of a function of u and a function of v, say

$$\mathrm{f}(u, v) = \mathrm{f}_1(u) \, \mathrm{f}_2(v)$$

and if further the limits of integration for u are independent of v, and those for v are independent of u, that is the integration is over a rectangle in the (u, v) plane, with sides parallel to the axes, then

$$\int f(u, v)\, du = f_2(v) \int f_1(u)\, du$$

since v is constant in the integration over u. Also $\int f_1(u)\, du$ is independent of v since the integrand and the limits of integration are independent of v. Hence the integration over v gives in this case

$$\int dv \left\{ \int f(u, v)\, du \right\} = \left[\int f_1(u)\, du \right] \left[\int f_2(v)\, dv \right] \tag{1}$$

and the double integral is reduced to the product of two single integrals, as in the example of the last paragraph, Method 2. Such a double integral is said to be *separable* in u and v. It must be remembered that this property depends not only on the form of the integrand but also on the domain of integration.

9.45. *Expressions for area and volume elements in terms of cylindrical polar and spherical polar coordinates*

Three coordinate systems, viz. rectangular cartesian, cylindrical polar (r, θ, z) and spherical polar (r, θ, ϕ) have pride of place in the solution of physical problems. The r of cylindrical polars is a different quantity from the r of spherical polars, but confusion will not result since the two systems are *alternatives* and are (effectively) never both used in the same problem. Similarly the two quantities θ are different. Fig. 9.3 shows the relation between cylindrical polar coordinates and an associated rectangular cartesian system, namely

$$r = \sqrt{(x^2 + y^2)}$$

$$\tan \theta = y/x$$

$$z = z$$

$$(\text{or } x = r \cos \theta,\ y = r \sin \theta,\ z = z)$$

Fig. 9.4 shows spherical polar coordinates r, θ, ϕ in relation to an associated rectangular cartesian system.

We now have

$$r = \sqrt{(x^2 + y^2 + z^2)}$$
$$\tan \theta = \sqrt{(x^2 + y^2)}/z$$
$$\tan \phi = y/x$$

(or $x = r \sin \theta \cos \phi$, $y = r \sin \theta \sin \phi$, $z = r \cos \theta$.)

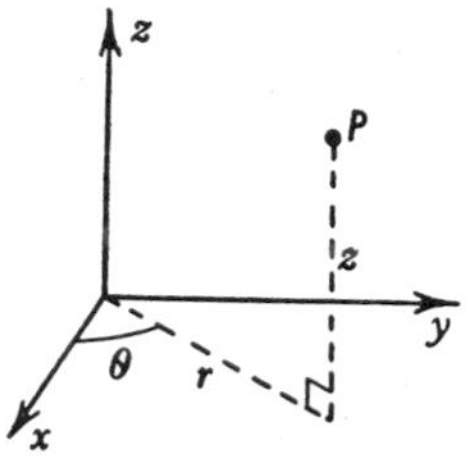

FIG. 9.3

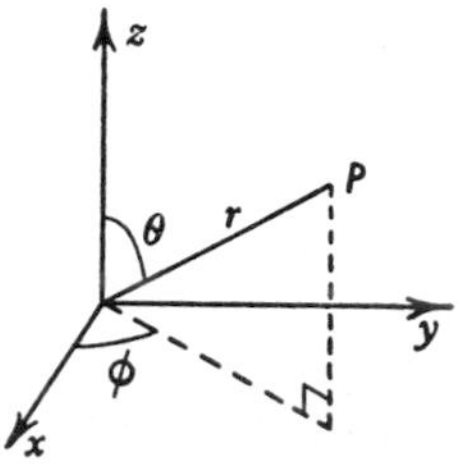

FIG. 9.4

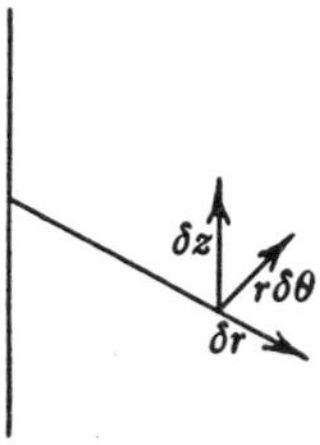

FIG. 9.5

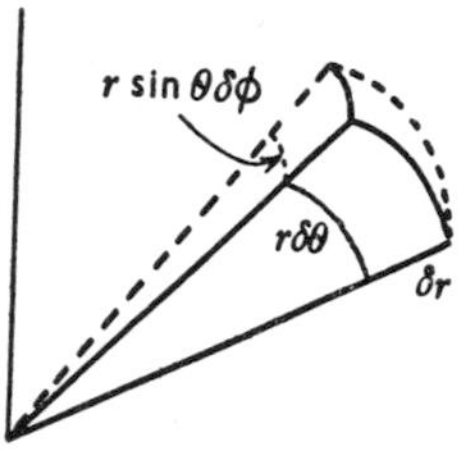

FIG. 9.6

In cylindrical polars the length elements associated with increments δr, $\delta\theta$, δz are respectively (see Fig. 9.5) δr, $r\,\delta\theta$, δz. A volume can thus be written

$$\delta V = r\,\delta r\,\delta\theta\,\delta z$$

while $r\,\delta\theta\,\delta r$, $r\,\delta\theta\,\delta z$ and $\delta r \delta z$ are three mutually perpendicular area elements.

In spherical polars Fig. 9.6 the length elements associated with increments δr, $\delta\theta$, $\delta\phi$ are, respectively δr, $r\,\delta\theta$ and $r \sin\theta\,\delta\phi$, this last quantity being otherwise expressible as $\sqrt{(x^2 + y^2)}\,\delta\phi$ in terms of associated cartesian coordinates x, y. Hence

$$\delta V = r^2 \sin\theta\,\delta r\,\delta\theta\,\delta\phi$$

and the three area elements perpendicular to the coordinate directions are $r^2 \sin\theta\,\delta\theta\,\delta\phi$, $r \sin\theta\,\delta r\,\delta\phi$ and $r\,\delta\theta\,\delta r$ respectively.

9.46. *Repeated integrals and convergence difficulties*

The reader may by now cherish the illusion that almost any repeated integral $\int dx \int f(x, y)\, dy$ can be equally well expressed as $\int dy \int f(x, y)\, dx$ or as $\int f(x, y)\, dA$, with analogous equivalences for triple integrals. We shall show by means of an example that this is not the case, even when the example apparently describes a physically meaningful situation.

Example

Consider the magnetic field at the origin due to a uniformly magnetised cylinder of dipole moment I per unit volume parallel to its axis, the cylinder being situated with its centre at the origin.

Let us take the axis of the cylinder as z-axis. From considerations of symmetry it can be seen that the resultant field at the origin must be in the z-direction. Using cylindrical polar coordinates a typical volume element is $r\, dr\, d\theta\, dz$, and the magnetic moment of this element is $Ir\, dr\, d\theta\, dz$. The z component of the magnetic field at the origin due to a magnetic dipole M, with its axis in the z-direction, at a point whose cylindrical polar coordinates are (r, z), is $M(2z^2 - r^2)/(z^2 + r^2)^{5/2}$. Hence the expression for the field at the origin due to the volume considered is

$$H_z = \int_{z=-b}^{b} \int_{\theta=0}^{2\pi} \int_{r=0}^{a} \frac{I(2z^2 - r^2)}{(z^2 + r^2)^{5/2}}\, r\, dr\, d\theta\, dz$$

Since θ occurs only in the factor $d\theta$ we may integrate this at once, and obtain

$$H_z = 2\pi I \int_{z=-b}^{b} \int_{r=0}^{a} \frac{(2z^2 - r^2)}{(z^2 + r^2)^{5/2}}\, r\, dr\, dz \qquad (1)$$

Method 1

Let us first integrate (1) by performing the r-integration before the z-integration. The r-integration gives

$$\int_{r=0}^{a} \frac{2z^2 - r^2}{(z^2 + r^2)^{5/2}}\, r\, dr = \left[\frac{r^2}{(z^2 + r^2)^{3/2}}\right]_{r=0}^{a} = \frac{a^2}{(z^2 + a^2)^{3/2}} \qquad \text{if } z \neq 0$$

When $z=0$ there is a singularity at the lower limit $r=0$, but, by the standard treatment of improper integrals, H_z can be evaluated,

$$H_z = 2\pi I a^2 \left\{ \int_{-b}^{0} (z^2+a^2)^{-3/2}\,\mathrm{d}z + \int_{0}^{b} (z^2+a^2)^{-3/2}\,\mathrm{d}z \right\}$$

$$= 2\pi I \left[z/(z^2+a^2)^{\frac{1}{2}} \right]_{-b}^{b}$$

$$= 4\pi I b/(a^2+b^2)^{\frac{1}{2}} \tag{2}$$

Method 2

Let us now carry out the integration of (1) by performing the z-integration first. This gives

$$\int_{z=-b}^{b} \frac{2z^2-r^2}{(z^2+r^2)^{5/2}}\, r\,\mathrm{d}z = -\left[\frac{rz}{(z^2+r^2)^{3/2}} \right]_{z=-b}^{b}$$

$$= -\frac{2br}{(r^2+b^2)^{3/2}} \quad \text{if } r \neq 0 \tag{3}$$

If $r=0$, the integrand has a singularity at $z=0$, but the result (3) still applies if the integral is given its 'principal value' defined by

$$\lim_{\epsilon \to 0} \left[\int_{z=-b}^{-\epsilon} + \int_{z=\epsilon}^{b} \right] 2z^{-3}\,\mathrm{d}z$$

Integration with respect to r then gives

$$H_z = 2\pi I \int_{r=0}^{a} \frac{-2br}{(r^2+b^2)^{3/2}}\,\mathrm{d}r = 4\pi I b \left[\frac{1}{(r^2+b^2)^{1/2}} \right]_{r=0}^{a}$$

$$= 4\pi I \left[\frac{b}{(a^2+b^2)^{1/2}} - 1 \right] \tag{4}$$

The results (2) and (4) do not agree ; the difference between them is in fact $4\pi I$. From this it appears that the double integral (1), with order of integration unspecified does not unambiguously define any quantity ; different values are obtained with different methods of integration. It is also clear that the difference arises from the singularity in the integrand of (1) at the origin, and the answer depends on the shape of the elements by which the singularity is approached in the limiting processes.

In the physical context to which formula (1) refers, both the results (2) and (4) give physically significant quantities ;

(4) gives the 'magnetic field' and (2) the 'magnetic induction' at a point of a magnetised substance. It is clearly of practical importance to know whether an expression in the form of a multiple integral does or does not define a unique quantity, and whether the order of integration of a repeated integral may be inverted. These questions are considered in the next section.

9.47. *Convergence properties of repeated integrals*

It can be shown that if $f(x, y)$ is a continuous function of (x, y) in a finite region A, then $\int_A f\, dA$ is uniquely defined, and can consequently be evaluated either as $\int dx \left(\int f\, dy\right)$ or as $\int dy \left(\int f\, dx\right)$ or in a number of other ways using other variables. This result will be referred to as 'theorem (1)'.

This theorem (1) covers one of the three important types of area integral which occur in practical work. The second type is that in which $f(x, y)$ becomes infinite within the region of integration; the integral considered in 9.46 is of this kind. The third type is that in which the function $f(x, y)$ is continuous but the region of integration is infinite, e.g. the total charge induced on an infinite conducting surface A by a point charge outside it could be expressed in the form $\int \sigma\, dA$. Integrals of these second and third types are closely analogous to the improper and infinite integrals we have already discussed for the case of a single variable, and their rigorous definition follows the same lines. What we are concerned with here is whether a formal expression does or does not define a meaningful quantity: and it will be most useful to give, not further theorems, but illustrations of the mode of procedure which is applicable to such cases.

Example 1

Convergence of the improper integral $\int_\tau (f/r^n)\, d\tau$, where f is a continuous function of position and the region of integration τ is a finite volume which includes the origin $r=0$ (r is the r of spherical polar coordinates).

Let S denote the surface bounding τ, S_2 be any surface inside S and surrounding the origin O, and τ_2 the volume between S and S_2. Then $\int_{\tau_2} (\mathrm{f}/r^n)\, d\tau$ has a unique value (by theorem (1)). If $\lim_{S_2 \to 0} \int_{\tau_2} (\mathrm{f}/r^n)\, d\tau$ tends to a unique limit I then the improper integral $\int_{\tau} (\mathrm{f}/r^n)\, d\tau$ exists and has this unique value; otherwise the improper integral does not define a unique quantity. The condition for the existence of the limit I may be alternatively formulated as follows (cf. the analogous condition for the convergence of a series 2.63): for any chosen $\epsilon > 0$ there must exist a surface S_1 such that for all surfaces S_2 inside S_1 and surrounding O

$$\left| \int_{\tau_{12}} (\mathrm{f}/r^n)\, d\tau \right| < \epsilon$$

where τ_{12} is the volume between S_1 and S_2.

Now let r_1 be the greatest value of r on S_1, and let r_2 be the least value of r on S_2 and let G be the greatest value of $|\mathrm{f}|$ within the sphere of radius r_1. Then

$$\left| \int_{\tau_{12}} (\mathrm{f}/r^n)\, d\tau \right| \leqslant G \int_{r=r_2}^{r=r_1} (1/r^n)\, d\tau$$

$$= G \int_{\phi=0}^{2\pi} \int_{\theta=0}^{\pi} \int_{r=r_2}^{r_1} \frac{r^2 \sin\theta\, dr\, d\theta\, d\phi}{r^n}$$

since the conditions of Theorem 1 are satisfied in the region of integration

$$= \begin{cases} 4\pi G \left[\dfrac{r^{3-n}}{(3-n)} \right]_{r_2}^{r_1} & n < 3 \\ 4\pi G \Big[\log r \Big]_{r_2}^{r_1} & n = 3 \\ 4\pi G \left[\dfrac{1}{-(n-3)\, r^{n-3}} \right]_{r_2}^{r_1} & n > 3 \end{cases}$$

Of these three expressions only the first can be made less than ϵ, for all r_2, by a suitable choice of r_1, viz. r_1 such that

$$\frac{4\pi G\, r_1^{\,3-n}}{3-n} < \epsilon \quad \text{i.e.} \quad r_1 < \left\{ \frac{\epsilon(3-n)}{4\pi G} \right\}^{1/(3-n)}$$

in the other two cases for every r_1, r_2 can be chosen so that the expression becomes arbitrarily large.

In general, then, $\int_{\tau} (\mathrm{f}/r^n)\, d\tau$ converges to a unique limit if $n < 3$. A slight modification of the foregoing work, replacing the greatest by the least value of $|\mathrm{f}|$, establishes that $\int_\tau (\mathrm{f}/r^n)\,\mathrm{d}\tau$ is actually divergent for $n \geqslant 3$ if f is continuous and non-zero at the origin.

Example 2

Convergence of the infinite integral $\int e^{-r^2}\,\mathrm{d}A$ where $r^2 = x^2 + y^2$, the region of integration being the whole of the (x, y) plane.

Let S_1 be the boundary of any finite area A_1 in the plane ; then the infinite integral exists if $\lim\limits_{S_1 \to \infty} \int e^{-r^2}\,\mathrm{d}A$ exists and is independent of the way in which $S_1 \to \infty$. As in Example 1 we replace this condition by an equivalent one : for convergence we must show that for any $\epsilon > 0$ there exists a boundary S_1 such that for all boundaries S_2 outside S_1

$$\left| \int_{A_{12}} e^{-r^2}\,\mathrm{d}A \right| < \epsilon$$

where A_{12} is the region between S_1 and S_2.

Let r_1 be the least value of r on S_1, and r_2 the greatest value of r on S_2. Then

$$\left| \int_{A_{12}} e^{-r^2}\,\mathrm{d}A \right| \leqslant \int_{\theta=0}^{2\pi} \int_{r=r_1}^{r_2} e^{-r^2}\, r\,\mathrm{d}r\,\mathrm{d}\theta$$

$$= \pi \Big[-e^{-r^2} \Big]_{r_1}^{r_2} = \pi \Big[e^{-r_1^2} - e^{-r_2^2} \Big]$$

$$< \epsilon$$

for all S_2 provided that $r_1^2 > -\log_e (\epsilon/\pi)$.

Hence $\int_{x,\,y\text{ plane}} e^{-r^2}\,\mathrm{d}A$ is uniquely defined and can be evaluated either as $\int_0^\infty \int_0^\infty e^{-(x^2+y^2)}\,\mathrm{d}x\,\mathrm{d}y$ or as $\int_0^\infty \int_0^{2\pi} e^{-r^2}\, r\,\mathrm{d}\theta\,\mathrm{d}r$ (or otherwise)

Corollary. $\int_{-\infty}^{\infty} e^{-x^2}\,\mathrm{d}x = \sqrt{\pi}$

We have just shown that

$$\int_{y=-\infty}^{\infty} \int_{x=-\infty}^{\infty} e^{-(x^2+y^2)}\,\mathrm{d}x\,\mathrm{d}y = \int_{r=0}^{\infty} \int_{\theta=0}^{2\pi} e^{-r^2}\, r\,\mathrm{d}\theta\,\mathrm{d}r$$

i.e.
$$\int_{y=-\infty}^{\infty} \mathrm{d}y \int_{x=-\infty}^{\infty} e^{-x^2} \,.\, e^{-y^2}\,\mathrm{d}x = \int_{r=0}^{\infty} 2\pi e^{-r^2}\, r\,\mathrm{d}r$$

i.e. $$\int_{y=-\infty}^{\infty} e^{-y^2}\,dy\left(\int_{-\infty}^{\infty} e^{-x^2}\,dx\right)=\pi\left[-e^{-r^2}\right]_0^{\infty}$$

or $$\left\{\int_{-\infty}^{\infty} e^{-x^2}\,dx\right\}^2=\pi \quad \text{since} \int_a^b f(y)\,dy \equiv \int_a^b f(x)\,dx$$

whence $$\int_{-\infty}^{\infty} e^{-x^2}\,dx=\sqrt{\pi}$$

9.48. *Change of variable in multiple integrals : Jacobians*

The displacement in the x, y plane corresponding to an increment δu in a variable u has components $\frac{\partial x}{\partial u}\,\delta u$, $\frac{\partial y}{\partial u}\,\delta u$ in the x, y directions respectively. Thus if u, v is a pair of variables which can be used instead of x, y to specify position in the x, y plane, the displacements due to increments δu, δv are specified by $\left(\frac{\partial x}{\partial u}\,\delta u, \frac{\partial y}{\partial u}\,\delta u\right)$ and $\left(\frac{\partial x}{\partial v}\,\delta v, \frac{\partial y}{\partial v}\,\delta v\right)$ respectively.

The area in the x, y plane (Fig. 9.7) corresponding to increments δu, δv, is therefore

$$\delta A=\left\{\frac{\partial x}{\partial u}\cdot\frac{\partial y}{\partial v}-\frac{\partial y}{\partial u}\cdot\frac{\partial x}{\partial v}\right\}\delta u\,\delta v \qquad (1)$$

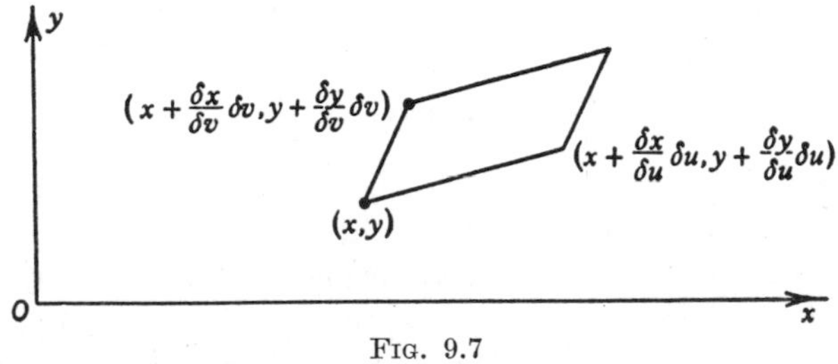

FIG. 9.7

(compare equation (2) of 17.42, and the comment on representation of areas).

Note : this expression for δA is only positive if the rotation from the δu-direction $\left(\frac{\partial x}{\partial u}\,\delta u, \frac{\partial y}{\partial u}\,\delta u\right)$ into the δv-direction is in the same sense as the rotation from the x into the y-axis. This association of a sign with the sense is usually an advantage in physical applications, but should it be undesirable we substitute the rule

$$\delta A=\left|\frac{\partial x}{\partial u}\frac{\partial y}{\partial v}-\frac{\partial y}{\partial u}\frac{\partial x}{\partial v}\right|\delta u\,\delta v$$

Using (1) we get the theorem.

Theorem. If $x=\phi(u, v)$ and $y=\psi(u, v)$ where, for constant v, ϕ and ψ are single-valued differentiable functions of u, and, for constant u, ϕ and ψ are single-valued differentiable functions of v, and if $f(x, y)=F(u, v)$, then

$$\iint f(x, y)\, dx\, dy=\iint F(u, v)\left\{\frac{\partial x}{\partial u}\frac{\partial y}{\partial v}-\frac{\partial y}{\partial u}\frac{\partial x}{\partial v}\right\} du\, dv$$

the limits of integration being chosen to correspond to the same boundaries in the x, y plane in the two cases.

The function $J(u, v)=\left\{\frac{\partial x}{\partial u}\frac{\partial y}{\partial v}-\frac{\partial y}{\partial u}\frac{\partial x}{\partial v}\right\}$ is called the Jacobian of the transformation and is customarily denoted by the symbol $\frac{\partial(x, y)}{\partial(u, v)}$: we note that its value is

$$\begin{vmatrix} \frac{\partial x}{\partial u} & \frac{\partial x}{\partial v} \\ \frac{\partial y}{\partial u} & \frac{\partial y}{\partial v} \end{vmatrix}$$

using the determinant notation (chap 18).

A change of variables in a triple integral can be carried out in a similar way provided that the old coordinates are expressible as single-valued differentiable functions of the new. Thus

$$\iiint f(x, y, z)\, dx\, dy\, dz=\iiint F(u, v, w)\frac{\partial(x, y, z)}{\partial(u, v, w)}\, du\, dv\, dw$$

where
$$\frac{\partial(x, y, z)}{\partial(u, v, w)}=\begin{vmatrix} \frac{\partial x}{\partial u} & \frac{\partial x}{\partial v} & \frac{\partial x}{\partial w} \\ \frac{\partial y}{\partial u} & \frac{\partial y}{\partial v} & \frac{\partial y}{\partial w} \\ \frac{\partial z}{\partial u} & \frac{\partial z}{\partial v} & \frac{\partial z}{\partial w} \end{vmatrix}$$

and similarly for any number of variables.

Example 1

Given that $x=r\cos\theta$, $y=r\sin\theta$, find the expression for an area element in polar coordinates (r, θ).

$$\delta A=\frac{\partial(x, y)}{\partial(r, \theta)}\,\delta r\,\delta\theta=\left(\frac{\partial x}{\partial r}\frac{\partial y}{\partial \theta}-\frac{\partial y}{\partial r}\frac{\partial x}{\partial \theta}\right)\delta r\,\delta\theta$$

$$=[\cos\theta\,(r\cos\theta)-\sin\theta\,(-r\sin\theta)]\,\delta r\,\delta\theta$$

$$=r\delta r\delta\theta$$

2. Find, by the same method, the expression for a volume element in spherical polar coordinates r, θ, ϕ. Verify by a triple integration in terms of these coordinates that the volume of a sphere of radius a is $\frac{4}{3}\pi a^3$.

9.49. *Jacobians and the independence of functions*

If $\mathrm{u}(x, y, z)$, $\mathrm{v}(x, y, z)$, and $\mathrm{w}(x, y, z)$ are three functions of (x, y, z), they are said to be ‘not independent’ if the value of one of them, say $\mathrm{w}(x, y, z)$, is deducible from the values of the other two without reference to the values of (x, y, z); otherwise they are said to be ‘independent’. For example, the functions

$$\mathrm{u}(x, y, z)=x+y+z\,;\quad \mathrm{v}(x, y, z)=x^2+y^2+z^2\,;$$

$$\mathrm{w}(x, y, z)=xy+yz+zx-1 \qquad (1)$$

are not independent since there is an identical relation

$$u^2-v-2w-2=0 \qquad (2)$$

between them for all values of x, y, z; and hence if values of u and v are specified the value of w is determined, whatever the values of (x, y, z) which give those values of u and v. But the functions

$$\mathrm{u}(x, y, z)=x+y+z\,;\quad \mathrm{v}(x, y, z)=x^2+2y^2+z^2$$

$$\mathrm{w}(x, y, z)=xy+yz+zx-1 \qquad (3)$$

are independent because there is no such identical relation between them.

If three functions are given, it may not be obvious whether they are related, that is, if there exists some identical relation $\phi(u, v, w)=0$ between them, for all (x, y, z). We shall now see that this question can be answered by examining their Jacobian.

First suppose that the functions u, v and w are related by some relation $\phi(u, v, w)=0$ for all (x, y, z). Since ϕ is independent of x, $(\partial\phi/\partial x)_{y,z}=0$, and similarly

$$(\partial\phi/\partial y)_{z,x}=(\partial\phi/\partial z)_{x,y}=0,$$

whence

$$\left.\begin{aligned}\frac{\partial\phi}{\partial u}\frac{\partial u}{\partial x}+\frac{\partial\phi}{\partial v}\frac{\partial v}{\partial x}+\frac{\partial\phi}{\partial w}\frac{\partial w}{\partial x}=0\\ \frac{\partial\phi}{\partial u}\frac{\partial u}{\partial y}+\frac{\partial\phi}{\partial v}\frac{\partial v}{\partial y}+\frac{\partial\phi}{\partial w}\frac{\partial w}{\partial y}=0\\ \frac{\partial\phi}{\partial u}\frac{\partial u}{\partial z}+\frac{\partial\phi}{\partial v}\frac{\partial v}{\partial z}+\frac{\partial\phi}{\partial w}\frac{\partial w}{\partial z}=0\end{aligned}\right\} \tag{4}$$

These equations are consistent only if

$$\begin{vmatrix}\dfrac{\partial u}{\partial x} & \dfrac{\partial v}{\partial x} & \dfrac{\partial w}{\partial x}\\ \dfrac{\partial u}{\partial y} & \dfrac{\partial v}{\partial y} & \dfrac{\partial w}{\partial y}\\ \dfrac{\partial u}{\partial z} & \dfrac{\partial v}{\partial z} & \dfrac{\partial w}{\partial z}\end{vmatrix}=0$$

or, in the contracted notation introduced in 9.48, if

$$\frac{\partial(u, v, w)}{\partial(x, y, z)}=0 \tag{5}$$

Hence if the Jacobian does not vanish there can be no relation $\phi(u, v, w)=0$ between the functions u, v, w; that is, these functions of (x, y, z) are independent.

On the other hand, the volume in the (u, v, w) space corresponding to increments $\delta x, \delta y, \delta z$ is $\dfrac{\partial(u, v, w)}{\partial(x, y, z)}\,\delta x\,\delta y\,\delta z$, and if the relation (5) is satisfied, this is zero; that is the region generated in (u, v, w) space by variations in (x, y, z) is a surface, $\phi(u, v, w)=0$ say; that is for all (x, y, z) there is a definite relationship between (u, v, w). Thus the functions (u, v, w) are dependent or independent according as the Jacobian $\partial(u, v, w)/\partial(x, y, z)$ does or does not vanish.

Similar results apply to two functions (u, v) of two independent variables (x, y), and more generally for n functions of n variables; the functions are dependent or independent according as the corresponding Jacobian does or does not vanish.

Example

To determine whether the functions $u = 2x + y$; $v = 4x(x + y + 1) + y(y + 2) + 3$ are independent we evaluate

$$\frac{\partial(u, v)}{\partial(x, y)} = \begin{vmatrix} \dfrac{\partial u}{\partial x} & \dfrac{\partial v}{\partial x} \\ \dfrac{\partial u}{\partial y} & \dfrac{\partial v}{\partial y} \end{vmatrix} = \begin{vmatrix} 2 & 8x + 4y + 4 \\ 1 & 4x + 2y + 2 \end{vmatrix} = 0$$

u and v are thus dependent functions. In fact $v = u^2 + 2u + 3$.

CHAPTER TEN

DIFFERENTIAL EQUATIONS: GENERAL REMARKS

10.1. Occurrence of differential equations

One of the most important applications of the ideas and techniques of differentiation and integration is to the derivation and solution of differential equations.

A large part of physics, and also of engineering, is concerned with continuous distributions, either in space or time or both. The laws of physics are usually statements about the rates of variation of quantities in such distributions, and, when formulated mathematically, lead most naturally to differential equations. The consequences of the physical laws in any particular set of circumstances are then worked out by solving the appropriate differential equation. A very large part of mathematical physics is therefore concerned first with the formulation and then with the solution of differential equations.

There are many standard techniques by which the solution of differential equations may be attempted : many of these will be mentioned in ensuing chapters. Guidance in the matter of formulating the equations is less easy to give, but a lead is often obtained by asking oneself questions like the following : What entities are present? How is their presence felt? What physical laws are known to relate them? What maintains the status quo in any region or, more generally, how are losses or gains accounted for? The following examples from different realms of applied science illustrate the process of formulating differential equations.

10.11. *Variation of pressure with height in the atmosphere*

The ' entity ' we are concerned with is the air which makes itself felt by its pressure or weight. The status quo is maintained if the weight of any volume is balanced by the difference between the upward and downward forces on it. The mathematical formulation therefore proceeds as follows :

Consider the equilibrium of the air in a vertical cylinder of cross section A and height dz (Fig. 10.1). The weight of this air, which is (A dz) ρg, is balanced by the forces due to the pressures p and $p+\mathrm{d}p$ on its ends, so that

$$(p+\mathrm{d}p)A - pA + \rho g A\,\mathrm{d}z = 0$$

where ρ is the density and g is the acceleration due to gravity. Hence

$$\mathrm{d}p/\mathrm{d}z = -g\rho \qquad (1)$$

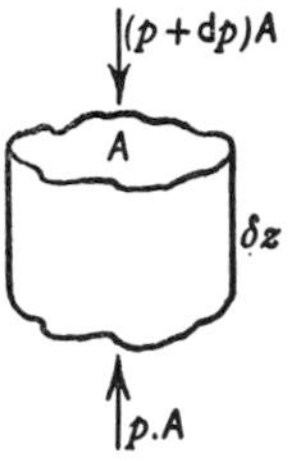

FIG. 10.1

If ρ is known as a function of height $\rho=\rho(z)$ say, this is the desired equation. If $\rho(z)$ is not known, but the temperature $T(z)$ at height z is a known function of z, we can eliminate ρ from (1) by using the physical law

$$p = R\rho T(z)$$

where R is a constant. We then find

$$\frac{\mathrm{d}p}{\mathrm{d}z} = -gp/RT(z) \qquad (2)$$

If the variation of temperature with height is given, this is a differential equation for the variation of pressure with height.

10.12. *The series resonant circuit*

Let a charge be applied to the plates of a condenser of capacitance C in series with a coil of inductance L and resistance R (Fig. 10.2). On completing the circuit a current will flow and the charge on the condenser will change with time; we require the differential equation which it satisfies.

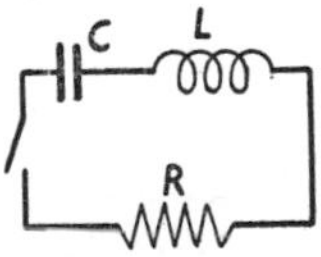

FIG. 10.2

The entities concerned are the electric charge and the hardware of the circuit (viz. condenser, inductance and resistance). Charge makes itself felt by the field it produces, and this is most conveniently expressed, in problems of electric circuits, in terms of e.m.f. The motion of the charge is governed by the physical law: the total back e.m.f. in the circuit is zero (compare (v)a of 6.51), and the back e.m.f.'s produced by condenser, resistance and inductance are respectively

$$q/C\;;\quad Ri\;;\quad L\,\mathrm{d}i/\mathrm{d}t$$

where the condenser plates have charges $\pm q$, and $i=\mathrm{d}q/\mathrm{d}t$ = rate of transport of charge, i.e. is the magnitude of the electric current. Using these laws we obtain the equation

$$L\frac{\mathrm{d}^2q}{\mathrm{d}t^2} + R\frac{\mathrm{d}q}{\mathrm{d}t} + \frac{1}{C}q = 0 \qquad (1)$$

for the time variation of q. The potential V across the condenser, $V = q/C$, will satisfy the same equation :

$$L\frac{\mathrm{d}^2V}{\mathrm{d}t^2} + R\frac{\mathrm{d}V}{\mathrm{d}t} + \frac{1}{C}V = 0 \qquad (2)$$

10.13. *Forced oscillations*

An extension of the previous problem is the determination of the current in a series resonant circuit connected to a generator supplying an e.m.f. varying with time (Fig. 10.3), thus

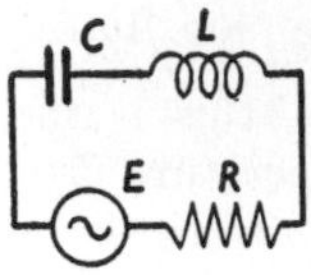

FIG. 10.3

$$E = \mathrm{f}(t)$$

We now obtain the following differential equation for V

$$L\frac{\mathrm{d}^2V}{\mathrm{d}t^2} + R\frac{\mathrm{d}V}{\mathrm{d}t} + \frac{1}{C}V = \frac{1}{C}\mathrm{f}(t) \qquad (1)$$

10.14. *Production of variable concentrations by mixing*

As it is difficult to view over-familiar problems with the same detachment as new ones, our final example is of a less hackneyed type. It also illustrates the way in which coupled equations arise.

Suppose we have a cascade of vessels the outlet of each constituting the inlet of the next (Fig. 10.4). Suppose that all inlet and outlet rates are steady, those for the nth vessel being R_n and R_{n+1} respectively, and that the input to the first vessel is a solution whose concentration differs from that of the initial contents of at least one of the vessels in the cascade. The problem is to formulate the equations governing the subsequent variations of concentration in all the vessels. Efficient mixing is assumed.

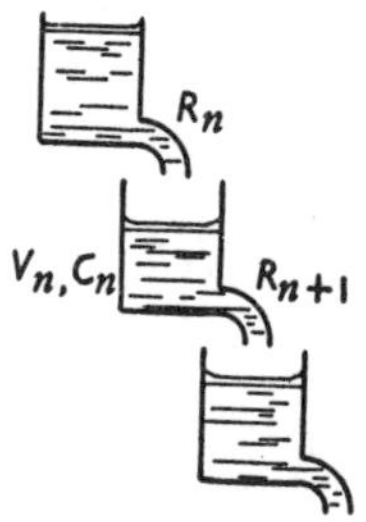

FIG. 10.4

The entities involved are the amounts of solvent and solute. Let the concentrations of solute in the first, second, third etc. vessels be C_1, C_2, C_3 ... and the total volumes of solvent plus solute be V_1, V_2, V_3. ... Gains and losses are accounted for in the following way : the rate of increase of total volume in any vessel is equal to the difference between inlet and outlet rates ; and the rate of increase of amount of solute is equal to the difference between inlet and outlet rates for the solute. Thus

$$\mathrm{d}V_n/\mathrm{d}t = R_n - R_{n+1}$$

$$\mathrm{d}(V_nC_n)/\mathrm{d}t = R_nC_{n-1} - R_{n+1}C_n$$

If there are N vessels we get $2N$ equations for the $2N$ unknowns $V_1 \ldots V_N$ and $C_1 \ldots C_N$, the input concentration C_0 into the first vessel being supposed known.

10.2. Partial differential equations

In each of the examples discussed above, there has been one independent variable, either x or t. For example in equation (1) of 10.12 although three variables t, q, $i = \mathrm{d}q/\mathrm{d}t$ appear, if we consider the actual behaviour of the current in the circuit, we see that for any particular value of t the values of the other two are also determined. Thus q and i cannot vary independently of t; if the value of t is specified, then q and i are fixed. Equations containing one independent variable only, such as t in this example, are called ordinary differential equations and are characterised by the presence of total derivatives.

A problem of much greater complexity arises when the variation of a function in two or more dimensions is considered; for example the bending of a thin plate, or the variation of the electrostatic potential in a region of space. The equation obtained in the latter case is the so-called Laplace-Poisson equation and is of fundamental importance as it is encountered in all parts of mathematical physics. We shall consider its derivation as an example of the way partial differential equations are obtained, and especially of the details of argument which ensure that, when several independent small quantities are involved, no source of significant variation is overlooked by too easy-going an attitude to the order of magnitude of small quantities.

The entities in which we are interested, namely the electrostatic potential and electric charge, are each related to electric field, the former by the definition of potential, the latter by a known physical law, viz. Gauss's theorem. The required equation will be obtained by (1) formulating the known relationships in mathematical terms and (2) eliminating the components of electric field.

The difference in electrostatic potential V between two points is minus the work done by the field (components E_x E_y E_z) on unit charge moving from one point to the other, thus

$$-\int_{\mathsf{x}=\alpha}^{x} E_{\mathsf{x}}\, \mathrm{d}\mathsf{x} = V(x, y, z) - V(\alpha, y, z) \tag{1}$$

where we use x to distinguish the variable of integration from the upper limit, x (compare 5.9), α is a constant reference coordinate and E_{x} is written for $E_x(\mathsf{x}, y, z)$. By 8.6 we know that

$$E_x = \frac{\partial}{\partial x} \int_\alpha^x E_{\mathsf{x}}\, \mathrm{d}\mathsf{x}$$

so, using (1) we find $E_x = -\partial V/\partial x$, and similarly $E_y = -\partial V/\partial y$, $E_z = -\partial V/\partial z$.

Gauss's theorem states that the total flux of electric induction (D) out of any closed surface is equal to $4\pi \times$ (enclosed charge) : if the surface intersects no matter, the induction is equal to the electric intensity or field, and we shall confine our attention to this case. Then Gauss's theorem is expressed mathematically,

$$\int E_n \, \mathrm{d}S = 4\pi q \tag{2}$$

where E_n is the component of the electric field measured along the normal to the surface element dS ; the integration is taken over the whole closed surface S, (cf. 9.41) and q is the charge within the surface.

It will simplify our investigation if, for our surface, we choose a rectangular box with sides parallel to the cartesian axes of x, y, z (Fig. 10.5). We are free to do this because Gauss's theorem is true for surfaces of all shapes ; the choice of a more general form of the surface would result in much algebraical complexity and little corresponding gain in information.

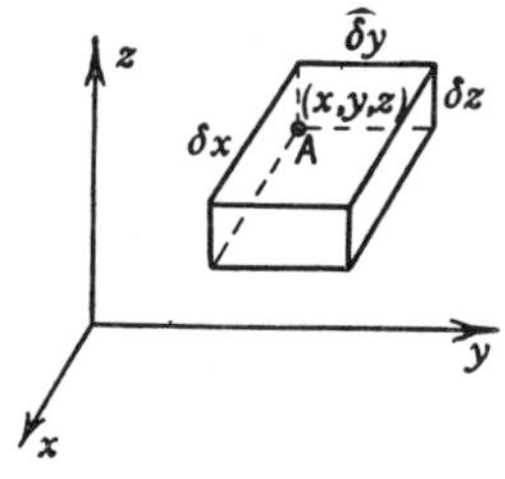

FIG. 10.5

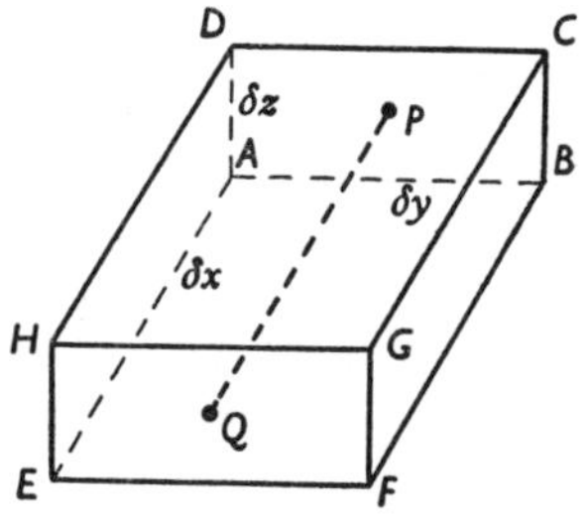

FIG. 10.6

Let vertex A of the box (Figs. 10.5 and 10.6) be situated at the point (x, y, z) and let the sides AE, AB, AD parallel to the axes be of length δx, δy, δz respectively. Faces $ABCD$ and $EFGH$ are both perpendicular to the x-axis, so for any point Q in $EFGH$, $E_n = E_x$, while for any point P in $ABCD$, $E_n = -E_x$. If P, Q are *corresponding* points on the two faces i.e. P is the point (x, y_1, z_1) and Q is the point

$(x+\delta x, y_1, z_1)$, where $y<y_1<y+\delta y$ and $z<z_1<z+\delta z$, a simplification results from considering the two points simultaneously, for then

$$E_n(P)+E_n(Q)=E_x(x+\delta x, y_1, z_1)-E_x(x, y_1, z_1)$$
$$=\left(\frac{\partial E_x}{\partial x}\right)_P . \delta x+O(\delta x^2)$$

(We assume the existence of first and second order partial derivatives: exceptional cases require the use of additional physical laws e.g. at discontinuities due to a change of dielectric constant.)

Moreover $$\left(\frac{\partial E_x}{\partial x}\right)_P=\left(\frac{\partial E_x}{\partial x}\right)_A+O(\delta y)+O(\delta z),$$

where $\left(\frac{\partial E_x}{\partial x}\right)_P$ and $\left(\frac{\partial E}{\partial x}\right)_A$ denote the values of $\left(\frac{\partial E_x}{\partial x}\right)_{y,z}$ at P and A respectively.

Hence the contribution of the two faces $ABCD$ and $EFGH$ to $\int E_n\,\mathrm{d}S$ is

$$\delta y\,\delta z\left\{\left(\frac{\partial E_x}{\partial x}\right)_A+O(\delta x)+O(\delta y)+O(\delta z)\right\}\delta x$$
$$=\delta\tau\left\{\left(\frac{\partial E_x}{\partial x}\right)_A+O(\epsilon)\right\}$$

where $\delta\tau$ is the volume of the box and ϵ is the greatest of δx, δy, δz.

Similarly the contributions from the faces perpendicular to the y and z axes are

$$\delta\tau\left\{\left(\frac{\partial E_y}{\partial y}\right)_A+O(\epsilon)\right\} \quad \text{and} \quad \delta\tau\left\{\left(\frac{\partial E_z}{\partial z}\right)_A+O(\epsilon)\right\}$$

Hence

$$\int E_n\,\mathrm{d}S=\delta\tau\left(\frac{\partial E_x}{\partial x}+\frac{\partial E_y}{\partial y}+\frac{\partial E_z}{\partial z}\right)_A+O(\epsilon)$$

From Gauss's theorem (2) this is $4\pi\,\delta q$ where δq is the δ charge within the volume $\delta\tau$. Hence

$$\left(\frac{\partial E_x}{\partial x}+\frac{\partial E_y}{\partial y}+\frac{\partial E_z}{\partial z}\right)_A=4\pi\frac{\delta q}{\delta\tau}+O(\epsilon)$$

and on taking the limit as δx, δy, δz all tend to zero

$$\frac{\partial E_x}{\partial x}+\frac{\partial E_y}{\partial y}+\frac{\partial E_z}{\partial z}=4\pi\rho \tag{3}$$

where

$$\rho = \lim_{\delta\tau \to 0} (\delta q/\delta\tau)$$

ρ is called the 'charge density'; it is the charge per unit volume.

The relation (3) can be expressed in terms of the potential V by means of the relations $E_x = -\partial V/\partial x$, $E_y = -\partial V/\partial y$, $E_z = -\partial V/\partial z$:

$$\frac{\partial^2 V}{\partial x^2} + \frac{\partial^2 V}{\partial y^2} + \frac{\partial^2 V}{\partial z^2} = -4\pi\rho \tag{4}$$

and in this form is called 'Poisson's equation'. Laplace's equation is obtained by putting $\rho = 0$; it is the equation satisfied by the potential in charge-free regions.

10.3. The solution of differential equations

There are two possible meanings to the word 'solution' when applied to differential equations. In the example

$$\frac{d^2y}{dx^2} + y = x^2 \tag{1}$$

it can be verified by differentiation that the function $y = x^2 - 2$ satisfies this equation and so does

$$y = x^2 - 2 + A \cos x + B \sin x \tag{2}$$

for any constant values of A and B.

If the word 'solution' were always held to imply a solution of this kind, that is, an explicit formula for y in the form of a finite sum of elementary functions, then the majority of differential equations would have no solution. If a broader view is taken however, and we ask instead whether there is a function y for which

$$\frac{d^2y}{dx^2} + xy = 0$$

(whether or not we can express y in terms of a finite number of elementary functions), then the answer is that there is such a function. It is not however an elementary function and if asked what sort of function it is, the best answer is simply that it is a function that satisfies the equation. Differential equations in fact are a most prolific source of new transcendental functions. In the present chapter we shall confine attention to certain limited classes of differential equation having elementary solutions.

10.4. The order of a differential equation

The differential equation

$$\phi\left(x, y, \frac{dy}{dz}, \dots, \frac{d^n y}{dx^n}\right) = 0 \tag{1}$$

where ϕ is an arbitrary function and $d^n y/dx^n$ is the highest derivative of y occurring in it, is said to be of order n. For example, the following equations are of the first order.

$$dy/dx + ay = x^2 \tag{2}$$

$$dy/dx + y^2 = \sin x \tag{3}$$

$$(dy/dx)^3 + dy/dx + y = \log \cos x \tag{4}$$

$$\log (dy/dx) + (dy/dx)^2 = x \tag{5}$$

The following are of second order

$$d^2y/dx^2 + \omega^2 y = 0 \tag{6}$$

$$d^2y/dx^2 + k\, dy/dx + \omega^2 y = \sin px \tag{7}$$

$$(d^2y/dx^2)^2 + (dy/dx)^3 + \sin y = \cos x \tag{8}$$

From this point of view an algebraic equation may be said to be of order zero.

10.41. *The degree of a differential equation*

If the function ϕ is such that the terms involving the highest derivative, $d^n y/dx^n$, form a polynomial of degree m in that derivative (with coefficients which may depend on x, y and all the lower derivatives) then the equation is said to be of the mth degree and nth order. Of the equations in 10.4, numbers (2), (3), (6) and (7) are of the first degree, equation (8) is of the second degree and (4) is of the third degree. Equation (5) is not of finite degree since it cannot be put into the specified form.

10.42. *Linear and non-linear equations*

A differential equation is said to be 'linear' (in y) if it reduces to the very special form

$$f_0(x) \cdot \frac{d^n y}{dx^n} + f_1(x) \cdot \frac{d^{n-1}y}{dx^{n-1}} + \dots + f_n(x) \cdot y + f_{n+1}(x) = 0 \tag{1}$$

in which the coefficients f_r are functions of x only. It may be of any order, but is necessarily of the first degree. Equations (2), (6) and (7) of 10.4 are linear: the others are non-linear. If in equation (1) the function f_{n+1} is zero, the equation is said to be ' homogeneous ' (in y).

Linear equations have a number of important properties which very considerably simplify their solution. These are considered in Chapter 11. Non-linear equations on the other hand, even of the first order and first degree, usually prove intractable; in spite of much effort, few widely applicable methods have been evolved and each equation has to be tackled as a separate problem by special methods, and often with small chance of success. For the commonest soluble non-linear equations the reader is referred to Piaggio, *Differential Equations*.

However, even if no formal solution of a differential equation can be obtained, it is usually possible to obtain an approximation to a solution by a numerical process. Such numerical techniques are of great importance in many realms of research, but for further information the reader is referred to the special texts on the subject, e.g. Hartree, *Numerical Methods*.

10.5. Use of Laplace transforms for solving linear equations

The Laplace transform is so powerful a tool that in some branches of engineering and physics it is partially displacing traditional methods of approaching linear differential equations. We shall adopt the view that its early introduction to the student both provides him with an immediately useful rule of thumb method of tackling quite a wide range of problems and, in the process, gives him an opportunity of discovering for himself some of the features of linear differential equations before coming to their formal study in Chapter 11.

A great advantage of the Laplace transform method over most alternative methods is that it is systematic and virtually invariable: a standard prescription is given whereby, in conjunction with certain tables like Table 1 below, a trial solution can be obtained. This trial solution must, at least until the more advanced theory of Chapter 15 has been studied, be verified by direct substitution in the original equation and in any subsidiary conditions which were postulated.

Suppose we have a linear equation in which the left-hand side is the sum of numerical multiples of y, $\mathrm{d}y/\mathrm{d}x$, $\mathrm{d}^2y/\mathrm{d}x^2$ etc., and the right-hand side is a function of x. We first multiply each side of the equation by e^{-px} and then integrate both sides with respect to x from 0 to ∞. This first step is the same in all applications of the method. The left-hand side so obtained is called the Laplace transform of the original left-hand side, and the new right-hand side is the Laplace transform of the old right-hand side.

Suppose the original right-hand side was $\mathrm{f}(x)$. The new right-hand side is

$$\int_0^\infty e^{-px}\,\mathrm{f}(x)\,\mathrm{d}x$$

$$=\bar{\mathrm{f}}(p) \tag{1}$$

say, where the notation $\bar{\mathrm{f}}$ is used to denote the transform of the original function f, and $\bar{\mathrm{f}}$ is a function of p because after the integration on the right-hand side has been performed and the limits inserted the definite integral no longer depends on x but does depend on the number p. Thus, for example, if

$$\mathrm{f}(x)=e^{-ax};\ \bar{\mathrm{f}}(p)=\int_0^\infty e^{-px}e^{-ax}\,\mathrm{d}x=\int_0^\infty e^{-(p+a)x}\,\mathrm{d}x=1/(p+a) \tag{2}$$

For very many functions $\mathrm{f}(x)$, the integration is straightforward and the corresponding values of $\bar{\mathrm{f}}(p)$ can be found. Since extensive tables exist giving the form of $\bar{\mathrm{f}}(p)$ for given forms of $\mathrm{f}(x)$, it is often unnecessary to do more than refer to the tables for the required transform. In other cases a little elementary rearrangement enables the transform to be found with ease, thus, if $\mathrm{f}(x)=\alpha_1\mathrm{f}_1(x)+\alpha_2\mathrm{f}_2(x)+\alpha_3\mathrm{f}_3(x)$ where α_1, α_2, α_3 are constants and the transforms of $\mathrm{f}_1(x)$, $\mathrm{f}_2(x)$, $\mathrm{f}_3(x)$ are known,

$$\bar{\mathrm{f}}(p)=\alpha_1\bar{\mathrm{f}}_1(p)+\alpha_2\bar{\mathrm{f}}_2(p)+\alpha_3\bar{\mathrm{f}}_3(p) \tag{3}$$

Again, if the transform of $\mathrm{f}(x)$ is known, the Laplace transform of $\mathrm{f}'(x)$ can easily be found by integration by parts, for

$$\bar{\mathrm{f}}'(p)=\int_0^\infty e^{-px}\frac{\mathrm{df}}{\mathrm{d}x}\,\mathrm{d}x=\Big[e^{-px}\,\mathrm{f}(x)\Big]_0^\infty+\int_0^\infty pe^{-px}\,\mathrm{f}(x)\,\mathrm{d}x$$

$$=-\mathrm{f}(0)+p\bar{\mathrm{f}}(p) \tag{4}$$

The Laplace transforms of higher derivatives can be found in a similar way by repeated integration by parts.

Examples. 1. Show that if $f(x)=x$, $\bar{f}(p)=1/p^2$

2. Show that if $f(x)=1$, $\bar{f}(p)=1/p$

3. Show that if $\left.\begin{array}{ll} f(x)=g(x) & x\geqslant 0 \\ \neq g(x) & x<0 \end{array}\right\} \bar{f}(p)=\bar{g}(p)$

A short working list of some of the most useful transforms is given in Table 1.

Table 1

	$f(x)$	$\bar{f}(p)$
(i)	c (constant)	c/p
(ii)	x	$1/p^2$
(iii)	x^n	$n!/p^{n+1}$
(iv)	e^{-ax}	$1/(p+a)$
(v)	$x^n e^{-ax}$	$n!/(p+a)^{n+1}$
(vi)	$\cos \omega x$	$p/(p^2+\omega^2)$
(vii)	$\sin \omega x$	$\omega/(p^2+\omega^2)$
(viii)	$e^{-ax} \sin \omega x$	$\omega/\{(p+a)^2+\omega^2\}$
(ix)	$e^{-ax} \cos \omega x$	$(p+a)/\{(p+a)^2+\omega^2\}$
(x)	$x \sin \omega x$	$2\omega p/\{p^2+\omega^2\}^2$
(xi)	$x \cos \omega x$	$(p^2-\omega^2)/\{p^2+\omega^2\}^2$
(xii)	$\sinh \omega x$	$\omega/(p^2-\omega^2)$
(xiii)	$\cosh \omega x$	$p/(p^2-\omega^2)$
(xiv)	$J_0(x)$	$1/\surd(p^2+1)$
(xv)	$J_n(x)$	$1/[\surd(p^2+1)\{p+\surd(p^2+1)\}^n]$
(xvi)	$x^{n/2} J_n(2\surd x)$	$p^{-n-1}e^{-1/p}$
(xvii)	$\operatorname{erfc}(a/2\surd x)$	$p^{-1}e^{-a\surd p}$
(xix)	$(\pi x)^{-1/2}e^{-a^2/4x}$	$p^{-1/2}e^{-a\surd p}$
(xx)	$\operatorname{erf} \surd x$	$1/(p+p^{3/2})$
(xxi)	$\alpha_1 f_1(x)+\alpha_2 f_2(x)$	$\alpha_1 \bar{f}_1(p)+\alpha_2 \bar{f}_2(p)$
(xxii)	df/dx	$p\bar{f}(p)-f(0)$
(xxiii)	d^2f/dx^2	$p^2\bar{f}(p)-pf(0)-f'(0)$

Further important results will be given in Chapter 15. Some unfamiliar functions such as the Bessel functions J_n and the error functions erf and erfc have been included for the benefit of more advanced readers who wish to use the table. For workers who require extensive tables, reference may be made to *Tables of Integral Transforms*, vol. 1, Bateman manuscript project, McGraw-Hill.

Let us now apply the Laplace transform method to some simple linear differential equations.

Example 1

Find the solution of $dy/dx + 2y = e^{-x}$ subject to the condition $y = 3$ when $x = 0$. Using results (xxi), (xxii) and (iv) we find for our transformed equation,

$$(p\bar{y} - 3) + 2\bar{y} = 1/(p+1)$$

whence

$$\bar{y} = (3p+4)/\{(p+1)(p+2)\}$$

$$= 1/(p+1) + 2/(p+2) \tag{5}$$

(see Chap. 3 for partial fractions technique).

Now from (iv) of Table 1 we see that $1/(p+1)$ is the transform of e^{-x} and $1/(p+2)$ is the transform of e^{-2x}, and using (xxi) this tells us that (5) is the transform of $e^{-x} + 2e^{-2x}$. Since (5) is the transform of y, the rule of thumb solution of our problem is

$$y = e^{-x} + 2e^{-2x} \tag{6}$$

Now, although if (6) is true (5) is satisfied, we have no guarantee that (6) is the *only* expression for y which satisfies (5). So before we can say that (6) is the required solution it is necessary to check that it does in fact satisfy both the given differential equation and the given condition $y = 3$ when $x = 0$.

Check : If (6) is true, $dy/dx + 2y = -e^{-x} - 4e^{-2x} + 2e^{-x} + 4e^{-2x} = e^{-x}$ and $y(0) = 1 + 2 = 3$.

The expression (6) is therefore the required solution of the given differential equation.

Example 2

Solve the equation $d^2y/dx^2 + dy/dx + y = 0$ subject to the conditions $y = 0$ at $x = 0$ and $y = 1$ at $x = 1$.

Taking the Laplace transform of the equation we find

$$\{p^2\bar{y} - 0 - y'(0)\} + \{p\bar{y} - 0\} + \bar{y} = 0$$

$$\bar{y} = y'(0)/(p^2 + p + 1)$$

$$= \frac{2}{\sqrt{3}}\, y'(0) \cdot \frac{\sqrt{3}/2}{(p+\frac{1}{2})^2 + \frac{3}{4}}$$

which, apart from the constant factor $2y'(0)/\sqrt{3}$ is of the form (viii). The presence of the unknown quantity $y'(0)$ causes no trouble since it is a constant, namely the value of dy/dx at the initial point $x = 0$,

Hence the rule of thumb solution is

$$y = \frac{2}{\surd 3} y'(0) \,.\, e^{-\frac{1}{2}x} \sin(\surd 3x/2) \tag{7}$$

Check : From (7),

(i) $\dfrac{d^2y}{dx} + \dfrac{dy}{dx} + y$

$$= \frac{2}{\surd 3} y'(0) e^{-x/2} \left[\left(\tfrac{1}{4} \sin \frac{\surd 3}{2} x - \frac{\surd 3}{2} \cos \frac{\surd 3}{2} x - \tfrac{3}{4} \sin \frac{\surd 3}{2} x \right) + \left(\frac{\surd 3}{2} \cos \frac{\surd 3}{2} x - \tfrac{1}{2} \sin \frac{\surd 3}{2} x \right) + \sin \frac{\surd 3}{2} x \right]$$

$= 0$

(ii) When $x = 0$, $y = 0$

(iii) When $x = 1$, $y = \dfrac{2}{\surd 3} y'(0) e^{-\frac{1}{2}} \sin\left(\dfrac{\surd 3}{2}\right)$

Thus all conditions are satisfied if we put the unknown constant $y'(0) = \dfrac{\surd 3}{2} e^{1/2} \Big/ \sin\left(\dfrac{\surd 3}{2}\right)$. The required solution is thus

$$y = e^{-\frac{1}{2}(x-1)} \sin(\surd 3x/2)/\sin(\surd 3/2)$$

Example 3

Solve the equation $d^2y/dx^2 + \omega^2 x = 0$ with conditions $y = 2$, $dy/dx = 1$ at $x = 0$ by the Laplace transform method.

Example 4

Solve $dy/dx - y = x^2$ subject to the condition $y = -6$ when $x = 2$ (Use partial fractions).

Example 5

Solve $d^2y/dx^2 + 3\, dy/dx + 2y = e^{-x}$ subject to no additional conditions. (Two unknown constants $y(0)$ and $y'(0)$ will appear in the answer.)

The reader will find that many of the examples of the next chapter can be solved by the Laplace transform method, with $y(0)$ and $y'(0)$ regarded as arbitrary constants. We repeat the warning, however, that, until chapter 15 has been mastered, the transform method is merely a rule of thumb procedure for finding a *trial* solution, and the validity of this solution must be checked by substitution in the given equations.

10.6. The existence of solutions of differential equations, and the role of the arbitrary constants

In general, a differential equation has not one but an infinite number of solutions because of the occurrence of arbitrary constants. For example the first-order equation

$$dy/dx + y^2 = 0 \tag{1}$$

has the solution

$$y = 1/(x + A) \tag{2}$$

with one constant A which is 'arbitrary' in the sense that the function (2) is a solution of equation (1) for any constant value of A; and the second-order equation (1) of 10.3 has the solution (2) of 10.3 with two constants which are 'arbitrary' in the same sense.

We will now examine the question of the existence of solutions of a differential equation and show how it is related to the occurrence of arbitrary constants in the general solution.

Consider an equation of first order and first degree,

$$dy/dx = f(x, y) \tag{3}$$

For a given value x_0 of x, y is not determined by the differential equation; any value y_0 may be specified provided only that $f(x_0, y_0)$ is defined. When y_0 has been chosen, $(dy/dx)_0$ is uniquely specified, and since $\delta y \simeq (dy/dx)_0\, \delta x$ we shall anticipate that the value $y_0 + \delta y$ of y at the adjacent point $x = x_0 + \delta x$ will be uniquely determined and, continuing step by step in the same way, that a unique solution can be built up for every chosen initial value y_0.

If we use only the approximate relation $\delta y \simeq (dy/dx)_0\, \delta x$ we can only prove the existence of an approximate solution of (3). A more satisfactory demonstration of the existence of an exact solution can be obtained by constructing a sequence of successive approximations $Y_{(1)}, Y_{(2)} \ldots$ and showing that the limit of this sequence is a function satisfying equation (3) at and near the starting point $x = x_0$.

We postulate that for some sufficiently small a, b and some finite value of K,

$$| f(x, y_1) - f(x, y_2) | \leqslant K \,| y_1 - y_2 |$$

for all points (x, y_1), (x, y_2) in the region $| x - x_0 | \leqslant a$, $| y - y_0 | \leqslant b$. This condition is satisfied if $f(x, y)$ is continuous and $\partial f/\partial y$ exists in the region. We now define

$$Y_0 = y_0; \quad Y_1(x) = y_0 + \int_{x_0}^{x} f(t, Y_0(t))\, dt; \ \ldots \ Y_{n+1}(x) = y_0 + \int_{x_0}^{x} f(t, Y_n(t))\, dt.$$

Then, so long as the Y_n involved remain in the range $| y - y_0 | \leqslant b$, and x in the range $| x - x_0 | \leqslant a$,

$$| Y_{n+1} - Y_n | = \left| \int_{x_0}^{x} \{f(t, Y_n(t)) - f(t, Y_{n-1}(t))\}\, dt \right| \leqslant \int_{x_0}^{x} K \,| Y_n(t) - Y_{n-1}(t) |\, dt.$$

To prove that the Y_n do remain in the required range when the range of x is suitably restricted we note that

$$| Y_1 - Y_0 | = \left| \int_{x_0}^{x} \mathrm{f}(t, y_0)\, \mathrm{d}t \right| \leqslant A \mid x - x_0 \mid.$$

where A is the greatest value of $\mathrm{f}(x, y_0)$ in $| x - x_0 | \leqslant a$, so

$$| Y_2 - Y_1 | \leqslant KA \mid x - x_0 \mid^2/2!$$

$$\cdots\cdots\cdots$$

$$| Y_n - Y_{n-1} | \leqslant K^{n-1}A \mid x - x_0 \mid^n/n!$$

whence
$$| Y_n - y_0 | \leqslant A\,(e^{K|x-x_0|} - 1)/K$$

$$\leqslant b \text{ provided } | x - x_0 | \leqslant \frac{1}{K} \log\left(1 + \frac{Kb}{A}\right).$$

Hence, if $| x - x_0 | \leqslant \alpha$ where α is the smaller of a and

$$\frac{1}{K} \log\left(1 + \frac{Kb}{A}\right),$$

$$| Y_n - Y_{n-1} | \leqslant K^{n-1} A \alpha^n \mid n!$$

i.e. in the interval $| x - x_0 | \leqslant \alpha$, the sequence of Y_n's converges uniformly to a limit $Y(x)$.

Then
$$Y(x) - y_0 = \lim_{n\to\infty} \int_{x_0}^{x} \mathrm{f}(t,\ Y_n(t)\, \mathrm{d}t = \int_{x_0}^{x} \mathrm{f}(t,\ Y(t))\, \mathrm{d}t$$

and
$$\mathrm{d}Y/\mathrm{d}x = \mathrm{f}(x,\ Y).$$

The function $Y(x)$ thus satisfies equation (3) in the interval $| x - x_0 | < \alpha$. Proceeding step by step in the same way we find that for every initial choice of y_0 there exists a unique solution $Y(x)$ (depending on y_0) : this can be expressed by saying that there is a one-parameter family of solutions $y = \mathrm{F}(x\ ;\ y_0)$ of the first order equation (3).

For a second order equation $\mathrm{d}^2y/\mathrm{d}x^2 = \mathrm{f}(x, y, \mathrm{d}y/\mathrm{d}x)$, $\mathrm{d}y/\mathrm{d}x$ is no longer determined when x_0, y_0 are given : $\mathrm{d}y/\mathrm{d}x = y_0'$ can be independently specified. In this case there is a two-parameter family of solutions

$$y = \mathrm{F}(x\ ;\ y_0, y_0')$$

Now consider the situation when the given differential equation is not of the first degree, so that the highest derivative is not given *uniquely* in terms of x, y and derivatives of lower orders. Suppose the differential equation is of degree m and of the first order, $\phi(x, y, \mathrm{d}y/\mathrm{d}x) = 0$ say. Then the equation will be satisfied if either

$$\mathrm{d}y/\mathrm{d}x = \mathrm{f}_1(x, y),\ \mathrm{d}y/\mathrm{d}x = \mathrm{f}_2(x, y),\ \ldots,\ \text{or } \mathrm{d}y/\mathrm{d}x = \mathrm{f}_m(x, y). \quad (4)$$

At $x = x_0$ we can still assign an arbitrary value y_0 to y, and at every point dy/dx must be given by one of the equations (4). If we chose to satisfy $dy/dx = f_1(x, y)$ in the first elementary interval (x_0, y_0) to (x_1, y_1) and $dy/dx = f_2(x, y)$ in an adjacent interval (x_1, y_1) to (x_2, y_2), then, except in the exceptional case of $f_1(x_1, y_1) = f_2(x_1, y_1)$, there would be a discontinuity of slope at the point (x_1, y_1) where the intervals met, that is at (x_1, y_1) the derivative dy/dx would not exist and so the equation

$$\phi(x, y, dy/dx) = 0$$

would not be satisfied. Hence to satisfy the equation we must in general stick to just one of the equations (4), though there may be exceptional points (x_i, y_i) where two of the f's are equal, say $f_1(x_i, y_i) = f_3(x_i, y_i)$, and consequently two possible branches of the solution, one corresponding to $dy/dx = f_1$ the other to $dy/dx = f_3$ can arise at such exceptional points. Provided we recognise the possibility of such branching phenomena we may say that the general solution of every first-order differential equation is a one-parameter family ; of every second-order equation a two-parameter family and so on.

Conversely, a solution in which the number of essentially distinct arbitrary constants is equal to the order of the equation is known as the *general solution.* Some differential equations admit of a solution which is not the same as the general solution with any choice of the constants in the latter, but such 'singular solutions' are of comparatively infrequent occurrence in practical problems, and the general solution commonly provides us with all that we require.

CHAPTER ELEVEN

LINEAR DIFFERENTIAL EQUATIONS

11.1. Superposition properties of solutions of linear equations

Linear equations (10.42) are of frequent occurrence in physical problems. This is not so much because physical problems are accurately represented by linear equations but because the non-linear equations that would give a better representation are often intractable. A necessary first step in solving many physical problems is in fact to linearise the equations by suitable approximations; usually by assuming that the dependent variable remains small so that its square can be neglected.

Linear equations are of two kinds. There are, first, those which contain no term independent of the unknown function y; that is equations of the type

$$\mathrm{f}_0(x)\frac{\mathrm{d}^n y}{\mathrm{d}x^n}+\mathrm{f}_1(x)\frac{\mathrm{d}^{n-1}y}{\mathrm{d}x^{n-1}}+\ldots+\mathrm{f}_n(x)y=0; \tag{1}$$

these are called 'homogeneous' equations. Secondly, there are those which do contain a term independent of y,

$$\mathrm{f}_0(x)\frac{\mathrm{d}^n y}{\mathrm{d}x^n}+\mathrm{f}_1(x)\frac{\mathrm{d}^{n-1}y}{\mathrm{d}x^{n-1}}+\ldots+\mathrm{f}_n(x)y=\mathrm{g}(x); \tag{2}$$

these are called 'inhomogeneous'.

Such equations have two important properties which greatly simplify both the process of obtaining solutions and of representing them when found. Consider first the case of the linear equation (1), homogeneous in y. Suppose that $y=\mathrm{u}(x)$ and $y=\mathrm{v}(x)$ are two solutions of equation (1). Then the linear combination

$$y=A\mathrm{u}(x)+B\mathrm{v}(x) \tag{3}$$

for any constant values of A and B is also a solution. This follows immediately by substituting (3) into (1) and using the property of the functions $\mathrm{u}(x)$ and $\mathrm{v}(x)$ that they are solutions of (1).

By the same argument, if $u_1(x)$, $u_2(x)$, ... , $u_m(x)$ are solutions of (1), then so is

$$y = A_1 u_1(x) + A_2 u_2(x) + \dots + A_m u_m(x) \tag{4}$$

We say that the solutions of a linear homogeneous equation can be superposed, or that they satisfy a law of superposition.

If the functions $u_1(x)$, ... , $u_n(x)$ are n linearly independent solutions of equation (1), that is, if no one of them can be expressed as a linear combination of the others, the solution

$$y = A_1 u_1(x) + A_2 u_2(x) + \dots + A_n u_n(x) \tag{5}$$

is an n-parameter family of solutions of the nth order differential equation (1), and is therefore the 'general solution' of this equation in the sense of 10.6. It is further possible to show (see Ince, *Ordinary differential equations*, Chap. 5) that no function $f(x)$ which is not of the form (5) can be a solution of equation (1).

If the equation is not homogeneous, the superposition property in the above form, (4), no longer holds. Instead we have the following equally useful theorem: if $y = u(x)$ is one solution of the inhomogeneous equation (2) and $y = v(x)$ is any solution of the homogeneous equation obtained by putting $g(x)$ equal to zero in (2) then

$$y = u(x) + v(x)$$

is a solution of (2). This follows easily by substitution as in the previous case.

A slightly different statement of this property will make its power apparent. If $v(x)$ is any one solution of equation (2), and y is the general solution, then $[y - v(x)]$ is a solution of equation (1). It follows that if the general solution of equation (1) is given by (5), then the general solution of equation (2) is

$$y = v(x) + A_1 u_1(x) + A_2 u_2(x) + \dots + A_n u_n(x)$$

since this function both satisfies equation (2) and has the full quota of n independent constants.

Example

One solution of the equation

$$\frac{d^2y}{dx^2} + y = 5x + 7 \tag{6}$$

is

$$y = 5x + 7$$

since $d^2y/dx^2 = 0$ for this function. The general solution of the corresponding homogeneous equation $d^2z/dx^2 + z = 0$ is

$$z = A \cos x + B \sin x$$

(see 11.22). Hence the general solution of (6) is

$$y = 5x + 7 + A \cos x + B \sin x$$

Solutions of non-linear equations have no additive properties of this kind.

A solution $v(x)$ of equation (2) is usually called a ' particular integral ' of this equation, and the general solution $u(x)$ of the corresponding homogeneous equation (1) is called the ' complementary function '.

The process of obtaining solutions of linear differential equations, homogeneous or inhomogeneous, is greatly simplified if the coefficients $f_0, f_1, \ldots, f_n$ in (1) or (2) are constants, instead of being functions of x, and §§ 11.2–11.4 are restricted to this case. Equations in which the coefficients may vary with x are considered in 11.5.

11.11. *The operator D*

In the solution of linear differential equations, homogeneous or inhomogeneous, it is often convenient to use a single symbol D to denote the operation of differentiation with respect to the independent variable, and D^n to denote the operation of differentiating n times; that is, if $y = f(x)$, $D^n y = d^n y/dx^n$. Then the equation

$$\frac{d^n y}{dx^n} + a_1 \frac{d^{n-1}y}{dx^{n-1}} + \ldots + a_{n-1}\frac{dy}{dx} + a_n y = 0$$

can be written

$$D^n y + a_1 D^{n-1} y + a_2 D^{n-2} y + \ldots + a_{n-1} D y + a_n y = 0 \qquad (1)$$

The symbol D is called an ' operator ' because it signifies not a number but an operation, namely that of differentiation.

Further, $(D + a)$, regarded as an operator operating on a function $y = f(x)$, is defined by

$$(D + a)y = Dy + ay = dy/dx + ay \qquad (2)$$

As a natural extension of this we can write equation (1) as

$$(D^n + a_1 D^{n-1} + a_2 D^{n-2} + \ldots + a_{n-1} D + a_n)y = 0 \qquad (3)$$

or more shortly $\phi(D)y = 0$

where $\phi(\mathrm{D})$ stands for the operator in brackets in (3), and is formally a polynomial in D, of the nth degree.

Just as it is understood that $a(y+z)$ means that the operation of multiplication by a is carried out on the sum $y+z$, whereas $ay+z$ means that the operation of multiplication by a is carried out on y only, so the convention is that $(\mathrm{D}+a)(y+z)$ means that the operation represented by $(\mathrm{D}+a)$ is carried out on the sum $(y+z)$ whereas $(\mathrm{D}+a)\,y+z$ means that this operation is carried out on y only.

Although the symbol D stands for an operation, not a number, there are ways in which the behaviour of D resembles that of algebraic symbols standing for numbers. For example, with the conventions just explained regarding the use of brackets.

$$
\begin{aligned}
(\mathrm{D}+1)(\mathrm{D}-1)y &= (\mathrm{D}+1)\left(\frac{\mathrm{d}y}{\mathrm{d}x}-y\right) \quad \text{(from (2))} \\
&= \frac{\mathrm{d}}{\mathrm{d}x}\left(\frac{\mathrm{d}y}{\mathrm{d}x}-y\right)+\frac{\mathrm{d}y}{\mathrm{d}x}-y=\frac{\mathrm{d}^2y}{\mathrm{d}x^2}-y \\
&= (\mathrm{D}^2-1)y \qquad (4)
\end{aligned}
$$

for any twice-differentiable function y. Such an equivalence between the results of two operations, for any operand to which they can significantly be applied, is often expressed by suppressing the symbol for the operand and writing a relation between the corresponding operators themselves, in this case

$$(\mathrm{D}+1)(\mathrm{D}-1)=\mathrm{D}^2-1 \qquad (5)$$

The correspondence between (5) and the algebraical relation

$$(z+1)(z-1)=z^2-1$$

where z stands for a *number*, is neither trivial nor fortuitous. Let us see why it arises. All purely algebraic rules and relations not involving division can be derived from the five basic rules of elementary algebra,† namely the commutative and associative rules of addition and multiplication, and the distributive rule.

$$
\begin{array}{ll}
\text{I.} & a+b=b+a \\
\text{II.} & (a+b)+c=a+(b+c) \\
\text{III.} & ab=ba \\
\text{IV.} & (ab)c=a(bc) \\
\text{V.} & a(b+c)=ab+ac
\end{array}
$$

† From these laws all the other results of ordinary algebra can be deduced ; if any of the laws is altered or omitted, a different kind of 'algebra' will result cf. vector algebra, Chapter 17.

Any symbol which obeys these rules can be manipulated as an algebraic quantity, whether or not it represents a number. Now the symbol D satisfies all of these relations, provided that, in III only, the other symbol stands for a *constant*, not a function of x. If in III we replace b by D, we must understand that Da means the operation of multiplying the operand by a and differentiating the result, *not* the result of differentiating the constant a; the meaning of Da, as an operator, is in fact defined by $\mathrm{D}ay \equiv \frac{\mathrm{d}}{\mathrm{d}x}(ay)$ for any y; the relation $a\mathrm{D} = \mathrm{D}a$ is a relation between *operators* operating on a function of x.

Thus $$\mathrm{D}a = a\mathrm{D}$$

since $$\frac{\mathrm{d}}{\mathrm{d}x}(ay) = a\frac{\mathrm{d}y}{\mathrm{d}x}$$

11.12. *Properties of the linear operator* $\phi(\mathrm{D})$

(a) The linear differential equation with constant coefficients

$$\frac{\mathrm{d}^n y}{\mathrm{d}x^n} + a_1\frac{\mathrm{d}^{n-1}y}{dx^{n-1}} + \dots + a_n y = \mathrm{f}(x)$$

can be written $$\phi(\mathrm{D})y = \mathrm{f}(x)$$

where $\phi(\mathrm{D})$ is a polynomial in D, and is independent of x and y. It is often called a 'linear' operator; this does not mean that it is linear in D, but that the effect of applying it to a function $y+z$ is the sum of the effects of applying it to y and to z separately, that is

$$\phi(\mathrm{D})(y+z) = \phi(\mathrm{D})y + \phi(\mathrm{D})z$$

(b) The result of applying the linear differential operator $\phi(\mathrm{D})$ to the function e^{mx} is the function $\phi(m)e^{mx}$, where $\phi(m)$ is a *numerical* coefficient (that is to say, it is independent of the variable x). For

$$\mathrm{D}e^{mx} = me^{mx}$$

$$\mathrm{D}^2e^{mx} = m^2e^{mx} \text{ etc.}$$

and therefore $$\phi(\mathrm{D})e^{mx} = (\mathrm{D}^n + a_1\mathrm{D}^{n-1} + \dots + a_n)e^{mx}$$

$$= (m^n + a_1m^{n-1} + \dots + a_n)e^{mx}$$

$$= \phi(m)e^{mx}$$

(c) Let $v = \mathrm{v}(x)$ be any differentiable function of x; then

$$\phi(\mathrm{D})e^{ax}\mathrm{v}(x) = e^{ax}\phi(\mathrm{D}+a)\mathrm{v}(x)$$

For

$$\begin{aligned}\mathrm{D}(e^{ax}v) &= e^{ax}\mathrm{D}v + ae^{ax}v\\ &= e^{ax}(\mathrm{D}+a)v\end{aligned}$$

and then by induction

$$\mathrm{D}^n(e^{ax}v) = e^{ax}(\mathrm{D}+a)^n v$$

for any positive integral value of n. Hence if $\phi(\mathrm{D})$ is any polynomial in D it follows that

$$\phi(\mathrm{D})[e^{ax}v] = e^{ax}\phi(\mathrm{D}+a)v$$

Example 1

$$\begin{aligned}\mathrm{D}(x^2e^x) &= e^x(\mathrm{D}+1)x^2\\ &= e^x(2x+x^2)\end{aligned}$$

Example 2

$$\begin{aligned}\mathrm{D}^2(e^{mx}\cos\beta x) &= e^{mx}(\mathrm{D}+m)^2\cos\beta x\\ &= e^{mx}(\mathrm{D}^2+2m\mathrm{D}+m^2)\cos\beta x\\ &= e^{mx}(-\beta^2\cos\beta x - 2m\beta\sin\beta x + m^2\cos\beta x)\\ &= e^{mx}[(m^2-\beta^2)\cos\beta x - 2m\beta\sin\beta x]\end{aligned}$$

There is no convenient analogous formula for $\phi(\mathrm{D})[(\sin\beta x)v]$ or $\phi(\mathrm{D})[(\cos\beta x)v]$.

11.2. Linear homogeneous equations with constant coefficients

The clue that leads to the solution of this class of equation is that the elementary functions x^n (where n is a positive integer), e^x, $\sin x$, $\cos x$ and their products and sums all satisfy equations of this form. Conversely, and more important, any solution of a homogeneous linear equation with constant coefficients can be expressed as a finite sum of products of polynomials, exponentials and circular functions. This in fact is the common property which defines the class of so-called elementary functions. It links the exponential and trigonometric functions with the polynomials and distinguishes them from other transcendental functions.

The following examples illustrate this characteristic property.

(a) Any polynomial of degree $(n-1)$ satisfies the equation

$$\frac{\mathrm{d}^n y}{\mathrm{d}x^n} = 0$$

(*b*) The function $y = Ae^{-ax}$ satisfies the equation

$$\mathrm{d}y/\mathrm{d}x + ay = 0$$

(*c*) The functions $y = Ae^{-ax} \sin kx$ and $y = Ae^{-ax} \cos kx$ both satisfy the equation

$$\mathrm{d}^2y/\mathrm{d}x^2 + 2a\, \mathrm{d}y/\mathrm{d}x + (k^2 + a^2)y = 0$$

(*d*) The function $y = (Ax + B)e^{-ax}$ satisfies the equation

$$\mathrm{d}^2y/\mathrm{d}x^2 + 2a\, \mathrm{d}y/\mathrm{d}x + a^2y = 0$$

Various methods of solution of equations of this kind will now be illustrated.

11.21. *First-order equation*

The equation of the first order is

$$\mathrm{d}y/\mathrm{d}x + ky = 0 \tag{1}$$

This is known to be satisfied by $y = e^{-kx}$ (see 11.2, (*b*)). To find the general solution, put $y = \mathrm{w}(x)e^{-kx}$. Substitution in (1) gives $\mathrm{w}'(x) = 0$, hence $\mathrm{w}(x)$ must be some *constant*, and the *general* solution is

$$y = Ae^{-kx} \tag{2}$$

11.22. *Second-order equation*

The equation of the second order with constant coefficients occurs in many applications. Consider the equation

$$\mathrm{d}^2y/\mathrm{d}x^2 + k^2y = 0 \tag{1}$$

The functions $y = \cos kx$ and $y = \sin kx$ both satisfy it ; hence by the first superposition theorem of 11.1,

$$y = A \cos kx + B \sin kx \tag{2}$$

is a solution, for any constant values of A and B. It is, further, the *general* solution, and no function $y = \mathrm{f}(x)$ which is *not* of this form can be a solution of (1) (see 11.1). Independent proof of this last statement will now be given because the method, based on the replacement of the single unknown $\mathrm{f}(x)$ by two unknown functions $\mathrm{u}(x)$, $\mathrm{v}(x)$ is often useful in other contexts.

Any differentiable function of x, $y = \mathrm{f}(x)$, can be expressed in the form

$$y = \mathrm{u}(x) \cos kx + \mathrm{v}(x) \sin kx \tag{3}$$

where u(x) and v(x) are functions of x related by the condition

$$\mathrm{u}'(x) \cos kx + \mathrm{v}'(x) \sin kx = 0 \tag{4}$$

for (3) and (4) are both satisfied if

$$\left.\begin{aligned} y &= \mathrm{u}(x) \cos kx + \mathrm{v}(x) \sin kx \\ \text{and} \quad y' &= -k\mathrm{u}(x) \sin kx + k\mathrm{v}(x) \cos kx \end{aligned}\right\} \tag{5}$$

i.e. if

$$\left.\begin{aligned} \mathrm{u}(x) &= [ky \cos kx - y' \sin kx]/k \\ \mathrm{v}(x) &= [ky \sin kx + y' \cos kx]/k \end{aligned}\right\} \tag{6}$$

Now any solution of (1) must certainly be differentiable, and so expressible in the form (3) with u(x), v(x) satisfying the condition (4).

Differentiating (5) and using (3), we have

$$y'' + k^2 y = -k\mathrm{u}'(x) \sin kx + k\mathrm{v}'(x) \cos kx$$

Thus if y is to satisfy equation (1)

$$\mathrm{u}'(x) \sin kx - \mathrm{v}'(x) \cos kx = 0 \tag{7}$$

Equations (4) and (7) are two equations for u$'(x)$, v$'(x)$, and it follows from them that u$'(x) = 0$, v$'(x) = 0$ for all x. Hence for any function y satisfying equation (1), the functions u(x) and v(x) in (3) must both be constant, and this gives the general solution (2).

The equation

$$\mathrm{d}^2y/\mathrm{d}x^2 - k^2 y = 0 \tag{8}$$

can be solved as follows : first note that it is satisfied by the function e^{mx} provided that $m^2 - k^2 = 0$ i.e. $m = \pm k$. The equation (8) is therefore satisfied by

$$y = Ae^{kx} + Be^{-kx} \tag{9}$$

and, since it contains two arbitrary independent constants, this is the general solution. An alternative form of the solution is

$$y = A' \cosh kx + B' \sinh kx \tag{10}$$

A similar method of solution can be applied to the general second-order linear homogeneous equation with constant coefficients,

$$\mathrm{d}^2y/\mathrm{d}x^2 + 2a\, \mathrm{d}y/\mathrm{d}x + by = 0 \tag{11}$$

but the method fails to give the whole of the general solution when the two values of m are coincident i.e. when $a^2 = b$. The following method avoids the difficulty of this exceptional case (though there is no need for its greater complexity if the case $a^2 = b$ is not required). Using the notation of 11.11, equation (11) takes the form,

$$(\mathrm{D}^2 + 2a\mathrm{D} + b)y = 0 \tag{12}$$

Put $y = e^{-ax}z$. Then

$$\begin{aligned}(\mathrm{D}^2 + 2a\mathrm{D} + b)y &= (\mathrm{D}^2 + 2a\mathrm{D} + b)(e^{-ax}z)\\ &= e^{-ax}[(\mathrm{D} - a)^2 + 2a(\mathrm{D} - a) + b]z \quad [\text{by } (c) \text{ of } 11.12]\\ &= e^{-ax}[\mathrm{D}^2 + b - a^2]z\end{aligned}$$

Hence the auxiliary function z satisfies the equation

$$[\mathrm{D}^2 + (b - a^2)]z = 0 \tag{13}$$

This is of the form of equation (1) or (8) above according as $(b - a^2)$ is positive or negative, so the general solution of (11) can be written down from the solutions (2), (9) or (10) of equations (1) and (8). For $b - a^2 = 0$, equation (13) becomes simply $\mathrm{D}^2 z = 0$ whose general solution is $z = Ax + B$ where A and B are any constants.

Hence we have the general solution of equation (11)

(i) If $b - a^2 > 0$,

$$y = e^{-ax}[A \cos (b - a^2)^{1/2}x + B \sin (b - a^2)^{1/2}x] \tag{14}$$

(ii) If $b - a^2 = 0$,

$$y = e^{-ax}[Ax + B] \tag{15}$$

(iii) If $b - a^2 < 0$,

$$y = e^{-ax}[A \cosh (a^2 - b)^{1/2}x + B \sinh (a^2 - b)^{1/2}x] \tag{16}$$

or $y = Ae^{-m_1 x} + Be^{-m_2 x}$

where $(m_1, m_2) = a \pm (a^2 - b)^{1/2}$ (17)

Example. Behaviour of an electrical circuit

The following example will help to illustrate the relationship between these various solutions.

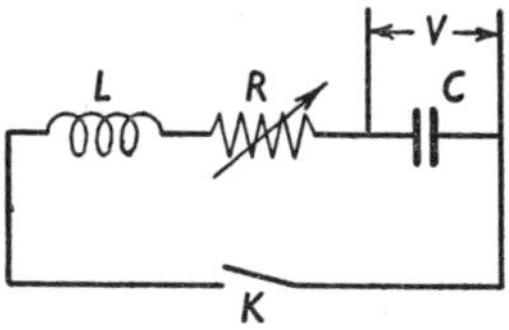

FIG. 11.1

A fixed inductance L and capacity C are joined in series with a variable resistance R (Fig. 11.1). On charging the condenser with the aid of an auxiliary battery and then discharging it by closing the key K, the subsequent behaviour of the potential difference across the condenser, $V = q/C$, will be governed by the equation (2) of 10.12 namely

$$L\frac{\mathrm{d}^2V}{\mathrm{d}t^2} + R\frac{\mathrm{d}V}{\mathrm{d}t} + \frac{1}{C}V = 0$$

which is of the type of equation (11), with t in place of x as independent variable.

If R is given a sufficiently large value so that $R^2 > 4L/C$, the relevant solution has the form (17) ; the potential difference V will gradually fall as the charge leaks slowly away through the resistance. If R is given successively smaller values, the voltage will fall more and more quickly and eventually when the resistance is sufficiently low (R^2 slightly less than $4L/C$), the exponential decay is replaced by a damped oscillatory variation of long period (see (14), with $b - a^2$ small and positive). Further decrease in R results in a shortening of the period and a decrease in the damping. Finally when R is very small ($R^2 \ll 4L/C$), the damping almost disappears and the voltage variation is nearly simple harmonic (see (14), with a small). Although there is a discontinuity in the analytical form of the solution as R passes through the critical value, $R = 2\surd(L/C)$, there is no corresponding discontinuity in the shape of the voltage-time curve, the one form changing continuously and smoothly into the other.

When, as in this example, the independent variable is the time variable t, the dependent variable (V in this example) is said to be underdamped, critically damped, or overdamped according as $b - a^2$ in equation (11) is negative, zero, or positive. If a is negative, y oscillates with continually increasing amplitude. This negative value of a corresponds to a negative resistance and is not possible in passive networks : negative resistances can however be simulated in circuits containing amplifiers and these provide an important method of generating oscillatory currents. A system for which a is negative is often said to have ' negative damping '.

11.23. *Homogeneous linear equations of higher order than the second ; constant coefficients*

Equations of order higher than the second occur usually through elimination of one or more dependent variables between two or more simultaneous first- or second-order equations. Apart from a steady increase in algebraical complexity with the order of the equation no new features appear in the solution.

Let the equation be

$$\phi(D)y = 0 \tag{1}$$

where $\phi(D)$ is a polynomial of degree n in D with real constant coefficients. Substitution of the trial solution $y = e^{mx}$ shows that this is a solution provided

$$\phi(m) = 0 \tag{2}$$

If this equation has n distinct roots, real or complex, the real roots correspond to solutions $A_j e^{m_j x}$ whereas the complex roots, which occur in conjugate pairs $m_j = k_j \pm i a_j$, correspond to solutions

$$e^{k_j x}\left[B_j \cos a_j x + C_j \sin a_j x\right]$$

as may be seen by writing $e^{\pm i a_j x} = \cos a_j x \pm i \sin a_j x$ and the general solution is the sum of such terms.

11.3. The inhomogeneous linear equation

The general form of the inhomogeneous linear equation is

$$\frac{\mathrm{d}^n y}{\mathrm{d}x^n} + a_1 \frac{\mathrm{d}^{n-1} y}{\mathrm{d}x^{n-1}} + \ldots + a_n y = \mathrm{f}(x) \tag{1}$$

The coefficients $a_1, \ldots, a_n$ may be functions of x in the general case.

11.31. *Transient and steady states*

The physical interpretation of particular integral and complementary function in a concrete example may help the reader to regard them in a friendly light. We shall consider the electrical example already formulated in 10.13: the circuit is redrawn in Fig. 11.2 and the equation relating the functions V (t) and f (t) is

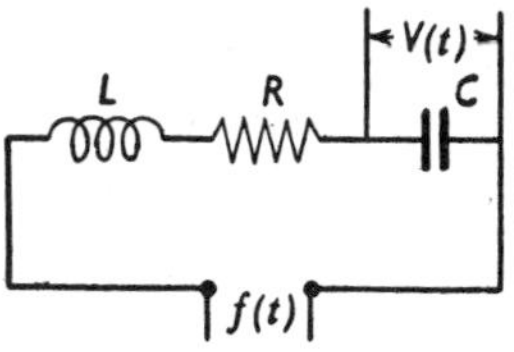

FIG. 11.2

$$LC\, \mathrm{d}^2 V/\mathrm{d}t^2 + RC\, \mathrm{d}V/\mathrm{d}t + V = \mathrm{f}(t) \tag{2}$$

This is of form (1) with t replacing x as the independent variable.

The circuit has been drawn in a form which explicitly shows f (t) as the input and V (t) as the quantity to be measured, or output potential. (It may be supposed that the output voltage is measured by a circuit of high impedance across the condenser so that the current taken is negligible.) Equation (1) may similarly be regarded as applying to a four terminal network (Fig. 11.3) specified by coefficients $a_1, \ldots, a_n$, the function f (x) being the 'input' and y (x) the 'output'. It is clear that if the output y were known, the input f could be deduced from equation (1) by straightforward differentiation, but that to find y given f requires the solution of a differential equation.

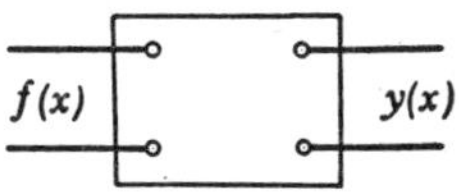

FIG. 11.3

We shall now anticipate the result and say that the output [V (t) or y (x)] is in general the sum of two parts, a forced response which is directly dependent on the input [f(t) or f(x)], and a secondary 'free response' which would be present even with zero input if the system were allowed to settle down from an initial state in which the condenser was charged and/or current was flowing. In passive networks the free response tends to zero as time increases and is transient in the normal sense of the word: in non-passive networks e.g. oscillator circuits, the free-response output may continue indefinitely when once started. A particular integral of equation (1) or (2) represents the forced response, and the complementary function represent the transient or free response of the circuit to any initial conditions.

Thus, suppose that in the system of Fig. 11.2 $v_1(t)$ is the forced response to input f(t) when V and $\mathrm{d}V/\mathrm{d}t$ are both zero at time $t=0$. Thus $V=v_1(t)$ is a particular integral of (2) satisfying $v_1=0$, $\mathrm{d}v_1/\mathrm{d}t=0$ at $t=0$.

Suppose also that $v_2(t)$ is the free response (transient) satisfying initial conditions $v_2=V_0$, $\mathrm{d}v_2/\mathrm{d}t=U_0$ at $t=0$. Then $v_2(t)$ satisfies the equation

$$L\,\mathrm{d}^2V/\mathrm{d}t^2+R\,\mathrm{d}V/\mathrm{d}t+V/C=0 \qquad (3)$$

With these definitions of v_1 and v_2 we see that the problem of satisfying (2) subject to initial conditions $V=V_0$, $\mathrm{d}V/\mathrm{d}t=U_0$ is solved by

$$V=v_1+v_2,$$

for (i) $L\,\mathrm{d}^2V/\mathrm{d}t^2+R\,\mathrm{d}V/\mathrm{d}t+V/C$

$$=L\,\mathrm{d}^2v_1/\mathrm{d}t^2+R\,\mathrm{d}v_1/\mathrm{d}t+v_1/c+L\,\mathrm{d}^2v_2/\mathrm{d}t^2+R\,\mathrm{d}v_2/\mathrm{d}t+v_2/c$$

$$=\qquad \mathrm{f}(t)/C \qquad + \qquad 0$$

and (ii) $V(0)=v_1(0)+v_2(0)=0+V_0$

$$(\mathrm{d}V/\mathrm{d}t)_0=(\mathrm{d}v_1/\mathrm{d}t)_0+(\mathrm{d}v_2/\mathrm{d}t)_0=0+U_0$$

Thus the result stated earlier has been confirmed.

In the above example we chose as our 'particular integral' that solution for which $v_1=0$, $\mathrm{d}v_1/\mathrm{d}t=0$ at $t=0$. The work could be paralleled with any other choice, $v_1=V_1$, $\mathrm{d}v_1/\mathrm{d}t=U_1$ say, in which case the corresponding conditions for the complementary function would be $v_2=V_0-V_1$, $\mathrm{d}v_2/\mathrm{d}t=U_0-U_1$. It often happens that one particular integral is of simpler algebraical form than any other, and it is then sometimes called *the* particular integral; this is not necessarily the one corresponding to a system starting from rest.

11.32. *Determination of particular integrals*

The most powerful systematic methods (Laplace Transforms, series solutions etc.) of obtaining the required solutions of a differential equation are described elsewhere (Chapters 10, 12,

14, 15). But in simple cases of the kind we are concerned with here, the less systematic method of 'trial solutions' often gives the answer even more quickly and easily.

From any particular integral of a linear differential equation, the general solution can be constructed by adding the complementary function. Hence *any* function which satisfies the equation, whether the function is guessed or systematically deduced, enables the required solution to be found.

The chosen 'trial function' should contain parameters the value of which must be determined (if possible) so that the trial function satisfies the differential equation. The student should not be unduly disturbed if the first trial function which he guesses does not satisfy the equation—he should try again. An appropriate trial solution in many cases is a function of similar form to the inhomogeneous term, or 'right-hand side' of the equation. Failing this a substitution of the form

$$y = z \times \text{complementary function}$$

is sometimes helpful.

11.33. *First-order equations*

The general first-order inhomogeneous linear equation with constant coefficients is

$$\mathrm{d}y/\mathrm{d}x + ay = \mathrm{g}(x) \tag{1}$$

Example

$$\mathrm{d}y/\mathrm{d}x + ay = e^{-bx} \tag{2}$$

The form of the right-hand side suggests a trial solution $y = Be^{-bx}$; substitution gives $(-b+a)Be^{-bx} = e^{-bx}$ and provided $b \neq a$ this is satisfied, for all x, if $B = 1/(a-b)$. Hence

$$y = e^{-bx}/(a-b) \tag{3}$$

is a particular integral.

In order to solve the general equation (1) we might try $y = B \,.\, \mathrm{g}(x+c)$, but no choice of B, c makes this a solution unless g is an exponential function or sine or cosine. Let us therefore try the substitution

$$y = z \times \text{complementary function}$$

$$= ze^{-ax} \tag{4}$$

Then by (c) of 11.12

$$(\mathrm{D}+a)y=(\mathrm{D}+a)[e^{-ax}z]=e^{-ax}\,\mathrm{D}z=e^{-ax}\,\mathrm{d}z/\mathrm{d}x$$

so that z has to be a solution of $\mathrm{d}z/\mathrm{d}x=e^{ax}\,\mathrm{g}(x)$. Hence

$$z=\int e^{ax}\mathrm{g}(x)\,\mathrm{d}x \tag{5}$$

and the solution of the differential equation (2) has been reduced to the evaluation of an integral (which it may or may not be possible to evaluate formally). More precisely (cf. eqn. 3 of 8.6)

$$z=\int_c^x e^{a\xi}\,\mathrm{g}(\xi)\,\mathrm{d}\xi \tag{6}$$

where c is some fixed lower limit of integration. Substitution in (4) then gives the solution of (1), namely

$$y=e^{-ax}\int_c^x e^{a\xi}\,\mathrm{g}(\xi)\,\mathrm{d}\xi \tag{7}$$

Different values of c give different particular integrals.

Example 1

$$\mathrm{d}y/\mathrm{d}x+ay=e^{-ax}\sin x$$

(7) gives $\quad y=e^{-ax}\int_c^x \sin\xi\,\mathrm{d}\xi=-e^{-ax}(\cos x-\text{constant})$

The simplest particular integral is thus $-e^{-ax}\cos x$ (with $c=\frac{1}{2}\pi$), while the choice $c=0$ would give $e^{-ax}(1-\cos x)$.

Example 2

Use (7) to find a solution of equation (2) in the exceptional case $a=b$ (compare with the solution (3) which fails).

11.34. *Second-order equations*

The use of trial solutions is also a valuable technique for finding particular integrals of second-order equations.

Example

$$\mathrm{d}^2y/\mathrm{d}x^2+2a\,\mathrm{d}y/\mathrm{d}x+by=e^{kx} \tag{1}$$

We have to find an output y which after differentiation in accordance with the equation will reproduce the input e^{kx}. Now the exponential e^{mx} is unique in that, apart from a constant factor, it reproduces itself after differentiation; hence the operation $(\mathrm{D}^2+\alpha\mathrm{D}+\beta)$ applied to the function e^{kx} will give a multiple of the input e^{kx}. We therefore make a trial solution

Ae^{kx}, where the coefficient A is to be determined. We find that A must satisfy

$$A\,(k^2+2ak+b)\,e^{kx}=e^{kx}$$

Provided $k^2+2ak+b\neq 0$, this can be satisfied *for all* x by taking $A=1/(k^2+2ak+b)$ and hence a particular integral is

$$y=e^{kx}/(k^2+2ak+b) \tag{2}$$

This method fails however if $k^2+2ak+b=0$.

A procedure applicable to any equation of the type

$$\mathrm{d}^2y/\mathrm{d}x^2+2a\,\mathrm{d}y/\mathrm{d}x+by=e^{kx}\,\mathrm{g}(x) \tag{3}$$

is to take out of the output function y the same exponential factor as occurs in the input, by writing $y=e^{kx}z$.

Then

$$(\mathrm{D}^2+2a\mathrm{D}+b)y=e^{kx}[(\mathrm{D}+k)^2+2a(\mathrm{D}+k)+b]z$$
$$=e^{kx}[\mathrm{D}^2+2(k+a)\mathrm{D}+(k^2+2ak+b)]z$$

so that the auxiliary function z satisfies the equation

$$[\mathrm{D}^2+2(k+a)\mathrm{D}+(k^2+2ak+b)]z=\mathrm{g}(x) \tag{4}$$

which may well be easier to solve than the original equation (3).

If $\mathrm{g}(x)$ is a polynomial of degree n, then provided $k^2+2ak+b\neq 0$ (4) has a polynomial solution of degree n, which can be found by substituting such a polynomial and equating coefficients. If however $k^2+2ak+b=0$ but $k+a\neq 0$, equation (4) becomes a first-order equation for $\mathrm{D}z=\mathrm{d}z/\mathrm{d}x$, namely

$$[\mathrm{D}+2(k+a)]\mathrm{D}z=\mathrm{g}(x)$$

which can be solved for $\mathrm{D}z$ by the method of the last paragraph whence z can be found by integration. [In fact, z will be a polynomial of degree $n+1$.] If both $k^2+2ak+b=0$ and $k+a=0$ (which can only occur if $k=a$, $b=a^2$), equation (4) becomes $\mathrm{D}^2z=\mathrm{g}(x)$, so that z is a polynomial of degree $(n+2)$. If, in the equation

$$\mathrm{d}^2y/\mathrm{d}x^2+2a\,\mathrm{d}y/\mathrm{d}x+by=\mathrm{f}(x) \tag{5}$$

$\mathrm{f}(x)$ is a sine or cosine, the most convenient way of obtaining a particular integral is usually by means of the complex representation of simple-harmonic quantities (see 6.5 and 11.33).

If $\mathrm{f}(x)$ is the product of a polynomial and a sine or cosine, say $\mathrm{f}(x)=\mathrm{h}(x)\cos mx$ where $\mathrm{h}(x)$ is a polynomial of degree n, then provided that the conditions $a=0$ and $b=m^2$ are not both satisfied, equation (5) has a solution

$$y=\mathrm{u}(x)\cos mx+\mathrm{v}(x)\sin mx \tag{6}$$

where $\mathrm{u}(x)$ and $\mathrm{v}(x)$ are polynomials of degree not higher than n.

These can be found by substitution and equating of coefficients of $x^k \cos mx$ and $x^k \sin mx$ separately ; the algebraical details are complicated unless the degree n of the polynomial is small.

For input functions $\mathrm{f}(x)$ other than sums or products, of polynomials, exponentials, and circular functions, equation (5) has usually no formal solution in finite terms.

Example

$$\frac{\mathrm{d}^2y}{\mathrm{d}x^2}+2a\frac{\mathrm{d}y}{\mathrm{d}x}+(a^2+1)y=4xe^{-ax}\cos x$$

Substitution of $y=e^{-ax}z$ gives

$$\frac{\mathrm{d}^2z}{\mathrm{d}x^2}+z=4x\cos x$$

Now put $z=\mathrm{u}(x)\cos x+\mathrm{v}(x)\sin x$. We find

$$(u''+2v'-4x)\cos x+(v''-2u')\sin x=0$$

This equation is satisfied if

$$u''+2v'=4x$$
$$v''-2u'=0$$

which have a solution $u=x$, $v=x^2$ (they have other solutions, but since we require only one solution to give a particular integral, we choose the simplest). Hence a particular integral is

$$y=e^{-ax}[x\cos x+x^2\sin x].$$

11.35. *Equations of any order*

Any linear inhomogeneous equation $\phi(\mathrm{D})y=\mathrm{g}(x)$, of order higher than the second, with constant coefficients can be reduced to a sequence of equations of the first and second order. For, if the *polynomial* $\phi(z)$ has linear factors $\mathrm{f}_1(z), \mathrm{f}_2(z), \ldots$ and irreducible quadratic factors $\mathrm{h}_1(z), \mathrm{h}_2(z), \ldots, \mathrm{h}_s(z)$, the operator $\phi(\mathrm{D})$ may be replaced by the product of operators

$$\mathrm{f}_1(\mathrm{D})\mathrm{f}_2(\mathrm{D})\ldots\mathrm{h}_1(\mathrm{D})\ldots\mathrm{h}_s(\mathrm{D}).$$

Then, putting $y_1=\mathrm{h}_s(\mathrm{D})y$, $y_2=\mathrm{h}_{s-1}(\mathrm{D})y_1, \ldots, y_r=\mathrm{f}_2(\mathrm{D})y_{r-1}$, we see that the equation $\phi(\mathrm{D})y=\mathrm{g}(x)$ is equivalent to the system of first and second order equations,

$$\left.\begin{aligned}\mathrm{f}_1(\mathrm{D})y_r&=\mathrm{g}(x)\\ \mathrm{f}_2(\mathrm{D})y_{r-1}&=y_r\\ &\cdots\cdots\\ \mathrm{h}_s(\mathrm{D})y&=y_1\end{aligned}\right\}\qquad(1)$$

We have seen in 11.33, 11.34 that any first-order or second-order linear equation with constant coefficients in which the inhomogeneous term is a product of polynomials, exponentials and sines or cosines has a solution of the same form. By solution of the successive equations (1) it follows that the same is true of an inhomogeneous linear equation of any order (with constant coefficients).

11.36. *Simple harmonic input functions*

This is the most frequent kind of input in physical applications, not only because of the importance of A.C. circuits but because of the usefulness of harmonic analysis in dealing with linear systems in general. In this context the independent variable is usually the time variable t, and the method of 6.5, 6.51 using the phase-amplitude diagram and the idea of complex impedances is the most convenient for this kind of input.

11.4. Simultaneous differential equations. Normal modes

A problem containing more than one dependent variable will give rise to a number of simultaneous differential equations.

Example

Coupled Oscillators

The behaviour of a system of two or more coupled oscillators is of considerable importance in several contexts. Fig. 11.4 shows an electrical arrangement which provides an example, namely two oscillatory circuits coupled together by mutual inductance M. The equations for q_1 and q_2, the charges on the two condensers, are :

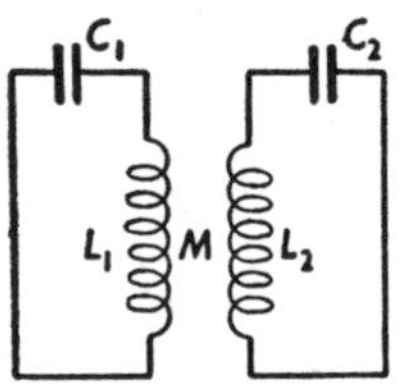

FIG. 11.4

$$L_1(\mathrm{d}^2q_1/\mathrm{d}t^2+\omega_1{}^2q_1)+M\ \mathrm{d}^2q_2/\mathrm{d}t^2=0 \tag{1}$$

$$L_2(\mathrm{d}^2q_2/\mathrm{d}t^2+\omega_2{}^2q_2)+M\ \mathrm{d}^2q_1/\mathrm{d}t^2=0 \tag{2}$$

where $\omega_1{}^2=1/L_1C_1$, $\omega_2{}^2=1/L_2C_2$. The solution satisfying specified initial conditions is most easily found by the method of Chapter 15 (Laplace Transforms).

If the general solution is required, two alternative methods are worth mentioning. The first is to eliminate either q_1 or q_2 from equations (1) and (2), obtaining a fourth-order equation for the other which can then be solved as indicated in 11.23. The elimination is most easily carried out on the equations expressed in operational form, $L_1(\mathrm{D}^2+\omega_1^2)q_1+MD^2q_2=0$ and $MD^2q_1+L_2(\mathrm{D}^2+\omega_2^2)q_2=0$, the result being

$$[L_1L_2(\mathrm{D}^2+\omega_1^2)(\mathrm{D}^2+\omega_2^2)-M^2\mathrm{D}^4]q_1=0$$

i.e. $$[(1-M^2/L_1L_2)\mathrm{D}^4+(\omega_1^2+\omega_2^2)\mathrm{D}^2+\omega_1^2\omega_2^2]q_1=0 \tag{3}$$

The quantity M^2/L_1L_2 is, for physical reasons, always less than unity, so the discriminant of the quadratic expression in D^2 on the left-hand side, viz $(\omega_1^2+\omega_2^2)^2-4(1-M^2/L_1L_2)\omega_1^2\omega_2^2$ lies between $(\omega_1^2+\omega_2^2)^2$ and $(\omega_1^2-\omega_2^2)^2$ and is therefore positive. After dividing by the positive factor $(1-M^2/L_1L_2)$, equation (3) may therefore be factorised

$$(\mathrm{D}^2+\gamma_1^2)(\mathrm{D}^2+\gamma_2^2)q_1=0 \tag{4}$$

where we have written the constants as γ_1^2 and γ_2^2 since both their sum and their product, and hence the numbers themselves, are positive.

The general solution is a linear combination of solutions of $(\mathrm{D}^2+\gamma_1^2)q=0$ and $(\mathrm{D}^2+\gamma_2^2)q=0$, that is

$$q_1=A_1\cos\gamma_1t+B_1\sin\gamma_1t+A_2\cos\gamma_2t+B_2\sin\gamma_2t \tag{5}$$

for (5) satisfies (4) and has four independent arbitrary constants.

The expression for q_2 must be derived from (5) without introducing further arbitrary constants. Elimination of $\mathrm{d}^2q_2/\mathrm{d}t^2$ from equations (1) and (2) gives

$$L_2M\omega_2^2q_2=((L_1L_2-M^2)\mathrm{D}^2+L_1L_2\omega_1^2)q_1 \tag{6}$$

from which q_2 can be found.

The above method becomes more and more cumbersome as the number of coupled equations increases, and the labour of elimination of variables becomes greater.

The second method avoids eliminations and the consequent unsymmetrical treatment of q_1 and q_2. It consists of first identifying particular solutions in which q_1 and q_2 vary with equal periodicities, and then showing that the general solution can be built up from these particular solutions.

It is convenient to use the representation of simple harmonic quantities by complex exponentials. We look for solutions, if any, in which q_1, q_2 vary harmonically with the same frequency i.e. $q_1=\mathscr{R}(Q_1e^{i\omega t})$, $q_2=\mathscr{R}(Q_2e^{i\omega t})$. We note that if $Q_1e^{i\omega t}$, $Q_2e^{i\omega t}$ satisfy (1) and (2) their real parts also satisfy the same equations. Substitution of $q_1 = Q_1 e^{i\omega t}$ and $q_2 = Q_2 e^{i\omega t}$ in (1), (2) gives,

$$L_1(\omega_1^2 - \omega^2)Q_1 - M\omega^2 Q_2 = 0$$
$$L_2(\omega_2^2 - \omega^2)Q_2 - M\omega^2 Q_1 = 0$$

The values of Q_1/Q_2 given by the two equations are consistent only if

$$(1 - M^2/L_1L_2)\omega^4 - (\omega_1^2 + \omega_2^2)\omega^2 + \omega_1^2\omega_2^2 = 0 \qquad (7)$$

This can be compared with equation (3) : we see that D^2 in (3) occurs in a way closely similar to $(-\omega^2)$ in (7), and therefore that the solutions to (7) are $\omega^2 - \gamma_1^2 = 0$, $\omega^2 - \gamma_2^2 = 0$. The special solutions with these frequencies are called *normal modes.*

When $\omega^2 = \gamma_1^2$, $Q_2/Q_1 = L_1(\omega_1^2 - \gamma_1^2)/M\gamma_1^2$, so there are corresponding normal modes

$$q_1 = \cos \gamma_1 t, \ (Q_1 = 1)$$
$$q_2 = \{L_1(\omega_1^2 - \gamma_1^2) \cos \gamma_1 t\}/M\gamma_1^2$$

and

$$q_1 = \sin \gamma_1 t, \ (Q_1 = -i)$$
$$q_2 = \{L_1(\omega_1^2 - \gamma_1^2) \sin \gamma_1 t\}/M\gamma_1^2$$

Two further independent modes arise from the alternative $\omega^2 = \gamma_2^2$ and correspond to q_1 proportional to $\cos \gamma_2 t$ and $\sin \gamma_2 t$ respectively.

Equations (1), (2) are linear, so the sum of arbitrary multiples of the four independent particular solutions which we have found is also a solution : this sum contains four independent arbitrary constants and is therefore the general solution, viz.

$$q_1 = A_1 \cos \gamma_1 t + B_1 \sin \gamma_1 t + A_2 \cos \gamma_2 t + B_2 \sin \gamma_2 t$$
$$q_2 = (A_1 \cos \gamma_1 t + B_1 \sin \gamma_1 t)L_1(\omega_1^2 - \gamma_1^2)/M\gamma_1^2$$
$$+ (A_2 \cos \gamma_2 t + B_2 \sin \gamma_2 t)M\gamma_2^2/L_2(\omega_2^2 - \gamma_2^2)$$

That this is in agreement with (5), (6) can be verified if it is borne in mind that γ_1 and γ_2 satisfy (7).

11.5. Linear equations with variable coefficients

We will now consider linear differential equations in which the coefficients, instead of being constant, are functions of the independent variable x. The superposition theorems of 11.1 are not restricted to equations with constant coefficients, and still apply.

Linear equations of the second and higher orders are not usually integrable by elementary methods. Solutions exist in the general sense that the differential equation defines a function of the independent variable, but this function is not usually elementary. Some exceptional classes of equations of the second order which have elementary solutions are discussed in 11.52.

11.51. *First order linear equations with variable coefficients*

We now confine ourselves to the first order linear equation

$$\mathrm{d}y/\mathrm{d}x + \mathrm{P}(x)y = \mathrm{Q}(x) \tag{1}$$

where P and Q are functions of x only.

The technique is to multiply both sides of the equation by a function $\phi(x)$ such that the left-hand side, which then starts off with the term $\phi(x)\,\mathrm{d}y/\mathrm{d}x$ is in fact equal to $\mathrm{d}[\phi(x)\,.\,y]/\mathrm{d}x$.

The function ϕ must thus be such that $\phi(x)\mathrm{P}(x) = \mathrm{d}\phi/\mathrm{d}x$ i.e. $\phi'(x)/\phi(x) = \mathrm{P}(x)$, whence $\log \phi(x) = \int \mathrm{P}(x)\,\mathrm{d}x$, that is

$$\phi(x) = \exp\left\{\int \mathrm{P}(x)\,\mathrm{d}x\right\} \tag{2}$$

Equation (1) then takes the form

$$\mathrm{d}[\phi(x)y]/\mathrm{d}x = \phi(x)\mathrm{Q}(x) \tag{3}$$

where $\phi(x)$ is the known function given by (2). Thus the solution of equation (1) is

$$y = \left\{\int \phi(x)\mathrm{Q}(x)\,\mathrm{d}x\right\} \Big/ \phi(x) \tag{4}$$

It can be seen that the arbitrary constant of integration in (2) merely provides a factor throughout in (3), which can be cancelled, and is therefore irrelevant. The constant of integration in the indefinite integral in (4), however, is necessary in order to obtain the *general* solution.

It follows from (4) that if in (1) P and Q are elementary functions of x, the solution of (1) is either an elementary function or is expressible in terms of integrals of elementary functions.

Example

$$\frac{\mathrm{d}y}{\mathrm{d}x} + \frac{y}{x} = x^2$$

The integrating factor is $\exp\left(\int (1/x)\,\mathrm{d}x\right) = \exp(\log x) = x$. On multiplication by it the equation becomes

$$x\,\mathrm{d}y/\mathrm{d}x + y = x^3$$

of which the left-hand side is $\mathrm{d}(xy)/\mathrm{d}x$. Hence, integrating

$$xy = \tfrac{1}{4}x^4 + C$$

$$y = \tfrac{1}{4}x^3 + C/x$$

The first term is a particular integral, the second the complementary function.

11.52. *Second-order linear equations with variable coefficients*

The general equation of this type is

$$\mathrm{d}^2y/\mathrm{d}x^2 + \mathrm{P}(x)\,\mathrm{d}y/\mathrm{d}x + \mathrm{Q}(x)\,y = \mathrm{R}(x) \qquad (1)$$

As in all linear systems the principle of superposition (§11.1) applies and the solution is consequently of the form

$$y = Au + Bv + w$$

where $Au + Bv$ is the complementary function, i.e. the general solution of the homogeneous equation obtained by putting $\mathrm{R}(x) = 0$ in (1), and w is a particular integral of (1).

This equation is without doubt the backbone of mathematical physics. One context in which it occurs is in the solution of partial differential equations and especially from the method of ' separation of the variables ' (16.2). Only for a few equations of the form (1) does an elementary solution exist ; even the simple equation

$$\frac{\mathrm{d}^2y}{\mathrm{d}x^2} + xy = 0$$

has no solution in finite terms in elementary functions.

There are, however, one or two classes of this general type which yield to an elementary treatment.

11.53. *Equations homogeneous in x*

The equations

$$\frac{\mathrm{d}^2y}{\mathrm{d}x^2} + \frac{a}{x}\frac{\mathrm{d}y}{\mathrm{d}x} + \frac{b}{x^2}y = \mathrm{f}(x) \qquad (1)$$

and

$$x^2\,\mathrm{d}^2y/\mathrm{d}x^2 + ax\,\mathrm{d}y/\mathrm{d}x + by = \mathrm{g}(x) \qquad (2)$$

are said to be homogeneous in x, the term referring strictly to the linear operators

$$\left(\frac{d^2}{dx^2}+\frac{a}{x}\frac{d}{dx}+\frac{b}{x^2}\right) \quad \text{and} \quad \left(x^2\frac{d^2}{dx^2}+ax\frac{d}{dx}+b\right)$$

which are of order -2 and 0 in x respectively.

The coefficients of these equations can be reduced to constants by a change of independent variable. Put $x=e^t$ so that $dx/dt=e^t$ Then if z is any variable depending on x (and so on t)

$$\frac{dz}{dx}=\frac{dz}{dt}\bigg/\frac{dx}{dt}=e^{-t}\frac{dz}{dt}$$

In particular

$$dy/dx=e^{-t}\,dy/dt \quad \text{so} \quad x\,dy/dx=dy/dt \tag{3}$$

$$\frac{d^2y}{dx^2}=\frac{d}{dx}\left(\frac{dy}{dx}\right)=e^{-t}\frac{d}{dt}\left(e^{-t}\frac{dy}{dt}\right)=e^{-2t}\left(\frac{d^2y}{dt^2}-\frac{dy}{dt}\right)$$

so that

$$x^2\,d^2y/dx^2=d^2y/dt^2-dy/dt \tag{4}$$

The process could be extended to all orders of derivative.

Substitution of (3) and (4) in (2) give

$$d^2y/dt^2+(a-1)\,dy/dt+by=g(e^t) \tag{5}$$

This can be solved completely by the methods of §11.3 or Chapter 15. Notice that the characteristic role played by the exponential function e^{mt} in solving equation (5) implies a similar importance of the function x^m in the solution of (1) and (2). Using this hint it may be possible to avoid the explicit change of variable from x to t. For example to find the complementary function of (2), i.e. the complete solution of

$$x^2\,d^2y/dx^2+ax\,dy/dx+by=0, \tag{6}$$

we can make a trial solution $y=x^m$. This satisfies equation (6) provided

$$[m(m-1)+am+b]\,x^m=0$$

and the roots m_1, m_2, if distinct, give the solution

$$y=Ax^{m_1}+Bx^{m_2}$$

If the roots are coincident ($b=\frac{1}{4}(a-1)^2$, $m_1=m_2=\frac{1}{2}(1-a)$), the substitution $y=Ax^mz$ leads to a soluble equation for z, and the solution

$$y=x^m(A+B\log x)$$

Example

Poisson's equation for the electrostatic potential ϕ in space due to a charge distribution (charge density ρ) which is symmetrical about an axis, $r=0$, can be written

$$\frac{d^2\phi}{dr^2}+\frac{1}{r}\frac{d\phi}{dr}=-4\pi\rho$$

i.e.
$$r^2\frac{d^2\phi}{dr^2}+r\frac{d\phi}{dr}=-4\pi\rho r^2 \tag{7}$$

which is of the form (2).

Let $r=e^t$, $\phi(r)=F(t)$ and $D=\dfrac{d}{dt}$. Then in terms of t as independent variable equation (7) becomes

$$D^2F=-4\pi\rho e^{2t}$$

where, on the right-hand side ρ will now be expressed as a function of t.

For any given density distribution ρ, the potential $\phi=F(t)$ can now be obtained by two integrations.

11.54. *Solution when a part of the complementary function is known*

If one solution of the equation

$$d^2y/dx^2+P(x)\,dy/dx+Q(x)\,y=0 \tag{1}$$

for the complementary function can be obtained (e.g. by trial), the whole solution of the inhomogeneous equation

$$d^2y/dx^2+P(x)\,dy/dx+Q(x)\,y=R(x) \tag{2}$$

can be obtained as follows. Let $y=u(x)$ be the known solution of (1). Introduce an auxiliary dependent variable z defined by

$$y=zu$$

Then
$$\frac{dy}{dx}=z\frac{du}{dx}+\frac{dz}{dx}u$$

$$\frac{d^2y}{dx^2}=z\frac{d^2u}{dx^2}+2\frac{dz}{dx}\frac{du}{dx}+\frac{d^2z}{dx^2}u$$

Substituting these into (2) and collecting the terms involving the different derivatives of z we find that z must satisfy the equation

$$u\frac{d^2z}{dx^2}+\left(2\frac{du}{dx}+Pu\right)\frac{dz}{dx}+\left(\frac{d^2u}{dx^2}+P\frac{du}{dx}+Qu\right)z=R$$

Now u satisfies equation (1) and therefore the coefficient of z vanishes. Hence by introducing $v = \mathrm{d}z/\mathrm{d}x$ as a further auxiliary dependent variable we obtain the first order equation

$$u\frac{\mathrm{d}v}{\mathrm{d}x} + \left(2\frac{\mathrm{d}u}{\mathrm{d}x} + \mathrm{P}u\right)v = \mathrm{R} \qquad (3)$$

for v. In this equation, u and $\mathrm{d}u/\mathrm{d}x$ are known functions of x, so it can be solved completely by the method of 11.51 to give v as a function of x containing one arbitrary constant. A second arbitrary constant appears when v is integrated to give z. The complete solution is then given by

$$y = uz$$

Example

$$(x^2-1)\frac{\mathrm{d}^2y}{\mathrm{d}x^2} - 2x\frac{\mathrm{d}y}{\mathrm{d}x} + 2y = 2(x^2-1)^2$$

By trial it is found that $y = x$ is a solution of the equation for the complementary function. We therefore put $y = xz$, compare 11.32, so that

$$\frac{\mathrm{d}y}{\mathrm{d}x} = x\frac{\mathrm{d}z}{\mathrm{d}x} + z, \quad \frac{\mathrm{d}^2y}{\mathrm{d}x^2} = x\frac{\mathrm{d}^2z}{\mathrm{d}x^2} + 2\frac{\mathrm{d}z}{\mathrm{d}x}$$

Then z must satisfy

$$(x^2-1)\left[x\frac{\mathrm{d}^2z}{\mathrm{d}x^2} + 2\frac{\mathrm{d}z}{\mathrm{d}x}\right] - 2x\left[x\frac{\mathrm{d}z}{\mathrm{d}x} + z\right] + 2xz = 2(x^2-1)^2$$

The terms in z go out leaving a first-order equation in $\mathrm{d}z/\mathrm{d}x = v$,

$$x(x^2-1)\,\mathrm{d}v/\mathrm{d}x - 2v = 2(x^2-1)^2 \qquad (4)$$

The integrating factor of the expression $\mathrm{d}v/\mathrm{d}x - [2/x(x^2-1)]v$ is found to be $x^2/(x^2-1)$; hence we multiply (4) by $x/(x^2-1)^2$ giving

$$\frac{x^2}{x^2-1}\frac{\mathrm{d}v}{\mathrm{d}x} - \frac{2x}{(x^2-1)^2}v = 2x$$

whence

$$\frac{\mathrm{d}}{\mathrm{d}x}\left[\left(\frac{x^2}{x^2-1}\right)v\right] = 2x$$

$$[x^2/(x^2-1)]v = x^2 + A$$

$$\mathrm{d}z/\mathrm{d}x = v = x^2 - 1 + A(x^2-1)/x^2 = x^2 - 1 + A(1 - 1/x^2)$$

whence $\qquad z = \tfrac{1}{3}x^3 - x + A(x + 1/x) + B$

and finally $\qquad y = xz = \tfrac{1}{3}x^4 - x^2 + A(x^2+1) + Bx.$

11.55. *Removal of first-order term*

It is always possible to remove the first-order term from a second-order linear equation by the substitution $y = uz$ where u is to be chosen suitably and z is a new dependent variable. This step does not necessarily make the equation integrable, but is useful in reducing the algebraical detail. It is an almost essential preliminary if the equation has to be solved numerically. Let the equation be

$$\frac{d^2y}{dx^2} + P(x)\frac{dy}{dx} + Q(x)\,y = R(x) \tag{1}$$

and put $y = uz$.

Then $$\frac{dy}{dx} = u\frac{dz}{dx} + u'z, \quad \frac{d^2y}{dx^2} = u\frac{d^2z}{dx^2} + 2u'\frac{dz}{dx} + u''z$$

and z must satisfy

$$u\frac{d^2z}{dx^2} + (2u' + Pu)\frac{dz}{dx} + (u'' + Pu' + Qu)\,z = R$$

The first-order term disappears if u is so chosen that

$$2u' + Pu = 0$$

$$u = e^{-\frac{1}{2}\int P\,dx}$$

In particular, if $P = 2/x$, then $u = e^{-\log x} = 1/x$, so that equation (1) can be written

$$\frac{d^2}{dx^2}(xy) + Q(x).(xy) = xR(x) \tag{2}$$

as can be seen directly on expanding the first term on the left-hand side by Leibnitz's theorem. The form (2) is very often the most convenient form in which to work with an equation in which the terms involving derivatives are $\dfrac{d^2y}{dx^2} + \dfrac{2}{x}\dfrac{dy}{dx}$.

Example

The equation

$$\frac{d^2\phi}{dr^2} + \frac{2}{r}\frac{d\phi}{dr} + \frac{\omega^2}{c^2}\phi = 0 \tag{3}$$

occurs in wave motion with spherical symmetry. Taking $r\phi$ as dependent variable, the equation becomes

$$\frac{d^2}{dr^2}(r\phi)+\frac{\omega^2}{c^2}(r\phi)=0$$

of which the complete solution is

$$r\phi=A\cos(\omega r/c)+B\sin(\omega r/c)$$

and hence the complete solution of (3) is

$$\phi=[A\cos(\omega r/c)+B\sin(\omega r/c)]/r$$

CHAPTER TWELVE

SERIES SOLUTIONS, EIGENVALUE PROPERTIES, AND FOURIER SERIES

12.1. Solution by series of second-order linear equations with variable coefficients

As mentioned in 11.52 a second-order differential equation with variable coefficients in general has no elementary solution. An analytical solution of the differential equation must therefore be sought among functions defined by infinite processes such as infinite series, infinite products, integrals, limits of sequences, and so on. The most useful of these forms are the infinite series and the definite integral.

In this chapter we shall consider solutions in the form of infinite series : series in ascending powers of x are particularly useful when numerical values of the solution are wanted at small values of the argument ; asymptotic series (see 14.3) have a similar use for large values of the argument.

12.11. *Example of solution by series*

To illustrate the procedure we use the method of solution by series to solve the first order equation

$$\frac{\mathrm{d}y}{\mathrm{d}x}=y \tag{1}$$

The method of solution of second (or higher) order linear equations is basically the same. (The general solution of equation (1) has already been obtained in 11.21 but we shall proceed as though we had no prior knowledge of the solution.) We make the trial solution

$$y=a_0+a_1x+a_2x^2+\dots+a_rx^r\dots \tag{2}$$

This gives

$$\mathrm{d}y/\mathrm{d}x=a_1+2a_2x+3a_3x^2+\dots+(r+1)a_{r+1}x^r\dots \tag{3}$$

We cannot at the moment assert that term by term differentiation is justified, but when the radius of convergence of the series (2) is eventually found, the theorem of 7.6 will apply and the process will be justified a posteriori for values of x within this region. Taking equation (1) in the form

$$dy/dx - y = 0$$

and inserting the series (2) and (3) we find that the coefficient of x^r on the left is

$$(r+1)a_{r+1} - a_r$$

and hence by comparing coefficients

$$a_{r+1} = \frac{1}{(r+1)} a_r \tag{4}$$

From this we find, putting $r = 0, 1, 2, \ldots$ in succession,

$$a_1 = a_0$$

$$a_2 = \tfrac{1}{2}a_1 = a_0/2!$$

$$a_3 = \tfrac{1}{3}a_2 = a_0/3!$$

and in general $\quad a_r = a_0/r!$

The series is therefore

$$y = a_0(1 + x + x^2/2! + \ldots + x^r/r! \ldots) \tag{5}$$

The radius of convergence is given by

$$\frac{1}{R} = \lim_{r\to\infty} \frac{a_{r+1}}{a_r} = \lim_{r\to\infty} \frac{1}{r+1} \tag{6}$$

and hence the series converges (absolutely and uniformly) for all values of x including complex values. This justifies the steps taken in deriving it. The solution (5) contains one arbitrary constant a_0 and is therefore complete.

The usefulness of the series method of solution will obviously be increased if we know the circumstances under which it can be expected to work. Therefore, before proceeding to the solution of second-order equations by series, we will engage on a more general discussion of series solutions.

12.12. *Ordinary points and singular points*

Consider the general equation

$$p_0(x)\, d^2y/dx^2 + p_1(x)\, dy/dx + p_2(x)\, y = q(x) \tag{1}$$

We shall discuss the solution y in a finite range of the independent variable x, and, to avoid unessential complications, we will assume that p_0, p_1, p_2 and q are single-valued and possess derivatives of all orders in this range.

Except at points (if any) where $\mathrm{p}_0(x)=0$, this equation can be solved for $\mathrm{d}^2y/\mathrm{d}x^2$ in terms of x, y and $\mathrm{d}y/\mathrm{d}x$, say

$$\mathrm{d}^2y/\mathrm{d}x^2=\mathrm{f}(x, y, \mathrm{d}y/\mathrm{d}x) \tag{2}$$

the function f possessing derivatives of all orders. Then from the existence theorem of 10.6 it follows that a solution exists satisfying given conditions $y=y_0$, $\mathrm{d}y/\mathrm{d}x=y_0'$ at $x=x_0$, and that it is unique.

The zeros of $\mathrm{p}_0(x)$ are called singular points of the equation and all other points are ordinary points. The equation is said to have a singularity at its singular points.

Writing $\mathrm{d}^2y/\mathrm{d}x^2=\mathrm{f}(x, y, \mathrm{d}y/\mathrm{d}x)$; $\mathrm{d}^3y/\mathrm{d}x^3=\mathrm{f}'(x, y, \mathrm{d}y/\mathrm{d}x)$; $\mathrm{d}^4y/\mathrm{d}x^4=\mathrm{f}''(x, y, \mathrm{d}y/\mathrm{d}x)$ etc., we see that if initial conditions $y=y_0$, $\mathrm{d}y/\mathrm{d}x=y_0'$ are postulated at any ordinary point $x=x_0$, $\mathrm{d}^2y/\mathrm{d}x^2$, $\mathrm{d}^3y/\mathrm{d}x^3$, ... can also be evaluated at that point. The Taylor expansion of y can therefore be written down, viz.

$$y_0+(x-x_0)y_0'+\tfrac{1}{2}(x-x_0)^2\, y_0''+\dots \tag{3}$$

That the radius of convergence of this series in $(x-x_0)$ is greater than zero, and that the second derivative of the series is equal to $\mathrm{f}(x, y, \mathrm{d}y/\mathrm{d}x)$ can be demonstrated provided that p_0, p_1, p_2 and q are analytic functions (see 13.32). It follows that the series (3) represents a function which satisfies (2) and hence satisfies (1), as well as satisfying the initial conditions. So, from the uniqueness property mentioned above, (3) can be identified with the solution y of the given differential equation.

We thus have the result: at every ordinary point $x=x_0$, the equation $p_0\,\mathrm{d}^2y/\mathrm{d}x^2+p_1\,\mathrm{d}y/\mathrm{d}x+p_2y=q$, with initial conditions $y=y_0$, $\mathrm{d}y/\mathrm{d}x=y_0'$, has a solution which can be expressed as a Taylor series in $(x-x_0)$.

The existence theorem does not hold at the singular points of the equation, nor of course can equation (2) be deduced from (1) when $p_0=0$, so we may expect some sort of exceptional behaviour at such points. Consider for example the equation

$$x^2\,\mathrm{d}^2y/\mathrm{d}x^2+x\,\mathrm{d}y/\mathrm{d}x-y=0$$

There is one singular point only, $x=0$. The general solution is

$$y=Ax+B/x$$

The initial conditions $y=y_0$, $\mathrm{d}y/\mathrm{d}x=y_0'$, at $x=x_0$ can be satisfied provided $x_0 \neq 0$. At the singular point $x=0$ such initial conditions cannot in general be satisfied ; only if $y_0=0$ (corresponding to $B=0$) is there a solution, namely $y=y_0'x$.

12.13. *Series solution of Legendre's equation of order n*

This equation is

$$(1-x^2)\frac{\mathrm{d}^2y}{\mathrm{d}x^2}-2x\frac{\mathrm{d}y}{\mathrm{d}x}+n(n+1)y=0 \tag{1}$$

There are singularities at $x=\pm 1$; further, in most physical applications x is the cosine of an angle and hence only the range $-1\leqslant x\leqslant 1$, corresponding to real angles, is of significance. We look for a solution with $y=y_0$, $\mathrm{d}y/\mathrm{d}x=y_0'$, at $x=0$, which is an ordinary point.

The solution can be obtained as in the example of 12.11 by substituting

$$y=a_0+a_1x+a_2x^2+\ldots \tag{2}$$

in equation (1) and equating to zero the coefficients of the different powers of x, but in the present case the use of a method based more directly on Taylor series is considerably shorter. Using Taylor's theorem, we have that the coefficient a_r in (2) is

$$a_r=y^{(r)}(0)/r! \tag{3}$$

$y^{(r)}(0)$ being the value of the rth derivative of y at $x=0$. But for any value of x, we have by differentiating equation (1) r times,

$$(1-x^2)\,\mathrm{D}^{r+2}y-2rx\mathrm{D}^{r+1}y-r(r-1)\,\mathrm{D}^ry$$
$$-2[x\mathrm{D}^{r+1}y+r\mathrm{D}^ry]+n(n+1)\,\mathrm{D}^ry=0$$

and in particular for $x=0$

$$y^{(r+2)}(0)+[n(n+1)-r(r+1)]y^{(r)}(0)=0$$

Hence $y^{(r+2)}(0)=-[n(n+1)-r(r+1)]y^{(r)}(0)$

$$=-(n-r)(n+r+1)y^{(r)}(0) \tag{4}$$

Hence from (3) and (4)

$$a_{r+2}/a_r=y^{(r+2)}(0)/(r+1)(r+2)y^{(r)}(0)=-\frac{n(n+1)-r(r+1)}{(r+1)(r+2)} \tag{5}$$

From the recurrence relation (5) the values of the coefficients a_r can be derived in succession from $a_0=y_0$, $a_1=y_0'$; since it is a relation between alternate derivatives, the odd coefficients a_{2r+1} are independent of a_0 and the even coefficients independent of a_1; hence the general solution separates into an even series and an odd series, each separately a solution of the equation.

$$y=a_0[1+(a_2/a_0)x^2+(a_4/a_0)x^4+\ldots]$$
$$+a_1x[1+(a_3/a_1)x^2+(a_5/a_1)x^4+\ldots]$$

If n is an integer, one or other of these series terminates and the equation has a polynomial solution, which is called a Legendre polynomial. If n is even, the even series terminates; for example, the values $n=0$, 2, 4 give the polynomials

$$n=0,\ y=a_0$$
$$n=2,\ y=a_0(1-3x^2)$$
$$n=4,\ y=a_0[1-10x^2+(35/3)x^4]$$

Similarly $n=1$, 3, 5 give

$$n=1,\ y=a_1x$$
$$n=3,\ y=a_1[x-(5/3)x^3]$$
$$n=5,\ y=a_1[x-(14/3)x^3+(21/5)x^5]$$

These polynomials are the only solutions of equation (1) which are finite both at $x=+1$ and at $x=-1$, and their importance in physical problems is a consequence of this property. To complete the definition of the Legendre polynomial it is necessary to specify the value of a_0 or a_1 in each case, see Chapter 16.

For non-terminating solutions (the odd solution if n is even, the even solution if n is odd, and both solutions if n is not an integer), it can be seen from (5) that $|a_{r+2}/a_r|\to 1$ as $r\to\infty$, so that the series converge at all ordinary points ($-1<x<1$) of equation (1). It is found from the ratio comparison tests however that at $x=\pm 1$ (the singular points of the equation) the series diverge. For integral n there is divergence at both $+1$ and -1. For non-integral n it is possible to find a solution which is finite at $x=+1$ or *alternatively* a solution finite at $x=-1$, but no solution finite at both singular points (cf. 12.15.)

12.14. *Behaviour of solutions at singular points*

The homogeneous equation

$$x^2\,\mathrm{d}^2y/\mathrm{d}x^2+ax\,\mathrm{d}y/\mathrm{d}x+by=0 \qquad (1)$$

has a singularity at $x=0$; in consequence one cannot expect to find a solution at the origin of the form

$$y=y_0+y_1x+\dots$$

except in the trivial case $a=b=0$. In fact, as we have already found in 11.53, the solution of (1) is in general of the form

$$y=Ax^{\alpha_1}+Bx^{\alpha_2}$$

where α_1 and α_2 are the roots of the auxiliary equation

$$\alpha^2+(a-1)\alpha+b=0$$

If the roots are equal, the solution is more complicated; we find as in 11.53,

$$y=x^{\alpha}(A+B\log x)$$

It appears then that a singularity of the type possessed by equation (1) results in solutions which for small x are of the form $y=x^r$ or $y=x^r\log x$ where r is not necessarily integral or even rational and may be either positive or negative. If $r<0$, solutions of both these types are infinite at $x=0$; and if $r>0$, $y(0)=0$, so in general if $r\neq 0$ we cannot satisfy a finite initial condition $y=y_0$.

Although at $x=0$ the solution of the homogeneous equation (1) may be infinite or many-valued, still more extreme singularities can occur in the solutions of other types of differential equation; for example, $y=\exp(1/x)$, which is a solution of the differential equation $x^2\,dy/dx+y=0$, tends to infinity more rapidly near $x=0$ than does any (negative) power of x. It is useful to distinguish between equations which reduce, in the neighbourhood of a singular point, to the homogeneous form, and equations which give rise to singularities of higher order. Suppose that the equation

$$p_0(x)\,d^2y/dx^2+p_1(x)\,dy/dx+p_2(x)y=0 \tag{2}$$

has a singularity at $x=x_0$; write $x=x_0+z$ and evaluate the coefficients $p(x_0+z)$ in terms of z if possible. The result will be of the form

$$(a_1z+a_2z^2+\dots)\,d^2y/dx^2+(b_0+b_1z+\dots)\,dy/dx+(c_0+c_1z+\dots)y=0$$

where we have omitted a_0 in the first coefficients so as to make $z=0$ a singularity. Now if $b_0=0$ and $a_1=0$ the equation is essentially of homogeneous form for small z and we can expect approximate solutions such as

$$y = z^r = (x - x_0)^r$$

or

$$y = z^r \log z = (x - x_0)^r \log (x - x_0)$$

in the neighbourhood of $x = x_0$. If in addition the coefficients c_0, or b_1 vanish, however, the argument fails and we lose this guide to what may be expected.

We now make the following definition. Let the linear equation (2) be divided throughout by the coefficient of $\mathrm{d}^2y/\mathrm{d}x^2$, to give the form

$$\mathrm{d}^2y/\mathrm{d}x^2 + \mathrm{q}_1(x)\,\mathrm{d}y/\mathrm{d}x + \mathrm{q}_2(x)y = 0\,;$$

then if $x\mathrm{q}_1(x)$ and $x^2\mathrm{q}_2(x)$ remain finite as $x \to 0$ the singularity at $x = 0$ is called a regular singularity. In all other cases, including those where the functions $\mathrm{p}_0(x)$, $\mathrm{p}_1(x)$, $\mathrm{p}_2(x)$ have no power series expansions at $x = 0$, the singularity will be called irregular.

12.15. *Behaviour of solutions of Legendre's equation at singular points*

That for non-integral values of n Legendre's equation

$$(1 - x^2)\,\mathrm{d}^2y/\mathrm{d}x^2 - 2x\,\mathrm{d}y/\mathrm{d}x + n(n+1)y = 0 \tag{1}$$

has solutions which are finite at $x = +1$ or $x = -1$ but not both can be demonstrated by the method of the last section. Let us investigate the behaviour of y near $x = -1$.

Put $x = -1 + z$, then $1 - x^2 = z(2 - z)$, and

$$z(2 - z)\,\mathrm{d}^2y/\mathrm{d}z^2 + 2(1 - z)\,\mathrm{d}y/\mathrm{d}z + n(n+1)y = 0 \tag{2}$$

We are interested in the behaviour near $z = 0$. We see that as $z \to 0$,

$$z\mathrm{p}_1(z)/\mathrm{p}_0(z) = z \,.\, \frac{2(1-z)}{z(2-z)} \to 1$$

$$z^2\mathrm{p}_2(z)/\mathrm{p}_0(z) = z^2\,\frac{n(n+1)}{z(2-z)} \to 0$$

Applying the results of 12.14 we therefore expect equation (1) to have at least one solution of the form

$$y = z^c(a_0 + a_1 z + a_2 z^2 + \ldots + a_r z^r + \ldots) \tag{3}$$

The investigation now follows a course which is only a slight extension of the series solution method described in 12.11. We shall describe the steps fully because this sort of work is often called for in the study of the equations of mathematical physics.

When (3) is substituted in (2), the left-hand side takes the form of a series, possibly involving non-integral powers of z, for

$$dy/dz = z^{c-1}[ca_0 + (c+1)a_1 z + \dots + (c+r)a_r z^r + \dots]$$

$$d^2y/dz^2 = z^{c-2}[c(c-1)a_0 + (c+1)ca_1 z + \dots + (c+r)(c+r-1)a_r z^r + \dots]$$

Equation (2) can be satisfied only if in the left hand side each power of z separately vanishes. Dealing first with the lowest power of z, which arises from the terms $2z\,d^2y/dz^2$ and $2\,dy/dz$, and is a multiple of z^{c-1}, we obtain the so-called *indicial equation*

$$[c(c-1)+c]a_0 = 0 \tag{4}$$

which determines the index c. For in the assumed form (3) it is implied that z^c is the highest power of z which is a factor i.e. that $a_0 \neq 0$, so (4) gives $c^2=0$ i.e. $c=0$.

For higher powers of z, the coefficients in the left-hand side of (2) can all be written in the same form, the general expression for the coefficient of z^{c+r} being

$$2(c+r+1)(c+r)a_{r+1} - (c+r)(c+r-1)a_r + 2(c+r+1)a_{r+1} - 2(c+r)a_r + n(n+1)a_r$$

Equating this to zero gives the *recurrence relation*,

$$a_{r+1}/a_r = [(c+r)(c+r+1) - n(n+1)]/2(c+r+1)^2 \tag{5}$$

For $c=0$ this gives

$$a_{r+1}/a_r = [r(r+1) - n(n+1)]/2(r+1)^2 \tag{6}$$

and by putting $r=0, 1, 2\dots$ in turn, all the coefficients can be determined as multiples of a_0.

Thus Legendre's equation for any n has one series solution $y = a_0 + a_1 z + \dots$ which is finite near $z=0$.

If n is an integer, the series terminates, yielding a polynomial of degree n which is finite for all points, including the other singular point $x=+1$ i.e. $z=2$; this agrees with the results of 12.12. If n is non-integral, however, the series (2) does not terminate, and its radius of convergence is $\lim_{r\to\infty}(a_r/a_{r+1}) = 2$ i.e. the series converges for $|z|<2$. For $z=2$,

$$\frac{a_{r+1}z^{r+1}}{a_r z^r} = 1 - \frac{1}{r} - O\left(\frac{1}{r^2}\right)$$

so by Note 2 of 2.66 the series diverges at $z=2$. This completes the verification of the statements made at the beginning of this section.

12.16. *Bessel's equation*

As a second example of the series method of investigating solutions of differential equations we take Bessel's equation

$$x^2\,\mathrm{d}^2y/\mathrm{d}x^2 + x\,\mathrm{d}y/\mathrm{d}x + (x^2 - n^2)y = 0 \tag{1}$$

n is a constant, and in the most general case, complex. We shall however consider real values only for the moment, and it is then sufficient to take $n \geqslant 0$. The equation has a regular singularity at $x=0$. We therefore expect one solution at least to be of the form

$$y = x^c[a_0 + a_1x + a_2x^2 + \ldots + a_rx^r + \ldots] \tag{2}$$

Substituting this trial solution into equation (1) we find for the coefficient of the lowest degree term x^c

$$[c(c-1) + c - n^2]\,a_0 = 0$$

The indicial equation therefore has two solutions

$$c = \pm n$$

The coefficient of x^{c+1} is

$$[(c+1)c + c + 1 - c^2]\,a_1 = 0$$

and hence $a_1 = 0$. For $r > 1$ the coefficient of x^{c+r} is

$$(c+r)(c+r-1)\,a_r + (c+r)\,a_r + a_{r-2} - n^2a_r$$

and hence the a's are given by the recurrence formula

$$\frac{a_r}{a_{r-2}} = -\frac{1}{(c+r)^2 - n^2} = -\frac{1}{(c+r+n)(c+r-n)} \tag{3}$$

Taking $c = +n$ this becomes

$$a_r/a_{r-2} = -1/r(2n+r)$$

hence the even coefficients are given by

$$a_2 = -\frac{1}{2(2n+2)}\,a_0 = -\frac{1}{2^2(n+1)}\,a_0$$

$$a_4 = -\frac{1}{4(2n+4)}\,a_2 = \frac{1}{2^4(2!)(n+1)(n+2)}\,a_0$$

$$a_{2r} = (-1)^r\,\frac{1}{2^{2r}(r!)(n+1)(n+2)\ldots(n+r)}\,a_0$$

and all the odd coefficients vanish.

Hence a first solution of Bessel's equation corresponding to the index $c = +n$ is

$$y_1 = a_0x^n\left[1 - \frac{1}{1!(n+1)}\left(\frac{x}{2}\right)^2 + \frac{1}{2!(n+1)(n+2)}\left(\frac{x}{2}\right)^4 - \ldots + \frac{(-1)^r}{r!(n+1)\ldots(n+r)}\left(\frac{x}{2}\right)^{2r} + \ldots\right] \tag{4}$$

The radius of convergence is infinitely large in accordance with the fact that $x=0$ is the only (finite) value of x at which Bessel's equation has a singularity.

Now unless n is an integer a second solution can be obtained by taking $c=-n$. This will give (for $n>0$) the solution,

$$y_2=a_0x^{-n}\left[1-\frac{1}{1!(-n+1)}\left(\frac{x}{2}\right)^2+\frac{1}{2!(-n+1)(-n+2)}\left(\frac{x}{2}\right)^4+\dots\right.$$
$$\left.+\frac{(-1)^r}{r!(-n+1)\dots(-n+r)}\left(\frac{x}{2}\right)^{2r}+\dots\right] \qquad (5)$$

with a singularity at $x=0$ (unless $n=0$), and if n is not an integer this series converges everywhere. However when n is an integer all the terms with $r\geqslant n$ will have the vanishing factor $(n-r)$ in the denominator. This indicates that there is not a solution of the form (5), and this case requires further discussion, as also does the case $n=0$ for which the indicial equation has equal roots. Particular values are assigned to a_0 in 16.5.

12.17. *Methods of obtaining a second solution*

As the general solution of a second order linear differential equation is a linear combination of two independent solutions, it is sometimes insufficient to confine one's attention to the solution of simplest form at a singularity. When the indicial equation has equal roots, as is the case for Legendre's equation $c^2=0$, or when, as in Bessel's equation for integral n, one of the two roots gives infinite coefficients in the corresponding series solution, a different method must be devised for investigating the second solution. Three methods may be mentioned here.

One is that of the introduction of an auxiliary variable in the way described in 11.54, where we now have $\mathrm{R}(x)=0$. That is, we put $y=zy_1$ where y_1 is the known first solution of the given equation.

Another method, suggested by the solution $x^m(A+B\log x)$ of the homogeneous equation $x^2y''+axy'+by=0$ when the indicial equation has equal roots (i.e. the case $b=\frac{1}{4}(a-1)^2$, see 11.53), is to substitute a form such as

$$y=y_1(x)\log x+\text{series}$$

into the differential equation. The required series is in fact always of the form $x^c\sum_{-k}^{\infty}b_rx^r$ where x^c is the lowest power of x

occurring in the series for $y_1(x)$, and k is an integer; the recurrence relation for the coefficients b_j and the value of k can be found by equating coefficients of the general power of x. This is often the simplest method to carry out in practice.

The third method is that of Frobenius (ref. Forsyth, *Treatise on Differential Equations* pp. 243–258) in which the actual equation is regarded as the limiting form of an equation with non-coincident roots of the indicial equation, $c=\gamma_1$ and $c=\gamma_1+\epsilon$ say. Then there will be two solutions

$$y_{\mathrm{I}}=z^{\gamma_1}[a_0+a_1z+a_2z^2+\ldots]$$

where the a's involve γ_1, and

$$y_{\mathrm{II}}=z^{\gamma_1+\epsilon}[a_0'+a_1'z+a_2'z^2+\ldots]$$

Now as $\epsilon\to 0$, $y_{\mathrm{II}}\to y_{\mathrm{I}}$ and the two distinct solutions coalesce. The difference $y_{\mathrm{II}}-y_{\mathrm{I}}$ however is also a solution and although this tends to 0 in the limit, the solution $(y_{\mathrm{II}}-y_{\mathrm{I}})/\epsilon$ will tend to $(\partial y/\partial c)_{c=\gamma}$ if this exists. Thus in addition to the first solution y_{I} we obtain an essentially different solution

$$y_2=\left(\frac{\partial y_{\mathrm{I}}}{\partial c}\right)_{c=\gamma}=z^{\gamma}\left(\frac{\partial a_0}{\partial c}+\frac{\partial a_1}{\partial c}z+\ldots\right)_{c=\gamma}+\log z\,.\,z^{\gamma}(a_0+a_1z+\ldots)$$

The idea behind Frobenius' method is of the greatest value in resolving degeneracies caused by equal roots. In quantum mechanics particularly a very useful method of separating states of otherwise equal energy is to imagine a small perturbation of the wave equation, for example by a small magnetic field. The premise on which it is based is essentially that a small change in the coefficients of the differential equation gives a small change in the solution. The conditions under which this is true are a matter for investigation ; it was actually shown by Frobenius that the method is valid without further condition at a regular singularity.

12.18. *Bessel's equation with integral n*

The first solution is provided by (4) of 12.16. In particular the $(r+1)$th term is, apart from an arbitrary factor a_0

$$\frac{(-1)^r x^n}{r!\,(n+1)\ldots(n+r)}\left(\frac{x}{2}\right)^{2r}\quad\text{i.e.}\quad\frac{(-1)^r\, n!\, x^n}{r!\,(n+r)!}\left(\frac{x}{2}\right)^{2r}$$

The expression for the second solution (5) of 12.16 fails when n is an integer because of the vanishing factor $(-n+n)$ in the denominator of every term after the nth. Of the three methods of finding a second solution which were surveyed in the last section, the first is not very convenient in this instance. The second can be conveniently applied. The recurrence relation is,

$$2(n+r)a_r+[(n+r)^2-n^2]b_r+b_{r-2}=0$$

where, from 12.16, $a_r=0$ unless r is positive and even. We see that $b_{r-2}=0$ when $r=-2n$, whence $k=2n$. The values of $b_{-2}, b_{-4} \dots b_{-2n}$ are uniquely determined by the recurrence relation as multiples of a_0, while $b_2, b_4, b_6 \dots$ are linear expressions in a_0 and the indeterminate coefficient b_0. The b_0 terms merely contribute an arbitrary multiple of y_1. Putting $b_0=0$, the second solution is

$$y_2=y_1 \log x+a_0x^{-n} \text{ [known power series of even terms]} \dots (1)$$

Frobenius' method may also be used. The method described in 12.17 for *coincident* roots of the indicial equation requires modification when the roots differ, $c=\alpha$, β say, where $\alpha-\beta=$positive integer. One now writes $Y(\epsilon)=\epsilon y(\beta+\epsilon)$ where $y(\alpha)$ is the first solution: in our present case $\alpha=n$, $\beta=-n$, so $Y(\epsilon)=\epsilon y(-n+\epsilon)$. Then $[\partial Y/\partial\epsilon]_{\epsilon=0}$ is Frobenius' second solution.

12.2. General properties of second-order linear equations

We shall now discuss a number of properties of the solutions of second-order linear equations with variable coefficients which can be deduced without requiring a knowledge of the exact analytical or numerical form of the solution. The theory of the general linear equations of order n has been worked out also, but as the second-order equation is sufficient for nearly all physical problems, we confine the discussion to this case, namely

$$\mathrm{p}_0(x)\, \mathrm{d}^2y/\mathrm{d}x^2+\mathrm{p}_1(x)\, \mathrm{d}y/\mathrm{d}x+\mathrm{p}_2(x)y=0 \qquad (1)$$

together with its inhomogeneous counterpart with $q(x)$ on the right-hand side.

12.21. *Independence of solutions*

At any ordinary point, that is, one where $p_0(x)$ is not zero, equation 12.2 (1) has two linearly independent solutions. Consequently if two linearly independent solutions $y=u_1$, $y=u_2$ are known the complete solution of the equation is

$$y=Au_1+Bu_2$$

We now set up a criterion for the linear independence of two differentiable functions $u_1(x)$ and $u_2(x)$. Two functions $u_1(x)$, $u_2(x)$ are said to be linearly dependent if there exist non-zero constants c_1, c_2 such that

$$c_1u_1(x)+c_2u_2(x)=0 \tag{1}$$

for all x; otherwise they are said to be linearly independent. If u_1 and u_2 are differentiable (as they must be if they are solutions of equation 12.2 (1)), it follows from (1) that also

$$c_1u_1'(x)+c_2u_2'(x)=0 \tag{2}$$

and hence, by elimination of c_1 and c_2 from (1) and (2)

$$\begin{vmatrix} u_1(x) & u_2(x) \\ u_1'(x) & u_2'(x) \end{vmatrix} =0 \tag{3}$$

for all x. The function of x represented by the left-hand side of (3) is called the ‘ Wronskian ’ of the functions $u_1(x)$ and $u_2(x)$, and will be written $W(x)$ or W. Thus $W(x)=0$ for all x is a necessary condition for the linear dependence of $u_1(x)$ and $u_2(x)$; and correspondingly $W(x)\neq 0$ for some x is a sufficient condition for linear independence.

Now consider the implications for two functions $y=u_1(x)$, $y=u_2(x)$ which satisfy the equation 12.2, so that

$$p_0u_j''=-(p_1u_j'+p_2u_j) \quad (j=1, 2)$$

We have $$W=u_1u_2'-u_1'u_2$$

so that
$$\begin{aligned} p_0W' &= p_0(u_1u_2''-u_1''u_2) \\ &= -u_1(p_1u_2'+p_2u_2)+u_2(p_1u_1'+p_2u_1) \\ &= -p_1(u_1u_2'-u_1'u_2)=-p_1W \end{aligned}$$

so that $$W(x)=W_0e^{-\int (p_1/p_0)\,dx}$$

where W_0 is a constant.

Hence, so long as $p_0 \neq 0$, $W(x)$ can be zero only if $W_0 = 0$, in which case W is zero everywhere. Thus if W vanishes at any one point x_0 in an interval $a < x < b$ all points of which are ordinary points of the second-order equation satisfied by u_1 and u_2 (this implies $p_0 \neq 0$), then the solutions are linearly dependent.

If W is non-zero anywhere in such an interval it is non-zero everywhere and the two solutions are linearly independent and form a fundamental pair of solutions.

12.22. *The method of 'variation of parameters'*

The following method enables the inhomogeneous equation

$$p_0(x)\, d^2y/dx^2 + p_1(x)\, dy/dx + p_2(x)y = q(x) \tag{1}$$

to be solved if two linearly independent solutions u_1, u_2 of the associated homogeneous equation

$$p_0(x)\, d^2y/dx^2 + p_1(x)\, dy/dx + p_2(x)y = 0 \tag{2}$$

are known.

Let y be the required solution of (1), and define two auxiliary functions $V_1(x)$, $V_2(x)$ by the equations (compare 11.22, equations (3), (4))

$$V_1 u_1 + V_2 u_2 = y \tag{3}$$

$$V_1' u_1 + V_2' u_2 = 0 \tag{4}$$

On differentiating (3) and using (4), we find

$$y' = V_1' u_1 + V_2' u_2 + V_1 u_1' + V_2 u_2' = V_1 u_1' + V_2 u_2' \tag{5}$$

and a second differentiation then gives

$$y'' = V_1 u_1'' + V_2 u_2'' + V_1' u_1' + V_2' u_2' \tag{6}$$

In the interest of brevity we introduce the symbol L to stand for the differential operator $p_0 \dfrac{d^2}{dx^2} + p_1 \dfrac{d}{dx} + p_2$, so that $L(y) = q(x)$ is an abbreviated way of writing equation (1). With this convention we find from equations (5) and (6) that

$$L(y) = V_1 L(u_1) + V_2 L(u_2) + p_0(V_1' u_1' + V_2' u_2')$$

But from (1) and (2) $L(y) = q(x)$ and $L(u_1) = L(u_2) = 0$, so

$$p_0(x)(V_1' u_1' + V_2' u_2') = q(x) \tag{7}$$

Equations (4) and (7) now enable us to find V_1' and V_2' as explicit functions of x. These expressions can then be integrated, so that the solution y is determined from equation (3).

In fact
$$V_1 = -\int \frac{u_2(x)q(x)}{W(x)p_0(x)}\,dx$$
$$V_2 = +\int \frac{u_1(x)q(x)}{W(x)p_0(x)}\,dx$$
where W(x) is the *Wronskian*
$$W(x) = \begin{vmatrix} u_1 & u_2 \\ u_1' & u_2' \end{vmatrix} = u_1 u_2' - u_1' u_2 \neq 0$$
since u_1 and u_2 are linearly independent.

12.3. Eigenvalue problems

A very important class of second-order linear differential equations contain an unspecified constant in the coefficient p_2. On the other hand, it is typical of the physical problems in which such equations arise that there are more stringent boundary conditions than could normally be satisfied by the solution if a value were arbitrarily assigned to the originally unspecified constant.

For example, the harmonic vibrations of a stretched string are mathematically determined by the wave equation,
$$\frac{\partial^2 Y}{\partial x^2} = \frac{1}{c^2}\frac{\partial^2 Y}{\partial t^2} \tag{1}$$
the condition that the time variation of y should be everywhere simple-harmonic with the same frequency,
$$Y = y(x)\cos(\omega t + \epsilon) \tag{2}$$
where ω and ϵ are unspecified, and the boundary conditions
$$Y = 0 \qquad \text{at } x = 0,\ l \text{ (all } t) \tag{3}$$

On inserting the harmonic expression (2) in the wave equation (1) and into the boundary condition (3), we find that the variation of the amplitude y(x) with x must satisfy the equation
$$\frac{d^2 y}{dx^2} = -\frac{\omega^2 y}{c^2} \quad (\omega \text{ unspecified}) \tag{4}$$
and the conditions
$$y = 0 \quad \text{at } x = 0,\ l. \tag{5}$$
The only solution of (4) satisfying the condition $y = 0$ at $x = 0$ is
$$y = A\sin(\omega x/c)$$
hence at $x = l$, $y = A\sin(\omega l/c)$.

Thus the further boundary condition $y=0$ at $x=l$ can (apart from the trivial case $A=0$) be satisfied only if ω has one of the special set of values which ensures that

$$\omega l/c = n\pi \quad (n \text{ integral}).$$

Hence the originally unspecified constant ω is, by reason of the boundary conditions, restricted to one of a discrete set of possible values $\omega = n\pi c/l$. The physical interpretation of this result is that the natural harmonics of a stretched string of length l have frequencies $\omega/2\pi = nc/2l$, $n=1, 2, 3 \ldots$

The values to which the constant ω^2 in equation (4) is restricted by the boundary conditions are called 'characteristic values' or 'eigenvalues', and the corresponding solutions—in the above example the functions $A \sin(n\pi x/l)$—are called eigenfunctions.

12.31. *Examples of eigenvalue problems: Sturm-Liouville systems*

We shall find in Chapter 16 that the solution of Laplace's equation in spherical polar coordinates leads to the equation

$$(1-x^2)\frac{\mathrm{d}^2 y}{\mathrm{d}x^2} - 2x\frac{\mathrm{d}y}{\mathrm{d}x} + \left[l - \frac{m^2}{1-x^2}\right]y = 0 \quad (l \text{ unspecified})$$

i.e.
$$\frac{\mathrm{d}}{\mathrm{d}x}\left[(1-x^2)\frac{\mathrm{d}y}{\mathrm{d}x}\right] + \left[l - \frac{m^2}{1-x^2}\right]y = 0 \qquad (1)$$

with the conditions that y should be finite at $x = +1, -1$. This constitutes an eigenvalue problem.

The typical form of the equations of wave mechanics (on which so much of modern physics depends) is

$$-\frac{h^2}{8\pi^2 m}\nabla^2\psi + V\psi = \lambda\psi \qquad (2)$$

where h is Planck's constant, m is the mass of the electron, λ an unspecified constant representing the total energy, and V is a known function representing the potential energy: the determination of the eigenvalues $\lambda = \lambda_1, \lambda_2, \ldots$ etc. amounts to the discovery of the possible energy levels of the system. The 'boundary' conditions on ψ are customarily that ψ is single-valued and finite at all points in a region. For the hydrogen atom $V = -e^2/r$ where r is the radial distance of the electron from the proton. The solution of equation (2) can then be reduced by methods which will be described in Chapter 14 to the solution of three subsidiary eigenvalue problems of which the first is essentially the same as the stretched string problem treated in 12.3, the second is identical with (1) above (with the boundary conditions as stated there), and the third is that of solving

$$\frac{d^2y}{dx^2}+\frac{2}{x}\frac{dy}{dx}+\left\{\frac{8\pi^2m}{h^2}\left(\frac{e^2}{x}+\lambda\right)-\frac{n(n+1)}{x^2}\right\}y=0 \tag{3}$$

with the boundary conditions y finite at $x=0$ and $y\to 0$ as $x\to+\infty$. Equation (3) can also be written

$$\frac{1}{x^2}\frac{d}{dx}\left\{x^2\frac{dy}{dx}\right\}+\left\{\frac{8\pi^2m}{h^2}\left(\frac{e^2}{x}+\lambda\right)-\frac{n(n+1)}{x^2}\right\}y=0 \tag{4}$$

In all these eigenvalue problems the differential equations are special cases of the general form

$$\frac{d}{dx}\left\{k(x)\frac{dy}{dx}\right\}+\{\lambda g(x)-h(x)\}y=0 \tag{5}$$

where $k(x)$, $g(x)$ and $h(x)$ are known real functions of x, and λ is an unspecified constant whose eigenvalues are to be found. The boundary conditions are every bit as important as the equations. We shall consider here only one type, which however is particularly important in applications: this consists of the homogeneous linear boundary conditions

$$\left.\begin{aligned}\alpha_1 y(a)+\alpha_2 y'(a)&=0\\ \beta_1 y(b)+\beta_2 y'(b)&=0\end{aligned}\right\} \tag{6}$$

where α_1, α_2, β_1, β_2 are known constants and $x=a$, $x=b$ are given endpoints. We shall further assume that in the range $a\leqslant x\leqslant b$ the functions dk/dx, $g(x)$ and $h(x)$ are continuous, and $g(x)$ and $k(x)$ are non-zero. If the endpoints a, b are finite, equation (5) with boundary conditions (6) is said to constitute a Sturm-Liouville system. For a full discussion of such a system see, for example, Ince *Ordinary Differential Equations*, Chap. 9–11. We note that the boundary conditions $y(a)=y(b)=0$ form a particular case of the boundary conditions (6), as do also the conditions $y'(a)=y'(b)=0$.

The properties of Sturm-Liouville systems derived in 12.32, 12.33 hold also when either or both of the limits a, b is infinite

12.32. *Orthogonality of eigenfunctions of Sturm-Liouville systems*

Suppose that $\lambda=\lambda_1$, λ_2 are two different eigenvalues of the Sturm-Liouville equation and that Y_1 and Y_2 are eigenfunctions corresponding to these eigenvalues, i.e. $Y_1(x)$ and $Y_2(x)$ satisfy the boundary conditions (6) of the last section and

$$\frac{d}{dx}\left\{k\frac{dY_1}{dx}\right\}+(\lambda_1 g-h)\,Y_1=0 \tag{1}$$

$$\frac{d}{dx}\left\{k\frac{dY_2}{dx}\right\}+(\lambda_2 g-h)\,Y_2=0 \tag{2}$$

Multiply (1) by Y_2 and (2) by Y_1 and subtract.

$$\frac{d}{dx}\left\{k\left(Y_2\frac{dY_1}{dx}-Y_1\frac{dY_2}{dx}\right)\right\}+(\lambda_1-\lambda_2)\,gY_1Y_2=0 \tag{3}$$

and integration from $x=a$ to $x=b$ gives

$$(\lambda_2-\lambda_1)\int_a^b gY_1Y_2\,dx=\Big[k(Y_2Y_1'-Y_1Y_2')\Big]_{x=a}^{b}$$

But at $x=a$ the boundary conditions ensure that

$$\alpha_1Y_1+\alpha_2Y_1'=0$$

and

$$\alpha_1Y_2+\alpha_2Y_2'=0$$

so at $x=a$, $Y_2Y_1'-Y_1Y_2'=0$†, and similarly $Y_2Y_1'-Y_1Y_2'=0$ at $x=b$. Hence, since by hypothesis $\lambda_1\neq\lambda_2$,

$$\int_a^b gY_1Y_2\,dx=0 \tag{4}$$

This is known as the orthogonality property of eigenfunctions corresponding to different eigenvalues. In the fairly common case $g=$constant the orthogonality property (4) takes the simple form

$$\int_a^b Y_1Y_2\,dx=0 \tag{5}$$

Example

The system $d^2y/dx^2+\lambda y=0$ with boundary conditions $y(0)=0$, $y(\pi)=0$ has solutions

$$y_1=\sin x \qquad (\lambda=\lambda_1=1)$$

$$y_2=\sin 2x \qquad (\lambda=\lambda_2=4)$$

† We note that Y_1, Y_2 are solutions of two *different* equations namely (1) and (2) respectively, so the theorems of 12.21 are not relevant.

In this system $g(x)=1$, so the orthogonality theorem states that

$$\int_0^\pi \sin x \sin 2x \, dx = 0$$

12.33. *Reality of eigenvalues*

We first show that the eigenvalues $\lambda=\lambda_1, \lambda_2, \ldots$ of a Sturm-Liouville system are necessarily *real* numbers, provided that in the boundary conditions the coefficients $\alpha_1, \alpha_2, \beta_1, \beta_2$ are real.

Suppose that $\lambda=\lambda_1$ were a complex eigenvalue, and y_1 is a corresponding (non-zero) eigenfunction, that is

$$\frac{d}{dx}\left\{k\frac{dy_1}{dx}\right\}+(\lambda_1 g-h)\,y_1=0 \tag{1}$$

then, taking the conjugate complex,

$$\frac{d}{dx}\left\{k\frac{dy_1^*}{dx}\right\}+(\lambda_1^* g-h)\,y_1^*=0 \tag{2}$$

(That equation (2) is a consequence of equation (1) can be proved by putting $y_1=\phi_1+i\psi$, $\lambda_1=\mu_1+i\nu_1$, in (1) and separating and reassembling real and imaginary parts).

Hence λ_1^* is also an eigenvalue of the original Sturm-Liouville equation and y_1^* is a corresponding eigenfunction. Hence by the argument of the last section

$$(\lambda_1^*-\lambda_1)\int_a^b g y_1^* y_1 \, dx = 0$$

We do not yet know whether λ_1 is real or complex, i.e. we do not know whether λ_1 and λ_1^* are equal or unequal, so we cannot use eqn. (4) of 12.32. On the other hand we know that $y_1^*y_1 \geqslant 0$, and $y_1^*y_1=0$ only when $y_1=0$; and g is supposed non-zero and continuous, and hence always has the same sign in the range $a \leqslant x \leqslant b$. Thus since the trivial case $y_1 \equiv 0$ has been excluded, $\int_a^b g y_1^* y_1 \, dx \neq 0$, so we must have $\lambda_1^*=\lambda_1$, i.e. λ_1 real.† Thus all the eigenvalues of a Sturm-Liouville system are real numbers.

This result throws light on, for example, the problems of quantum mechanics. It suggests the sort of mathematical reason which ensures that all the eigenvalues of the total energy

† This conclusion is not necessarily valid if the coefficients in the boundary conditions are complex.

parameter λ are real. Moreover, although the actual boundary conditions in many problems of quantum mechanics are not of Sturm-Liouville type [e.g., the third equation, (3) of 12.31, for the hydrogen atom problem has boundary conditions referring to an infinite range, and in (1) of 12.31, $k=0$ at both ends of the range and the boundary conditions specify not values but only finiteness at the ends of the range] nevertheless the same *method* of proof can frequently be applied to these slightly different conditions to establish in many cases that the eigenvalues will all be real.

12.34. *Expansions in eigenfunctions*

The orthogonality theorem of 12.32 enables us to calculate the coefficients in a so-called Sturm-Liouville expansion. Let $f(x)$ be an arbitrary function, subject to conditions which will be examined later, and suppose that it can be expanded in the form

$$f(x)=a_1 Y_1(x)+\ldots+a_r Y_r(x)+\ldots=\sum_s a_s Y_s(x)$$

valid in $a<x<b$ where the Y's are the eigenfunctions of any Sturm-Liouville system. Then if both sides are multiplied by $g(x)\,Y_r(x)$ and integrated from a to b we find that all terms on the right vanish but one with $s=r$ and we obtain

$$\int_a^b g(x)\,f(x)\,Y_r(x)\,dx=a_r\int_a^b g_r\{Y_r(x)\}^2\,dx$$

whence
$$a_r=\int_a^b gf\,.\,Y_r\,dx\Big/\int_a^b g\,.\,Y_r^2\,dx \qquad (1)$$

The term-by-term integration on the right is valid if for example the series converges uniformly in (a, b) but we defer considerations of this kind for the moment.

The orthogonality theorem therefore provides us with a selection operator by the aid of which we can pick out one term in the Sturm-Liouville expansion.

The corresponding selection operator for a power series expansion (Taylor series) is that of differentiating r times and then putting $x=0$; since integration is a much less exacting process than differentiation we might anticipate that eigenfunction expansions can often be used when power series expansions fail.

Example

Expand $\sin^2 x$ $(0 \leqslant x \leqslant 2\pi)$ in terms of the eigenfunctions of $d^2y/dx^2 = \lambda y$ with boundary conditions $dy/dx = 0$ at $x = 0, 2\pi$.

We must first obtain the eigenfunctions of the specified equation with the specified boundary conditions, and we note in passing that the eigenfunctions here will not be the same as those in the example of 12.32 because the boundary conditions have been altered. In order to have two zeros of dy/dx we must prescribe oscillatory not exponential solutions, so $\lambda = -\omega^2$ (ω real),

$$y = A \cos \omega x + B \sin \omega x$$

$$dy/dx = -A\omega \sin \omega x + B\omega \cos \omega x$$

From the boundary conditions we find $B = 0$ and $\omega \,.\, 2\pi = n\pi$ so the eigenfunctions are $\cos \frac{1}{2}nx$, $n = 0, 1, 2, \ldots$ (we may omit the coefficient A because the correct multipliers are determined by the expansion method).

The desired expansion is therefore of the form,

$$\sin^2 x = a_1 + a_2 \cos \tfrac{1}{2}x + a_3 \cos x + a_4 \cos 3x/2 + \ldots \qquad (2)$$

The function g, i.e. the coefficient of λy is equal to -1, so, multiplying (2) by -1, $-\cos \frac{1}{2}x$, $-\cos x$, ... respectively and integrating we find

$$-\int_0^{2\pi} \sin^2 x \, dx = -2\pi a_1 \qquad \text{from which } a_1 = \tfrac{1}{2}$$

$$-\int_0^{2\pi} \sin^2 x \cos \tfrac{1}{2}x = -a_2 \int_0^{2\pi} \cos^2 \tfrac{1}{2}x \, dx \quad \text{from which } a_2 = 0$$

and similarly $a_3 = a_4 = 0$, $a_5 = -\frac{1}{2}$, $a_6 = a_7 = \ldots = 0$.

Thus the expansion gives $\sin^2 x = \frac{1}{2}(1 - \cos 2x)$. In this case then, the expansion correctly represents the function.

Indeed the set of all the eigenfunctions corresponding to given boundary conditions in *any* Sturm-Liouville system has this important property, that any well-behaved continuous function with the same boundary conditions can be approximated to any desired order of accuracy by a linear combination of functions of the set. This is expressed by saying the eigenfunctions form a ‘ complete ’ set. To prove this statement is beyond our present scope, though the reader who has familiarised himself with the concepts of measure and Lebesgue integration in 8.5 is well-prepared for work along these lines :

for a full discussion the reader is referred to Courant-Hilbert, *Die Methoden der Mathematischen Physik* or *Methods of Mathematical Physics*, vol. II.

Although a still wider definition is possible, for our purposes we can define a *well-behaved* continuous function to be any continuous function with only a finite number of turning points i.e. of maxima and minima. Thus certain functions of unusual behaviour, like $\sin(1/x)$ in a range embracing the origin, are excluded (compare also 8.4).

An expansion in terms of cosines and/or sines such as that in the above example is known as a Fourier series or expansion. Expansions in terms of Legendre functions and Bessel functions will be mentioned in 17.33 and 17.82.

12.4. Fourier series

12.41. *Sine series for odd functions*

An arbitrary well-behaved continuous *odd* function $f_1(x)$ (Note: $f_1(-x) = -f_1(x)$ for an odd function), subject to the boundary condition $f_1(x)=0$ at $x=c$ can be expressed in $|x| \leqslant c$ as $\sum_{n=1}^{\infty} a_n \sin(n\pi x/c)$. For the functions $\sin(n\pi x/c)$, $n=1, 2, 3, \ldots$ are the eigenfunctions of the equation $d^2y/dx^2 + \lambda y = 0$ with boundary conditions $y=0$ at $x=0$ and $x=c$. The function $f_1(x)$, which is zero at $x=0$ because it is an odd function, and is also zero at $x=c$, can therefore be represented in the range $0 \leqslant x \leqslant c$ by the series; and since $\sin(-n\pi x/c) = -\sin(n\pi x/c)$ this at the same time ensures that the series is equal to the function throughout the whole range $-c \leqslant x \leqslant c$.

If now we have a function $F_1(x)$ for which $F_1(x) \neq 0$ at $x=c$, we can envisage an auxiliary function $f_1(x)$ which coincides with $F_1(x)$ everywhere except very close to $x=c$ where its value descends rapidly but continuously to zero. The function $f_1(x)$ can be made to approximate $F_1(x)$ as closely as we wish except at the point $x=c$ itself (and hence also at $x=-c$). Since $f_1(x)$ can be expressed as $\sum_{n=1}^{\infty} a_n \sin(n\pi x/c)$ in $-c \leqslant x \leqslant c$, it follows that an odd function $F_1(x)$ can be represented by the same series in $-c < x < c$, the endpoints of the range now being excluded. Similarly *any* well-behaved function $F(x)$ can be represented in $0 < x < c$ by such a series.

The coefficients a_n can be evaluated as in the last section, using the orthogonality property of the eigenfunctions, viz.

$$\int_{-c}^{c} \sin(m\pi x/c) \sin(n\pi x/c)\, dx = 0 \qquad n \neq m$$
$$= c \qquad n = m$$

as can be verified by elementary integration. To evaluate the coefficient a_m in the series

$$f_1(x) = \sum_{n=1}^{\infty} a_n \sin(n\pi x/c) \qquad (1)$$

we multiply both sides by $\sin(m\pi x/c)$ and integrate, thus

$$\int_{-c}^{c} f_1(x) \sin(m\pi x/c)\, dx = c \,.\, a_m$$

whence
$$a_m = \frac{1}{c}\int_{-c}^{c} f_1(x) \sin(m\pi x/c)\, dx \qquad (2)$$

An odd function with a finite number of finite discontinuities can be approximated, except at the points of discontinuity, by a continuous function $f_1(x)$; it follows that except at the points of discontinuity such a function can be represented by the Fourier series (1) with coefficients given by (2).

Example 1

Show that the Fourier series for $f_1(x) = x$ in the interval $-\pi < x < \pi$ is $2(\sin x - \frac{1}{2}\sin 2x + \frac{1}{3}\sin 3x \ldots)$. A graph showing the sum of the first four terms is shown in Fig. 12.1.

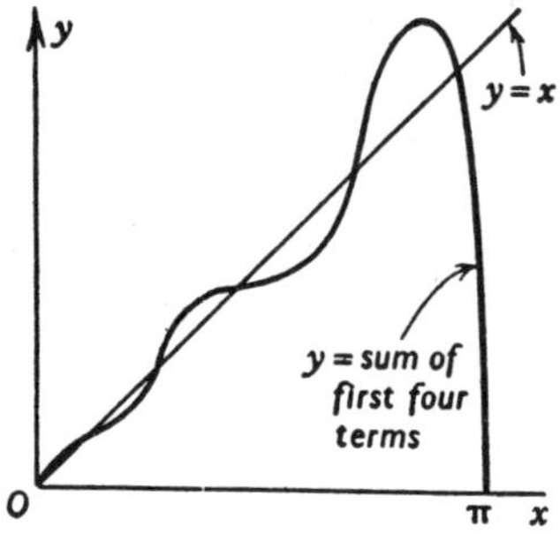

FIG. 12.1

Example 2

Find the Fourier series for the function $f_1(x) = +1 \quad 0 < x < 1$
$= -1 \quad -1 < x < 0$

and check by plotting the sum of the first three terms.
(Answer: $\sum_{m \text{ odd}} (4 \sin m\pi)/m\pi$).

12.42. *Cosine series for even functions*

An arbitrary well-behaved continuous *even* function $f_2(x)$ subject to the boundary condition $f_2'(x)=0$ at $x=c$ can be expressed in $|x|\leqslant c$ in the form $\sum_{n=0}^{\infty} b_n \cos(n\pi x/c)$. For the functions $\cos(n\pi x/c)$, $n=0, 1, 2, \ldots$ are the eigenfunctions of the equation $d^2y/dx^2+\lambda y=0$ with boundary conditions $y'=0$ at $x=0, c$; the function $f_2(x)$ can therefore be represented by the series in $0\leqslant x\leqslant c$, and, since $\cos(-n\pi x/c)=\cos(n\pi x/c)$, this ensures that the series represents $f_2(x)$ throughout the range $-c\leqslant x\leqslant c$. As for the sine series, the boundary condition on $f_2(x)$ can be relaxed provided we exclude the endpoints $\pm c$ from the expected range of validity of the series representation. Similarly the condition of continuity can be relaxed provided we exclude the points of (finite) discontinuity from the expected range of validity of the series representation.

The coefficients b_n in the Fourier cosine series

$$f_2(x)=\sum_{n=0}^{\infty} b_n \cos(n\pi x/c) \tag{1}$$

can be evaluated by using the orthogonality property of the eigenfunctions, for

$$\begin{aligned}\int_{-c}^{c} \cos(m\pi x/c)\cos(n\pi x/c)\,dx &= 0 && n\neq m\\ &= c && n=m\neq 0\\ &= 2c && n=m=0\end{aligned}$$

whence

$$\left.\begin{aligned} b_m &= \frac{1}{c}\int_{-c}^{c} f_2(x)\cos(m\pi x/c)\,dx \qquad m>0\\ b_0 &= \frac{1}{2c}\int_{-c}^{c} f_2(x)\,dx\end{aligned}\right\} \tag{2}$$

While it is essential that the expressions (1) of this section and the last can be written down without hesitation when required, there is no need to memorise the formulae (2) which can be readily derived when needed.

Example

Show that the Fourier cosine expansion of x^2 in the range $-1\leqslant x\leqslant 1$ is $\frac{1}{3}+4\sum_{1}^{\infty}(-1)^n \cos n\pi x/n^2\pi^2$.

12.43. *General Fourier series*

Any function $F(x)$ can be expressed as the sum of an odd function and an even function, $F(x) = f_1(x) + f_2(x)$ say (see 2.23). From 12.41 and 12.42 it follows that :

Any function which is well-behaved and continuous in $-c < x < +c$ or which has only a finite number of finite discontinuities can be expanded as a Fourier series,

$$F(x) = \sum_{n=1}^{\infty} a_n \sin(n\pi x/c) + \sum_{n=0}^{\infty} b_n \cos(n\pi x/c) \qquad (1)$$

where the coefficients a_m, b_m can be evaluated by multiplying (1) by $\sin(m\pi x/c)$ and $\cos(m\pi x/c)$ respectively and integrating from $-c$ to $+c$.

It can be seen from (1) that

$$F(x-c) = \sum_{n=1}^{\infty} A_n \sin(n\pi x/c) + \sum_{n=0}^{\infty} B_n \cos(n\pi x/c) \qquad 0 < x < 2c \quad (2)$$

where $A_n = (-1)^{n+1} a_n$ and $B_n = (-1)^n b_n$. Thus any function can be represented in any range $0 < x < 2c$ by a series (2) of the same form as (1): it is in fact basically the same series. The coefficients A_m and B_m are found most directly from (2) by multiplying by $\sin(m\pi x/c)$ and $\cos(m\pi x/c)$ respectively and integrating from $x = 0$ to $x = 2c$.

The usual way of finding a Fourier series for any function in a range $x = a$ to $x = b$ is to move the origin to the midpoint or the initial point of the range by making the substitution

$$u = x - \tfrac{1}{2}(a+b) \text{ or } u = x - a,$$

and then to proceed by the methods already described using u instead of x as the variable.

12.44. *Uniqueness of representation*

$$\text{If } \sum_{n=1}^{\infty} a_n \sin(n\pi x/c) + \sum_{n=0}^{\infty} b_n \cos(n\pi x/c)$$

$$= \sum_{n=1}^{\infty} \alpha_n \sin(n\pi x/c) + \sum_{n=0}^{\infty} \beta_n \cos(n\pi x/c) \qquad -c < x < c \quad (1)$$

then $a_n = \alpha_n$; $b_n = \beta_n$ for all n.

This follows by the usual method, namely multiplying by $\sin(n\pi x/c)$, $\cos(n\pi x/c)$ respectively and integrating, bearing in mind the orthogonality relations stated in 12.41, 12.42 and the further orthogonality relation

$$\int_{-c}^{c} \sin(m\pi x/c)\cos(n\pi x/c)\,dx = 0 \quad \text{all } m, n.$$

It should be noted that (1) can also be written

$$\sum_{1}^{\infty} (a_n - \alpha_n)\sin(n\pi x/c) + \sum_{0}^{\infty} (b_n - \beta_n)\cos(n\pi x/c) = 0$$

We have said that this can only be true if $(a_n - \alpha_n) = 0$, $(b_n - \beta_n) = 0$ for all n, that is, we have established the linear independence of the eigenfunctions $\sin(n\pi x/c)$, $\cos(n\pi x/c)$ for all $n \geqslant 0$. The properties of linear independence and of uniqueness of expansions are closely linked : either property follows from the other when there are no convergence difficulties.

Thus no function defined in $-c < x < c$ has two different Fourier expansions in terms of the eigenfunctions $\sin(n\pi x/c)$, $\cos(n\pi x/c)$: the expansion in terms of these eigenfunctions of any function whose value is given throughout $-c < x < c$ is unique.

If the range $-c < x < c$ were wider than the range in which equality between the series and the given function is postulated, the situation would be different. The postulated equality would then tell us only that equation (1) is true in the smaller range, so the integrals of the two sides throughout the larger range $-c < x < c$ would not necessarily be equal, and we could no longer deduce that $a_n = \alpha_n$, $b_n = \beta_n$.

We note for example, that in the range $-\pi < x < \pi$, the Fourier series

$$x = 2(\sin x - \tfrac{1}{2}\sin 2x + \tfrac{1}{3}\sin 3x - \ldots)$$

is the unique expansion of x in terms of sines or cosines of integral multiples of x. In the reduced range $0 < x < \pi$ however, there are numerous other possibilities, such as

$$x = \frac{\pi}{2} - \frac{4}{\pi}\left(\cos x + \frac{\cos 3x}{3^2} + \frac{\cos 5x}{5^2} + \ldots\right)$$

$$x = \pi - 2(\sin x + \tfrac{1}{2}\sin 2x + \tfrac{1}{3}\sin 3x + \ldots)$$

$$x = \frac{\pi}{2} - (\sin 2x + \tfrac{1}{2}\sin 4x + \tfrac{1}{3}\sin 6x + \ldots).$$

The reader may verify the last two expansions by finding the Fourier series of x appropriate to the ranges $0 < x < 2\pi$ and

$0<x<\pi$ respectively. The first series is obtained from the cosine expansion of $x-\frac{1}{2}\pi$ in the range $0<x<\pi$.

12.45. *Fourier analysis and complex Fourier series*

The terms of any Fourier series are unchanged if x is replaced by $x+2c$, that is the Fourier series defines a periodic function, period $2c$. This function coincides with $\mathrm{F}(x)$ in the range $-c<x<c$. If however $\mathrm{F}(x)$ is also periodic with period $2c$, the Fourier series represents it everywhere. This obviously constitutes a particularly economical application. The expression of a *periodic* function as a Fourier series is usually called Fourier analysis.

We have already seen that when dealing with oscillations the complex representation $e^{i\omega t}$ is often more convenient than the real functions $\cos \omega t$ or $\sin \omega t$. For the same reason it is often convenient to use the complex Fourier expansion

$$\mathrm{f}(x)=\sum_{n=-\infty}^{\infty} C_n \exp(in\pi x/c) \tag{1}$$

where the coefficients C_n are in general complex numbers. We note that the right hand side is the same as

$$C_0+\sum_{n=1}^{\infty}\left\{C_{-n}(\cos n\pi x/c - i\sin n\pi x/c)+C_n(\cos n\pi x/c + i\sin n\pi x/c)\right\},$$

that is

$$C_0+\sum_{n=1}^{\infty}(C_{-n}+C_n)\cos n\pi x/c+\sum_{n=1}^{\infty}(iC_n-iC_{-n})\sin n\pi x/c$$

which is of the same form as our previous Fourier expansions apart from the occurrence of complex numbers.

In order to deduce the value of C_m we multiply both sides of (1) by the conjugate complex of $\exp(im\pi x/c)$, that is by $\exp(-im\pi x/c)$ before integrating from $-c$ to $+c$. It is then found that

$$C_m=\frac{1}{2c}\int_{-c}^{c}\mathrm{f}(x)\,.\,\exp(-im\pi x/c)\,\mathrm{d}x \tag{2}$$

The device of using the conjugate complex rather than the function itself as the integrating factor is appropriate for all complex eigenfunction series, whether Fourier series or series of Bessel functions, Legendre functions etc.

12.5. Function space

A useful correlation with matrix and vector algebra is provided by the concept of function space. Suppose we are interested in all the functions which can be formed from linear combinations of three given linearly independent functions f_1, f_2, f_3, i.e. we are interested in all functions of the form

$$f = \alpha_1 f_1 + \alpha_2 f_2 + \alpha_3 f_3$$

If the coefficients $\alpha_1, \alpha_2, \alpha_3$ are given the function f is known, so we may say that the point $(\alpha_1, \alpha_2, \alpha_3)$ in a three-dimensional space represents the function f. At unit distances along the three axes are the points (1, 0, 0), (0, 1, 0), (0, 0, 1) corresponding to $f = f_1$, $f = f_2$, $f = f_3$ respectively. The three axes may therefore be referred to as the f_1, f_2, f_3 axes.

In the same way if we are concerned with linear combinations of n linearly independent functions $f = \alpha_1 f_1 + \alpha_2 f_2 + \dots + \alpha_n f_n$ we may think of the coefficients α_i as coordinates in an n-dimensional space whose axes may be referred to as the axes of $f_1, f_2, \dots, f_n$ respectively.

To approximate as closely as we please to an arbitrary function $f(x)$ even in a finite range $a \leqslant x \leqslant b$ it is necessary to have an expansion with an infinite number of terms. The corresponding infinite set of coefficients is said to define a point in ‘ function-space ’, a space with an infinite number of dimensions but otherwise closely analogous to the three-dimensional and n-dimensional spaces introduced above.

We have already stated that an arbitrary well-behaved continuous function in $a < x < b$ can be expanded in terms of the eigenfunctions of any Sturm-Liouville system with boundaries at (a, b). We shall show below that, as for Fourier series, the eigenfunctions are linearly independent and hence the expansion is unique thus the eigenfunctions of any Sturm-Liouville system constitute a just sufficient set of axes for the infinite-dimensional function space associated with the range $a < x < b$.

To examine the question of linear independence suppose there is a linear relation

$$C_1 Y_1 + C_2 Y_2 + \dots + C_s Y_s + \dots = 0 \tag{1}$$

between the eigenfunctions Y_s for which the values of λ are all different. Multiply by gY_r and integrate from a to b. Then because of the orthogonality relation $\int_a^b gY_rY_s\,dx=0$ if $s\neq r$, it follows that (1) reduces to $C_r=0$; this applies for each value of r. Hence there is no relation (1) with non-zero coefficients between the eigenfunctions Y_s, and this is the property described by calling these functions linearly independent. The uniqueness of the expansion in terms of these functions follows almost immediately, as in 12.44.

If we think of α_1 as the ' component ' of f in the Y_1 direction, the natural interpretation of the orthogonality law for eigenfunctions is that the corresponding axes in function space are, in a geometrical sense, orthogonal. For the equation $\int_a^b gY_iY_j\,dx=0$ ensures that the component of Y_i in the Y_j direction is zero, and conversely, i.e. the directions Y_i, Y_j are perpendicular.

If $Z_1, Z_2, Z_3 \ldots$ are eigenfunctions of a second Sturm-Liouville equation also with range $a\leqslant x\leqslant b$, then if it is so desired, any function f can be referred to axes of $Z_1, Z_2, Z_3, \ldots$ instead of to $Y_1, Y_2, Y_3 \ldots$, i.e. any point in function space can be referred either to the one or to the other set of axes : the algebraic process of transforming an expansion in terms of one set of eigenfunctions into an expansion in terms of a second set is equivalent to a rotation of axes in function space. If a function is represented by a finite point on one system then it must have a finite representation in any other system. This is a valuable result since it implies that the vast amount of work done on the conditions of validity of Fourier expansions applies practically unchanged to Sturm-Liouville systems in general.

CHAPTER THIRTEEN

FUNCTIONS OF A COMPLEX VARIABLE

13.1. Introduction

A mathematical relation

$$y = \mathrm{f}(x) \tag{1}$$

between real variables x and y is used in physical problems to represent the relation between two physical variables.

The relation

$$w = \mathrm{f}(z) \tag{2}$$

between complex variables is mathematically not very different from (1). The complex number z is inserted into the formula represented by the symbol f and the various operations performed just as in (1). The only difference is that in addition to the processes of ordinary arithmetic we use the relation $i^2 = -1$, thus ensuring that powers of i do not appear in the final form for the number w. In physical applications however equation (2) represents much more than equation (1). For z and w do not now represent single variables. Each represents two separate variables; moreover the equation itself represents two separate real equations. For example, contrast the real equation

$$y = x^2 \tag{3}$$

with the complex equation

$$w = z^2 \tag{4}$$

If $z = x + iy$, and $w = u + iv$ we find from equation (4)

$$u + iv = x^2 - y^2 + i \, . \, 2xy \tag{5}$$

hence equation (4) is equivalent to the two real equations

$$\left. \begin{aligned} u &= x^2 - y^2 \\ v &= 2xy \end{aligned} \right\} \tag{6}$$

obtained by equating the real and imaginary parts of (5).

This economy of expression has already been noticed in Chapter 6 and in particular in 6.51 where the single equation

$$e = zi$$

(with the special use of i for current as explained in that section) includes both the relationship between the amplitudes and that between the phases of the e.m.f. and current. The application to alternating currents is however only one of the applications of functions of a complex variable to scientific problems. The subject turns out to be unexpectedly rewarding. First, as the connection between the complex variable and the position of a point in a plane would lead us to expect, the theory can be applied to many two-dimensional problems ; in particular it will appear that any function of the complex variable $x+iy$, within a very wide class, is intimately connected with one of the most important of the equations of mathematical physics, namely Laplace's equation, which in two dimensions is

$$\frac{\partial^2\phi}{\partial x^2}+\frac{\partial^2\phi}{\partial y^2}=0$$

This equation is of basic importance in electrostatics, hydrostatics, the theory of gravitation, and potential theory in general.

Secondly there are two rather more specialised applications concerning mathematical technique rather than the representation of physical problems. The definite integral of a function of a real variable can in a number of cases be most easily evaluated indirectly from a related complex integral ; and some properties of real power series can only be fully understood when related to the behaviour of the corresponding complex series. These last two applications are examples of the use of the complex number in its primary role, namely as an extension of the idea of number.

13.2. Functions of a complex variable

Let $z = x + iy$ be a complex variable. To specify z is to assign a pair of values to x and y ; to say that a quantity can be calculated when z is given is therefore equivalent to saying that the quantity is a function of x and y. The phrase ‘ function of a complex variable ’ or ‘ function of z ’ is sometimes used (and we shall follow this usage) to mean nothing more than a function of x and y which is, or can be, written down in terms of z and the conventional algebraic signs : in this sense $x^2 - y^2 + 2ixy = z^2$, $x - iy = z^*$ and $\log (x^2 + y^2) = 2 \log | z |$, are all functions of z; and it would be logically permissible to introduce a new convention of notation to denote any function of x and y in terms of z, e.g. to put $x^3 \cos y = \mathrm{g}(z)$, and having defined the notation, to call the function a function of z.

Some people prefer to restrict the phrase 'functions of z' to quantities which, like z^2 but unlike z^*, may be roughly described by saying that $x + iy$ occurs as a single entity, without separating the symbols x and y; but there is some difficulty in formulating a precise definition. The difficulties of definition can be overcome only if we agree to narrow our class of functions of z to those which are differentiable with respect to z in the sense which will be explained in 13.3. Members of this narrow class are better known as analytic functions of z, but the phrase 'functions of z' is also sometimes used in this restricted sense.

We shall use the words 'function of z' to mean any member of the wider class of functions of x and y which can be written down in terms of the symbol z, $w = \mathrm{f}(z)$ say.

13.21. *Representation of complex functions on the Argand diagram*

The equation
$$w = \mathrm{f}(z) \tag{1}$$
when w and z are complex contains a good deal more information than can be exhibited by a single graph such as suffices for functions of a real variable. For if $w = u + iv$, equation (1) gives two equations of the form
$$\left.\begin{aligned} u &= \mathrm{u}(x, y) \\ v &= \mathrm{v}(x, y) \end{aligned}\right\} \tag{2}$$
specifying the values of two separate (but usually related) functions of two variables. A function of two variables can be represented either by a three-dimensional model or more conveniently by means of contour lines drawn in the (x, y) plane, or, as we may conveniently say, in the z-plane. Thus to represent (1) graphically we draw, in the z-plane, the contours $u = 0, \pm 1, \pm 2$ etc. and the contours $v = 0, \pm 1, \pm 2$, etc.; that is the families of curves
$$\mathrm{u}(x, y) = 0, \ \pm 1 \text{ etc.}$$
$$\mathrm{v}(x, y) = 0, \ \pm 1 \text{ etc.}$$

The process can be best illustrated by an example :

$$w = 1/z$$

Here $$u + iv = 1/(x + iy) = (x - iy)/(x^2 + y^2)$$

so that $$u = x/(x^2 + y^2) \qquad v = -y/(x^2 + y^2)$$

The curves $u =$ constant in the z-plane are thus the curves

$$x^2 + y^2 - (x/u) = 0$$

This can be rearranged into the form

$$(x - 1/2u)^2 + y^2 = 1/4u^2,$$

which, for each value of u, represents a circle centred at $(1/2u, 0)$ and of radius $| 1/2u |$, see Fig. 13.1. The curves $v =$ constant are similarly circles centred at $(0, -1/2v)$ and of radius $| 1/2v |$. The surface represented by the u-contours can be visualised as an infinitely high pinnacle to the right of the origin and an infinitely deep well just to the left.

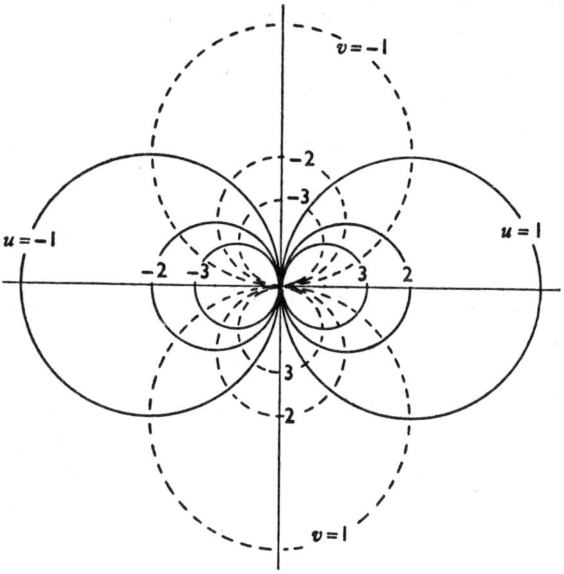

FIG. 13.1

The v-curves are lines of greatest slope on the u-surface. Notice that every u-curve and every v-curve passes through the origin ; it follows conversely that neither u nor v is defined at the origin.

13.22. *Representation by modulus and phase of* f(z)

Instead of plotting contours of u and v, we can equally well exhibit the properties of f(z) by means of the contours of the modulus and phase of f(z). Thus if

$$w = \mathrm{f}(z) = Re^{i\phi}$$

then R and ϕ are functions of position on the Argand diagram and can be represented by the families of contours R = constant, ϕ = constant.

Example

$$w = z^2$$

In this case we find $R = r^2$; and $\phi = 2\theta$. The three-dimensional surface corresponding to the R-contours is therefore a paraboloid of revolution, and the ϕ contours can be visualised for example as

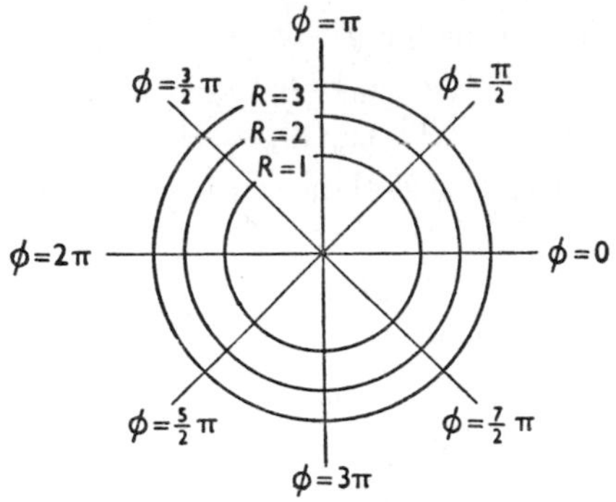

FIG. 13.2

the successive rungs in a staircase spiralling about a line through the origin (Fig. 13.2). Notice however that an increase of 2π in ϕ does not affect the value of w, which remains single valued at every point in the plane although ϕ is multi-valued.

13.23. *The complex function as a transformation of the z-plane*

A third representation, analogous in some ways to the first, discussed in 13.21, is very important in the application of complex functions to potential problems. Let $w = \mathrm{f}(z)$ be the function to be represented. Then to each value of z there corresponds one (or more) values of w; consequently to each point (x, y) in the z-plane there corresponds one (or more) points (u, v) in what we will call the w-plane.

The relation between (u, v) and (x, y) is determined by the equation

$$u + iv = \mathrm{f}(x + iy) \tag{1}$$

A graphical representation of $f(z)$ can therefore be obtained by taking a number of specified points such as Z in the z-plane and calculating the corresponding points W in the w-plane; or more systematically we may take a coordinate grid in the z-plane and plot the corresponding curves in the w-plane (Fig. 13.3).

Example 1

$$w = z^2$$

Putting
$$u + iv = (x + iy)^2$$
we have
$$\left.\begin{aligned} u &= x^2 - y^2 \\ v &= 2xy \end{aligned}\right\} \tag{2}$$

The grid line $x = x_0$ in the z-plane transforms to the curve specified by

$$\left.\begin{aligned} u &= x_0^2 - y^2 \\ v &= 2x_0 y \end{aligned}\right\}$$

or eliminating the parameter y

$$u = x_0^2 - (v/2x_0)^2$$

i.e.
$$v^2 = 4x_0^2 [x_0^2 - u] \tag{3}$$

This is a parabola in the w-plane with vertex at $u = x_0^2$ and latus rectum $4x_0^2$.

The line
$$y = y_0$$
becomes
$$\left.\begin{aligned} u &= x^2 - y_0^2 \\ v &= 2xy_0 \end{aligned}\right\}$$

or after elimination of x

$$u = (v/2y_0)^2 - y_0^2$$

i.e.
$$v^2 = 4y_0^2 (u + y_0^2) \tag{4}$$

which is again a parabola, with vertex at $-y_0^2$ and latus rectum $4y_0^2$.

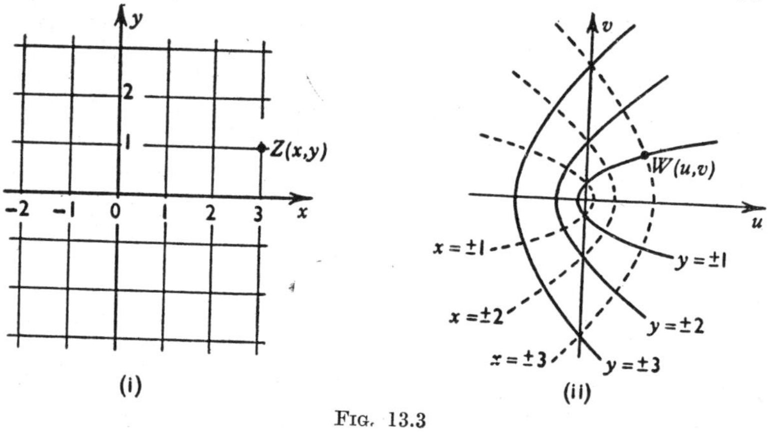

FIG. 13.3

It will be noticed that the points (x, y) and $(-x, -y)$ both transform to the same point (u, v) given by (2). For any given point Z in the z-plane there is one and only one point W in the w-plane but for each W there are two corresponding points Z.

A physical process that corresponds to this transformation of the z-plane can be pictured as follows :

Take an elastic sheet representing the z-plane and mark on it a pair of axes and a grid of lines $x=$ constant, $y=$ constant. Now cut the membrane along the x-axis and discard one half, say the lower half. Keeping the membrane in one plane and the origin fixed rotate the negative x-axis through 180° into contact with the positive axis. Join the edges together so that the line $x=-a$ runs smoothly into the line $x=+a$. A little thought will show that the grid lines of Fig. 13.3 (i) are deformed into something resembling 13.3 (ii). Notice for example that the portion of the sheet near the origin will tend to go into compression in the process, thereby closing up the grid lines in this region, while at large distances the sheet is highly expanded and the grid lines become widely separated.

Example 2

$$w=z^{1/2}$$

We write $w^2=z$, giving $u^2-v^2=x$

and $$2uv=y$$

The line $x=x_0$ therefore transforms to the hyperbola $u^2-v^2=x_0$ and $y=y_0$ transforms to $2uv=y_0$. (Fig. 13.4)

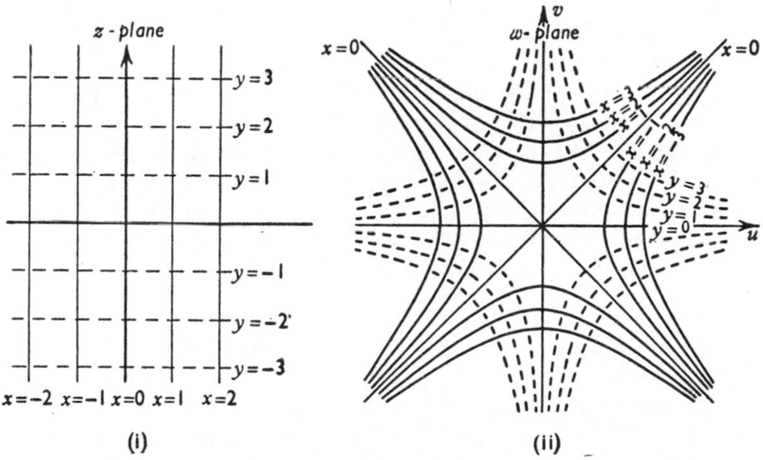

FIG. 13.4

In this case any point Z other than the origin transforms to two different points of the form (u, v) and $(-u, -v)$.

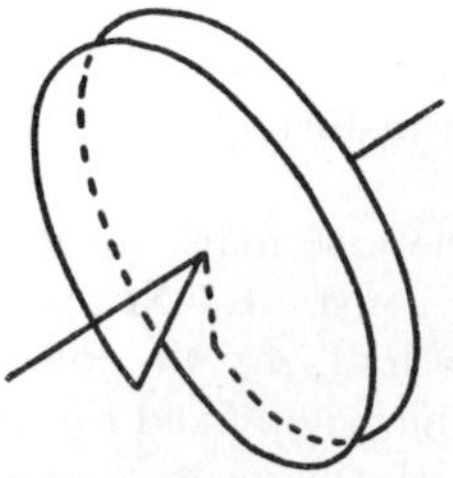

FIG. 13.5

In polar coordinates the point (r, θ) transforms to $(r^{1/2}, \frac{1}{2}\theta)$ and the same point written as $(r, \theta+2\pi)$ transforms to $(r^{1/2}, \frac{1}{2}\theta+\pi)$. A simple device for depicting this is to imagine the z-plane to be occupied by a double membrane consisting of two turns of a spiralling surface as in Fig. 13.5. The lower turn contains the points with phases between -2π and 0 and the second turn contains those with phases between 0 and 2π. Phases between 2π and 4π could similarly be accommodated in a third layer and so on but it is sufficient in this case to suppose instead that these points revert to the first layer.

We can imagine that the end of the second turn is continued smoothly into the beginning of the first turn in some way, for example by means of threads passing through holes along the x-axis in the intermediate sheet. A particle moving continuously in a circle round the origin in the z-plane is imagined to alternate between the two sheets, a cycle performed in the lower sheet being followed by one in the upper sheet and so on.

Now draw a set of superimposed grid lines on both sheets in the z-plane. Cut the threads that connect the end of the second sheet to the beginning of the first and unfold the two layers into a single surface, the line $\theta=0$ remaining fixed in direction. Rejoin the two free edges (corresponding to $\theta=-2\pi$ and $\theta=+2\pi$ in the z-plane) along what is now the negative u axis in the w-plane; the grid of lines of Fig. 13.4 (i) will now transform to the hyperbolae of Fig. 13.4 (ii). Notice that the whole of the lower sheet in the z-plane is compressed into the upper half of the w-plane, and that the upper sheet of the z-plane goes into the lower half of the w-plane.

To summarise the three methods of representing a given function we note that in the first the curves $u=$constant, $v=$constant are plotted on the z-plane, in the second the curves $R=$constant, $\phi=$constant are plotted; in the third the contours $x=$constant, $y=$constant are plotted on the w-plane.

The first and second methods are commonly used for the numerical representation of a complex function. The third is the basis of a very useful application of complex variable theory to potential problems; this is discussed under the title 'conformal transformations' in most advanced books on electricity and magnetism.

13.3. Differential and integral relations

In some cases a function $w = \mathrm{f}(z)$ can be differentiated with respect to z in much the same way as if w and z were real. Consider the function

$$w = z^2$$

To calculate the derivative of w we allow z to change by δz; then

$$w + \delta w = (z + \delta z)^2$$

whence

$$\delta w / \delta z = 2z + \delta z$$

and therefore $\lim\limits_{|\delta z| \to 0} (\delta w/\delta z) = 2z$ independently of arg δz, and may be called the derivative of the function w.

In general, a derivative of a function $w = \mathrm{f}(z)$ exists if, and only if, a unique limit

$$\lim_{|\delta z| \to 0} [\{\mathrm{f}(z + \delta z) - \mathrm{f}(z)\}/\delta z]$$

exists, independent of the sequence of values by which $\delta x \to 0$ and $\delta y \to 0$. The derivative is equal to the common limit derived from all such sequences, and is denoted by $\mathrm{d}w/\mathrm{d}z$ or by $\mathrm{f}'(z)$. The familiar rules for finding derivatives of sums, products, etc., can be established as for functions of a real variable.

However, the quantity $\mathrm{d}w/\mathrm{d}z$ is certainly of a more intricate nature than the slope of a graph of w against z since, for one thing, values of z cannot be conveniently represented by points in a straight line but only by points of a two-dimensional surface. Furthermore, it is not possible to decide by inspection whether a function $w = \mathrm{u}(x, y) + i\mathrm{v}(x, y)$ is or is not differentiable with respect to z. The nature of the derivative may be illuminated by re-stating the definition of a derivative in terms of the variation of w in the Argand z-plane; we shall afterwards proceed to find a criterion for the existence of $\mathrm{d}w/\mathrm{d}z$.

13.31. *The Cauchy-Riemann relations*

Let Z be the point (x, y) and Z' the point $(x + \delta x, y + \delta y)$. Then if the R.H.S. exists

$$\frac{\mathrm{d}w}{\mathrm{d}z} = \lim_{Z' \to Z} \frac{\mathrm{u}(x + \delta x, y + \delta y) + i\mathrm{v}(x + \delta x, y + \delta y) - \{\mathrm{u}(x, y) + i\mathrm{v}(x, y)\}}{\delta z} \tag{1}$$

The limit (1) can be said to exist only if its value is independent of the path along which $Z' \to Z$. For example, two possible paths of approach are shown in Fig. 13.6. The first, when ZZ' is sufficiently small, is parallel to the x-axis and $\delta z = \delta x$, so if the limit (1) is evaluated for this path the result is

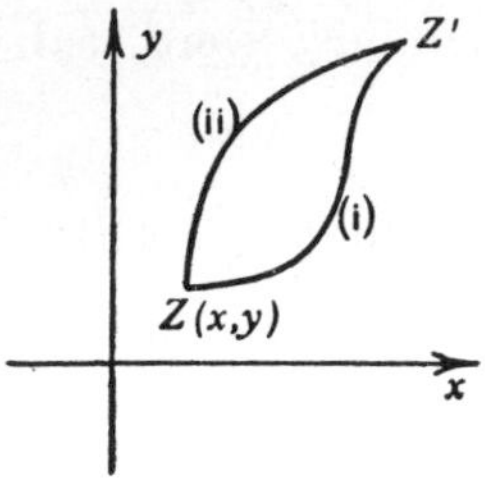

FIG. 13.6

$$\frac{\partial u}{\partial x} + i\frac{\partial v}{\partial x}.$$

For the second path, however ZZ' becomes parallel to the y-axis and hence $\delta z = i\,\delta y$, so that the R.H.S. of (1) has the value

$$\frac{1}{i}\frac{\partial u}{\partial y} + \frac{\partial v}{\partial y}.$$

If (1) is independent of path it follows that

$$\frac{\partial u}{\partial x} + i\frac{\partial v}{\partial x} = \frac{\partial v}{\partial y} - i\frac{\partial u}{\partial y}$$

i.e.
$$\frac{\partial u}{\partial x} = \frac{\partial v}{\partial y} \quad \text{and} \quad \frac{\partial v}{\partial x} = -\frac{\partial u}{\partial y} \tag{2}$$

Equations (2) are thus necessary conditions for the differentiability of the function w with respect to z: they are known as the Cauchy-Riemann relations.

We shall now show that, if u and v are differentiable functions of (x, y), the Cauchy-Riemann relations are also *sufficient* to ensure the differentiability of the function w.

For then

$$\mathrm{u}(x+\delta x, y+\delta y) - \mathrm{u}(x, y) = \left(\frac{\partial u}{\partial x} + \epsilon\right)\delta x + \left(\frac{\partial u}{\partial y} + \eta\right)\delta y$$

where ϵ and η tend to zero when δx and δy both tend to zero. Similarly

$$\mathrm{v}(x+\delta x, y+\delta y) - \mathrm{v}(x, y) = \left(\frac{\partial v}{\partial x} + \epsilon'\right)\delta x + \left(\frac{\partial v}{\partial y} + \eta'\right)\delta y$$

Hence

$$\frac{\delta w}{\delta z} = \left[\left(\frac{\partial u}{\partial x} + i\frac{\partial v}{\partial x}\right)\delta x + \left(\frac{\partial u}{\partial y} + i\frac{\partial v}{\partial y}\right)\delta y \right.$$
$$\left. + (\epsilon + i\epsilon')\,\delta x + (\eta + i\eta')\,\delta y\right] \Big/ (\delta x + i\delta y)$$

Now using the Cauchy-Riemann relations

$$\left(\frac{\partial u}{\partial y}+i\,\frac{\partial v}{\partial y}\right)\delta y=\left(-\frac{\partial v}{\partial x}+i\,\frac{\partial u}{\partial x}\right)\delta y=\left(\frac{\partial u}{\partial x}+i\,\frac{\partial v}{\partial x}\right)i\,\delta y$$

Also

$$\delta x/|\,\delta x+i\,\delta y\,|\leqslant 1 \text{ so } |\,(\epsilon+i\epsilon')\,\delta x/(\delta x+i\,\delta y)\,|\leqslant|\,\epsilon+i\epsilon'\,|\to 0$$

as δx and δy both $\to 0$. Similarly $(\eta+i\eta')\,\delta y/(\delta x+i\,\delta y)\to 0$ as δx and $\delta y\to 0$. Thus

$$\frac{\delta w}{\delta z}=\frac{\partial u}{\partial x}+i\,\frac{\partial v}{\partial x}+\zeta$$

where $\zeta\to 0$ when δx and δy both $\to 0$. Hence $\lim\limits_{|\delta z|\to 0}\dfrac{\delta w}{\delta z}$ exists and in fact

$$\frac{\mathrm{d}w}{\mathrm{d}z}=\frac{\partial u}{\partial x}+i\,\frac{\partial v}{\partial x}$$

This derivative may be expressed in any of the alternative forms

$$\frac{\partial v}{\partial y}+i\,\frac{\partial v}{\partial x} \quad\text{or}\quad \frac{\partial u}{\partial x}-i\,\frac{\partial u}{\partial y} \quad\text{or}\quad \frac{\partial v}{\partial y}-i\,\frac{\partial u}{\partial y}$$

by using the Cauchy-Riemann relations.

We have thus established that if u and v are differentiable functions of x and y, the Cauchy-Riemann relations constitute a necessary and sufficient condition that $w=\mathrm{u}(x, y)+i\mathrm{v}(x, y)$ should possess a derivative $\mathrm{d}w/\mathrm{d}z$ where $z=x+iy$.

13.32. *Analytic functions*

Let a function $\mathrm{f}(x+iy)$ be defined at all points (x, y) in a given region of the Argand diagram. If the function is single-valued and has a unique derivative $\mathrm{df}/\mathrm{d}z$ at all points in the region then it is said to be *analytic* in this region. Other terms in use are regular and holomorphic.

Analytic functions are well-behaved. Being differentiable once they are necessarily continuous. As we shall see in 13.39 they have derivatives of all orders. It will appear, however, in 13.76 that no function except a constant can be analytic everywhere ; with this trivial exception every function becomes non-analytic either at some finite point in the z-plane, or else at infinity.

Examples

Verify that the Cauchy-Riemann relations hold at all finite points in the z-plane for the following functions —

1. $w = z^2$
2. $w = z^3$
3. $w = e^x(\cos y + i \sin y)$

Show that the following functions are analytic except at the isolated points stated.

4. $w = 1/z$, $z = 0$
5. $w = 1/(z - a)$, $z = a$
6. $w = 1/(z^2 + a^2)$, $z = \pm ia$
7. $w = z^{1/2}$ $(-\pi < \arg z \leqslant \pi)$, $z = 0$ (see also 13.41)

Show that the following functions are not analytic except possibly at isolated points

8. $w = |z|$
9. $w = z^*$

The last two examples show that a function of z is not necessarily analytic merely because it can be expressed in terms of z with the aid of special devices such as modulus signs etc.

13.33. *Laplace's equation*

We now show that if $f(z)$ is an analytic function, its real and imaginary parts $u(x, y)$ and $v(x, y)$ both satisfy Laplace's equation. We have to assume for the present that the second derivatives of u and v exist; this restriction in the proof is removed in 13.39 where it is shown that derivatives of all orders of an analytic function exist.

From the Cauchy-Riemann relations we have

$$\frac{\partial u}{\partial x} = \frac{\partial v}{\partial y}$$

$$\frac{\partial u}{\partial y} = -\frac{\partial v}{\partial x}$$

Differentiate the first with respect to x and the second with respect to y.

$$\frac{\partial^2 u}{\partial x^2} = \frac{\partial^2 v}{\partial x\, \partial y}$$

$$\frac{\partial^2 u}{\partial y^2} = -\frac{\partial^2 v}{\partial y\, \partial x}$$

Hence adding and using 9.14

$$\frac{\partial^2 u}{\partial x^2}+\frac{\partial^2 u}{\partial y^2}=\frac{\partial^2 v}{\partial x\,\partial y}-\frac{\partial^2 v}{\partial y\,\partial x}=0$$

Similarly we can show

$$\frac{\partial^2 v}{\partial x^2}+\frac{\partial^2 v}{\partial y^2}=0$$

Example

$$\mathrm{f}(z)=z^3$$

For this function

$$\mathrm{u}(x, y)=x^3-3xy^2\ ;\quad \mathrm{v}(x, y)=3x^2y-y^3$$

$$\frac{\partial^2 u}{\partial x^2}+\frac{\partial^2 u}{\partial y^2}=6x-6x\quad ;\quad \frac{\partial^2 v}{\partial x^2}+\frac{\partial^2 v}{\partial y^2}=6y-6y$$

$$=0 \qquad\qquad =0$$

13.34. *Functions of z in the narrow sense*

We shall now indicate briefly the connection between the Cauchy-Riemann relations and the condition that $w=u+iv$ shall be a function in the restricted (and ill-defined) sense that x and y occur only in the combination $x+iy$.

Let w be any differentiable function of the real variables x and y, in the sense of Chapter 9, and let α, β $(\neq\alpha)$ be any real constants. If $s=x+\alpha y$ and $t=x+\beta y$ then $x=(\beta s-\alpha t)/(\beta-\alpha)$ and $y=(t-s)/(\beta-\alpha)$; w may be expressed as a function of the new variables s, t, and

$$\frac{\partial w}{\partial t}=\frac{\partial w}{\partial x}\frac{\partial x}{\partial t}+\frac{\partial w}{\partial y}\frac{\partial y}{\partial t}$$

$$=\left[-\alpha\frac{\partial w}{\partial x}+\frac{\partial w}{\partial y}\right]\Big/(\beta-\alpha)$$

If $\dfrac{\partial w}{\partial y}=\alpha\dfrac{\partial w}{\partial x}$, then $\dfrac{\partial w}{\partial t}=0$, and it follows that w is a function of $s=x+\alpha y$ alone.

The Cauchy-Riemann relations tell us that

$$\frac{\partial u}{\partial y}+i\frac{\partial v}{\partial y}=i\left(\frac{\partial u}{\partial x}+i\frac{\partial v}{\partial x}\right),\ \text{that is, that}\ \frac{\partial w}{\partial y}=i\frac{\partial w}{\partial x}$$

If i were a real number this relation would ensure that w was a function of $(x+iy)$ alone.

Thus the ill-defined concept of a function in which x and y occur only in the combination $x+iy$ can profitably be replaced by the precise concept of a function satisfying the Cauchy-Riemann relation, that is, an analytic function.

13.35. *Integration*

The integral of a function $f(z)$ of the complex variable z can, like the integral of a function of a real variable, be defined by the aid of Riemann sums. Let A and B be two points in the z-plane, Fig. 13.7, and let the path of integration be divided into segments by intermediate points, $Z_1, \ldots, Z_{n-1}$. Let the endpoints of the segments be denoted by the complex numbers $z_0=a$, z_1, ... $z_n=b$, and let ξ_1 be any point in the first segment, ξ_2 any point in the second and so on. We form the sum

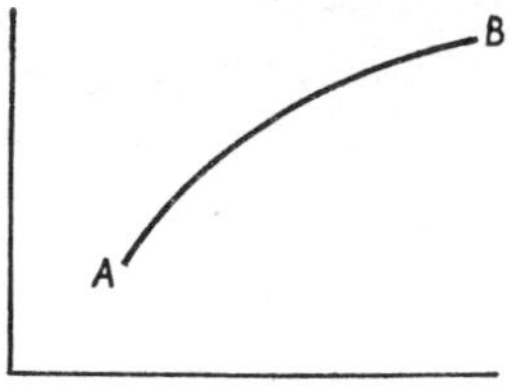

FIG. 13.7

$$S_n=f(\xi_1)(z_1-z_0)+f(\xi_2)(z_2-z_1)+\ldots+f(\xi_n)(z_n-z_{n-1}) \tag{1}$$

For any finite value of n this sum can be evaluated by a straightforward application of the rules of complex algebra. Let the number of segments now be increased in such a way that every interval z_r-z_{r-1} tends to zero as n tends to infinity. If S_n tends to a limit S whose value is independent both of the mode of subdivision into segments and of the method of selection of $\xi_1, \xi_2, \ldots$ etc. within these segments, this limit is called the Riemann integral of $f(z)$ along the specified path.

This definition is not identical in form with the definition of the Riemann integral used in 8.3. Indeed we could not now form sums $L_n=\sum m_r\, dz_r$ and $U_n=\sum M_r\, dz_r$ because it is meaningless to talk of the ' least ' and ' greatest ' values (m_r, M_r) of a function $f(z)$ which takes complex values. It is not difficult to see, however, that if z and ξ are restricted to real values, and if $f(z)$ is real when z is real, the definition of an integral as the limit of sum (1), when this is independent of the mode of subdivision and the selection of the ξ's, is equivalent to the definition of the Riemann integral. For if the (real) ξ's are chosen so that $f(\xi_i)$ is the least value taken by $f(x)$ in the ith interval, S_n corresponds to the Riemann sum L_n (see 8.3). Similarly another appropriate choice of ξ's makes $S_n=U_n$;

so $\lim S_n$ exists if and only if $\lim L_n = \lim U_n$, and then $\lim S_n = \lim L_n = \lim U_n =$ Riemann integral. The definition of the Riemann integral of a function of a complex variable is therefore consistent with the definition of the Riemann integral of a real function of a real variable.

If the point A is fixed then the integral certainly depends on the upper limit of integration, but it will also depend in general on the path of integration from A to B. Hence we cannot infer that the integral defines a function of the upper limit alone. In the next section, however, we prove a very remarkable theorem which enables us to assert this when the integrand $\mathrm{f}(z)$ is analytic.

Examples

The following results are easily proved :

1. $\int_A^B \mathrm{f}\,\mathrm{d}z = -\int_B^A \mathrm{f}\,\mathrm{d}z$ the paths of integration being the same.

2. $\int_A^B \mathrm{f}\,\mathrm{d}z + \int_B^C \mathrm{f}\,\mathrm{d}z = \int_A^C \mathrm{f}\,\mathrm{d}z$, the path AC being the combined paths AB and BC.

3. $\int_A^B \mathrm{d}z = z_B - z_A = b - a$ say, independent of path.

4. $\int_A^B [\mathrm{f}_1(z) + \mathrm{f}_2(z)]\,\mathrm{d}z = \int_A^B \mathrm{f}_1\,\mathrm{d}z + \int_A^B \mathrm{f}_2\,\mathrm{d}z.$

5. If the path of integration is parallel to the x-axis e.g. from $A=(a, c)$ to $B=(b, c)$ then

$$\int_{a+ic}^{b+ic} \mathrm{f}(z)\,\mathrm{d}z = \int_a^b \mathrm{f}(x+ic)\,\mathrm{d}x$$

6. If the path of integration is parallel to the y-axis e.g. from $A=(c, a)$ to $B=(c, b)$ then

$$\int_{c+ia}^{c+ib} \mathrm{f}(z)\,\mathrm{d}z = i\int_a^b \mathrm{f}(c+iy)\,\mathrm{d}y$$

An integral round a *closed* curve C in the z-plane is known as a ‘ contour integral ’, and is indicated by an integral sign drawn through a circle, $\oint$, with a suffix if necessary to specify the contour C of integration (compare also with the line integrals of 9.32).

13.36. *Cauchy's theorem*

Let f(z) be analytic at all points within and on a closed curve C in the z-plane. Cauchy's theorem states that for such a function

$$\oint_C \mathrm{f}(z)\,\mathrm{d}z = 0$$

The theorem also implies of course that the integrals along the two paths from a point P to a point Q (see Fig. 13.8) are equal ; for the integral round the closed path is, in effect, the integral from P to Q via one path, added to the integral in the reverse direction via the other path.

FIG. 13.8

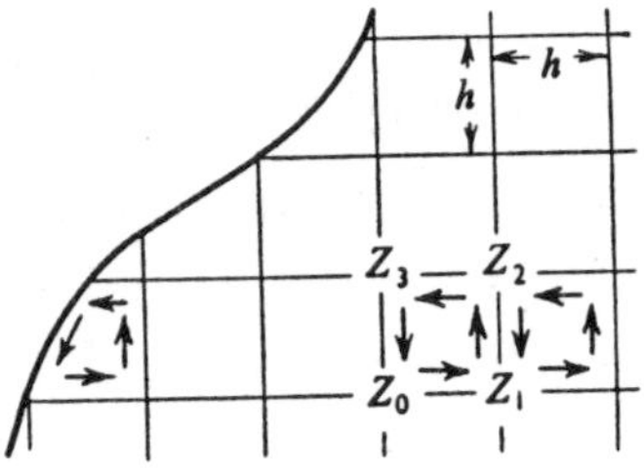

FIG. 13.9

To prove the theorem we draw a square mesh of side h sub-dividing the area within the curve into a number of squares plus a number of irregular shapes bounded on one side by the curve C. Now consider the sum of the integrals obtained by circulating in the same sense round the periphery of each elementary cell. The contribution from any complete or incomplete side of a square within C cancels with another such contribution because every path except those on the boundary of C is traversed once in each direction (Fig. 13.9). The sum of these integrals is therefore equal to the integral along the closed path C. Consider now the integral around one of the squares, $Z_0Z_1Z_2Z_3$. At Z_0, let $z = z_0 \equiv x_0 + iy_0$ and $\mathrm{f}(z) = \mathrm{f}_0$; at any point in the neighbourhood we have

$$\frac{\mathrm{f}(z) - \mathrm{f}_0}{z - z_0} = \mathrm{f}_0' + \alpha$$

where $\alpha \to 0$ as $z \to z_0$ i.e. $\mathrm{f}(z) = \mathrm{f}_0 + \mathrm{f}_0'(z - z_0) + \alpha(z - z_0)$. Therefore the integral round the square is

$$\mathrm{f}(z)\,\mathrm{d}z = \mathrm{f}_0 \oint \mathrm{d}z + \mathrm{f}_0' \oint (z - z_0)\,\mathrm{d}z + \oint \alpha(z - z_0)\,\mathrm{d}z \qquad (1)$$

The first integral on the R.H.S vanishes : for (see Examples 2 and 3 of 13.35),

$$\oint \mathrm{d}z = (z_1 - z_0) + (z_2 - z_1) + (z_3 - z_2) + (z_0 - z_3) = 0$$

The second integral also vanishes. For on the segment Z_0Z_1, $z - z_0 = x + iy_0 - (x_0 + iy_0) = x - x_0$ and $\mathrm{d}z = +\mathrm{d}x$, while on the segment Z_2Z_3, $z - z_0 = x + i(y_0 + h) - (x_0 + iy_0) = x - x_0 + ih$ and $\mathrm{d}z = -\mathrm{d}x$; and using the results of 13.35, Examples 1, 2 and 4, we find that

$$\int_{z_0}^{z_1} (z - z_0)\,\mathrm{d}z + \int_{z_2}^{z_3} (z - z_0)\,\mathrm{d}z$$

$$= \int_{x_0}^{x_0+h} (x - x_0)\,\mathrm{d}x - \int_{x_0}^{x_0+h} (x - x_0 + ih)\,\mathrm{d}x$$

$$= -\int_{x_0}^{x_0+h} ih\,\mathrm{d}x = -ih^2$$

Similarly using Example 6 the remaining two segments contribute the amount

$$\int_{z_1}^{z_2} (z - z_0)\,\mathrm{d}z - \int_{z_0}^{z_3} (z - z_0)\,\mathrm{d}z = \int_{y_0}^{y_0+h} ih\,\mathrm{d}y = +ih^2$$

The two contributions therefore cancel.

There remains the contribution from the third term in (1), viz.,

$$\oint \alpha(z - z_0)\,\mathrm{d}z$$

Let α_m be the greatest value reached by $|\alpha|$ on the boundary of the square. Since the greatest value reached by $|z - z_0|$ is the diagonal $\sqrt{2}h$, the modulus of the integral is certainly less than

$$\oint \alpha_m \sqrt{2}h\,|\mathrm{d}z| = \sqrt{2}\alpha_m h \oint |\mathrm{d}z|$$

$$= 4\sqrt{2}\alpha_m h^2$$

Now we have seen that $\oint_C \mathrm{f}(z)\,\mathrm{d}z$ is equal to the sum of the integrals round the cells into which the area inside C has been divided. Since for each square

$$\left|\oint \mathrm{f}(z)\,\mathrm{d}z\right| \leqslant 4\sqrt{2}\,\alpha_m h^2 = 4\sqrt{2}\,\alpha_m \times (\text{area of cell}),$$

it follows that the sum of the contributions from all complete squares within C is certainly not greater in modulus than $M\,4\sqrt{2}A$ where A is the combined area of these squares, and M is the greatest value reached by $|\alpha|$ on any square. Now the $|\alpha|$'s and therefore

M can be reduced indefinitely by making h tend to zero; further although A will increase during this process it cannot exceed the area enclosed by C. Hence the contribution from complete squares within C can be made arbitrarily small by taking a sufficiently close mesh.

There remain the contributions from the irregular shapes bounded on one side by a segment of C. We again have

$$\oint dz = 0 \quad \text{and} \quad \oint (z - z_0)\, dz = \oint \tfrac{1}{2} d(z^2) - z_0 \oint dz = 0 \quad \text{(cf. Ex. 3)},$$

and need only consider the contributions from $\oint \alpha (z - z_0)\, dz$. These also become arbitrarily small when $h \to 0$, provided that the curve C is of finite length. For the contribution from the straight portions

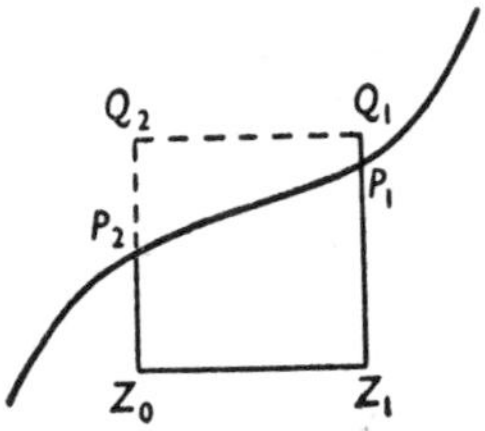

FIG. 13.10

of any one of these shapes, e.g. $P_2Z_0Z_1P_1$ (Fig. 13.10) is certainly less than

$$\alpha_m \sqrt{2}h \oint |\, dz \,| < 4\, \alpha_m \sqrt{2}h^2$$

and the contribution from the segments of C is less than

$$\alpha_m \sqrt{2}h \int_{P_1}^{P_2} |\, dz \,|$$

where α_m is the greatest value of $|\,\alpha\,|$ within or on $Z_0Z_1P_1P_2$. Hence the contribution has modulus less than

$$4\alpha_m \sqrt{2}h^2 + \alpha_m \sqrt{2}h \int dz$$

and summing over all these peripheral circuits, we obtain an amount less than

$$M4\sqrt{2}A_1 + \sqrt{2}MhS$$

Here M is the greatest of the α_m's and tends to zero† with h; A_1 is the area of the squares traversed by the curve and S is the total

† This can be proved fairly easily if $f'(2)$ is continuous. Without this assumption the proof of Gauchy's theorom is more subtle.

length of curve C. We note that since no such square has any point further than $\sqrt{2}h$ from C, $A_1 \leqslant 2\sqrt{2}hS$ Hence $\left|\oint_C f(z)\,dz\right| \leqslant \epsilon$ where ϵ can be made arbitrarily small by reducing the mesh size h.

Hence
$$\oint_C f(z)\,dz = 0$$

13.37. *Extension of Cauchy's theorem*

One or two useful extensions of Cauchy's theorem should be noticed. Let C_1 and C_2 be two curves such that C_1 encloses C_2 completely, and suppose that $f(z)$ is analytic on these curves and in the annular space between them. Then by bridging the annulus with two paths S_1 and S_2 as shown (Fig. 13.11) we can regard the path $C_1S_1C_2S_2$ as a single curve C to which the theorem applies, giving

$$\oint_C f(z)\,dz = 0$$

The contributions from S_1 and S_2 cancel since the two paths can be made to coincide. Also the paths C_1 and C_2 are traversed

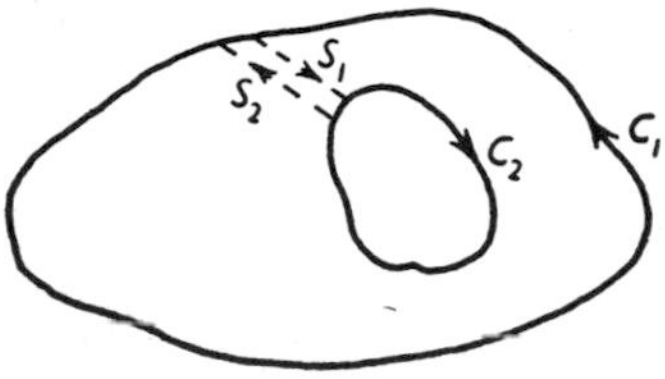

FIG. 13.11

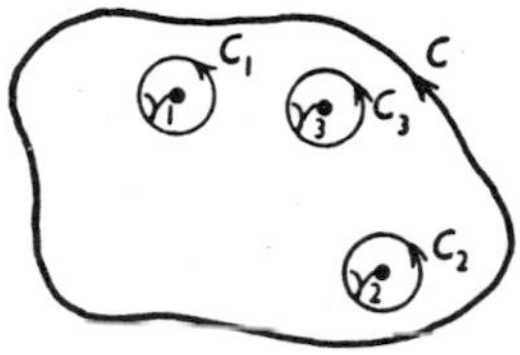

FIG. 13.12

in opposite directions. It follows that if the separate integrals are taken in the same sense, then

$$\oint_{C_1} f(z)\,dz = \oint_{C_2} f(z)\,dz \tag{1}$$

This result implies that a closed path of integration may be deformed from C_1 to C_2 without affecting the integral provided that the integrand is analytic at all intervening points. This can be extended to the cases in which there are two or more isolated points within a contour at which the integrand is not analytic. For example in Fig. 13.12 if $f(z)$ is analytic at all points within C except γ_1, γ_2 and γ_3, then

$$\oint_C f(z)\,dz = \oint_{C_1} f(z)\,dz + \oint_{C_2} f(z)\,dz + \oint_{C_3} f(z)\,dz$$

where C_1, C_2 and C_3 are small circles surrounding the non-analytic points. These circles may be diminished indefinitely or C may be allowed to expand without limit, provided always that no new singularities are brought inside C.

Example

For any simple closed curve C encircling the point $z=\alpha$,

$$\oint_C dz/(z-\alpha)=2\pi i.$$

Let C_1 be a circle with centre at α and radius a, sufficiently small for C_1 to lie entirely within C. Then, by the result (1),

$$\oint_C dz/(z-\alpha)=\oint_{C_1} dz/(z-\alpha)$$

Also on C_1, $z-\alpha=a(\cos\theta+i\sin\theta)=ae^{i\theta}$, and

$$dz=a(-\sin\theta+i\cos\theta)\,d\theta=iae^{i\theta}\,d\theta$$

Hence $\oint_{C_1} dz/(z-\alpha)=\oint_{\theta=0}^{2\pi} i\,d\theta=2\pi i$, and this is also the value of

$$\oint_C dz/(z-\alpha).$$

13.38. *Integration as the inverse of differentiation for analytic functions*

Let $f(z)$ be analytic in a region and let S_1 and S_2 be any two paths from A to B (Fig. 13.13). Then since the integral round the closed path S_1, S_2 vanishes, it follows that the integral $\int_{z=a}^{b} f(z)\,dz$

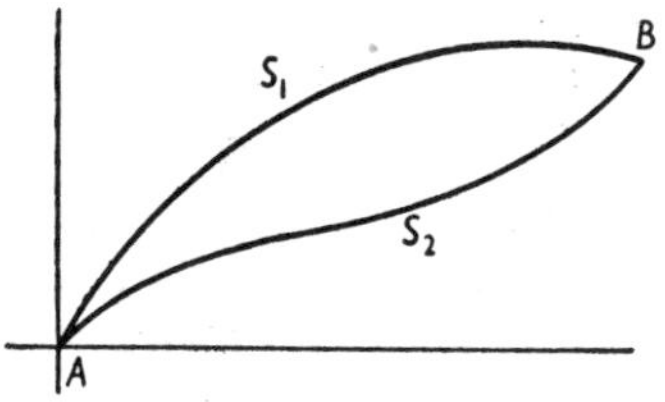

FIG. 13.13

depends only on a and b and not on the path taken. Similarly, for fixed a, the integral

$$F(z)=\int_a^z f(\zeta)\,d\zeta \tag{1}$$

depends on its upper limit only and defines a function of z corresponding exactly to the indefinite integral in the case of the real variable : in particular we can show that the Riemann integral (1) satisfies the equation $F'(z) = f(z)$.

For,

$$F(z+\delta z) - F(z) = \int_z^{z+\delta z} f(\zeta)\, d\zeta$$

$$= \int_0^{\delta z} f(z+\zeta)\, d\zeta$$

Now $f(z)$ is analytic and therefore possesses a derivative, so $f(z+\zeta) = f(z) + \zeta[f'(z) + \epsilon]$ where $\epsilon \to 0$ as $\zeta \to 0$. Hence

$$F(z+\delta z) - F(z) = \delta z\, f(z) + O(\delta z)^2$$

It follows that $\lim_{\delta z \to 0} \dfrac{F(z+\delta z) - F(z)}{\delta z}$ exists and is equal to $f(z)$. Hence $F'(z) = f(z)$ for all values of z for which $f(z)$ is analytic.

Conversely if $F(z)$ is a function for which $F'(z) = f(z)$, then the (Riemann) integral

$$\int_a^z f(\zeta)\, d\zeta = F(z) + \text{constant}$$

i.e. to find $\int f(z)\, dz$ for an analytic function it is sufficient to find a function $F(z)$ for which $F'(z) = f(z)$. The proof is straightforward, for if we write $G(z) = \int_a^z f(\zeta)\, d\zeta$ we have already proved that $G'(z) = f(z)$, hence $\dfrac{d}{dz}[F(z) - G(z)] = 0$, that is, $F(z) - G(z)$ is independent of z, or $G(z) = F(z) + \text{constant}$, as required.

Example 1

The function $f(z) = z^n$, $n \geqslant 0$, is analytic at all finite points. Also $(d/dz)(z^{n+1})/(n+1)) = z^n$. Hence $\int z^n\, dz = z^{n+1}/(n+1) + C$.

Example 2

$$\int e^{\alpha z}\, dz = \frac{e^{\alpha z}}{\alpha} + C$$

13.39. *Cauchy's integral formula and the higher derivatives of an analytic function*

In this section we shall prove a result of considerable importance, namely formula (5) below. Let $f(z)$ be a function which is analytic inside and on a simple closed curve C. We shall use the symbol z to stand for any chosen point inside C, and ζ for a running variable either round the contour C or round some other curve lying wholly inside or on C. For any ζ in or on C the quantity $f(\zeta)/(\zeta - z)$ is an analytic function of ζ except at $\zeta = z$ where the denominator vanishes. Hence

$$\int_C \frac{f(\zeta)}{\zeta - z} d\zeta = \int_{C_1} \frac{f(\zeta)}{\zeta - z} d\zeta$$

where C_1 is a circle with centre $\zeta = z$ and radius a sufficiently small to ensure that C_1 lies inside C. As $f(\zeta)$ is analytic inside C, it is differentiable at z. Therefore, for any $\epsilon > 0$ we can ensure that $|f(\zeta) - f(z)| < \epsilon$ everywhere on C_1 by choosing a sufficiently small.

But

$$\int_{C_1} \frac{f(\zeta)}{\zeta - z} d\zeta = f(z) \int_{C_1} \frac{d\zeta}{\zeta - z} + \int_{C_1} \frac{f(\zeta) - f(z)}{\zeta - z} d\zeta$$

$$= 2\pi i\, f(z) + \int_{\theta=0}^{2\pi} \{f(\zeta) - f(z)\} i\, d\theta$$

using result (1) 13.37 to get the first term, and applying the same method (since on C_1, $\zeta = z + ae^{i\theta}$) to obtain the second term.

Now $|i\{f(\zeta) - f(z)\}| = |\{f(\zeta) - f(z)\}|$, hence

$$\left| \int_{\theta=0}^{2\pi} \left\{ f(\zeta) - f(z) \right\} i\, d\theta \right| \leqslant \epsilon \int_0^{2\pi} d\theta = 2\pi\epsilon$$

This, moreover, is true for all positive ϵ, so the L.H.S. must be zero, whence

$$\int_C \frac{f(\zeta)}{\zeta - z} d\zeta = 2\pi i\, f(z)$$

or

$$f(z) = \frac{1}{2\pi i} \int_C \frac{f(\zeta)}{\zeta - z} d\zeta \qquad (1)$$

This is Cauchy's integral formula, which expresses the value of the analytic function f at an internal point in terms of an integral involving only values of f on the curve C itself.

By means of this theorem we can prove the important result that an analytic function has derivatives of all orders.

Let z be any point inside the contour C, and let $z + \delta z$ be a neighbouring point also within C.

Then

$$f(z) = \frac{1}{2\pi i} \int_C \frac{f(\zeta)}{\zeta - z} d\zeta$$

and

$$f(z + \delta z) = \frac{1}{2\pi i} \int_C \frac{f(\zeta)}{\zeta - z - \delta z} d\zeta$$

Hence
$$f'(z) = \lim_{|\delta z| \to 0} \frac{f(z+\delta z) - f(z)}{\delta z}$$
$$= \lim_{|\delta z| \to 0} \frac{1}{2\pi i} \int_C \frac{f(\zeta)}{(\zeta - z)(\zeta - z - \delta z)} d\zeta \tag{2}$$
Now we use algebraical identity
$$\int_C \frac{f(\zeta)}{(\zeta - z)(\zeta - z - \delta z)} d\zeta = \int_C \frac{f(\zeta)}{(\zeta - z)^2} d\zeta + \delta z \int_C \frac{f(\zeta)\, d\zeta}{(\zeta - z)^2(\zeta - z - \delta z)} \tag{3}$$
Since $f(\zeta)$ is analytic, and z and $z+\delta z$ are both within C, the integrand of the second integral on the right-hand side of (3) is finite at all points of C; also the length of the curve C is finite. Hence this integral is finite, and as $\delta z \to 0$, its contribution to the integral on the left-hand side of (3) tends to 0.

Hence
$$f'(z) = \frac{1}{2\pi i} \int_C \frac{f(\zeta)}{(\zeta - z)^2} d\zeta \tag{4}$$

By a similar argument we can prove that if $f^{(n)}(z)$ exists and has the value
$$f^{(n)}(z) = \frac{n!}{2\pi i} \int_C \frac{f(\zeta)}{(\zeta - z)^{n+1}} d\zeta \tag{5}$$
then $f^{(n+1)}(z)$ exists and has the value given by replacing n by $(n+1)$ in formula (5). Now formulae (1) and (4) show that (5) holds for $n=0$ and $n=1$, hence by induction it holds generally.

13.4. Singularities

Any point in the z-plane at which $f(z)$ is not analytic, e.g. because $F'(z)$ is not uniquely defined, is called a *singular point* of the function. It will be shown in 13.76 that the only function that has no singular points is a constant. Every other function is singular somewhere, possibly at infinity.

A singularity in which a linear factor in the denominator becomes zero is called a simple pole. Examples of functions with simple poles are

1. $1/(z+a)$; pole at $z = -a$
2. $1/(z^2+a^2)$; poles at $z = \pm ia$
3. $1/(z-a)(z-b)(z-c)$; poles at $z=a$, b, and c

If a function $F(z)$ with a simple pole at $z=a$ is expressed
$$F(z) = f(z)/(z-a)$$

the value of the numerator at $z=a$, namely $f(a)$, is called the 'residue' of $F(z)$ at $z=a$ (see also 13.78). We note that if C is a small contour encircling the pole, on which contour the function $F(z)$ is analytic,

$$\int_C F(z)\,dz=\int_C \frac{f(z)}{z-a}\,dz=2\pi i\, f(a) \tag{1}$$

by Cauchy's integral theorem of the last section. That is, *the value of the contour integral encircling the pole is $2\pi i$ times the residue.*

Multiple poles can also be defined. For example, the function $f(z)=1/z^2$ has a double pole at the origin, and the function $1/(z-a)^2$ has a double pole at $z=a$. Poles of higher orders are exhibited by the functions $1/(z-a)^n$, $1/(z^2+a^2)^n$ where n is any positive integer. These have obvious connections with Cauchy's integral formula for higher derivatives.

13.41. *Branch points*

A second type of singularity rather more elusive than the pole (which is not very different from its counterpart in the real variable) is a branch point. The function $f(z)=z^{\frac{1}{2}}$ discussed in 13.23 Example 2 provides the simplest example. This function is not single valued and therefore is not analytic according to the definition of 13.32. However it is easily made analytic in the following way. In 13.23 we saw that the two values of $z^{\frac{1}{2}}$ arise because the identical points (r, θ) and $(r, \theta+2\pi)$ in the z-plane transform to two different points in the w-plane; further we saw how this state of affairs could be imagined as the unwrapping of a double sheet representing the z-plane into a single sheet representing the w-plane. If, however, the z-plane is restricted by some means to one sheet then in the unwrapping process one half only of the w-plane is formed and the other half, containing the duplicated points, is suppressed. A simple way of making this restriction is to make a barrier in the z-plane along a line from the origin to infinity in any direction, for example along the negative x-axis. If we take the positive x-axis to be the line $\theta=0$ (rather than $\theta=2\pi$ etc.) and if we agree not to use circuits in the z-plane crossing the negative axis, then the value of θ at all points in the z-plane is restricted to the range

$$-\pi<\theta\leqslant\pi$$

(Notice that we have taken the value of θ for a point on the negative x axis to be $+\pi$ and not $-\pi$.) The corresponding values of $w=z^{\frac{1}{2}}$ are then confined to the right-hand half of the w-plane.

Now consider the values of w for values of z which are close together but at opposite sides of the barrier (fig. 13.14), i.e. consider

$$z_1 = re^{i(\pi - \frac{1}{2}\delta)}$$

$$z_2 = re^{-i(\pi - \frac{1}{2}\delta)}$$

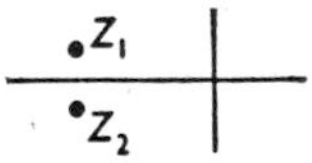

FIG. 13.14

We note that $$z_1 - z_2 = re^{i\pi}[e^{-\frac{1}{2}i\delta} - e^{-2\pi i}e^{\frac{1}{2}i\delta}]$$

$$= -r[e^{-\frac{1}{2}i\delta} - e^{\frac{1}{2}i\delta}]$$

so that as $\delta \rightarrow 0$, $$z_1 \rightarrow z_2.$$

But $$w_1 = z_1^{\frac{1}{2}} = r^{\frac{1}{2}}\, e^{i(\frac{1}{2}\pi - \frac{1}{4}\delta)}$$

$$w_2 = z_2^{\frac{1}{2}} = r^{\frac{1}{2}}\, e^{-i(\frac{1}{2}\pi - \frac{1}{4}\delta)}$$

$$w_1 - w_2 = r^{\frac{1}{2}}\, e^{\frac{1}{2}i\pi}[e^{-\frac{1}{4}i\delta} - e^{-\pi i}\, e^{\frac{1}{4}i\delta}]$$

$$= i\, r^{\frac{1}{2}}[e^{-\frac{1}{4}i\delta} + e^{\frac{1}{4}i\delta}]$$

so that as $\delta \rightarrow 0$, $$w_1 - w_2 \rightarrow 2ir^{\frac{1}{2}}$$

i.e. w_1 does not $\rightarrow w_2$ as $z_1 \rightarrow z_2$.

Thus we have made the function w single-valued at the expense of its continuity.

It should perhaps be mentioned that the negative real axis is not the only possible choice of barrier : any line or curve extending from the origin to infinity in the z-plane ensures that θ is uniquely specified for each z, and hence that $z^{\frac{1}{2}}$ is one-valued.

Either of the two functions which $z^{\frac{1}{2}}$ represents (generally called the two ' branches ' of $z^{\frac{1}{2}}$) is analytic except at the barrier. But the position of the barrier may be shifted at will, except that it must always pass through the origin. The origin is thus a point, and indeed the only point, at which the function cannot be made analytic, and this is essentially bound up with the fact that at the origin the two branches of the function are indistinguishable : to indicate these special characteristics the origin is called a *branch point*.

It is usually possible to envisage an n-valued function of z as consisting of n ' branches ' in different sheets connected only at branch points, i.e. points at which two or more branches become indistinguishable and the function cannot be made analytic.

Other examples of functions with branch points follow.

Example 1

$(z-a)^{\frac{1}{2}}$. There is now a branch point at $z=a$. The function can be made single valued by a barrier in the z-plane from $z=a$ to infinity.

Example 2

$1/(z-a)^{\frac{1}{2}}$. There is again a branch point at $z=a$, but in this case the function does not exist at the branch point. The function might be said to have a pole and a branch point at $z=a$, but in fact, it is not usual to speak of poles of non-integral order.

Example 3

$(z^2-a^2)^{\frac{1}{2}}$. There are here two branch points, at $z=\pm a$. The function can be made single valued in this case by a barrier joining the branch points ; it is not necessary for the barrier to go to infinity. To see this consider a point Z moving in a circular path of radius b about one of the branch points, say $z=a$. Then the position of Z is represented by

$$z=a+be^{i\theta}$$

During the course of the cycle θ will increase from 0 to 2π. We have to find the path of the corresponding point W in the w-plane.

We have
$$\begin{aligned} w^2 &= z^2-a^2 \\ &= 2abe^{i\theta}+b^2e^{2i\theta} \\ &= 2ab[e^{i\theta}+(b/2a)e^{2i\theta}] \qquad (a>0,\ b>0) \end{aligned}$$

When $\theta=\pi$, $w^2=2ab[-1+(b/2a)]$, so the corresponding point of the w^2-curve lies on the real axis, and is to the left or right of the origin according as $b<2a$ or $b>2a$. If $b<2a$ the w^2-path does not subtend a complete angle of 2π about the origin until $\theta=2\pi$. If $b>2a$ however, the w^2-path subtends an angle of 2π when θ reaches π, and by the time $\theta=2\pi$, the w^2-path has described an angle of 4π about the origin.

Since $\arg w^2=2 \arg w$, the angle subtended at the origin by the w-path when $\theta=2\pi$ is π or 2π according as $b<2a$ or $b>2a$ (see Figs. 13.15). In the latter case ($b>2a$), the values of w corresponding to $2\pi\leqslant\theta\leqslant4\pi$ repeat the values obtained for θ in the range $0\leqslant\theta\leqslant2\pi$, which is consistent with w being a one-valued function of z ; but when $b<2a$, the two representations of z, namely $z=a+be^{i\theta}$ and $z=a+be^{i(2\pi+\theta)}$ lead to two different values of w ; i.e. w is no longer a single-valued function.

We have thus verified that, the function z can be made single valued by a barrier joining the two branch points $\pm a$.

The reader should not suppose, however, that a function can be made single valued by linking any two branch points by a barrier in this way. The function

$$w = \surd(z-a) + \surd(z+a)$$

has branch points at $z = \pm a$, as before, but is single valued only for paths which encircle neither point.

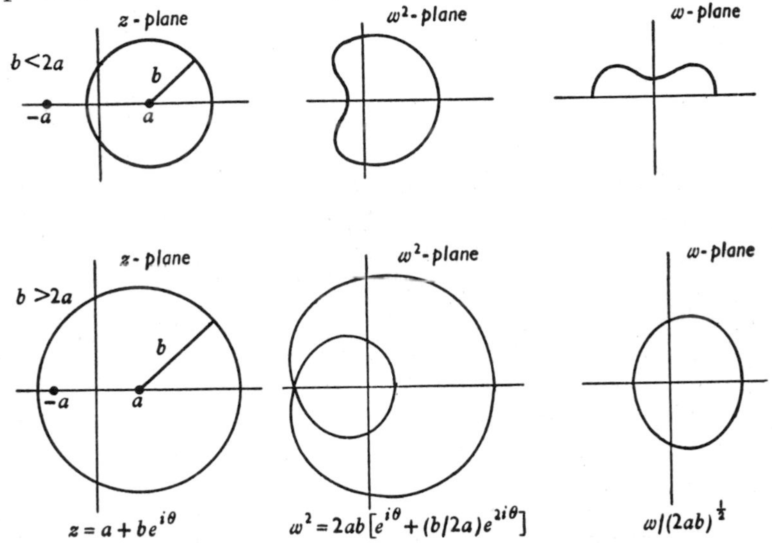

FIG. 13.15

13.5. Polynomials, rational functions and algebraic functions of a complex variable

These are all defined in a way closely similar to the corresponding functions of a real variable. Some simple but important characteristics of these functions are worth stating.

13.51. *Polynomials*

Polynomials in z, i.e. functions of the form

$$f(z) = a_0 z^n + a_1 z^{n-1} + \dots + a_n \tag{1}$$

are single valued and analytic at all finite points of the z-plane and have no poles or branch points. The polynomial has n zeros, as we shall show in 13.9, corresponding to n factors (not necessarily distinct)

$$f(z) = a_0 (z-\alpha_1)(z-\alpha_2) \dots (z-\alpha_n) \tag{2}$$

13.52. *Rational functions*

If p (z), q (z) are polynomials, then the ratio

$$r(z)=p(z)/q(z)$$

is a rational function. It will have zeros at the zeros of p (z) and poles simple or multiple, at the simple or repeated zeros of q (z). It is analytic except at these poles.

13.6. Power series; definition of convergence; absolute convergence

To define a function that is not algebraic, we need an infinite process of some kind, just as in the theory of the real variable. Of the available processes, namely infinite sequences, infinite series, infinite products, integrals and solutions of differential equations, the simplest is the infinite power series, such as

$$w=a_0+a_1z+a_2z^2+\ldots+a_nz^n+\ldots \tag{1}$$

This defines a value of w for every point z at which the series converges, and a function so defined is obviously single valued and as we shall show is in fact analytic at all points within the region of convergence.

The following definitions and theorems (13.61–62) are closely analogous to those we have already met in dealing with real power series.

Definition of convergence. The series $\sum_{r=1}^{\infty} a_rz^r$ converges to a limit w if for any $\epsilon>0$ there exists a number n_0 such that $\left|\sum_{r=1}^{n} a_rz^r - w\right| < \epsilon$ for all $n>n_0$.

A necessary condition for convergence is that $|a_nz^n|\to 0$ as $n\to\infty$. This is easily proved. The reader should notice the geometrical interpretation of the result in the Argand diagram (Fig. 13.16).

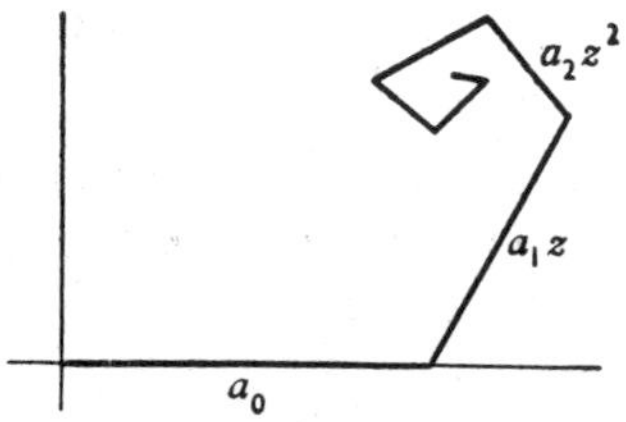

FIG. 13.16

The limit of the series is a point given by the vector sum of displacements representing the successive terms, and these displacements must eventually tend to zero if the series is to have a limit.

Absolute convergence. If the real series

$$|a_0|+|a_1z|+|a_2z^2|+\ldots+|a_nz^n| \qquad (2)$$

obtained by taking the moduli of the terms in series (1) converges, then series (1) is said to converge absolutely. If series (1) converges for some z whereas (2) does not, then series (1) is said to converge conditionally. Notice that the sum of series (2) is the total length of the segments in Fig. 13.16 placed end to end in a straight line.

13.61. *The first ratio test*

Since from example 1 of 6.41,

$$|a_{n+1}z^{n+1}/a_nz^n|=|a_{n+1}z^{n+1}|/|a_nz^n|,$$

the real series (2) of the above paragraph converges if for all n greater than a certain value n_0

$$|(a_{n+1}/a_n)z|<k \qquad \text{where } k<1$$

If, further, $\lim|a_{n+1}/a_n|$ exists and is denoted by the real number $1/R$ it follows that (1) converges absolutely if

$$|z|<R$$

If $|z|=R$ a closer examination is required. If $|z|>R$ then (2) certainly diverges. It is also possible to show that for $|z|>R$ series (1) diverges also.

13.62. *The circle of convergence*

The results of 13.61 can be summarised with the aid of the Argand diagram. Draw a circle of radius R, about the origin (Fig. 13.17); then the series (1) of 13.6 converges absolutely, for all values of z lying within the circle and diverges for all values outside. This simple theorem provides a good example of the way in which the complex variable unifies the isolated results obtained in real variable theory. The real infinite series

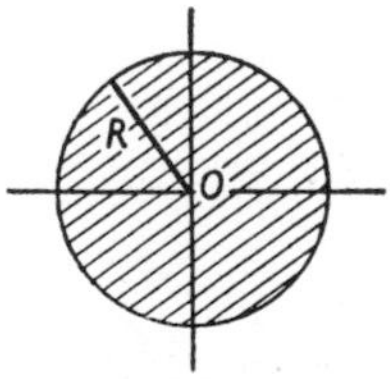

FIG. 13.17

$$1+x+x^2+\ldots+x^n$$

converges absolutely to $1/(1-x)$ provided that $|x|<1$. The restriction at $x=+1$ is not unexpected because the function $1/(1-x)$ is unbounded here; at $x=-1$ the function is apparently well-behaved, yet it cannot be expanded as $1+x+x^2+\ldots$ when $x\leqslant -1$. If we ask what characteristic of the function ‘causes’ the failure there is no neat answer in terms of real variable theory. But directly we consider the function of a complex variable $1/(1-z)$ we can describe the situation as follows. The function has a singularity at $z=1$ and therefore cannot be represented at $z=1$, by a convergent series; thus any representation of the function as a power series must have radius of convergence $\leqslant 1$, and consequently no power series can represent the function when $|z|>1$: in particular when $z=x=-1$ the series $1+x+x^2+\ldots$ does not converge to $1/(1-x)$.

Similarly the function $(a^2+z^2)^{1/2}$ can be expanded to give the series

$$(a^2+z^2)^{1/2}=a[1+\tfrac{1}{2}(z/a)^2-\tfrac{1}{8}(z/a)^4+\ldots]$$

The singularities at $z=\pm ia$ restrict the convergence to the interior of a circle of a radius a, as is easily verified directly. Thus in spite of the well-behaved appearance of the function the series fails for $z=x>a$ and for $z=x<-a$.

The region of convergence of a power series in z is always the interior of a circle about the origin in the z-plane. This is not so for other series. For example the series

$$1+a_1(z-1)+a_2(z-1)^2+$$

converges (if at all) in a circle about the point $z=1$.

13.63. *Behaviour on the circle of convergence*

A power series can be conditionally convergent only on its circle of convergence. Consider the four series:

$$1+z+z^2+z^3+\ \ldots\ +z^n\ldots \qquad (a)$$

$$1+z+2z^2+3z^3+\ \ldots\ +nz^n\ldots \qquad (b)$$

$$1+z+\frac{z^2}{2}+\frac{z^3}{3}+\ \ldots\ +\frac{z^n}{n}\ldots \qquad (c)$$

$$1+z+\frac{z^2}{2^2}+\frac{z^3}{3^2}+\ \ldots\ +\frac{z^n}{n^2}\ldots \qquad (d)$$

The radius of convergence is unity in each case. On the circle $|z|=1$ the reader may verify that series (*a*) oscillates finitely at all points except at $z=1$ where it diverges to $+\infty$. Series (*b*) oscillates infinitely except at $z=1$ where it diverges to $+\infty$. Series (*c*) is conditionally convergent except at $z=1$ where it diverges to $+\infty$; to see this, write the $(n+1)$th term in the form

$$\frac{z^n}{n}=\frac{1}{n}(\cos n\theta+i\sin n\theta)$$

and use the results of 4.22 (Dirichlet's test). Finally series (*d*) converges absolutely on the circle since it converges even at $z=1$ (2.63).

13.7. Infinite series of functions of a complex variable

13.71. *Uniform convergence*

A series $\sum \mathrm{f}_r(z)$ or a sequence $\mathrm{S}_n(z)$ of functions of z is said to converge uniformly in a region of the z-plane to a limit $\mathrm{f}(z)$ if for any $\epsilon>0$ there exists a number n_0 independent of z such that

$$\left|\sum_1^n \mathrm{f}_r(z)-\mathrm{f}(z)\right|<\epsilon$$

or

$$|\mathrm{S}_n(z)-\mathrm{f}(z)|<\epsilon$$

whenever $n>n_0$.

A power series is easily seen to be uniformly convergent in any region lying within the circle of convergence. For let R be the radius of convergence and let $d<R$ be the greatest value of $|z|$ in the region; then since the series is absolutely convergent for $z=d$ (see 13.61, 13.62) we can, for any given $\epsilon>0$, find a value n_0 such that

$$\sum_{n+1}^{\infty} |a_n|\, d^n<\epsilon$$

whenever $n\geqslant n_0$; hence for any z in the region

$$\left|\sum_{n+1}^{\infty} a_n z^n\right|\leqslant \sum_{n+1}^{\infty} |a_n|\, d^n<\epsilon$$

whenever $n>n_0$.

13.72. *Continuity of infinite series*

Let $f_\nu(z)$ be an infinite set of continuous functions, and let the series $\sum_0^\infty f_\nu(z)$ be convergent in some region of the z-plane, to a limit

$$S(z) = \sum_0^\infty f_\nu(z)$$

The function of z so defined is not necessarily continuous. A sufficient condition for continuity (at all internal points of the region) is, as in 4.21, that the series converges uniformly.

13.73. *Integration of infinite series*

If a series of continuous functions $\sum_0^\infty f_\nu(z)$ is uniformly convergent to a function $S(z)$ in a region, the series formed by integrating term by term, along a given finite path in the region, is equal to the integral of $S(z)$ along that path, that is

$$\int_C S(z)\,dz = \sum_0^\infty \int_C f_\nu(z)\,dz.$$

Write
$$S(z) - S_n(z) = R_n(z)$$

Then from the uniform convergence of the series we can deduce that for all z in the region

$$R_n(z) < \epsilon \quad \text{whenever } n \geqslant n_0$$

Hence
$$\int_C S(z)\,dz - \int_C S_n(z)\,dz = \int R_n(z)\,dz$$
$$\leqslant \int |R_n(z)|\,dz$$
$$< \epsilon l$$

where l is the length of the path C.

But
$$\int_C S_n(z)\,dz = \int_C \sum_0^n f_\nu(z)\,dz$$
$$= \sum_0^n \int_C f_\nu(z)\,dz$$

the interchange being permissible for a finite sum. Hence by taking $n > n_0$ we can ensure that

$$\left| \int_C S(z) - \sum_0^n \int_C f_\nu(z)\, dz \right| < \epsilon l$$

which is arbitrarily small. Hence

$$\int_C S(z)\, dz = \sum_{\nu=0}^{\infty} \left\{ \int_C f_\nu(z)\, dz \right\}$$

13.74. *Differentiation of infinite series*

The derivative of the sum of an infinite series is equal to the sum of the series obtained by differentiating term by term, provided the derived series so obtained converges uniformly.

This follows from the previous section and the theorem of 13.38. Let

$$S(z) = \sum f_r(z)$$

be the series, and let

$$S^{(1)}(z) = \sum f_r'(z) \tag{1}$$

be the series obtained by term by term differentiation. If this series converges uniformly in a region, then it can be integrated term by term along any path in the region to give

$$\begin{aligned} \int_a^z S^{(1)}(z)\, dz &= \sum \int_a^z f_r'(z)\, dz \\ &= \sum \{ | - f_r(a) \} \,|\, f_r(z) \\ &= S(z) - S(a) \,| \end{aligned}$$

Hence from the theorem of 13.38

$$S^{(1)}(z) = S'(z)$$

that is
$$\sum \frac{d}{dz} f_\nu(z) = \frac{d}{dz} \sum f_\nu(z)$$

13.75. *Differentiation of power series*

A power series can be differentiated term by term within its circle of convergence; that is, $\frac{d}{dz} \sum a_n z^n = \sum n a_n z^{n-1}$.

This can be established in much the same way as the corresponding result for real series, 7.61, or from the results of 13.6 ff and 13.74.

13.76. *Taylor's series*

Suppose that $f(z)$ is analytic on and inside a simple closed curve C, and let z_0 be a point inside C. Then

$$f(z)=f(z_0)+(z-z_0)f'(z_0)+\ldots+\frac{(z-z_0)}{n!}f^{(n)}(z_0)+\ldots$$

provided that $|z-z_0|<b$, where b is the distance from z_0 to the nearest point of the contour C.

Proof. Let C_1 be a circle with centre z_0 and radius $a<b$, then from Cauchy's integral formula (see 13.39)

$$f(z)=\frac{1}{2\pi i}\int_{C_1}\frac{f(\zeta)}{\zeta-z}d\zeta$$

Now

$$\frac{1}{\zeta-z}=\frac{1}{\zeta-z_0}\left[1\Big/\left\{1-\frac{z-z_0}{\zeta-z_0}\right\}\right]$$

$$=\frac{1}{\zeta-z_0}+\frac{z-z_0}{(\zeta-z_0)^2}+\ldots+\frac{(z-z_0)^n}{(\zeta-z_0)^{n+1}}+\ldots$$

provided that $|(z-z_0)/(\zeta-z_0)|<1$, that is provided that

$$|z-z_0|<|\zeta-z_0|,$$

which is satisfied because $|z-z_0|<a<b\leqslant|\zeta-z_0|$. Hence

$$f(z)=\frac{1}{2\pi i}\int_{C_1}\left\{\frac{f(\zeta)}{\zeta-z_0}+\frac{(z-z_0)f(\zeta)}{(\zeta-z_0)^2}+\ldots+\frac{(z-z_0)^n f(\zeta)}{(\zeta-z_0)^{n+1}}+\ldots\right\}d\zeta$$

where the series under the sign of integration, like the series for $1/(\zeta-z)$, is uniformly convergent, so that the integral of the series is equal to the sum of the integrals of its terms, i.e.

$$f(z)=f(z_0)+(z-z_0)f'(z_0)+\ldots+\frac{(z-z_0)^n}{n!}f^{(n)}(z_0)+\ldots$$

Corollary. A function which is analytic for all finite values of z, and is bounded as $|z|\to\infty$, is a constant.

For, using its Taylor expansion at the origin ($z_0=0$)

$$f(z)=f(0)+zf'(0)+\ldots+\frac{z^n}{n!}f^{(n)}(0)+\ldots$$

and it can be shown (see Titchmarsh, *Theory of Functions* §2.5) that this can be bounded as $|z|\to\infty$ for all $\arg z$ only if $f'(0)=f''(0)=\ldots=f^{(n)}(0)=\ldots=0$. Hence $f(z)=f(0)=\text{constant}$.

13.77. *Laurent series*

If $f(z)$ has a singularity at $z=z_0$ it can be represented near $z=z_0$ by a series in $(z-z_0)$ only if negative as well as positive powers of $(z-z_0)$ are included.

If $f(z)$ is analytic in an annular region about z_0, but excluding the point z_0 itself we can derive the required series by a method similar to that used in the last paragraph. We have

$$f(z)=\frac{1}{2\pi i}\oint_C \frac{f(\zeta)}{\zeta-z}\,d\zeta$$

where C is a closed contour within and on which $f(z)$ is analytic. A circle C, with centre z_0 no longer satisfies this condition, but the contour C consisting of a circle C_1, a second circle C_2 also with centre z_0 described in the opposite sense to C_1, and two coincident paths with opposite senses joining C_1 to C_2 somewhat as in Fig. 13.11 is acceptable provided both C_1 and C_2 lie in the annular region within which $f(z)$ is analytic. Since an analytic function is a single-valued function, the integrals in opposite senses along the two coincident paths give zero contribution to $\oint_C$. Hence

$$f(z)=\frac{1}{2\pi i}\oint_{C_1} \frac{f(\zeta)}{\zeta-z}\,d\zeta-\frac{1}{2\pi i}\oint_{C_2} \frac{f(\zeta)}{\zeta-z}\,d\zeta \tag{1}$$

At all points in the region between C_1 and C_2, $|z-z_0|<b_1$ where b_1 is the radius $|\zeta-z_0|$ of the larger of the two circles, C_1. Hence, as in the last section,

$$\frac{1}{2\pi i}\oint_{C_1} \frac{f(\zeta)}{\zeta-z}\,d\zeta=\frac{1}{2\pi i}\oint_{C_1}\left\{\frac{f(\zeta)}{\zeta-z_0}+\frac{(z-z_0)\,f(\zeta)}{(\zeta-z_0)^2}+\dots\right\}d\zeta$$

$$=\alpha_0+\alpha_1(z-z_0)+\dots+\alpha_n(z-z_0)^n+\dots \tag{2}$$

say, where the constants α_0, α_1 etc. can be expressed as integrals with respect to ζ, but can no longer be explicitly evaluated as $f(z_0)$, $f'(z_0)$ etc. since Cauchy's integral formula holds only for functions analytic throughout the whole of the interior of C_1, not merely in an annular portion of it.

For the second integral in (1) we note that $1/|z-z_0|<1/b_2$

where b_2 is the radius $|\zeta - z_0|$ of the smaller of the two circles, C_2. Hence

$$\frac{1}{z-\zeta}=\frac{1}{z-z_0}\left(1-\frac{\zeta-z_0}{z-z_0}\right)^{-1}$$

$$=\frac{1}{z-z_0}+\frac{\zeta-z_0}{(z-z_0)^2}+\dots+\frac{(\zeta-z_0)^{n-1}}{(z-z_0)^n}+\dots$$

which is uniformly convergent for all z in the region between C_1 and C_2, so

$$-\frac{1}{2\pi i}\oint_{C_2}\frac{f(\zeta)}{(\zeta-z)}\,d\zeta=\frac{\beta_1}{z-z_0}+\frac{\beta_2}{(z-z_0)^2}+\dots+\frac{\beta_n}{(z-z_0)^n}+\dots \quad (3)$$

From (1), (2) and (3) we find

$$f(z)=\sum_{n=0}^{\infty}\alpha_n(z-z_0)^n+\sum_{n=1}^{\infty}\beta_n(z-z_0)^{-n} \quad (4)$$

This series for $f(z)$ is called its Laurent series. We note that

$$\beta_1=\frac{1}{2\pi i}\oint_{C_2}f(\zeta)\,d\zeta\,;\quad \beta_n=\frac{1}{2\pi i}\oint_{C_2}(\zeta-z_0)^{n-1}f(\zeta)\,d\zeta$$

13.78. *The theorem of residues*

The important process of integrating a function of a complex variable round a closed path in the complex plane has already been mentioned in 13.36 where it was shown that if a function $f(z)$ is analytic on and within a closed curve C, the contour integral

$$\oint_C f(z)\,dz=0$$

We now aim at finding the value of the contour integral $\oint_C f(z)\,dz$ for functions $f(z)$ which have a finite number of singularities $z_1, z_2, \dots, z_n$ within the contour but which are analytic elsewhere within and on it. The usefulness of being able to evaluate contour integrals of this kind will be seen in Chapter 15 (Laplace Transforms).

In the first place we replace the path C as in 13.37 by a number of small circles C_1, C_2, C_3 etc. each one enclosing only one singularity, so that the required integral is expressible,

$$\oint_C f(z)\,dz=\oint_{C_1}f(z)\,dz+\oint_{C_2}f(z)\,dz+\dots+\oint_{C_n}f(z)\,dz \quad (1)$$

In the neighbourhood of z_1, $f(z)$ may be expanded as a Laurent series, and in practice the coefficient β_1 of $1/(z-z_1)$ is usually fairly easy to find by ordinary algebraical methods. But by 13.77

$$\beta_1 = \frac{1}{2\pi i}\oint_{C_1} f(z)\,dz\,; \quad \text{i.e.} \quad \oint_{C_1} f(z)\,dz = 2\pi i\beta_1 \tag{2}$$

The quantity β_1, which is the coefficient of $1/(z-z_1)$ in the Laurent expansion of $f(z)$ is called the residue at z_1 in extension of the definition of 13.4, and from (1) and (2) we now deduce the important theorem, *If* $f(z)$ *is one-valued and analytic on and inside a closed contour* C *apart from a finite number of singularities* $z_1, z_2, \ldots, z_n$ *within* C, *then*

$$\oint_C f(z)\,dz = 2\pi i \begin{pmatrix}\textit{sum of the residues at}\\ \textit{the points } z_1, z_2, \ldots, z_n\end{pmatrix} \tag{3}$$

Example 1

Evaluate $\oint_C \frac{e^{zt}}{(z^2-1)}\,dz$ where C is a simple contour enclosing both the singularities $z = +1$ and $z = -1$.

At $z = +1$,

$$e^{zt}/(z^2-1) = \frac{e^{(z-1)t}}{(z-1)+2}\cdot\frac{e^t}{z-1} = \frac{1}{2}\frac{e^t}{z-1}\,(1+\text{powers of } z-1).$$

The residue is $\frac{1}{2}e^t$. Similarly at $z = -1$, the residue is $-\frac{1}{2}e^{-t}$, whence $\oint_C e^{zt}\,dz/(z^2-1) = \sinh t$.

Example 2

Prove that if C is the circle $|z| = 1$, and if $0 < k < 1$,

$$\oint_C dz/(1-kz)(z-k) = 2\pi i/(1-k^2).$$

13.8. The elementary transcendental functions

We now come to the functions e^z, $\cos z$, $\sin z$ and their inverses $\log z$, $\cos^{-1} z$, $\sin^{-1} z$. The definition of any transcendental function must of necessity involve a limiting process, such as an infinite sequence, an infinite series, an integral, the solution of a differential equation etc. Of these we choose to define e^z for all values of z, by the infinite series

$$e^z = 1 + z + \frac{z^2}{2!} + \ldots + \frac{z^n}{n!} + \ldots. \tag{1}$$

First we must determine the radius of convergence of (1). From the ratio test, the series converges absolutely if

$$\lim \left| \frac{a_{n+1} z^{n+1}}{a_n z^n} \right| < 1$$

that is, if $$\lim_{n \to \infty} |z|/n < 1$$

This is evidently true for all finite values of z and hence the series (1) defines an analytic function at all points in the z-plane; i.e. the radius of convergence is infinite.

Now absolutely convergent series can be multiplied term by term to give an absolutely convergent product series. Hence as in the real case (3.8) we find that

$$e^{z_1} e^{z_2} = e^{z_1 + z_2}$$

This justifies the use of the index notation although, when z is complex there can of course be no direct interpretation of e^z as a product of z factors e. It also shows that

$$e^z = e^{x+iy} = e^x e^{iy} = e^x (\cos y + i \sin y).$$

Differentiation of (1) gives the result

$$\frac{\mathrm{d}}{\mathrm{d}z} e^z = e^z$$

so that e^z is a solution of the differential equation

$$\mathrm{d}w/\mathrm{d}z = w$$

with the boundary condition $w = 1$ at $z = 0$. That

$$e^z = \lim_{n \to \infty} (1 + z/n)^n$$

is easily established by an extension of the argument of 5.3. The details are left as an exercise.

The trigonometric functions $\sin z$ and $\cos z$ are defined by the series

$$\sin z = z - \frac{z^3}{3!} + \frac{z^5}{5!} - \dots \frac{(-1)^n z^{2n+1}}{(2n+1)!} + \dots$$

and $$\cos z = 1 - \frac{z^2}{2!} + \frac{z^4}{4!} - \dots \frac{(-1)^n z^{2n}}{(2n)!} + \dots$$

both of which converge at all points in the z-plane.

It follows immediately that for all z

$$\cos z + i \sin z = e^{iz}$$

In particular for z real and equal to θ, we have

$$\cos\theta + i\sin\theta = e^{i\theta}$$

Similarly

$$\cos\theta - i\sin\theta = e^{-i\theta}$$

whence

$$\cos\theta = \tfrac{1}{2}(e^{i\theta} + e^{-i\theta})$$

$$\sin\theta = \frac{1}{2i}(e^{i\theta} - e^{-i\theta})$$

Finally notice that $\sin z$ and $\cos z$ both satisfy

$$\frac{d^2w}{dz^2} = -w$$

the former satisfying the conditions $w=0$, $w'=1$, the second $w=1$, $w'=0$ at $z=0$.

13.81. *The logarithmic function*

We define $\log z$ as the inverse function to e^z. Hence the relation

$$w = \log z$$

implies no more and no less than

$$z = e^w$$

The properties of the logarithmic function are easily deduced :

1. The index rule gives

$$\log z_1 z_2 = \log z_1 + \log z_2 \qquad (1)$$

2. Since the exponential function $z = e^w$ satisfies

$$dz/dw = z$$

the logarithmic function $w = \log z$ must satisfy

$$\frac{dw}{dz} = \frac{1}{z}$$

i.e.

$$\log z = w = \int (1/z)\, dz$$

apart from a constant of integration. Since $w=0$ at $z=1$ we can use the definite integral

$$\log z = \int_1^z d\zeta/\zeta \qquad (2)$$

3. A power series for log z cannot be given, since log z is not defined for $z=0$; but from formula (2), we have

$$\log(1+z)=\int_1^{1+z} d\zeta/\zeta=\int_0^z dw/(1+w) \quad \text{where } w=\zeta-1$$
$$=\int_0^z (1-w+w^2-\ldots)\,dw$$

The integrand is uniformly convergent inside the unit circle and can therefore be integrated term by term to give

$$\log(1+z)=z-\frac{z^2}{2}+\frac{z^3}{3}\ldots \tag{3}$$

These properties are closely analogous to those of the logarithmic function of a real variable. We now consider the properties having no real analogue. The first is the multi-valued property of the complex logarithm.

Putting $z=re^{i\theta}$ we find immediately that

$$\log z=\log r+i\theta$$

and, since for a given z, θ is not unique, it follows that log z is not unique. In fact to any given z there correspond an infinite number of values of log z differing by integral multiples of $2\pi i$.

To obtain a single-valued function we must select one of these values by some convention. The simplest is to suppose that the phase of z is restricted to the values

$$-\pi<\arg z\leqslant\pi.$$

The corresponding value of log z is then called the principal value and is denoted by Log z.† When z is real this principal value agrees with the definition of the logarithm of a real variable.

Example 1

$$\log(-1)=i(2n+1)\pi$$
$$\operatorname{Log}(-1)=i\pi$$

Example 2

$$\log e=1+2ni\pi$$
$$\operatorname{Log} e=1$$

† Some older text-books, including Hardy, *Pure Mathematics*, employ the opposite convention.

13.82. *The trigonometric functions*

The functions $\sin z$ and $\cos z$ are easily discussed by means of the identities

$$\sin z \equiv (e^{iz} - e^{-iz})/2i$$
$$\cos z \equiv (e^{iz} + e^{-iz})/2$$

Further, the hyperbolic functions $\sinh z$ and $\cosh z$ do not differ materially from $\sin z$ and $\cos z$; thus

$$\sinh z \equiv \tfrac{1}{2}(e^{z} - e^{-z}) \equiv (1/i) \sin iz$$
$$\cosh z \equiv \tfrac{1}{2}(e^{z} + e^{-z}) \equiv \cos iz$$

To remember that $\sinh z = -i \sin iz$ rather than $+i \sin iz$ notice that for small z, $\sinh z \simeq z$, $\sin iz \simeq iz$; the correct form then follows easily. Similarly

$$\sinh iz = i \sin z \text{ etc.}$$

The other trigonometric functions $\tan z$, $\operatorname{cosec} z$, etc. and their hyperbolic counterparts are defined in terms of sin, cos, sinh and cosh as in real variable theory.

13.9. Existence of roots of an algebraic equation

The fundamental theorem of algebra, as it is often called, is that every algebraic equation of degree n has n roots. This theorem can be proved in an elementary manner as follows.

Let the equation be

$$\mathrm{f}(z) \equiv z^n + a_1 z^{n-1} + \ldots + a_n = 0 \tag{1}$$

where the coefficients are real or complex constants. Put $z = Re^{i\theta}$; then for sufficiently large values of R we can neglect all terms but the first and write

$$\mathrm{f}(z) \simeq R^n e^{in\theta}$$

that is, $$\mathrm{f} \equiv \mathrm{u}(x, y) + i\mathrm{v}(x, y) \simeq R^n (\cos n\theta + i \sin n\theta)$$

The curves

$$\mathrm{u}(x, y) = 0\,; \quad \mathrm{v}(x, y) = 0$$

therefore tend asymptotically to the straight lines

$$\cos n\theta = 0\,; \quad \sin n\theta = 0$$

i.e. $n\theta = (m + \tfrac{1}{2})\pi$: $n\theta = m\pi$ respectively.

Let the curves $u = 0$, $v = 0$ meet the circle C of radius R in the points $U_1, \ldots, U_n$ and $V_1, \ldots, V_n$. From the asymptotic forms it follows that for sufficiently large R these points are distributed at nearly equal intervals round the circumference and in the order $V_1 U_1 V_2 U_2 \ldots U_n$.

We have to show that it is not possible to complete the u, v curves inside the circle without having at least one where a curve $u=0$ crosses a curve $v=0$. Such a point of intersection must give a root of the equation, since

$$f(z)=u+iv=0$$

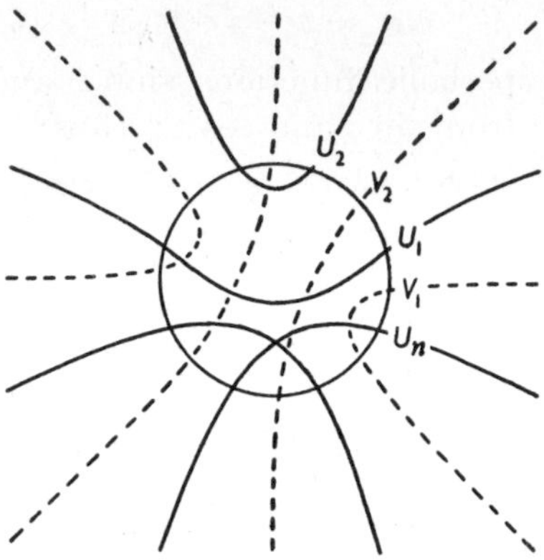

FIG. 13.18

The proof uses the fact that u and v are continuous : this is true because each is a real polynomial (see eqn. (3)). We notice that the circumference of the circle $|z|=R$ is divided by the points U_1 U_2 etc., into arcs on which u is alternately positive and negative, and that V_1 V_2 etc., fall one in each arc. Let us say that two V's are 'connected' if it is possible to join them by a line not crossing any curve $u=0$. Since u is continuous it follows that u has the same sign at two connected V's. Let all the points connected to V_1 be found, then all the points connected to the next remaining V (namely V_2) and so on until all of them are exhausted. From all the connected points select the pair V_r V_s that have the smallest angular separation on the circumference. Any two V's must be separated by at least one U, and two V's of the same sign must have an even number of U's between them, and therefore also at least one point V_t. This point cannot be connected to any other V within or at the ends of V_r V_s since V_r V_s is by hypothesis the closest pair of connected points; nor can it be connected to any V outside the arc V_r V_s, for the connecting path would cross the connecting path of V_r to V_s and this would imply connection between V_t and V_r. Now consider the curve $v=0$ which enters the circle at V_t. This must emerge from the circle at some point V_q to which V_t is not connected (since V_t is not

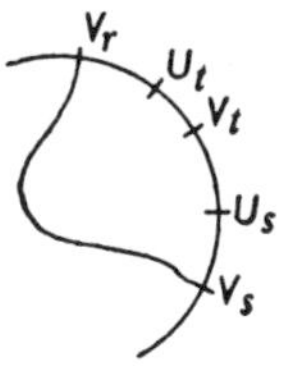

FIG. 13.19

connected to any other V). It follows that in going from V_t to V_q the locus $v=0$ cuts a curve $u=0$, and that if the point of intersection is (x_1, y_1) then $z_1 = x_1 + iy_1$ is a root of the original algebraic equation.

Dividing $f(z)$ by the factor $(z - z_1)$ we obtain an equation of degree $n-1$; this also has a root, and by $n-1$ repetitions we can find $n-1$ roots together with the first order equation $\alpha z + \beta = 0$ which provides the nth root.

The fundamental theorem cannot be extended immediately to transcendental equations. Thus, although it is true that the equation

$$\sin x = 0 \tag{2}$$

has infinitely many solutions, it is not true that the equation

$$e^z = 0 \tag{3}$$

has infinitely many. In fact there is no value of z in the finite part of the complex plane that satisfies (2); all the n solutions that one obtains from the approximation

$$1 + z + \ldots + z^n/n! = 0$$

recede to infinity as n increases.

CHAPTER FOURTEEN

THE USE OF INTEGRALS TO REPRESENT FUNCTIONS

14.1. Solutions of differential equations in series and by definite integrals

Power series such as those obtained in Chapter 12 as solutions of differential equations are an excellent means of calculating numerical solutions at sufficiently small values of the argument. They do not however lend themselves easily to the determination of the analytical properties of the function. For example take the absolutely convergent series

$$C(x) = 1 - \frac{x^2}{2!} + \frac{x^4}{4!} - \frac{x^6}{6!} + \dots$$

$$S(x) = x - \frac{x^3}{3!} + \frac{x^5}{5!} - \frac{x^7}{7!} + \dots$$

and try to prove directly from these series that

$$[C(x)]^2 + [S(x)]^2 = 1$$

Although this can be done, the manipulations are very awkward, and when the problem is not the proof of a known relation but the discovery of a new one, the limitations of a power-series solution are very evident.

Another form of solution, which is often more useful and more flexible for formal manipulation and derivation of analytical relationships, though not so useful for evaluating numerical values, is a solution in the form of a definite integral, in particular a contour integral.

14.2. Method of solution by contour integral

In principle the method of solution by means of an integral in the complex plane, that is a contour integral (13.35), can be regarded as a generalisation of the power series method. The latter can be summarised as follows. Let the differential equation be

$$\mathrm{L}y=0 \tag{1}$$

where L is a linear differential operator

$$\mathrm{L}=\mathrm{p}_0(x)\frac{\mathrm{d}^2}{\mathrm{d}x^2}+\mathrm{p}_1(x)\frac{\mathrm{d}}{\mathrm{d}x}+\mathrm{p}_2(x)$$

Choose a trial solution

$$y=\sum_{r=0}^{\infty} a_r x^{c+r} \tag{2}$$

and substitute it into the equation (1). This gives

$$\sum_{r=0}^{\infty} a_r \mathrm{L}\{x^{c+r}\}=0$$

and equating to zero the coefficient of the lowest power of x then determines c; the other terms determine a_r for $r=2, 3, \ldots$ (the initial conditions determining a_0 and a_1).

The definite integral method consists in making a trial substitution which we shall write for the moment in the form

$$y=\int_{\alpha}^{\beta} \mathrm{a}(r)\mathrm{K}(x, r)\,\mathrm{d}r \tag{3}$$

in order to emphasise the close analogy to the power series method. The role of the summation in (2) is taken over by the integral in (3); the role of the coefficients a_r by the function $\mathrm{a}(r)$, and the role of the arbitrary powers x^{c+r} by the arbitrary function of two variables $\mathrm{K}(x, r)$, which is known as the 'kernel' of the integral (3). The summation over $r=0$ to ∞ is replaced by an integration from $r=\alpha$ to β; these limits α, β are at our disposal, and in particular the integration may be along the real axis or on a closed or open contour in the complex r-plane. In what follows, to emphasise that it is in general a complex number, we shall use $\sigma=s+it$ to denote the variable of integration. Similarly the unknown function will be denoted not by $\mathrm{a}(r)$ but by $\mathrm{F}(\sigma)$.

The most generally useful kernels are the functions $e^{\sigma x}$ and $e^{i\sigma x}$ for paths of integration along the real or along the pure imaginary axis. These give rise to the Laplace and the Fourier integrals, and are then usually written in the forms e^{px} and $e^{i\omega x}$.

As an illustration of the method we consider the equation

$$\frac{\mathrm{d}^2y}{\mathrm{d}x^2}+xy=0 \tag{4}$$

We make the trial solution

$$y=\int_{\alpha}^{\beta} \mathrm{F}(\sigma)e^{\sigma x}\, \mathrm{d}\sigma$$

where the function $\mathrm{F}(\sigma)$ and the path of integration are to be chosen so that the differential equation is satisfied.

With this trial form of y, equation (4) becomes

$$\int_{\alpha}^{\beta} \mathrm{F}(\sigma)\, \sigma^2 e^{\sigma x}\, \mathrm{d}\sigma+\int_{\alpha}^{\beta} \mathrm{F}(\sigma) x e^{\sigma x}\, \mathrm{d}\sigma=0$$

that is,

$$\int_{\alpha}^{\beta} [\sigma^2\mathrm{F}(\sigma)+x\mathrm{F}(\sigma)]e^{\sigma x}\, \mathrm{d}\sigma=0 \qquad (5)$$

In writing, as we have done, $\mathrm{d}^2y/\mathrm{d}x^2=\int_{\alpha}^{\beta} \mathrm{F}(\sigma)\sigma^2 e^{\sigma x}\, \mathrm{d}\sigma$, it has been assumed that differentiation under the integral sign is permissible : justification of this step must of course wait until the form of $\mathrm{F}(\sigma)$ and the path of integration have been determined.

The next step is to express the left-hand side of (5) in the form

$$\mathrm{f}(x, \alpha, \beta)+\int_{\alpha}^{\beta} \phi(\sigma)e^{x\sigma}\, \mathrm{d}\sigma \qquad (6)$$

where the function $\phi(\sigma)$ is dependent on σ and $\mathrm{F}(\sigma)$ only. The object of this manœuvre is to separate as much as possible the variation with x from the variation with σ. If the left-hand side of (5) can be put in the form (6), and if values of α, β can be found for which $\mathrm{f}(x, \alpha, \beta)=0$ for all x, the only further requirement in order that (5) shall be satisfied is that $\phi(\sigma)=0$, that is, an equation determining the form of $\mathrm{F}(\sigma)$. In practice the form of $\mathrm{f}(x, \alpha, \beta)$ usually depends on the form of the function $\mathrm{F}(\sigma)$, so the condition $\phi(\sigma)=0$ is satisfied first, and α, β are determined subsequently.

A factor x in the integrand can be removed by an integration by parts, thus

$$\int_{\alpha}^{\beta} \mathrm{F}(\sigma)\,.\, x e^{x\sigma}\, \mathrm{d}\sigma=\Big[\mathrm{F}(\sigma)e^{x\sigma}\Big]_{\alpha}^{\beta}-\int_{\alpha}^{\beta} \mathrm{F}'(\sigma)e^{x\sigma}\, \mathrm{d}\sigma$$

so equation (5) is equivalent to

$$\Big[\mathrm{F}(\sigma)e^{x\sigma}\Big]_{\alpha}^{\beta}+\int_{\alpha}^{\beta} [\sigma^2\mathrm{F}(\sigma)-\mathrm{F}'(\sigma)]e^{x\sigma}\, \mathrm{d}\sigma=0 \qquad (7)$$

If the original equation had contained coefficients of quadratic or higher degree further integrations by parts would have been necessary. To satisfy equation (7) we first choose $F(\sigma)$ so that

$$F'(\sigma) - \sigma^2 F(\sigma) = 0$$

This gives
$$F(\sigma) = e^{\frac{1}{3}\sigma^3}$$

apart from the constant factor. Secondly we must choose α and β so that

$$\left[e^{\frac{1}{3}\sigma^3 + x\sigma}\right]_\alpha^\beta = 0 \quad \text{for all } x \tag{8}$$

The left-hand side of equation (8) is analytic in the finite part of the σ-plane, and hence any closed path of integration satisfies (8) automatically. However, such a choice leads to

$$\int_\alpha^\beta F(\sigma) e^{\sigma x}\, d\sigma = 0,$$

that is, it gives only the trivial solution $y=0$. We must therefore take an open path (for example one going to infinity); the obvious choice will be a path such that the function $e^{\frac{1}{3}\sigma^3 + x\sigma}$ tends to zero at both ends. Now, if we put $\sigma = re^{i\theta}$; then $\sigma^3 = r^3 e^{3i\theta}$ and will be real and negative if 3θ is an odd multiple of π, that is if $\theta = \pm\frac{1}{3}\pi$ or π. In each of these cases $e^{\frac{1}{3}\sigma^3 + x\sigma} \to 0$ as $r \to \infty$ for all finite x.

There are therefore three suitable paths of integration, A_1, A_2 and A_3 (see Fig. 14.1: the real part of $e^{3i\theta}$ is positive in the shaded and negative in the unshaded regions.) giving three possible integrals

$$y = \int_{A_j} e^{\sigma x + \frac{1}{3}\sigma^3}\, d\sigma, \quad (j = 1, 2, 3)$$

These are not independent since $\int_{A_1} - \int_{A_2} + \int_{A_3}$ is an integral round a closed contour and therefore vanishes. The integral along A_1 can be deformed into an angular path with apex at the origin (Fig. 14.2). This path can be further deformed into the imaginary axis since the real part of σ^3 on the dotted arcs is negative and hence there is no contribution from them at infinity. On the imaginary axis, we can put $\sigma = it$ and thus obtain

$$\int_{A_1} = i\int_{-\infty}^{\infty} e^{i(tx - \frac{1}{3}t^3)}\, dt = 2i\int_0^\infty \cos\left(tx - \tfrac{1}{3}t^3\right) dt, \tag{9}$$

the sine term disappearing. Apart from the multiplying factor (which can be replaced by any arbitrary constant), this is now a real integral. It converges very slowly however in comparison to the integral along the 60° path, along which the integrand falls off very steeply with σ.

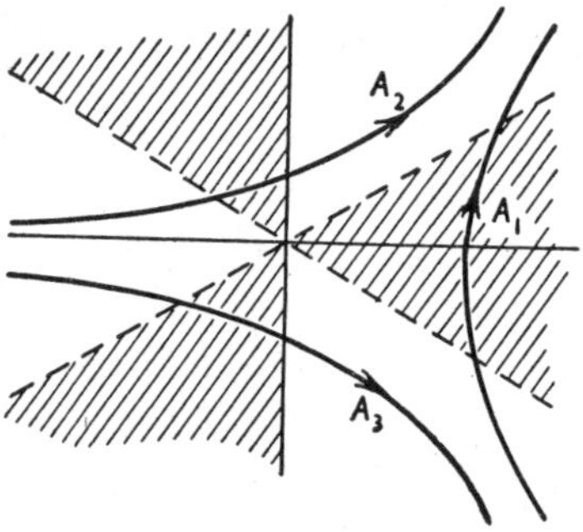

FIG. 14.1

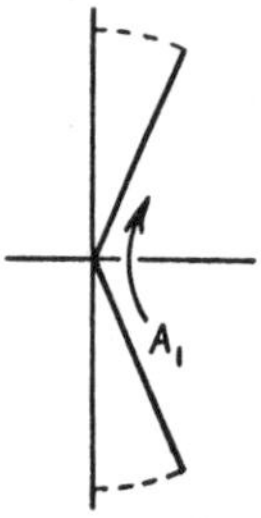

FIG. 14.2

The integral along either A_2 or A_3 provides a second solution as does also their sum. If we take the sum and deform both paths into right angles with the apex at the origin the contributions from the imaginary axis will be

$$i\int_0^\infty e^{i(tx-\frac{1}{3}t^3)}\,\mathrm{d}t \quad \text{from } A_2$$

and

$$i\int_0^{-\infty} e^{i(tx-\frac{1}{3}t^3)}\,\mathrm{d}t \quad \text{from } A_3$$

On replacing the dummy variable t (5.9) by $-t$ in the latter integral the sum becomes

$$i\int_0^\infty [e^{i(tx-\frac{1}{3}t^3)} - e^{-i(tx-\frac{1}{3}t^3)}]\,\mathrm{d}t = -2\int_0^\infty \sin\,(tx-\tfrac{1}{3}t^3)\,\mathrm{d}t$$

The two integrals along the real axis give

$$2\int_{-\infty}^0 e^{sx+\frac{1}{3}s^3}\,\mathrm{d}s = 2\int_0^\infty e^{-sx-\frac{1}{3}s^3}\,\mathrm{d}s$$

and hence the second solution is (apart from a multiplying factor)

$$\int_0^\infty [e^{-tx-\frac{1}{3}t^3} - \sin\,(tx-\tfrac{1}{3}t^3)]\,\mathrm{d}t \tag{10}$$

In principle the value of y at any chosen x could be found from either of the expressions (9) or (10) by a numerical integration. In practice this would be difficult to carry out; but explicit forms like (9) and (10) are nonetheless extremely valuable, particularly in deducing general relationships and properties for the functions they represent. Several examples will arise in the course of this and succeeding chapters.

14.3. Asymptotic expansions

One kind of expansion of a function in series is that called an ' asymptotic expansion '. This is, roughly speaking, a series whose early terms approximate the function for large values of the variable (see also 14.4). Asymptotic expansions are not always easy to find, but when the given function is expressible as an integral, one of the following methods may be successful : repeated integration by parts or direct examination of the behaviour of the integral for large values of x. The former method is usually the more straightforward, where it is applicable.

14.31. *Repeated integration by parts*

As an example of repeated integration by parts, consider the integral $\int_x^\infty e^{-u^2}\,du$. This can be written

$$\int_x^\infty e^{-u^2}\,du = \int_x^\infty (1/2u)(2ue^{-u^2})\,du$$

The function in the second bracket here is the derivative of $-e^{-u^2}$, so integration by parts gives

$$\int_x^\infty e^{-u^2}\,du = \Big[-(1/2u)e^{-u^2}\Big]_x^\infty + \int_x^\infty (-1/2u^2)e^{-u^2}\,du$$

$$= e^{-x^2}/2x - \int_x^\infty (1/2u^2)e^{-u^2}\,du$$

The integral here can now be written $\int_x^\infty (1/4u^3)(2ue^{-u^2})\,du$ and a similar integration by parts carried out ; and this procedure can be repeated as often as desired. The result is a series in inverse powers of x, namely

$$\int_x^\infty e^{-u^2}\,du = \frac{e^{-x^2}}{2x}\Bigg[1 - \frac{1}{2x^2} + \frac{1.3}{(2x^2)^2} - \frac{1.3.5}{(2x^2)^3} + \dots + (-1)^n \frac{1.3.5\dots(2n-1)}{(2x^2)^n} + R_{n+1}\Bigg] \qquad (1)$$

where R_{n+1}

$$=(-1)^{n+1}\,1\,.\,3\,.\,5\ldots(2n+1)\,2xe^{+x^2}\int_x^\infty (1/2u^2)^{n+1}\,e^{-u^2}\,du. \quad (2)$$

The expression (1) is the asymptotic expansion of $\int_x^\infty e^{-u^2}\,du$.

The ratio of consecutive terms in the bracket in (1) is given by

$$\frac{(n+1)\text{th term}}{n\text{th term}} = -\frac{(2n-1)}{2x^2}, \quad (3)$$

so the terms decrease in magnitude so long as $2n-1<2x^2$, but increase indefinitely as $n\to\infty$. The series in brackets in (1) therefore diverges, or rather oscillates infinitely if n is allowed to tend to infinity. It is not the infinite series, but the finite series obtained by taking a finite value of n and ignoring the remainder term in (1) which is useful in practice. That this provides a good representation of the function for large values of x is easily shown. If $|R_n|$ denotes the magnitude of the remainder after n terms in the bracket,

$$|R_n| = |(n+1)\text{th term}| - |R_{n+1}|$$

$$|R_n| < |(n+1)\text{th term}| \quad (4)$$

that is, $|R_n| < 1\,.\,3\ldots(2n-1)/(2x^2)^n$

Thus for finite n and sufficiently large x, R_n is very small, and the first n terms of the asymptotic expansion give a good approximation to the function. It can be seen from (4) and (3) that, for a given value of x, the optimum value of n is that for which the $(n+1)$th term of the asymptotic expansion has the smallest magnitude, that is, n is the greatest integer for which $2n-1<2x^2$.

14.32. *Value of an integral for large values of a parameter*

As an example of the second of the two methods mentioned in 14.3 we consider the integral

$$\mathrm{I}(x) = \int_{-\infty}^{\infty} \mathrm{f}(t)\,e^{-\frac{1}{2}x^2t^2}\,dt \quad (1)$$

Here the function $\mathrm{K}(x,t)=e^{-\frac{1}{2}x^2t^2}$ is the Gaussian error function; for a given value of x we see that its value $\to 0$ as $t\to\pm\infty$, and that its graph has a hump at $t=0$ whose width decreases as x increases (see Fig. 14.3). We assume the function $f(t)$ to have for small t a power series expansion, converging for $-\alpha<t<\alpha$, namely

$$f(t)=a_0+a_1t+a_2t^2+\ldots,$$

and to satisfy $f(t)\leqslant 0(t^k)$ for $|t|>\alpha$ with some finite k. Then

$$I(x)=\int_{-\alpha}^{\alpha} e^{-\frac{1}{2}x^2t^2}[a_0+a_1t+\ldots]\,dt+\int_{\alpha}^{\infty} e^{-\frac{1}{2}x^2t^2}[f(t)+f(-t)]\,dt. \qquad (2)$$

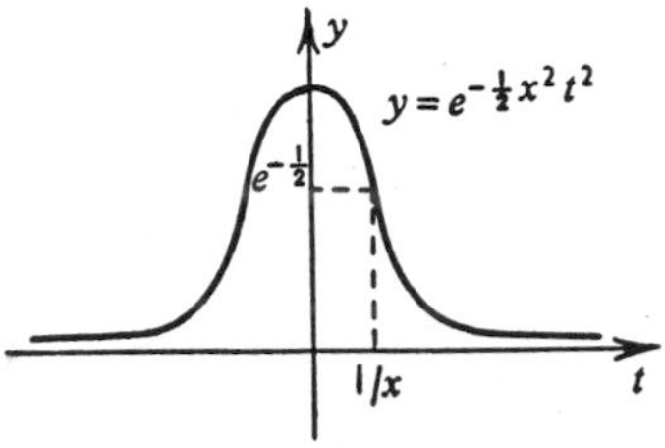

FIG. 14.3

Since $f(t)$ is integrable to infinity the last term is of order $e^{-\frac{1}{2}\alpha^2x^2}$ and this diminishes with very satisfactory rapidity as x increases. An approximation to $I(x)$ for large x can therefore be obtained (though its validity will require further investigation) by ignoring the second integral in (2). We note that

$$a_0\int_{-\alpha}^{\alpha} e^{-\frac{1}{2}x^2t^2}\,dt=(a_0/x)\int_{-\alpha x}^{\alpha x} e^{-\frac{1}{2}u^2}\,du,$$

and for sufficiently large x, $e^{-\frac{1}{2}u^2}$ is negligible for all $u>\alpha x$, so

$$a_0\int_{-\alpha}^{\alpha} e^{-\frac{1}{2}x^2t^2}\,dt\approx(a_0/x)\int_{-\infty}^{\infty} e^{-\frac{1}{2}u^2}\,du=(2\pi)^{\frac{1}{2}}\,a_0/x \text{ (see 9.47 Ex. 2).}$$

The later terms can be approximated in the same way, using the integrals†

$$\int_{-\infty}^{\infty} e^{-\frac{1}{2}x^2t^2}t^{2r}\,dt=(2\pi)^{\frac{1}{2}}\,1\,.\,3\,\ldots\,(2r-1)/x^{2r+1},$$

$$\int_{-\infty}^{\infty} e^{-\frac{1}{2}x^2t^2}t^{2r+1}\,dt=0.$$

† The first of these two integrals can be derived by differentiating r times with respect to x^2 the result $\int_{-\infty}^{\infty} e^{-\frac{1}{2}x^2t^2}\,dt=\frac{(2\pi)^{\frac{1}{2}}}{x}$ [see corollary of example 2 of 9.47 with $xt/\surd 2$ as variable]. The second integral is zero because $e^{-\frac{1}{2}x^2t^2}t^{2r+1}$ is an odd function of t, (tu) say, as the integral $=\int_0^{\infty} u(t)\,dt+\int_0^{\infty} u(-t)\,dt=0.$

We find

$$I(x) \approx (2\pi)^{\frac{1}{2}} \left(\frac{a_0}{x} + \frac{a_2}{x^3} + \frac{1 \cdot 3 a_4}{x^5} + \ldots + \frac{1 \cdot 3 \ldots (2r-1)}{x^{2r+1}} a_{2r} \ldots \right) \quad (3)$$

To investigate the convergence etc. of (3) we proceed in much the same way as in the last section. We write

$$I(x) = (2\pi)^{\frac{1}{2}} \left(\frac{a_0}{x} + \frac{a_2}{x^3} + \ldots \frac{1 \cdot 3 \ldots (2n-3)}{x^{2n-1}} a_{2n-2} \right) + R_{2n}(x)$$

$$= S_{2n}(x) + R_{2n}(x)$$

say, where S_{2n} is the sum of series (3) to the term in $1/x^{2n-1}$, and R_{2n} is the remainder.

That is,

$$R_{2n}(x) = \int_{-\infty}^{\infty} [f(t) - (a_0 + a_1 t + \ldots + a_{2n-1} t^{2n-1})] e^{-\frac{1}{2}t^2 x^2} \, dt$$

We note that if a_{2n}/a_{2n-2} tends to a finite limit as $n \to \infty$, the ratio of consecutive non-zero terms in S_∞,

$$\frac{\text{term in } 1 \mid x^{2n+1} \mid}{\text{term in } 1 \mid x^{2n-1} \mid} = \frac{2n-1}{x^2} \cdot \frac{a_{2n}}{a_{2n-2}}$$

$$\to \infty \quad \text{as} \quad n \to \infty$$

Thus, as in the example of the preceding section, the asymptotic series diverges. As before, however, this does not make the expansion valueless, for the convergence of a series is determined entirely by the behaviour of the terms for which $n > N$ where N is arbitrarily large, whereas the usefulness of an asymptotic expansion depends entirely on the behaviour of the early terms. It is however necessary to show that, for given n, the value of R_{2n} is small when x is sufficiently large. This we can do as follows.

In the range $-\alpha < t < \alpha$ we can write

$$| g(t) | \equiv | f(t) - (a_0 + a_1 t + \ldots + a_{2n-1} t^{2n-1}) | \leqslant A_n t^{2n} \quad (4)$$

for some finite A_n. For $|t| > \alpha$, $f(t) \leqslant O(t^k)$, so, for $2_n \geqslant k$, $g(t) \leqslant O(t^{2n})$. Hence $| g(t) | \leqslant B_n t^{2n}$ for some finite B_n and all t.

Then

$$x^{2n} \mid R_{2n}(x) \mid \leqslant B_n \int_{-\infty}^{\infty} x^{2n} t^{2n} e^{-\frac{1}{2}t^2 x^2}\, dt$$

$$= \frac{B_n}{x} \int_{-\infty}^{\infty} u^{2n} e^{-\frac{1}{2}u^2}\, du$$

$$= \frac{C_n}{x} \tag{5}$$

where C_n is finite. Hence

$$x^{2n} R_{2n}(x) \to 0 \quad \text{as } x \to \infty,$$

that is,

$$R_{2n}(x) = o(1/x^{2n})$$

The remainder after n terms is therefore very small if x is large. On the other hand we have seen that if x is kept fixed and n is allowed to increase indefinitely, the series diverges, i.e.

$$R_{2n}(x) \to \infty \quad \text{as } n \to \infty.$$

Thus if the asymptotic series (3) is regarded as an infinite series it diverges; but if regarded as a finite series plus a remainder, the remainder is very small for large values of x.

We may describe the matter in another way by saying that the operators $\lim_{n\to\infty}$, $\lim_{x\to\infty}$ do not commute when applied to $R_{2n}(x)$. Thus if x is allowed to increase first, then for any given n, however large, $R_{2n}(x) \to 0$. But if n increases first then for any fixed x, however large, $R_{2n}(x) \to \infty$. The source of this peculiar behaviour can be located in the non-uniform convergence of $e^{-\frac{1}{2}u^2} u^{2n}$. As u tends to infinity this tends to zero for all n but the convergence is non-uniform (4.2).

14.4. Poincaré's definition of an asymptotic expansion

Let S_n be the sum to the term in z^{-n} of an infinite, usually divergent, series of negative powers of z,

$$S_n = a_0 + \frac{a_1}{z} + \frac{a_2}{z^2} + \ldots + \frac{a_n}{z^n} \tag{1}$$

Then if $f(z)$ is a function such that in a given range of $\arg z$,

$$\lim_{|z|\to\infty} z^n [f(z) - S_n(z)] = 0 \tag{2}$$

for every fixed n, the series S_∞ is an asymptotic expansion of $f(z)$ (Poincaré's definition) in the given range.

The notation $\sim$ is used for asymptotic 'equality', thus

$$f(z) \sim a_0 + a_1/z + \dots + a_n/z^n + \dots .$$

We see that the examples of the previous sections satisfy Poincaré's definition of an asymptotic expansion with $\arg z = 0$. We may compare and contrast the condition (2) with the condition for the convergence of the series $S_n(z)$ to the limit $f(z)$, namely

$$\operatorname*{Lt}_{n\to\infty} [f(z) - S_n(z)] = 0.$$

Example

Consider the function $(2/\pi^{\frac{1}{2}}) \int_0^x e^{-u^2}\,du$. This function is called the 'error function' and is written erf x. The coefficient $2/\pi^{\frac{1}{2}}$ is introduced in order that erf x should tend to 1 as $x \to \infty$ (9.47). From formulae (1) and (2) of 14.31 with $n = \frac{1}{2}m$ it follows that if S_m is the sum, up to the term in $1/(2x^2)^{\frac{1}{2}m}$, of the series

$$1 - \frac{1}{2x^2} + \frac{1\,.\,3}{(2x^2)^2} - \frac{1\,.\,3\,.\,5}{(2x^2)^3} + \dots \tag{3}$$

then $$\pi^{\frac{1}{2}} x e^{x^2} (1 - \operatorname{erf} x) = S_m + R_{m+1}$$

where $|R_{m+1}| < 1\,.\,3\,.\,5 \dots (2n+1)/(2x^2)^{\frac{1}{2}m+1}$, (see inequality following (4) of 14·31).

Hence $x^m |R_{m+1}| < 1\,.\,3\,.\,5 \dots (2n+1)/2x^2$, and condition (2) is satisfied. Hence the series (3) is an asymptotic expansion, in the strict sense, of the function $\pi^{\frac{1}{2}} x e^{x^2} (1 - \operatorname{erf} x)$. It is convenient to write

$$\operatorname{erf} x \sim 1 - \frac{e^{-x^2}}{x} \left[1 - \frac{1}{2x^2} + \frac{1\,.\,3}{(2x^2)^2} - \dots \right] \tag{4}$$

and to call this formula the asymptotic expansion of erf x, although this is *not* in Poincaré's form.

For a given x greater than unity the terms diminish at first but begin to increase in magnitude after the rth where r is the integral part of $(\frac{1}{2} + x^2)$. The remainders R_n alternate in sign with n, so the correct value of the function for any given x must lie between successive values of S_n. The error is therefore always less than the last term retained.

14.41. *Properties of asymptotic series*

It is easily proved from Poincaré's definition (14.4) of an asymptotic series that the asymptotic expansions of $f(x)$ and $g(x)$ can always be added, subtracted, or multiplied to give those of the sum, difference, or product, respectively, of $f(x)$ and $g(x)$. Further, integration of an asymptotic series gives the asymptotic expansion of the integral. On the other hand, an asymptotic series can *not* necessarily be differentiated term by term.

A given analytic function has a unique asymptotic expansion. For if $f(z)$ has two expansions

$$f(z) \sim a_0 + \frac{a_1}{z} + \frac{a_2}{z^2} + \ldots + \frac{a_r}{z^r} + \ldots$$

$$f(z) \sim b_0 + \frac{b_1}{z} + \frac{b_2}{z^2} + \ldots + \frac{b_r}{z^r} + \ldots$$

then on forming the difference we find

$$0 \sim a_0 - b_0 + \frac{a_1 - b_1}{z} + \ldots + \frac{a_r - b_r}{z^r} + \ldots$$

and allowing z to tend to infinity [cf (2) of 14.4 with $n=0$] we find $a_0 = b_0$. Multiplying by z and going to the limit we find $a_1 = b_1$ and so on. Hence the expansion is unique. There is a proviso however; the expansion is unique only in a given part of the complex plane; the same function may have different expansions in different parts of the plane.

Note that there are many functions that tend to zero at infinity in some direction in the complex plane without having an expansion in inverse powers of z; for example the function e^{-z^2} tends to zero at infinity in all directions within 45° on either side of the real axis but has no asymptotic expansion of the form (1) of 14.4 since it diminishes more quickly than any inverse power of z. Hence if a function $f(z)$ has the expansion $f(z) \sim a_0 + a_1/z_1 + \ldots$ valid within this region, the function $f(z) + Ae^{-z^2}$ has the same expansion.

14.5. The method of steepest descents

An integral of the type $I(s)=\int_\alpha^\beta g(z)\,e^{sf(z)}\,dz$ (1)

or more generally

$$I(\sigma)=\int_\alpha^\beta g(z)\,e^{\sigma f(z)}\,dz \quad (\sigma=s+it) \tag{2}$$

where $f(z)$ is analytic, lends itself readily to asymptotic expansion. We shall consider the approximate evaluation of the integral $I(s)$ for large s.

Let $f(z)=u(x,y)+iv(x,y)$, and let contours $v(x,y)\equiv v=$constant be drawn in the z-plane. The path from α to β can be deformed so that it runs partly along these contours, $v=$constant and partly at right angles to them, i.e. along curves $u=$constant. The contribution to $I(s)$ from the latter will be ultimately very small. For we are interested only in large values of s for which the integrand oscillates very rapidly as v varies owing to the factor e^{ivs}; hence the integrand is alternately positive and negative, and if $g(z)$ is well-behaved the successive contributions to the integral tend to cancel. In other words the average value of the integrand over any sizeable length of path along a curve $u=$constant is small. It follows that only the parts along the contours $v=$constant are important, and these portions are lines of slope of u. The variable part of the exponential factor is now e^{su}. If u is large and negative in any portion, e^{su} is small and the contribution to the integral will be unimportant; the most significant parts of the path will be those where u is algebraically greatest. We therefore try to find a path along which algebraically large values of u are collected together in as small a region as possible. In geographical terms we try to find a path over the u-surface from α to β which keeps to low ground as much as possible and traverses high ground as quickly as possible.

Suppose that the points α and β are in two valleys on the u-contour diagram, separated by a pass, as in Fig. 14.4. The best path from α to β is obviously via the pass S; any other path must not only climb higher ground, but must be at the higher level over a greater distance. The profile of this path from α to β will be of the general shape of Fig. 14.5. There may of course be more than one pass to cross, in which case the contributions have to be determined separately.

The point S is a saddle point of $f(z)$ and the path through S is the line of steepest descent from S; the process is therefore

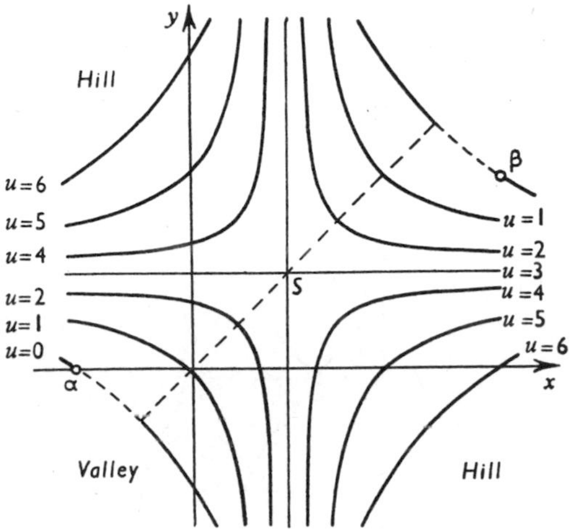

FIG. 14.4

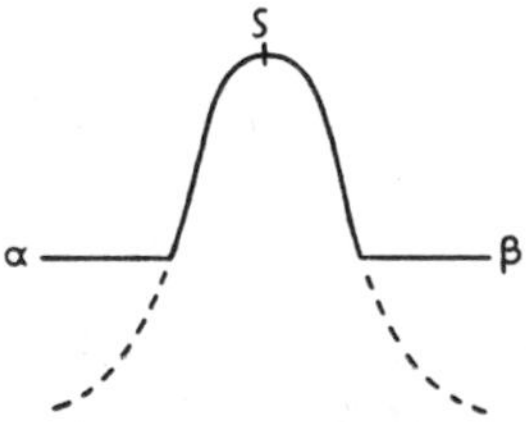

FIG. 14.5

known as the method of steepest descents. The details of calculation and of the way in which an asymptotic expansion is obtained are illustrated most easily by taking a particular case.

Example

Put $g(z)=1$ and $f(z)=\log z-z$ in the general form of integral (1), and let $\alpha=0$, $\beta=\infty$. Then

$$I(s)=\int_0^\infty e^{s(\log z-z)}\,dz=\int_0^\infty z^s e^{-sz}\,dz$$

This integral converges for positive values of s. To find the u-contours we note that

$$\log z - z = \log re^{i\theta} - z = (\log r + i\theta) - (x + iy)$$

so that
$$u = \log r - x$$

Now consider the contours $u = C$. For a contour through the origin, $C = -\infty$; and for a contour through any point at infinity for which $-\frac{1}{2} < \theta < \frac{1}{2}$, that is, through any point for which $x \to \infty$, we again have $C \to -\infty$. Thus the two termini lie in valleys. That these valleys are separated by a ridge is seen from a rough sketch of one or two of the contour lines $u \equiv \log r - x = C$ as in Fig. 14.6.

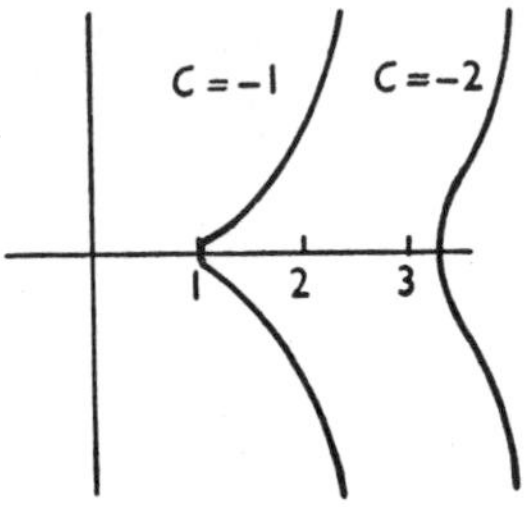

FIG. 14.6

The contours $u = -1, -2$, for example, separate the valley $u = -\infty$ in which the origin lies from the valley $u = -\infty$ at infinity. To locate the saddle point (or lowest point of the ridge to be crossed) of $\mathrm{f}(z) = \log z - z$ we differentiate:

$$\frac{\mathrm{d}}{\mathrm{d}z}(\log z - z) = (1/z) - 1$$

Thus the only stationary point of $\mathrm{f}(z)$ is at $z = 1$. We deduce from this fact together with our previous examination of the lie of the contours that $z = 1$ is the required saddle point of $\mathrm{f}(z)$. Moreover, at every point on the real axis $\frac{\mathrm{d}}{\mathrm{d}z}(\log z - z)$ is real so the line of steepest descent continues along the real axis. On this path between 0 and ∞, $\mathrm{f}(z)$ is everywhere negative, falling off rapidly in magnitude for $z \gg 1$. Putting $z = 1 + \zeta$ we have

$$\log z - z = -1 - \frac{\zeta^2}{2} + \frac{\zeta^3}{3} - \dots$$

and hence
$$\mathrm{I}(s) = e^{-s} \int_{-1}^{\infty} e^{-s(\frac{1}{2}\zeta^2 - \frac{1}{3}\zeta^3 + \dots)} \, \mathrm{d}\zeta$$

Now as s increases, the relevant range of ζ becomes smaller and smaller, and hence as a first approximation to $\mathrm{I}(s)$ we can ignore ζ^3 and higher terms, and write

$$\mathrm{I}(s)=e^{-s}\int_{-1}^{\infty} e^{-\frac{1}{2}s\zeta^2}\,\mathrm{d}\zeta$$

Further, since for large s the additional range from $\zeta=-\infty$ to -1 does not appreciably affect this integral (though it would completely alter the original one) we can write

$$\mathrm{I}(s)\simeq e^{-s}\int_{-\infty}^{\infty} e^{-\frac{1}{2}s\zeta^2}\,\mathrm{d}\zeta=e^{-s}(2\pi/s)^{\frac{1}{2}}$$

To find higher terms it is convenient to replace ζ by the substitution

$$\tfrac{1}{2}\xi^2=\tfrac{1}{2}\zeta^2-\tfrac{1}{3}\zeta^3+\tfrac{1}{4}\zeta^4-\ldots=\zeta-\log(1+\zeta) \qquad (3)$$

then

$$\mathrm{I}(s)=e^{-s}\int_{-\infty}^{\infty} e^{-\frac{1}{2}s\xi^2}\frac{\mathrm{d}\zeta}{\mathrm{d}\xi}\,\mathrm{d}\xi \qquad (4)$$

which is of the form considered in 14.32. To evaluate it, we require the series for $\mathrm{d}\zeta/\mathrm{d}\xi$ in powers of ξ. To obtain this, first differentiate (3) and obtain a differential equation for ζ as a function of ξ; this is

$$\zeta\,\mathrm{d}\zeta/\mathrm{d}\xi=\xi(1+\zeta)$$

and then substitute

$$\zeta=\xi+a_2\xi^2+a_3\xi^3+\ldots$$

and equate coefficients. The result is

$$\zeta\,\mathrm{d}\zeta/\mathrm{d}\xi=\mathrm{d}(\tfrac{1}{2}\zeta^2)/\mathrm{d}\xi=\xi+3a_2\xi^2+2(a_2{}^2+2a_3)\xi^3+5(a_2a_3+a_4)\xi^4+\ldots$$

$$\xi(1+\zeta)=\xi+\xi^2+a_2\xi^3+a_3\xi^4+\ldots$$

whence

$$a_2=\frac{1}{3},\ a_3=\frac{1}{36},\ a_4=-\frac{1}{270},\ a_5=\frac{1}{4320},\ \ldots$$

Higher terms can be calculated, but in practice this is seldom necessary; if the general term is required, this method is not suitable, and some method peculiar to the special problem must be used.

We now have

$$\frac{\mathrm{d}\zeta}{\mathrm{d}\xi}=1+\frac{2}{3}\xi+\frac{1}{12}\xi^2-\frac{2}{135}\xi^3+\frac{1}{864}\xi^4+\ldots$$

Substitution into formula (2), and use of formula (3) of 14.32, with $x^2=s$, gives

$$\mathrm{I}(s)\sim e^{-s}(2\pi/s)^{\frac{1}{2}}\left[1+\frac{1}{12s}+\frac{1}{288s^2}\cdots\right] \qquad (5)$$

This is the expansion of asymptotic type which we sought. We shall meet this series again later in connection with the factorial function (16.1).

CHAPTER FIFTEEN

LAPLACE TRANSFORMS

15.1. Existence of the Laplace transform

In 10.5 we considered the Laplace transform method as a rule of thumb technique, the results justifying the means. This attitude is not inappropriate when the results can be quickly checked by substitution into the differential equation. In more complicated problems, however, this is not always feasible, and as there is little satisfaction in spending time and labour in deriving results the validity of which is uncertain we must now look more closely into the analytical questions of the existence, convergence and other properties of the integrals that are used.

The Laplace transform method is of particular importance in a range of electrical and engineering problems, e.g. the analysis and design of control systems, in which the independent variable is usually the time. We shall therefore use t rather than x as the independent variable in the present chapter.

The integral $$\bar{\mathrm{f}}(p)=\int_0^{\infty} e^{-pt}\,\mathrm{f}(t)\,\mathrm{d}t \qquad (1)$$

if it exists, is the Laplace transform of $\mathrm{f}(t)$. The conditions for the existence of the Laplace transform can be stated as follows :

If (i) $\mathrm{f}(t)$ is integrable in every finite range $a<t<b$ $(0\leqslant a<b<\infty)$ and (ii) for some value of p, say $p=p_0$, the limit

$$\lim_{t\to\infty} e^{-p_0 t}\,|\,\mathrm{f}(t)\,| \text{ exists,}$$

then the infinite integral (1) converges absolutely for all $p>p_0$. These conditions are quoted here without proof though proof is not difficult ; roughly speaking condition (i) ensures that the integral over the finite part of the infinite range is well behaved, and condition (ii) that the contribution from large values of t is negligible for sufficiently large values of p.

Further, the integral $\int_0^{\infty} e^{-pt}\mathrm{f}(t)\,\mathrm{d}t$ converges uniformly for

$p \geqslant p_0 + \delta \, (\delta > 0)$, and consequently $\bar{\mathrm{f}}(p)$ is a continuous function of p for $p > p_0$.

To prove this, let L be a positive number greater than $e^{-p_0 t} \mid \mathrm{f}(t) \mid$ or all $t \geqslant M$, then

$$\left| \int_M^\infty e^{-pt}\mathrm{f}(t)\,\mathrm{d}t \right| = \left| \int_M^\infty e^{-p_0 t}\mathrm{f}(t) e^{-(p-p_0)t}\,\mathrm{d}t \right|$$

$$\leqslant \int_M^\infty e^{-p_0 t} \mid \mathrm{f}(t) \mid e^{-(p-p_0)t}\,\mathrm{d}t$$

$$\leqslant L e^{-(p-p_0)M}/(p-p_0)$$

This can be made less than ϵ by taking M greater than

$$(p-p_0)^{-1} \log [L/(p-p_0)\epsilon]$$

The last expression is a decreasing function of p; hence the value of M that makes the remainder negligible when $p = p_0 + \delta$ will suffice for all greater values of p. Hence the integral $\int_0^\infty e^{-pt}\mathrm{f}(t)\,\mathrm{d}t$ converges uniformly to $\bar{\mathrm{f}}(p)$ for all values of p greater than $p_0 + \delta$. Now a uniformly convergent integral of a continuous function is continuous. Hence $\bar{\mathrm{f}}(p)$ is continuous for all $p > p_0$ (but not necessarily at $p = p_0$).

From the definition (1), it is clear that the Laplace transform $\bar{\mathrm{f}}(p)$ of a function $\mathrm{f}(t)$ depends only on the behaviour of $\mathrm{f}(t)$ for $t > 0$. This shows that from the Laplace transform $\bar{\mathrm{f}}(p)$, it is essentially impossible to determine the behaviour of $\mathrm{f}(t)$ prior to $t = 0$. However, in application to problems in which a system of some kind is disturbed at $t = 0$ and the subsequent response is required, this limitation is immaterial. The given initial conditions summarise all we need to know of the previous history of the system, and how these initial conditions were reached is irrelevant.

15.2. The inverse Laplace transformation

If $\bar{\mathrm{f}}(p)$ is the Laplace transform of $\mathrm{f}(t)$, then $\mathrm{f}(t)$ is the inverse Laplace transform of $\bar{\mathrm{f}}(p)$.

15.21. *Uniqueness*

It is obvious that, if the Laplace transform of a given function $\mathrm{f}(t)$ exists, then it is also unique; the existence of a definite integral implies its uniqueness. It is not obvious, however, and in fact it is exceedingly remarkable at first sight that to a given function $\bar{f}(p)$, satisfying reasonable conditions of continuity, there is one and only one continuous or sectionally continuous function $f(t)$, defined for $t>0$. This means that under these conditions the inverse Laplace transformation is also unique. For suppose that a given function $\bar{f}(p)$ had two inverse transforms $f_1(t)$ and $f_2(t)$. Then

$$\int_0^\infty e^{-pt} f_1(t)\, dt = \bar{f}(p), \quad p>p_1 \tag{1}$$

$$\int_0^\infty e^{-pt} f_2(t)\, dt = \bar{f}(p), \quad p>p_2 \tag{2}$$

and the transform of the function $\Delta(t)$ defined as the difference

$$\Delta(t) = f_1(t) - f_2(t) \tag{3}$$

is evidently identically zero for all $p>p_0$; that is

$$\int_0^\infty e^{-pt} \Delta(t)\, dt = 0, \quad p>p_0 \tag{4}$$

where p_0 is the numerically greater of p_1, p_2.

Now we cannot deduce from this that $\Delta(t) \equiv 0$ for all t; in fact, we can easily see that this deduction would be invalid; for $\Delta(t)$ may be non-zero at isolated values of t without contributing to the integral in (4) (see end of 8.6). However if $f_1(t)$ and $f_2(t)$ are both sectionally continuous, so also is $\Delta(t)$, and the integral $\int_0^L e^{-pt}\Delta(t)\, dt$ can be approximated by a polynomial $\sum_{r=0}^{n} X^r \Delta_r$ where X is written for e^{-p}. Now the poly-nomial can be zero for all X in the range corresponding to $p>p_0$ only if each $\Delta_r = 0$ (see 3.14). The conditions of continuity imposed on $\bar{f}(p)$, $f_1(t)$ and $f_2(t)$ are sufficient to ensure that as n and L both tend to infinity, the corresponding result $\Delta(t) = 0$ remains true. [We omit rigorous proof.] We shall therefore regard the uniqueness of the inverse transform as established subject to the stated continuity conditions.

15.22. *Analytical formula*

We now investigate the problem of finding $f(t)$ if $\bar{f}(p)$ is given.

Suppose that $\bar{f}(p)$ is a known function of $p = p_1 + ip_2$, and that it is analytic for all p on and to the right of a given ordinate B

in the complex plane for which in general $p_1 = \text{const.} > 0$. The related function $\mathrm{f}(t)$ is required. We have therefore to solve the integral equation

$$\int_0^\infty e^{-pt}\mathrm{f}(t)\,\mathrm{d}t = \bar{\mathrm{f}}(p) \tag{1}$$

Let us follow the method described in the last chapter, taking as a trial solution

$$\mathrm{f}(t) = \int_\alpha^\beta e^{\sigma t}\mathrm{F}(\sigma)\,\mathrm{d}\sigma \tag{2}$$

where α, β and $\mathrm{F}(\sigma)$ have to be chosen to fit equation (1). Then inserting this value into (1) we have

$$\int_0^\infty e^{-pt}\int_\alpha^\beta e^{\sigma t}\mathrm{F}(\sigma)\,\mathrm{d}\sigma\,\mathrm{d}t = \bar{\mathrm{f}}(p)$$

that is

$$\int_0^\infty \int_\alpha^\beta e^{-(p-\sigma)t}\mathrm{F}(\sigma)\,\mathrm{d}\sigma\,\mathrm{d}t = \bar{\mathrm{f}}(p)$$

If we suppose the change of order of integration is valid, we can first perform the integration with respect to t, which is very simple and gives

$$\int_\alpha^\beta \frac{\mathrm{F}(\sigma)\,\mathrm{d}\sigma}{p-\sigma} = \bar{\mathrm{f}}(p)$$

Now $\bar{\mathrm{f}}$ is analytic in the region to the right of B in the p-plane. Let us suppose that in a region near the point $\sigma = p$ in the σ-plane (with a fixed value of p) the function $\mathrm{F}(\sigma)$ is analytic ; then by Cauchy's integral (13.39), if we take the path of integration to be a closed contour round the point $\sigma = p$ and in a clockwise direction we find

$$\bar{\mathrm{f}}(p) = \oint \frac{\mathrm{F}(\sigma)}{p-\sigma}\,\mathrm{d}\sigma = 2\pi i\,\mathrm{F}(p) \tag{3}$$

Hence $2\pi i\,\mathrm{F}(p)$ is actually the same function as $\bar{\mathrm{f}}(p)$ and is therefore analytic in the same region. If in addition $\bar{\mathrm{f}}(p) = O(1/p)$ at infinity (this implies that $\mathrm{f}(t)$ is finite for small t) then the closed contour can be deformed into the line B plus a circular arc at infinity along which the integrand in (3) is of order $(1/p^2)$ and therefore does not contribute. Hence (a) the function $2\pi iF$ and the function $\bar{\mathrm{f}}$ are the same under these restricted conditions and (*b*) the function f(*t*) corresponding to a given $\bar{f}(p)$ is

$$f(t)=\frac{1}{2\pi i}\int_B e^{\sigma t}\bar{f}(\sigma)\,d\sigma$$

or replacing the dummy variable σ by p

$$f(t)=\frac{1}{2\pi i}\int_B e^{pt}\bar{f}(p)\,dp \tag{4}$$

(The path of integration B is known as a Bromwich contour and is such that all poles of $\bar{f}$ are to its left.)

Having obtained the relation between F and $\bar{f}$ we can now justify the interchange of the order of integration from the stated restrictions on $\bar{f}(p)$. For if $\bar{f}(p)$ is analytic and $O(1/p)$ at infinity, then $F(\sigma)$ is also analytic on and to the right of B and is $O(1/\sigma)$ at infinity; hence the integral

$$\int_B e^{-(p-\sigma)x}F(\sigma)\,d\sigma$$

converges uniformly for all t in the range $0<t<\infty$ and can be integrated with respect to t under the integral sign in this range.

Thus the formula (4) has been established for deducing the f(t) corresponding to a given $\bar{f}(p)$. It may also be written

$$f(t)=\frac{1}{2\pi i}\int_{p_1-i\infty}^{p_1+i\infty} e^{pt}\bar{f}(p)\,dp \tag{5}$$

We note in passing that the formula gives a formal expression for f(t) for negative values of t, even though, as we saw in the last paragraph, these are not usually of practical significance. It can be shown in fact that $f(t)=0$ for $t<0$ (see example 2 below).

The formula (4) (or (5)) is not of merely academic interest. The research worker quite often arrives at functions $\bar{f}(p)$ which do not appear in any table of Laplace transforms. He must then examine the poles of $e^{pt}\bar{f}(p)$ in the complex p-plane and use the theorem of residues 13.78. With practice this process is often much less laborious than one might expect.

Example 1

Find by the inversion theorem the functions whose Laplace transforms are

$$\frac{1}{p}, \quad \frac{1}{p+a}, \quad \frac{p}{p^2+a^2}, \quad \frac{a}{p^2+a^2}, \quad \text{(cf. ex. 1 of 13.78)}$$

Answers : 1, e^{-ax}, $\cos ax$, $\sin a\alpha$.

Example 2

Show that if $\bar{f}(p)$ is analytic at all points to the right of the Bromwich contour then $f(t)=0$ for all $t<0$.

[If t is negative e^{pt} is exponentially small to the right of the Bromwich contour. An arc of closure contributes nothing to the integral and completes a contour within which $\bar{f}(p)$ is analytic. Hence

$$f(t)=\frac{1}{2\pi i}\oint e^{pt}\bar{f}(p)\, dp=0 \quad (t<0)]$$

15.3. Properties of the Laplace transform

We shall now develop the properties of the Laplace transform, bearing in mind its main application for our purpose, the solution of differential equations. We have seen in 10.5 that the principal steps in this process are (i) the conversion of the differential equations in t into algebraic equations in p, (ii) the expansion of the solution of the algebraic equation into a sum of simple terms, (iii) the interpretation of the solution with the aid of a list of standard forms.

Our aim in the following will be to build up a set of rules and theorems enabling us to extend the list of standard forms already at our disposal, and in particular to extend this list to the transforms of infinite series and to integrals. A table listing the main results will be found at the end of the chapter (15.9).

15.31. *Notation*

We will use the notation $f(t)\supset\bar{f}(p)$ to signify that the Laplace transform of $f(t)$ is $\bar{f}(p)$.

15.32. *Transforms of derivatives*

Let $f(t)$ be such that

(i) $f(t)\supset\bar{f}(p)$ for all $p>p_0$

(ii) $f(t)$ tends to a limit $f(0+)$ as t tends to 0 through positive values.

(iii) $f(t)$ is differentiable except possibly at isolated points of finite discontinuity.

Then $\frac{d}{dt}f(t) \supset p\bar{f}(p) - f(0+)$ for all $p > p_0$. (This statement is more exact than that given in §10.5.)

For $\frac{d}{dt}f(t) \supset \int_0^\infty e^{-pt}\frac{d}{dt}f(t)\,dt = \int_{t=0}^\infty e^{-pt}\,df(t)$

Integration by parts is permissible in the sense of 8.41. Therefore

$$\frac{d}{dt}f(t) \supset \left[e^{-pt}f(t)\right]_0^\infty + p\int_0^\infty e^{-pt}f(t)\,dt$$

$$= -f(0+) + p\bar{f}(p) \quad \text{for all } p > p_0 \qquad (1)$$

It will be noticed that $f(0-)$ will be characteristically zero in applications to initial-value problems.

For the higher derivatives, say the nth, $f(t)$ and its derivatives up to the $(n-1)$th must satisfy the conditions (i) to (iii). We then find by repeated integration by parts, or by induction, that

$$\frac{d^n}{dt^n}f(t) \supset -p^{n-1}f(0+) - p^{n-2}f'(0+) - \ldots - f^{(n-1)}(0+) + p^n\bar{f}(p)$$

$$(p > p_0) \qquad (2)$$

Example 1

The function $y = \cos \omega t$ satisfies the equation $\frac{d^2y}{dt^2} + \omega^2 y = 0$ with initial conditions $y_0 = 1$, $\dot{y}_0 = 0$. Hence its transform $\bar{y}(p)$ must satisfy

$$(p^2 + \omega^2)\bar{y} = py_0 + \dot{y}_0 = p$$

whence

$$\bar{y} = p/(p^2 + \omega^2)$$

Example 2

Similarly $y = \sin \omega t$ satisfies the same equation with $y_0 = 0$, $\dot{y}_0 = \omega$. Hence its transform is

$$\bar{y} = \omega/(p^2 + \omega^2)$$

These two results have already been given in 10.5 but the present method of derivation is worth noticing since it serves to associate the numerator p with the cosine function.

15.33. *Change of scale*

Let $f(t) \supset \bar{f}(p)$ for $p > p_0$, and let a be positive. Then

$$f(at) \supset (1/a)\bar{f}(p/a) \text{ for } p > ap_0 \qquad (1)$$

Example 1

$$e^t \supset 1/(p+1)\ ;\quad e^{at} \supset (1/a)/[(p/a)+1] = 1/(p+a)$$

Example 2

Prove the general result (1).

15.34. *The p-shift theorem*

If $f(t) \supset \bar{f}(p)$ for $p > p_0$, then $e^{at}f(t) \supset \bar{f}(p-a)$ for $p > p_0 + a$

For $$e^{at}f(t) \supset \int_0^\infty e^{-pt}e^{at}f(t)\,dt = \int_0^\infty e^{-(p-a)t}f(t)\,dt$$

If we put $p' = p - a$, this becomes $\int_0^\infty e^{-p't}f(t)\,dt$ which is $\bar{f}(p')$, provided $p' > p_0$; and hence

$$e^{at}f(t) \supset \bar{f}(p-a) \text{ provided } p > p_0 + a \tag{1}$$

Examples

$$1 \supset 1/p\ ;\quad e^{-at} \supset 1/(p+a)$$
$$t^n \supset n!/p^{n+1}\ ;\quad e^{-at}t^n \supset n!/(p+a)^{n+1}$$
$$\sin \omega t \supset \omega/(p^2+\omega^2)\ ;\quad e^{-at}\sin \omega t \supset \omega/[(p+a)^2+\omega^2]$$
$$\cos \omega t \supset p/(p^2+\omega^2)\ ;\quad e^{-at}\cos \omega t \supset (p+a)/[(p+a)^2+\omega^2]$$

15.35. *The t-shift theorems*†

If $f(t) = 0$ for $t < 0$ and if $f(t) \supset \bar{f}(p)$ for $p > p_0$, then provided $a > 0$

$$f(t-a) \supset e^{-ap}\bar{f}(p) \text{ for } p > p_0 \tag{1}$$

For $$f(t-a) \supset \int_0^\infty e^{-pt}f(t-a)\,dt = e^{-ap}\int_0^\infty e^{-pt'}f(t')\,dt' \quad (t' = t - a)$$

Now in the range $-a < t' < 0$ we have $f(t') = 0$ hence

$$f(t-a) \supset e^{-ap}\int_0^\infty e^{-pt'}f(t')\,dt' = e^{-ap}\bar{f}(p)$$

For positive shifts in t, we have the theorem: if $f(t) = 0$ for all $t < a$, where a is positive, and if $f(t) \supset \bar{f}(p)$ (for $p > p_0$), then $f(t+a) \supset e^{ap}\bar{f}(p)$ for $p > p_0$.

For as above we find

$$f(t+a) \supset e^{ap}\int_0^\infty e^{-pt}f(t)\,dt$$

Then provided $f(t) = 0$ in the range $0 < t < a$ we can write

$$f(t+a) \supset e^{ap}\int_0^\infty e^{-pt}f(t)\,dt = e^{ap}\bar{f}(p) \tag{2}$$

† These theorems are restated in abbreviated form in 15.4.

The result (2) can easily be misused: in particular its use will lead to error unless the condition $f(t)=0$ in $0<t<a$ is carefully confirmed in each application. For example, take $f_1(t)=t$ so that $\bar{f}_1(p)=1/p^2$. Then $f_1(t+a)=t+a$ and the transform of $t+a$ is $(1/p^2)+(a/p)$, which is not the same as e^{ap}/p^2. The point is that the formula does not apply to the function $f_1(t)=t$ because this function is not zero in the range $0<t<a$ (see Figs. 15.1).

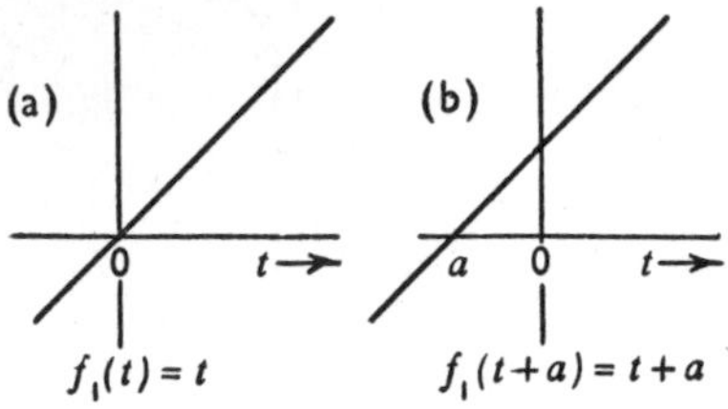

FIG. 15.1

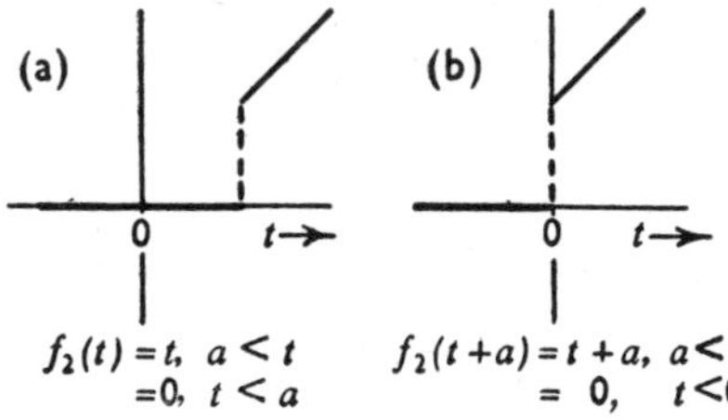

FIG. 15.2

If on the other hand we start with the function shown in Fig. 15.2(*a*), namely

$$f_2(t)=0,\ t<a$$
$$=t,\ t>a,$$

we find
$$\bar{f}_2(p)=\int_0^\infty e^{-pt}f_2(t)\,dt=\int_0^\infty e^{-pt}t\,dt$$
$$=(ae^{-pa}/p)+(e^{-pa}/p^2)=e^{-pa}[(a/p)+(1/p^2)]$$

from which the shift theorem (2) gives, correctly,

$$f_2(t+a)\supset(a/p)+(1/p^2)$$

15.4. Discontinuous functions

15.41. *The Heaviside unit function*

When using Laplace transforms, functions of the form

$$\left.\begin{aligned} f_1(t)&=0, \quad t<0\\ &=F_1(t), t>0 \end{aligned}\right\} \tag{1}$$

and of the form

$$\left.\begin{aligned} f_2(t) &= 0, \quad t<a \\ &= F_2(t), t>a \end{aligned}\right\} \tag{2}$$

occur frequently. It is convenient to write the function $f_1(t)$ of (1) as $f_1(t) = H(t)F_1(t)$ where $H(t)$ is the Heaviside unit function defined by

$$\left.\begin{aligned} H(t) &= 0 \quad t<0 \\ &= 1 \quad t>0 \end{aligned}\right\}$$

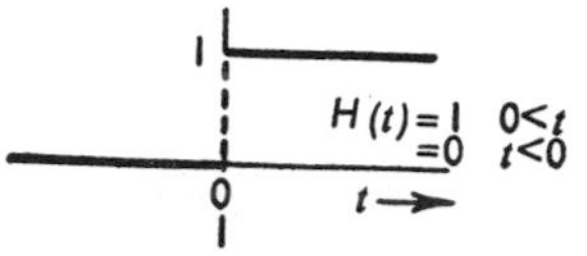

FIG. 15.3

(Fig. 15.3) and $F_1(t)$ may be defined for all t. In the same notation the function $f_2(t)$ can be written

$$f_2(t) = H(t-a)F_2(t)$$

The Laplace transform of $H(t)$ is

$$\overline{H}(p) = \int_0^\infty e^{-pt}\,dt = 1/p,$$

that is

$$H(t) \supset 1/p \quad (p>0). \tag{3}$$

Application of the t-shift theorem to this result gives

$$H(t-a) \supset (1/p)e^{-ap} \quad (a>0,\, p>0) \tag{4}$$

It has been pointed out in 15.1 that the Laplace Transform of a function does not of itself determine that function for $t<0$; that is, in terms of the notation of this section the Laplace transform of $F_1(t)$ is the same as that of $f_1(t) = F_1(t)H(t)$. However it was pointed out in 15.2 that the customary inversion formula, equation (4) of 15.2, does formally define a value of $f(t)$ for $t<0$, and gives the value zero. That is, inverting the transform $\bar{f}_1(p) = \overline{F}_1(p)$ this formula would give $f_1(t)$ rather than $F_1(t)$ or any other function having the same behaviour for $t>0$.

The reader may find the conditions of the t-shift theorems easier to remember when stated in abbreviated form using the unit function, namely

$$\text{(i) If } \mathrm{f}(t) = \mathrm{H}(t)\mathrm{F}(t) \supset \bar{\mathrm{f}}(p) \quad (p > p_0)$$

$$\text{Then } \mathrm{f}(t-a) \supset e^{-ap}\bar{\mathrm{f}}(p) \quad a > 0,\ p > p_0$$

$$\text{(ii) If } \mathrm{f}(t) = \mathrm{H}(t-a)\mathrm{F}(t) \supset \bar{\mathrm{f}}(p) \quad (p > p_0)$$

$$\text{Then } \mathrm{f}(t+a) \supset e^{ap}\bar{\mathrm{f}}(p) \quad a > 0,\ p > p_0$$

15.42. *Some applications of the t-shift theorems*

The t-shift theorems have some useful applications in connection with periodic functions, especially the piece-wise continuous functions which arise in switching cycles and time-base circuits. (i) Let $\mathrm{f}(t)$ be any function which is zero outside the range $0 < t < T$ (see Fig. 15.4, a), and has a Laplace transform $\bar{\mathrm{f}}(p)$ for $p > p_0$.

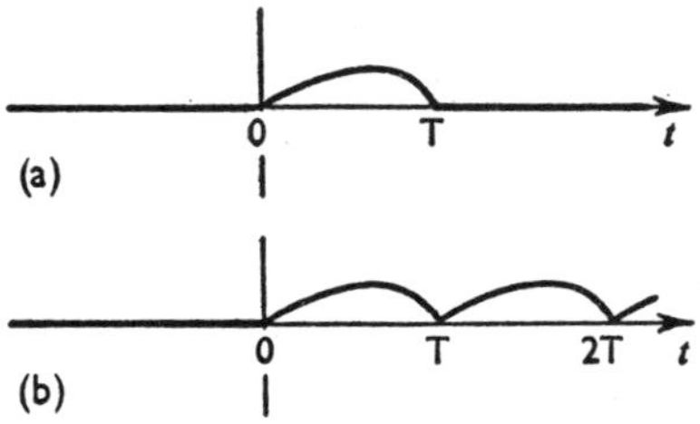

FIG. 15.4

Let $\mathrm{F}(t)$ be the periodic function defined by

$$\mathrm{F}(t) = 0,\ t < 0$$

$$\mathrm{F}(t) = \mathrm{f}(t),\ 0 < t < T$$

$$\mathrm{F}(t) = \mathrm{f}(t - rT),\ rT < t < (r+1)T$$

$\mathrm{F}(t)$ is thus the function formed by repeating the values of $\mathrm{f}(t)$ in each interval $rT < t < (r+1)T$ (see Fig. 15.4, b)

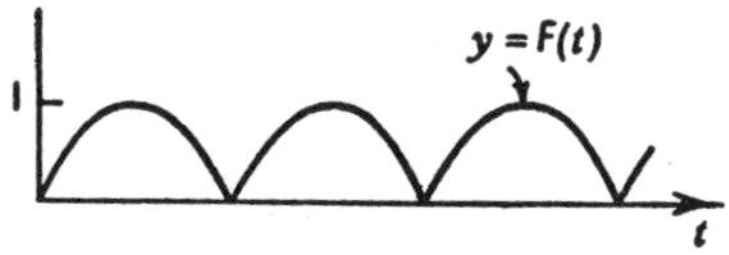

FIG. 15.5

We have therefore

$$\mathrm{F}(t) \supset \overline{\mathrm{F}}(p) = \int_0^\infty e^{-pt}\mathrm{F}(t)\,\mathrm{d}t$$

$$= \int_0^T e^{-pt}\mathrm{F}(t)\,\mathrm{d}t + \int_T^{2T} e^{-pt}\mathrm{F}(t)\,\mathrm{d}t + \ldots + \int_{rT}^{(r+1)T} e^{-pt}\mathrm{F}(t)\,\mathrm{d}t +$$

$$= \bar{\mathrm{f}}(p) + e^{-pT}\bar{\mathrm{f}}(p) + \ldots + e^{-rpT}\bar{\mathrm{f}}(p) + \ldots \text{ provided } p > p_0$$

$$= \bar{\mathrm{f}}(p)[1 + e^{-pT} + \ldots + e^{-rpT} + \ldots]$$

This is a geometric series and converges provided $p>0$, giving

$$\overline{\mathrm{F}}(p) = \bar{\mathrm{f}}(p)/(1 - e^{-pT}) \tag{1}$$

(ii) *Full wave rectification*

The rectified wave form shown in Fig. 15.5 is of the foregoing type with

$$\mathrm{f}(t) = \sin(\pi t/T) \qquad 0<t<T$$
$$= \quad 0 \qquad\qquad t<0,\ t>T$$

Then $\bar{\mathrm{f}}(p)$ may be calculated either directly or from the t-shift theorem. To use the second method notice that

$$\mathrm{f}(t) = \sin(\pi t/T)\mathrm{H}(t) + \sin[\pi(t-T)/T]\mathrm{H}(t-T), \tag{2}$$

for when $t<T$ the second term in (2) is zero, giving

$$\mathrm{f}(t) = \sin(\pi t/T), \qquad 0<t<T\,;$$

but when $t>T$, (2) gives

$$\mathrm{f}(t) = \sin(\pi t/T) + \sin[(\pi t/T) - \pi], \quad (t>T)$$

which is identically zero.

Now $\quad \sin(\pi t/T) \supset \pi T/(\pi^2 + p^2T^2), \qquad (p>0)$

so $\quad \sin(\pi t/T)\mathrm{H}(t) \supset \pi T/(\pi^2 + p^2T^2) \quad (p>0)$

Hence, using the t-shift theorem for the function (2)

$$\mathrm{f}(t) \supset \frac{\pi T}{\pi^2 + p^2T^2}(1 + e^{-pT})$$

and finally, from (1)

$$\overline{\mathrm{F}}(p)=\frac{\pi T}{\pi^2+p^2T^2}\,\frac{1+e^{-pT}}{1-e^{-pT}}=\frac{\pi T}{\pi^2+p^2T^2}\coth\tfrac{1}{2}pT$$

(see Fig. 15.6).

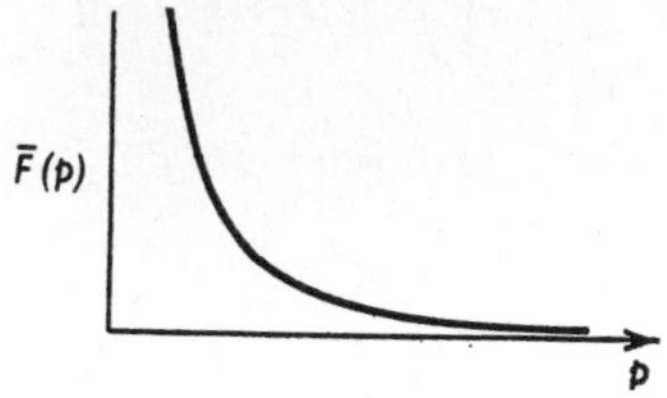

FIG. 15.6

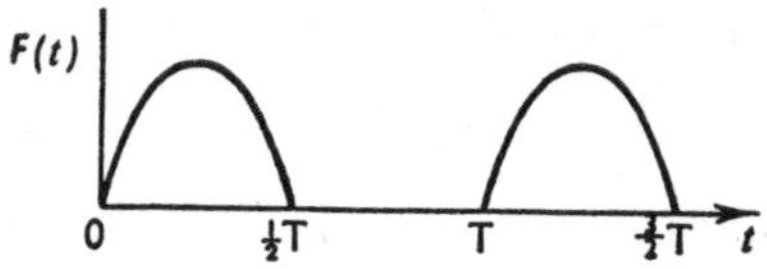

FIG. 15.7

(iii) *Half-wave rectification*

In this case we have (see Fig. 15.7)

$$\mathrm{f}(t)=\sin(2\pi t/T),\quad 0<t<\tfrac{1}{2}T$$

and by the change of scale theorem (§ 15.33)

$$\bar{\mathrm{f}}(p)=\tfrac{1}{2}\,\frac{\pi T}{\pi^2+(\frac{1}{2}p)^2T^2}\,(1+e^{-\frac{1}{2}pT})$$

Hence
$$\overline{\mathrm{F}}(p)=\frac{2\pi T}{4\pi^2+p^2T^2}\,\frac{1+e^{-\frac{1}{2}pT}}{1-e^{-pT}},\quad p>0$$

(iv) *Square wave*

The function $\mathrm{f}(t)$ in this case (see Fig. 15.8) is defined by

$$\mathrm{f}(t)=1,\ 0<t<\beta T$$
$$=0,\ \beta T<t$$

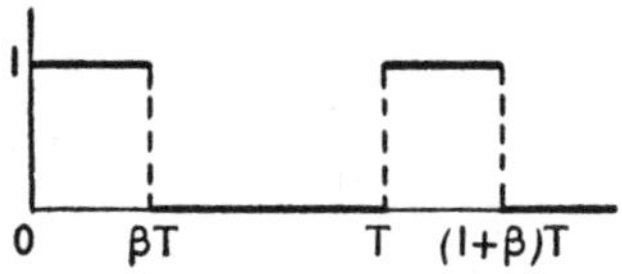

FIG. 15.8

and therefore can be written

$$\mathrm{f}(t)=\mathrm{H}(t)-\mathrm{H}(t-\beta T)$$

This gives
$$\bar{\mathrm{f}}(p)=(1-e^{-\beta Tp})/p$$

and for the periodic function

$$\overline{\mathrm{F}}(p)=(1-e^{-\beta pT})/p(1-e^{-pT})$$

If $$\beta=\tfrac{1}{2},\ \overline{\mathrm{F}}(p)=\frac{1}{p}\cdot\frac{1-e^{-\frac{1}{2}pT}}{1-e^{-pT}}=\frac{1}{p}\cdot\frac{1}{1+e^{-\frac{1}{2}pT}}$$

15.43. *The Dirac δ-function*

A function closely related to the Heaviside unit function is the Dirac δ-function. Instead of the abruptly discontinuous unit function let us first consider a differentiable function of similar general shape, for example

$$\mathrm{y}(t)=\tfrac{1}{2}+(2/\pi)\tan^{-1}(t/\epsilon)$$

where ϵ is very small but not zero (see Fig. 15.9 (a)).

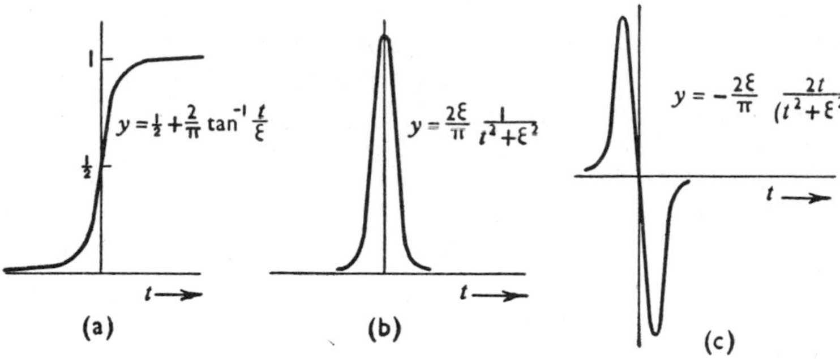

FIG. 15.9

Then although H(t) is not differentiable at $t=0$, y(t) is differentiable, and

$$\frac{\mathrm{dy}}{\mathrm{d}t}=\frac{2\epsilon}{\pi}\,\frac{1}{t^2+\epsilon^2}$$

If this is plotted for $\epsilon=0{\cdot}01$ say we obtain an impulse function, as shown in Fig. 15.9 (b). The Dirac δ-function is the idealised form of this when ϵ becomes very small. If we actually go to the limit as implied by $\epsilon\to 0$ then the function does not exist at $t=0$, and for $t\neq 0$ is without interest since it vanishes. However the function is very useful, in the same sense that point charges, particles and impulsive forces are useful. In discussing the properties of all such idealisations, it is only necessary to stop short of the limit $\epsilon=0$, and to take ϵ extremely small, say 10^{-10} units on the scale appropriate to the problem under consideration.

In this sense, the Dirac δ-function is the derivative of the Heaviside function; it has two essential properties

(i) $$\int_{\alpha}^{\beta} \delta(t)\,dt = \Big[\mathrm{H}(t)\Big]_{\alpha}^{\beta} = \mathrm{H}(\beta) - \mathrm{H}(\alpha)$$

In particular if $\alpha < 0 < \beta$

$$\int_{\alpha}^{\beta} \delta(t)\,dt = 1$$

(ii) If $f(t)$ is any function continuous at $t=a$, and if $\alpha < a < \beta$, then

$$\int_{\alpha}^{\beta} \delta(t-a)f(t)\,dt = f(a)$$

For $\delta(t-a)$ differs from zero only in the immediate neighbourhood of $t=a$, and since $f(t)$ is continuous at $t=a$, the value of $f(t)$ in the neighbourhood of $t=a$ differs from $f(a)$ by an amount which tends to zero with $(t-a)$. Hence

$$\int_{\alpha}^{\beta} \delta(t-a)f(t)\,dt = f(a)\int_{\alpha}^{\beta} \delta(t-a)\,dt + \eta = f(a) + \eta$$

where η can be made as small as we please by choosing the ϵ in the δ-function representation sufficiently small, so we may in fact write $\int_{\alpha}^{\beta} \delta(t-a)f(t)\,dt = f(a)$.

In particular if $a > 0$, $\int_{0}^{\infty} e^{-pt}\,\delta(t-a)\,dt = e^{-ap}$;

that is $$\delta(t-a) \supset e^{-ap} \quad (a>0) \tag{1}$$

It is also possible to introduce functions of a higher order of singularity by differentiating the δ-function, thus

$$\delta'(t) \simeq -\frac{2\epsilon}{\pi}\,\frac{2t}{(t^2+\epsilon^2)^2}$$

and so on. The form of $\delta'(t)$ is indicated in Fig. 15.9(c).

15.44. *Singular input functions and initial conditions*

If we try to obtain a result analogous to (1) of 15.43 for $a=0$, we find $\int_{\alpha}^{\infty} e^{-pt}\delta(t)\,dt = 1$ $(\alpha > 0)$, but $\int_{0}^{\infty} e^{-pt}\delta(t)\,dt$ is an improper integral with no well-defined value. Thus $\delta(t)$ has no true Laplace transform. If, because it is so convenient a form, we choose to write $\delta(t) \supset 1$, we must recognise that this is only a short-hand for $\delta(t-a) \supset e^{-ap}$ when a is extremely small. The need for a clear-cut convention of this kind is closely bound up with the interpretation of the initial conditions.

Let us consider a specific problem. Take for example the second-order equation

$$\frac{d^2y}{dt^2}+a\frac{dy}{dt}+by=f(t)$$

with initial conditions $y=y_0$, $\dfrac{dy}{dt}=\dot{y}_0$ at $t=0$. The transformed equation is (from 15.32)

$$(p^2+ap+b)\bar{y}=\bar{f}(p)+(p+a)y_0+\dot{y}_0$$

The right-hand side, however, is the transform of

$$f(t)+y_0\delta'(t)+(\dot{y}_0+ay_0)\,\delta(t)$$

provided $\delta(t)$ and $\delta'(t)$ are interpreted as $\delta(t-a)$, $\delta'(t-a)$ with a extremely small; so the original equation and initial conditions lead to the same solution as the equation

$$\frac{d^2y}{dt^2}+a\frac{dy}{dt}+by=f(t)+y_0\,\delta'(t)+(\dot{y}_0+ay_0)\,\delta(t)$$

with initial conditions $y=0$, $\dfrac{dy}{dt}=0$ at $t=0$. Thus a function on the right-hand side which is singular (i.e. like δ, δ', etc.) at $t=0$ has an effect equivalent to an instantaneous change in initial conditions. That $\delta(t)$ suitably represents an impulse is easily seen.

15.5. General results on the inversion of transforms

15.51. *Inverse of a quotient by partial fractions*

As mentioned in 10.5, a useful technique when inverting a Laplace transform, that is when finding the $f(t)$ corresponding to a given $\bar{f}(p)$, is that of expanding in partial fractions.

Let $\bar{f}(p)$ be a proper rational function of p, that is

$$\bar{f}(p)=h(p)/g(p)$$

where $h(p)$ and $g(p)$ are polynomials, the degree of $g(p)$ being greater than that of $h(p)$. Let the roots of $g(p)$ be real and distinct, and equal to $\alpha_1, \alpha_2, \ldots, \alpha_n$. Then $\bar{f}(p)$ is the Laplace transform of the function

$$\sum_{i=1}^{n} \frac{h(\alpha_i)}{g'(\alpha_i)} e^{\alpha_i t}$$

For, using the rule of 3.32

$$\frac{h(p)}{g(p)} = \sum_{i=1}^{n} \frac{h(\alpha_i)}{(p-\alpha_i)g'(\alpha_i)}$$

and $1/(p-\alpha_i)$ is the Laplace transform of $e^{\alpha_i t}$ for $p > \alpha_i$.

The rule does not break down when applied to non-repeated complex roots but it then expresses $f(t)$ in complex exponential form, which is often not the most convenient form. It does break down if applied to a repeated root α_i, real or complex, since then $g'(\alpha_i) = 0$. A general result can be obtained, but in practice it is more convenient to determine the partial fractions algebraically and use a list of transforms.

15.52. *Differentiation with respect to p*

Let conditions 15.1 (i) and (ii) for the existence of the Laplace transform

$$\bar{f}(p) = \int_0^\infty e^{-pt} f(t)\, dt \qquad p > p_0$$

be satisfied. Then the integral converges uniformly (see 15.1). Hence by 9.34 it is permissible to differentiate under the integral sign, provided the resulting integral converges, thus

$$-\frac{d}{dp}\bar{f}(p) = \int_0^\infty e^{-pt} t\, f(t)\, dt \tag{1}$$

The convergence of the right-hand side for $p = p_0 + \delta > p_0$ can be shown as follows:

$$\int_M^\infty e^{-pt} \mid t\, f(t) \mid dt = \int_M^\infty e^{-(p_0+\frac{1}{2}\delta)t} \mid t\, e^{-\frac{1}{2}t\delta} f(t) \mid dt$$

$< \int_M^\infty e^{-(p_0+\frac{1}{2}\delta)t} \mid f(t) \mid dt$ for M greater than the value of t for which $te^{-\frac{1}{2}t\delta} = 1$, $M > M_0$ say.

$< \epsilon$ for M sufficiently large, as proved in 15.1.

Thus the integral (1) is absolutely convergent and therefore is convergent. Hence

$$t\mathrm{f}(t) \supset -\frac{\mathrm{d}}{\mathrm{d}p}\bar{\mathrm{f}}(p), \quad p > p_0$$

15.53. *Integration with respect to p*

Similarly since the integral converges uniformly for all $p > p_0$ we can integrate under the integral sign and obtain

$$\int_p^\infty \bar{\mathrm{f}}(\lambda)\,\mathrm{d}\lambda = \int_0^\infty \mathrm{f}(t)\left\{\int_p^\infty e^{-\lambda t}\,\mathrm{d}\lambda\right\}\mathrm{d}t, \qquad p > p_0$$

$$= \int_0^\infty \mathrm{f}(t)(e^{-pt}/t)\,\mathrm{d}t, \qquad p > p_0$$

Hence $$\mathrm{f}(t)/t \supset \int_p^\infty \bar{\mathrm{f}}(\lambda)\,\mathrm{d}\lambda \qquad p > p_0$$

15.54. *The inversion of a product*

Let $$\mathrm{f}(t) \supset \bar{\mathrm{f}}(p) \qquad p > p_1$$
$$\mathrm{g}(t) \supset \bar{\mathrm{g}}(p) \qquad p > p_2$$

and let $\mathrm{F}(t)$ be the function of t defined by

$$\mathrm{F}(t) = \int_0^t \mathrm{f}(t-z)\mathrm{g}(z)\,\mathrm{d}z = \int_0^t \mathrm{f}(z)\mathrm{g}(t-z)\,\mathrm{d}z \qquad (1)$$

Then $$\mathrm{F}(t) \supset \bar{\mathrm{f}}(p)\bar{\mathrm{g}}(p), \text{ for } p > p_0$$

where p_0 is the greater of p_1, p_2.

Proof

The equality of the two integrals in (1) follows immediately from the substitution $z' = t - z$.

We can assume that for some finite values of K and p_0

$$|\mathrm{f}(t)| < Ke^{p_0 t}$$
$$|\mathrm{g}(t)| < Ke^{p_0 t}$$

and therefore $$|\mathrm{F}(t)| \leqslant \int_0^t |\mathrm{f}(t-z)|\,|\mathrm{g}(z)|\,\mathrm{d}z$$

$$< K^2 \int_0^t e^{p_0(t-z)}e^{p_0 z}\,\mathrm{d}z = K^2 t e^{p_0 t}$$

Hence $\int_0^\infty e^{-pt}\mathrm{F}(t)\,\mathrm{d}t$ converges for $p > p_0$ (from the proof of the convergence of the integral (1) of 15.52), so that the function $\mathrm{F}(t)$

has a Laplace transform for $p > p_0$. To evaluate it we apply the definition

$$\begin{aligned} \mathrm{F}(t) &\supset \int_0^\infty e^{-pt}\mathrm{F}(t)\,\mathrm{d}t \\ &= \int_{t=0}^\infty e^{-pt}\left\{\int_{z=0}^t \mathrm{f}(t-z)\mathrm{g}(z)\,\mathrm{d}z\right\}\mathrm{d}t \\ &= \int_{t=0}^\infty \int_{z=0}^t e^{-pt}\mathrm{f}(t-z)\mathrm{g}(z)\,\mathrm{d}z\,\mathrm{d}t \qquad (2) \end{aligned}$$

The integrand is a function of t and z; in the double integral (2), integration is first with respect to z from $z=0$ to t, and then with respect to t from 0 to ∞, i.e. over the triangular area of Fig. 15.10. Now the integral is known to be absolutely convergent for $p > p_0$,

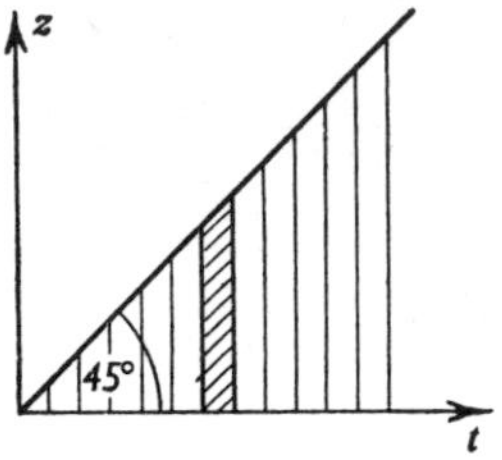

FIG. 15.10

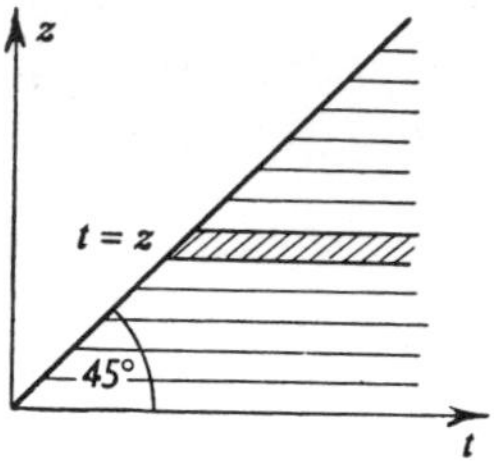

FIG. 15.11

and it can therefore be summed by any other method of subdivision, and in particular integrating first with respect to t and then with respect to z; the integration is then from $t=z$ to ∞ and then from $z=0$ to ∞ (see Fig. 15.11), this gives

$$\mathrm{F}(t) \supset \int_{z=0}^\infty \int_{t=z}^\infty e^{-pt}\mathrm{f}(t-z)\mathrm{g}(z)\,\mathrm{d}t\,\mathrm{d}z \qquad (3)$$

The integration over t is now easily effected by means of the t-shift theorem of 15.35, or directly by the substitution $t-z=t'$

thus
$$\int_z^\infty e^{-pt}\mathrm{f}(t-z)\,\mathrm{d}t = e^{-pz}\bar{\mathrm{f}}(p) \qquad p > p_1$$

Hence
$$\begin{aligned} \mathrm{F}(t) &\supset \int_0^\infty e^{-pz}\bar{\mathrm{f}}(p)\mathrm{g}(z)\,\mathrm{d}z \qquad && p > p_1 \\ &= \bar{\mathrm{f}}(p)\bar{\mathrm{g}}(p) && p > p_1,\ p > p_2 \end{aligned}$$

15.55. *Application of product theorem to standard input functions*

A familiar experimental method of assessing the fidelity of response of a telephone system or a radio receiver is to measure the steady state amplitude R of the response to a unit simple harmonic input, e.g. sin ωt. By varying the frequency ω the variation of R with ω can be found and from this the behaviour of the system to an arbitrary input can be estimated.

Other standard inputs are the unit step function or Heaviside input function $\mathrm{H}(t)$ and the unit impulse function $\delta(t)$. A study of the response of a system to the latter function brings to light an interesting interpretation of the product theorem.

Let the differential equation of the system be

$$\phi(\mathrm{D})y = \mathrm{f}(t) \tag{1}$$

where $y = y(t)$ is the output and $\mathrm{f}(t)$ the input. Then if the system is quiescent at $t=0$,

$$y(0) = y'(0) = \ldots = y^n(0) = 0 \tag{2}$$

Now we may assume that $y(t)$ satisfies the conditions of 15.32 and that y and its derivatives are continuous functions of t; then

$$\mathrm{D}^n y \supset p^n\bar{y} - p^{n-1}y(0) - \ldots - y^{n-1}(0) = p^n\bar{y}$$

on inserting the initial conditions (2). Hence

$$\phi(\mathrm{D})y \supset \phi(p)\bar{y}$$

The subsidiary equation derived from (1) is thus

$$\phi(p)\bar{y} = \bar{\mathrm{f}}(p)$$

with solution $\bar{y} = \bar{\mathrm{f}}(p)/\phi(p)$

Now let the input be the impulse function $\delta(t)$ whose transform is $\bar{\delta}(p) = 1$. Then

$$\bar{y} = \bar{\delta}(p)/\phi(p) = 1/\phi(p) = \bar{\mathrm{g}}(p)$$

say, and the corresponding output is given by

$$y(t) = \mathrm{g}(t)$$

A knowledge of the response $\mathrm{g}(t)$ to the δ-function input enables us to find $\phi(p) = 1/\bar{\mathrm{g}}(p)$ without prior knowledge of ϕ or the form of the differential equation of the system. Moreover, the response to an arbitrary function $\mathrm{f}(t)$ can be deduced from the observed form $\mathrm{g}(t)$. Thus

$$\bar{y} = \bar{\mathrm{f}}(p)/\phi(p) = \bar{\mathrm{f}}(p)\bar{\mathrm{g}}(p)$$

Hence, from the product theorem the response to $\mathrm{f}(t)$ is

$$y(t) = \int_0^t \mathrm{g}(t-z)\mathrm{f}(z)\,\mathrm{d}z$$

and the evaluation of this integral requires no knowledge of the system other than its response $g(t)$ to the unit impulse function.

Moreover one can now discern a kind of interpretation of this result and hence of the product theorem. For an electric circuit the unit impulse function could be used to represent a very high input voltage V applied for a time $1/V$. Similarly a general input function $f(t)$ can be regarded in some circumstances as a succession of impulses: thus in the time interval from z to $z+dz$ the magnitude of the voltage is $f(z)$ and the corresponding impulse is of magnitude $f(z)\,dz$, i.e. the impulse is $f(z)\,dz\,.\,\delta(t-z)$. Now the response to input $\delta(t-z)$ is, by definition, $g(t-z)$, so the response to $f(z)\,dz\,.\,\delta(t-z)$ is $f(z)\,dz\,.\,g(t-z)$ and, adding up the responses to all the impulses that have been applied up to time t, we obtain

$$y(t)=\int_0^t f(z)g(t-z)\,dz$$

15.6. Theorems on series and limits

15.61. *Series solution for small t*

It is often easy to expand $\bar{f}(p)$ as a series in negative powers of p. *When the series,*

$$\bar{f}(p)=\sum_{n=1}^{\infty} a_n p^{-n} \tag{1}$$

say, has a finite radius of convergence,

$$f(t)=\sum_{n=1}^{\infty} a_n t^{n-1}/(n-1)! \tag{2}$$

that is, the infinite series can be inverted term by term as could a finite series.

The series (2) is clearly a very useful expression for investigating the behaviour of $f(t)$ for small values of t.

To prove the theorem we use the result of 15.53, that the integral of a uniformly convergent series is equal to the series formed by integrating the terms one by one. The inverse transform of $\bar{f}(p)$,

$$f(t)=\frac{1}{2\pi i}\int_{p_1-i\infty}^{p_1+i\infty}\left(e^{pt}\sum a_n p^{-n}\right)dp$$

and, on the path of integration $e^{pt}=e^{p_1 t}(\cos p_2 t+i\sin p_2 t)$ where p_2 is variable. The series

$$e^{pt}\sum a_n p^{-n}=e^{p_1 t}\sum a_n(\cos p_2 t+i\sin p_2 t)p^{-n}$$

is uniformly convergent on the path of integration (cf. Abel's theorem, 4.22) provided we take p_1 greater than the radius of convergence of (1), for then on the path of integration $|p^{-1}|$ is less than the largest value for which (1) is convergent. Hence

$$\begin{aligned}\mathrm{f}(t)&=\frac{1}{2\pi i}\int_{p_1-i\infty}^{p_1+i\infty}\left(\sum_{n=1}^{\infty}e^{pt}a_n p^{-n}\right)dp\\ &=\sum_{n=1}^{\infty}\frac{1}{2\pi i}\left(\int_{p_1-i\infty}^{p_1+i\infty}e^{pt}a_n p^{-n}\,dp\right)\\ &=\sum_{n=1}^{\infty}a_n t^{n-1}/(n-1)!\end{aligned}$$

as required.

The above result can be extended to fractional powers: thus, *if*

$$\bar{\mathrm{f}}(p)=\sum_{n=1}^{\infty}b_n p^{-\nu_n}\qquad (\textit{all } \nu_n>0) \tag{3}$$

and if the series is uniformly convergent for $|p|\geqslant p_0$, *then*

$$\mathrm{f}(t)=\sum_{n=1}^{\infty}b_n t^{\nu_n-1}/(\nu_n-1)! \tag{4}$$

where the denominator is the factorial function which will be discussed in the next chapter.

It will be seen from (1) and (2) that for any function $\bar{\mathrm{f}}(p)$ which is expressible as a series in negative powers of p,

$$\lim_{t\to 0}\mathrm{f}(t)=\lim_{p\to\infty}p\bar{\mathrm{f}}(p). \tag{5}$$

since each side equals a_1. The result also holds in many cases involving fractional powers of p, cf. (3) and (4).

15.62. *Asymptotic expansions for large t*

Suppose that $p\bar{\mathrm{f}}(p)$ can be expressed as a series in positive powers of p, integral and non-integral,

$$\bar{\mathrm{f}}(p)=\sum_{n=0}^{\infty}a_n p^{n-1}+p^{-\alpha}\sum_{n=0}^{\infty}b_n p^n\qquad 0<\alpha<1 \tag{1}$$

Then if the series are convergent for $|p| < p_0$ say,

$$\mathrm{f}(t) \sim a_0 + \frac{1}{\pi} \sin(1-\alpha)\pi \sum_{n=0}^{\infty} (-1)^n b_n (n-\alpha)!\, t^{-n-1+\alpha} \tag{2}$$

where the sign $\sim$ is used for asymptotic equality (14.41).

For proof of this theorem and a more generalised form of the result the reader is referred to Carslaw and Jaeger, *Operational Methods in Applied Mathematics*, §126. We note that

$$\lim_{t\to\infty} \mathrm{f}(t) = \lim_{p\to 0} p\bar{\mathrm{f}}(p) \tag{3}$$

15.7. Solution of partial differential equations

The application of a Laplace transformation to a partial differential equation in two variables, which is linear with respect to one of the variables, reduces it to an ordinary differential equation. For example,

$$\frac{\partial^2 \mathrm{f}}{\partial x^2} = \frac{1}{c^2} \frac{\partial^2 \mathrm{f}}{\partial t^2} \tag{1}$$

$$\int_0^\infty \frac{\partial^2 \mathrm{f}}{\partial x^2} e^{-pt}\, \mathrm{d}t = \frac{1}{c^2} [p^2 \bar{\mathrm{f}} - p a_1(x) - a_2(x)] \text{ where } \mathrm{f}(x, 0) = a_1(x)$$

$$\mathrm{f}'(x, 0) = a_2(x)$$

i.e.
$$c^2 \frac{\partial^2 \bar{\mathrm{f}}}{\partial x^2} = p^2 \bar{\mathrm{f}} - p a_1(x) - a_2(x)$$

subject to the usual provisos about uniform convergence of the integral.

The symbol $\partial/\partial x$ denotes a variation with x keeping t constant, and as $\bar{\mathrm{f}}$ is not a function of t, the quantity $\partial^2 \bar{\mathrm{f}}/\partial x^2$ may be written $\mathrm{d}^2 \bar{\mathrm{f}}/\mathrm{d}x^2$, so we have,

$$c^2 \frac{\mathrm{d}^2 \bar{\mathrm{f}}}{\mathrm{d}x^2} - p^2 \bar{\mathrm{f}} = -p a_1(x) - a_2(x) \tag{2}$$

The solution of (2) may be tackled either by conventional means or by a further Laplace transform using a different symbol q say, instead of p, to avoid confusion. When $\bar{\mathrm{f}}$ has been found as a function of (x, p) its inverse (from tables or otherwise) gives the required solution of (1).

Whether the Laplace transform method is convenient in any

particular case depends very much on the boundary conditions. The next section will throw further light on this matter.

15.8. Other integral transforms

By an 'integral transform' of a function $f(t)$ is meant a function $F(\sigma)$ of an auxiliary variable σ, the 'parameter' of the transform, related to $f(t)$ by a definite integral of the type,

$$F(\sigma)=\int_a^b K(\sigma, t)f(t)\,dt$$

The Laplace transform is one of several integral transforms; p is the conventional symbol (instead of σ) for the parameter in this case, $K(p, t)=e^{-pt}$, and the limits are $a=0$, $b=\infty$.

Other integral transforms are obtained by using different functions K and different limits of integration. The function K is called the kernel of the transformation. Among the most important transforms are those associated with the names of Fourier, Hankel and Mellin. It is customary, though not essential, to use different symbols for the parameters in the various types of transform. This lessens the chance of, for example, using the wrong table of transforms, though unfortunately there are no universal conventions. We shall use the parameters ω (or n), ξ and s for Fourier, Hankel and Mellin transforms respectively.

15.81. *Infinite Fourier transforms*

The Fourier sine, cosine and exponential transforms have strong resemblances to the Fourier sine, cosine and exponential expansions of functions which were discussed in 12.4. The transforms and their inverses are:

Fourier sine transform,

$$F(\omega)=\sqrt{\frac{2}{\pi}}\int_0^\infty \sin(\omega t)\,f(t)\,dt\,;\quad f(t)=\sqrt{\frac{2}{\pi}}\int_0^\infty \sin(\omega t)F(\omega)\,d\omega$$

Fourier cosine transform,

$$F(\omega)=\sqrt{\frac{2}{\pi}}\int_0^\infty \cos(\omega t)\,f(t)\,dt\,;\quad f(t)=\sqrt{\frac{2}{\pi}}\int_0^\infty \cos(\omega t)F(\omega)\,d\omega$$

Fourier exponential transform,

$$F(\omega)=\frac{1}{\sqrt{2\pi}}\int_{-\infty}^\infty e^{i\omega t}f(t)\,dt\,;\quad f(t)=\frac{1}{\sqrt{2\pi}}\int_{-\infty}^\infty e^{-i\omega t}F(\omega)\,d\omega$$

Some authors sacrifice the symmetry in the above forms by omitting the numerical factor in the transforms : the value of the numerical factor in the inverse transforms must then be squared e.g. the sine transform is written $\int_0^\infty \sin(\omega t)\,\mathrm{f}(t)\,\mathrm{d}t$ and its inverse $\frac{2}{\pi}\int_0^\infty \sin(\omega t)\mathrm{F}(\omega)\,\mathrm{d}\omega$.

It will be seen that the sine and cosine transforms will in most cases exist if $\mathrm{f}(t)\to 0$ as $t\to\infty$, and the exponential transform if $\mathrm{f}(t)\to 0$ as $t\to\pm\infty$.

If the derivative of $\mathrm{f}(t)$ also tends to zero at $\pm\infty$, the Fourier exponential transform of the derivative is merely a multiple of $\mathrm{F}(\omega)$. If also the second derivative tends to zero at $\pm\infty$, the transform of the second derivative is a multiple of $\mathrm{F}(\omega)$, and so on. There is a similar result for the sine and cosine transforms except that in general the transform of a derivative involves both the sine and the cosine transform of the original function ; (on the other hand there is no restriction on the behaviour of the function or its derivatives at $-\infty$).

The above statements give the clue to the circumstances in which Fourier transforms may be expected to prove of value, namely in the solution of linear differential equations for which the boundary conditions require that the function and its derivatives vanish at one or more infinite boundaries. Vibrations or heat conduction in infinite sheets provide examples.

15.82. *Finite Fourier transforms*

The finite Fourier transform $\mathrm{F}(n)=\int_0^c \sin\left(\frac{n\pi x}{c}\right)\mathrm{f}(x)\,\mathrm{d}x$ has already been met in the formula for the coefficients of the terms in a Fourier sine expansion, 12.41, 12.43. Similarly the finite Fourier cosine transform appeared in 12.42. In our present notation we therefore have the pairs :

Finite Fourier sine transform,

$$\mathrm{F}(n)=\int_0^c \sin\frac{n\pi t}{c}\,\mathrm{f}(t)\,\mathrm{d}t\,;\quad \mathrm{f}(t)=\frac{2}{c}\sum_{n=1}^{\infty}\mathrm{F}(n)\sin\frac{n\pi t}{c}$$

Finite Fourier cosine transform,

$$\mathrm{F}(n)=\int_0^c \cos\frac{n\pi t}{c}\,\mathrm{f}(t)\,\mathrm{d}t\,;\quad \mathrm{f}(t)=\frac{1}{c}\mathrm{F}(0)+\frac{2}{c}\sum_{n=1}^{\infty}\mathrm{F}(n)\cos\frac{n\pi t}{c}$$

The main application of such transforms is to problems in which all relevant values of t lie in a finite interval $0<t<c$, e.g. problems on strips of finite width or finite rectangular plates.

15.83. *Mellin transforms*

For the Mellin transform,

$$\mathrm{F}(s)=\int_0^\infty t^{s-1}\mathrm{f}(t)\,\mathrm{d}t\,;\quad \mathrm{f}(t)=\frac{1}{2\pi i}\int_{c-i\infty}^{c+i\infty} t^{-s}\mathrm{F}(s)\,\mathrm{d}s$$

The transform of the derivative of $\mathrm{f}(t)$ is no longer easily expressed in terms of the transform of $\mathrm{f}(t)$, so this transform is unsuited to the solution of linear differential equations with constant coefficients. However, the transforms of $t\,\mathrm{df}/\mathrm{d}t$, $t^2\,\mathrm{d}^2\mathrm{f}/\mathrm{d}t^2$ etc. are readily expressible in terms of $\mathrm{F}(s)$, so the Mellin transformation is well suited to the solution of differential equations of the type,

$$a_n t^n\,\mathrm{d}^n\mathrm{f}/\mathrm{d}t^n+\ldots+a_1 t\,\mathrm{df}/\mathrm{d}t+a_0\mathrm{f}=\mathrm{g}(t)$$

15.84. *Hankel transforms*

When equations such as Poisson's equation or others expressing physical laws are expressed in terms of cylindrical coordinates, they are seldom linear equations with constant coefficients, so neither Laplace nor Fourier transforms are likely to be of use for their solution. In some cases Mellin transforms are useful, but more often the best transform to use is the Hankel transform. This is not unnatural, since the kernel of the Hankel transform involves a function intimately bound up with cylinders, called the Bessel function J_n. The definition and properties of Bessel functions will be discussed in the next chapter. In terms of these functions the Hankel transformation is :

$$\mathrm{F}(\xi)=\int_0^\infty t\mathrm{J}_n(\xi t)\mathrm{f}(t)\,\mathrm{d}t\,;\quad \mathrm{f}(t)=\int_0^\infty \xi\mathrm{J}_n(\xi t)\mathrm{F}(\xi)\,\mathrm{d}\xi$$

For further information on all the transforms mentioned in this section the reader is referred to Sneddon *Fourier Transforms*, and for tables of the transforms to *Tables of Integral Transforms*, Bateman Manuscript Project.

15.9. Table of Laplace transforms (supplementing the table of 10.5)

$f(t)$	$\bar{f}(p)$	
$f(at)$	$(1/a)\bar{f}(p/a)$	For explanation and conditions of validity, see the text.
$e^{at}f(t)$	$\bar{f}(p-a)$	
$f(t-a)$	$e^{-ap}\bar{f}(p)$	
$H(t-a)$	$(1/p)e^{-ap}$	
$\delta(t-a)$	e^{-ap}	
$tf(t)$	$-\frac{d}{dp}\bar{f}(p)$	
$f(t)/t$	$\int_p^\infty \bar{f}(\lambda)\, d\lambda$	
$\int_0^t f(t-z)g(z)\, dz$	$\bar{f}(p)\bar{g}(p)$	
$\sum_{i=1}^{\infty} \frac{h(\alpha_i)}{g'(\alpha_i)} e^{\alpha_i t}$	$h(p)/g(p)$	
$f^{(n)}(t)$	$p^n\bar{f} - p^{n-1}f(0+) - p^{n-2}f'(0+) \ldots - f^{(n-1)}(0)$	
$\sum_{n=1}^{\infty} a_n t^{n-1}/(n-1)!$	$\sum_{n=1}^{\infty} a_n p^{-n}$	
$\sim a_0$ (see 15.62)	$\sum_{n=0}^{\infty} a_n p^{n-1}$	
$\frac{1}{2\pi i}\int_{p_1-i\infty}^{p_1+i\infty} e^{pt}\bar{f}(p)\, dp$	$\bar{f}(p)$	

CHAPTER SIXTEEN

SPECIAL FUNCTIONS

In this chapter we consider certain important functions. Their properties are enumerated in some detail for reference purposes. The general reader will be primarily interested in the nature of the available information rather than in memorising all the details (at least at first).

16.1. The Factorial function

The familiar definition of factorial n for a positive integer n, namely

$$n! = n(n-1)(n-2)\ldots 3 \,.\, 2 \,.\, 1 \tag{1}$$

cannot be readily extended to provide a definition of the factorial function of a non-integral argument. It can however be shown, most simply by induction, that the definite integral $\int_0^\infty e^{-t} t^n \, dt$ has the value

$$\int_0^\infty e^{-t} t^n \, dt = n! \tag{2}$$

for positive integral n, and this result offers a means of defining the factorial function for fractional values, and indeed for complex values, of the argument.

To prove the result (2), suppose this result to hold for $n = m \geqslant 0$. Then by integration by parts

$$\int_0^\infty e^{-t} t^{m+1} \, dt = -\left[t^{m+1} e^{-t} \right]_0^\infty + (m+1) \int_0^\infty t^m e^{-t} \, dt \tag{3}$$

The integrated term vanishes at both limits since $m \geqslant 0$, and the integral in the second term is $m!$, since it is supposed that the result (2) holds for $n = m$. Hence (3) becomes

$$\int_0^\infty e^{-t} t^{m+1} \, dt = (m+1) \,.\, m! = (m+1)!$$

which is formula (2) for $n = m + 1$. Now (2) holds for $n = 1$, hence it holds for any positive integral value of n; that is, whenever $n!$ is defined by the elementary formula (1).

Now suppose that z is any number, real or complex, such that the infinite integral $\int_0^\infty e^{-t}t^z\, dt$ exists. Then $z!$ can be *defined* by

$$z! = \int_0^\infty e^{-t}t^z\, dt \tag{4}$$

This definition of the factorial function $z!$ embraces (1) but is of greater generality. The quantity $(-\frac{1}{2})!$ for example, cannot be expressed in a form comparable to (1), but is readily evaluated as a definite integral,

$$(-\tfrac{1}{2})! = \int_0^\infty e^{-t}t^{-\frac{1}{2}}\, dt = 2\int_0^\infty e^{-s^2}\, ds \quad (t = s^2)$$
$$= \sqrt{\pi}$$

We note also that the definition (4) gives $0! = \int_0^\infty e^{-t}\, dt = 1$.

The integral on the right-hand side of (4) is convergent at the upper limit for all z, and at the lower limit behaves like $\int t^z\, dt$, and so is convergent provided that $\mathscr{R}(z) > -1$, and divergent if $\mathscr{R}(z) < -1$. The expression (4) thus serves to define $z!$ for any z for which $\mathscr{R}(z) > -1$.

Instead of abandoning the concept of a factorial function in the excluded cases $\mathscr{R}(z) < -1$, we can again look for a property which is valid for all values of z for which $z!$ is defined by (4) (or (1)), but which suggests a new definition for $z!$ where (4) fails.

For all values of z for which the integrals are convergent and the integrated term vanishes, we have

$$(z+1)! = \int_0^\infty t^{z+1}e^{-t}\, dt = \Big[-t^{z+1}e^{-t}\Big]_0^\infty + \int_0^\infty (z+1)t^z e^{-t}\, dt$$
$$= (z+1)\, .\, z! \tag{5}$$

so that $\quad z! = (z+1)!/(z+1)$

We can use the relation (5) to define $z!$ when $(z+1)!$ is defined by (4) but $z!$ is not : that is, if $-2 < \mathscr{R}(z) < -1$ we can define $z!$ by

$$z! = (z+1)!/(z+1)$$

Similarly if $-3 < \mathscr{R}(z) < -2$, we can define $z!$ by

$$z! = (z+2)!/(z+2)(z+1),$$

and in fact, by repeated use of (5) we can define $z!$ for all those values of z excluded from direct definition by the definite integral (4), except for negative integral values.

16.11. *Analytic properties of the factorial function*

The function defined by 16.1 (4) is analytic at all points to the right of the line $x=-1$. For

$$\frac{\mathrm{d}}{\mathrm{d}z}(z!)=\int_0^\infty e^{-t}\log t\, t^z\,\mathrm{d}t$$

and this integral converges uniformly at all points in the z-plane to the right of $x=-1$. For points to the left of $x=-1$ we have

$$z!=(z+n)!/(z+n)\ldots(z+2)(z+1) \tag{1}$$

where n is sufficiently large to ensure $\mathscr{R}(z+n)>-1$. Thus, since $(z+n)!$ is analytic, $z!$ is analytic everywhere except at the negative integers where it has simple poles.

16.12. *The gamma function*

A second notation in common use for the factorial function $z!$ is $\Gamma(z+1)$. The symbol Γ is the Greek capital gamma, and the function is referred to as the gamma function. We follow H. and B. S. Jeffreys† in the adoption of the factorial notation and the name ‘ factorial function ’.

16.13. *Product of two factorials*

Consider the product of two factorial functions $m!$ and $n!$, where m amd n may be real or complex provided their real parts exceed -1. Then

$$m!\,n!=\int_0^\infty e^{-t}t^m\,\mathrm{d}t\int_0^\infty e^{-t}t^n\,\mathrm{d}t$$

and this can be rewritten as a double integral

$$\int_0^\infty\int_0^\infty e^{-(t+u)}t^m u^n\,\mathrm{d}t\,\mathrm{d}u \tag{1}$$

The integrand decreases exponentially as either t or u tends to infinity, so there are no convergence difficulties : the double integral converges absolutely and may be evaluated as an area integral over the first quadrant of the (u, t) plane using any convenient variables.

† *Methods of Mathematical Physics* (Cambridge, 1946), Chapter 15.

Put $v = u + t$ and divide the quadrant into strips by lines $v = \text{constant}$, and then into area elements $dv\,dt$ by lines

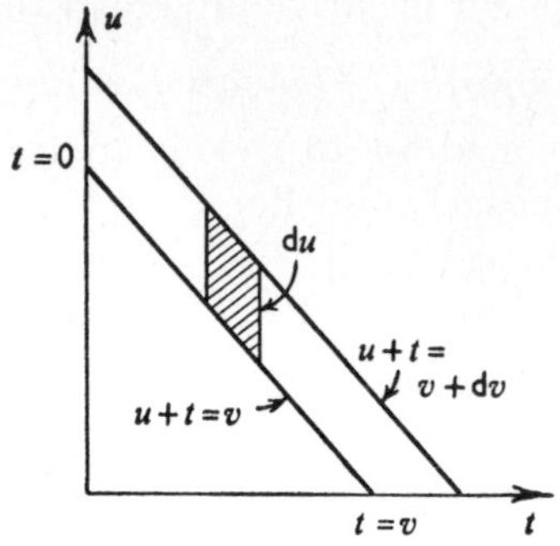

FIG. 16.1

$t = \text{constant}$. The limits of t in a strip are $t = 0$, $t = v$ (see Fig. 16.1). The integral (1) therefore takes the form

$$\int_{v=0}^{\infty} \int_{t=0}^{v} e^{-v} t^m (v-t)^n \, dv \, dt$$

or, putting $s = t/v$

$$\int_{v=0}^{\infty} \int_{s=0}^{1} e^{-v} v^{m+n+1} s^m (1-s)^n \, ds \, dv$$

$$= \int_{v=0}^{\infty} e^{-v} v^{m+n+1} \, dv \int_{s=0}^{1} s^m (1-s)^n \, ds$$

i.e. $$m!\,n! = (m+n+1)! \int_0^1 s^m (1-s)^n \, ds \tag{2}$$

The integral in (2), although of simple appearance, cannot be expressed as an elementary function except in special cases (e.g. when both m and n are integers, or when one of them is zero). We define the transcendental function $\mathrm{B}(m, n)$ of two variables by

$$\mathrm{B}(m, n) = \int_0^1 t^{m-1} (1-t)^{n-1} \, dt \tag{3}$$

in terms of this function, (2) can be written

$$m!\,n! = (m+n+1)!\,\mathrm{B}(m+1, n+1) \tag{4}$$

The function $\mathrm{B}(m, n)$ is called the beta function.

Two special cases may be mentioned in which equation (4) can be reduced to a relation between factorial functions alone.

These are the cases $n = \pm m$, and the results are (5) and (9) below.

When $n=m$ [$\mathscr{R}(m) > -1$], formula (2) becomes

$$m!\,m! = (2m+1)! \int_0^1 t^m (1-t)^m \,dt$$

The integrand is symmetrical about $t=\frac{1}{2}$, hence

$$(m!)^2 = 2\,.\,(2m+1)! \int_{1/2}^1 t^m (1-t)^m \,dt$$

Now if $v=(2t-1)^2$, $1-v=4t(1-t)$ and $\frac{1}{4}v^{-\frac{1}{2}}\,dv=dt$

Hence
$$(m!)^2 = 2(2m+1)! \int_0^1 (\tfrac{1}{4})^m (1-v)^m\,.\,\tfrac{1}{4}v^{-\frac{1}{2}}\,dv$$
$$= \tfrac{1}{2}(\tfrac{1}{4})^m (2m+1)! \int_0^1 (1-v)^m v^{-\frac{1}{2}}\,dv$$
$$= \tfrac{1}{2}(\tfrac{1}{4})^m (2m+1)!\,[m!\,(-\tfrac{1}{2})!/(m+\tfrac{1}{2})!]$$

using (2). Rearranged, and with $(-\frac{1}{2})!$ replaced by its value $\surd\pi$ (cf. 16.1), this gives the 'duplication formula'

$$(2m)! = (1/\pi)^{\frac{1}{2}}\, 4^m m!\,(m-\tfrac{1}{2})! \qquad (5)$$

When $n=-m$, formula (2) gives

$$m!\,(-m)! = \int_0^1 t^m/(1-t)^m \,dt \quad (-1<m<1)$$

and on making the substitution $t/(1-t)=e^z$, this becomes

$$m!\,(-m)! = \int_{-\infty}^{\infty} \tfrac{1}{2}[e^{mz}/(1+\cosh z)]\,dz \qquad (6)$$

The real integral (6) is best evaluated by contour integration in the complex plane; the appropriate contour is from $-\infty$ to $+\infty$ along the real axis and back from $+\infty+2\pi i$ to $-\infty+2\pi i$ (see Fig. 16.2). Cosh $i\pi=\cos\pi=-1$, so $z=i\pi$ is a pole of the integrand in (6). It is found that $2\pi i$ times the residue at the pole $z=i\pi$ is equal to $(1-e^{2\pi mi})$ times the integral (6). The final result is

$$m!\,(-m)! = m\pi/\sin m\pi \qquad (7)$$

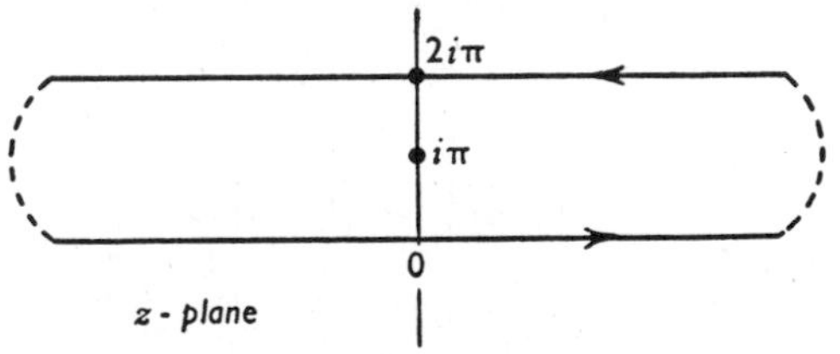

Fig. 16.2

This can be extended to values of m outside the range $-1<m<1$ by use of formula (1) of 16.11.

A corollary to this result is obtained by using the fact that

$$(-m)! = -m \,.\, (-m-1)!$$

Hence
$$m!\,(-m-1)! = -\pi/\sin m\pi \tag{8}$$

or
$$1/m! = -(1/\pi)(\sin m\pi)(-m-1)! \tag{9}$$

16.14. *Hankel's contour integral for z!*

The contour of integration C shown in Fig. 16.3 is sometimes useful in connection with the factorial function. By considering contributions from each portion of the path, it can be shown (see Whittaker and Watson, *Modern Analysis*, §12.22) that

$$\int_C (-t)^m e^{-t}\, dt = -2i[\sin(m+1)\pi](m!) \tag{1}$$

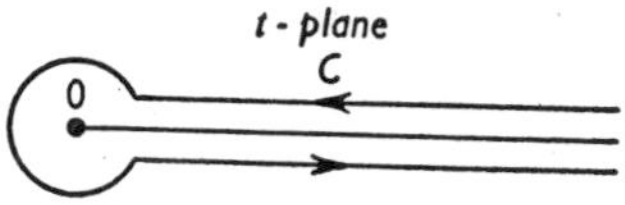

Fig 16.3.

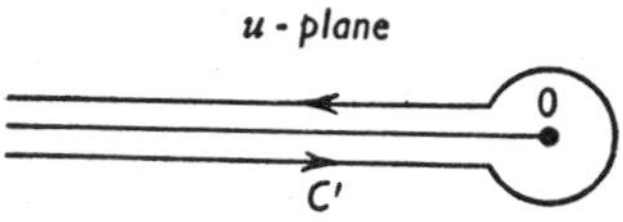

Fig. 16.4

Writing $-t=u$, the left-hand side becomes $\int_{C'} -u^m e^u\, du$ where C' is the contour shown in Fig. 16.4, and on replacing m by $-(n+1)$ and using (8) of 16.13 we get the alternative form of (1),

$$\int_{C'} u^{-(n+1)} e^u\, du = 2\pi i/n! \tag{2}$$

16.15. *Asymptotic expansion of z!*

The integral representation

$$z! = \int_0^\infty e^{-t} t^z\, dt \tag{1}$$

leads very easily to the first term and with increasing labour to further terms of the asymptotic expansion of $z!$. Put $t=uz$; $dt = z\, du$ then (1) becomes

$$z! = z^{z+1} \int_0^\infty e^{-uz} u^z\, du$$

$$= z^{z+1} \int_0^\infty e^{(-u+\log u)z}\, du$$

This is precisely the integral whose asymptotic expansion we found in 14.5, see formula (5). Hence

$$z! \sim z^{z+1}e^{-z}(2\pi/z)^{\frac{1}{2}}\left[1+\frac{1}{12z}+\frac{1}{288z^2}\cdots\right]$$

$$\sim(2\pi z)^{\frac{1}{2}}z^ze^{-z}\left[1+\frac{1}{12z}+\frac{1}{288z^2}+\cdots\right]$$

This is known as Stirling's expansion for $z!$. When $|z|$ is large, the approximation $(2\pi z)^{\frac{1}{2}}z^ze^{-z}$ is an extremely useful one, much used in statistical work, and of application in statistical mechanics. Even when z is small this approximation is quite a good one; for $z=1$ it gives the value $(2\pi)^{\frac{1}{2}}/e=0{\cdot}922$ as an approximation to 1!, though this value of z is by no means 'large'.

16.2. Functions of mathematical physics

Functions which arise in the course of solving Laplace's equation $\nabla^2\phi=0$, the heat conduction equation $\nabla^2\psi=\kappa\,\partial\psi/\partial t$, and the classical wave equation $\nabla^2\psi=\frac{1}{c^2}\,\partial^2\psi/\partial t^2$ are of great importance in physics. Exponentials, sines and cosines, Legendre functions and Bessel functions all belong to this category. These functions occur during the solution of any one of the three equations named above by the method of 'separation of variables' which we now describe.

Consider Laplace's equation, expressed in cartesian coordinates,

$$\frac{\partial^2\phi}{\partial x^2}+\frac{\partial^2\phi}{\partial y^2}+\frac{\partial^2\phi}{\partial z^2}=0 \qquad (1)$$

We note that the particular form $\phi(x, y, z)=\mathrm{X}(x)\,\mathrm{Y}(y)\,\mathrm{Z}(z)$ satisfies (1) provided that, for all (x, y, z),

$$\frac{\mathrm{d}^2X}{\mathrm{d}x^2}\,YZ+X\frac{\mathrm{d}^2Y}{\mathrm{d}y^2}\,Z+XY\frac{\mathrm{d}^2Z}{\mathrm{d}z^2}=0$$

i.e., dividing throughout by XYZ,

$$\frac{1}{X}\frac{\mathrm{d}^2X}{\mathrm{d}x^2}+\frac{1}{Y}\frac{\mathrm{d}^2Y}{\mathrm{d}y^2}+\frac{1}{Z}\frac{\mathrm{d}^2Z}{\mathrm{d}z^2}=0 \qquad (2)$$

Now the sum $\frac{1}{Y}\frac{\mathrm{d}^2Y}{\mathrm{d}y^2}+\frac{1}{Z}\frac{\mathrm{d}^2Z}{\mathrm{d}z^2}$ is independent of x, so $\frac{1}{X}\frac{\mathrm{d}^2X}{\mathrm{d}x^2}$, which is certainly independent of y and z, is also independent of x; that is, it must be constant. Similarly the second and third terms in (2) are each constant, hence

$$\frac{1}{X}\frac{d^2X}{dx^2}=\lambda_1\,;\quad \frac{1}{Y}\frac{d^2Y}{dy^2}=\lambda_2\,;\quad \frac{1}{Z}\frac{d^2Z}{dz^2}=\lambda_3 \tag{3}$$

where, because of (2), we require $\lambda_1+\lambda_2+\lambda_3=0$ i.e. if λ_1 and λ_2 are chosen arbitrarily, then we must have $\lambda_3=-(\lambda_1+\lambda_2)$. Thus the function $\phi=XYZ$ satisfies (1) when the functions X, Y, Z satisfy (3) with $\lambda_1+\lambda_2+\lambda_3=0$. In particular

$$\phi=\exp\,(\pm\lambda_1{}^{1/2}x\pm\lambda_2{}^{1/2}y\pm\lambda_3{}^{1/2}z) \tag{4}$$

(with $\lambda_1+\lambda_2+\lambda_3=0$) satisfies (1) for any combination of signs and any choice of λ_1, λ_2.

Moreover, since equation (1) is linear it follows that if $\phi=\phi_1$, $\phi=\phi_2$, $\phi=\phi_3$, ... , $\phi=\phi_n$ are all solutions, then so is $\phi=\sum a_i\phi_i$ the a's being constant.

We have not established that the general linear combination of the solutions (4) is a completely general solution of (1), but it is obviously sufficiently general to offer good hope of satisfying the requirements of a wide range of problems.

Example 1

Prove that the heat conduction equation $\nabla^2\psi=\kappa\,\partial\psi/\partial t$ is satisfied by the function $\psi=\phi e^{\lambda_4 t}$ where $\phi=\exp(\pm\lambda_1{}^{1/2}x\pm\lambda_2{}^{1/2}y\pm\lambda_3{}^{1/2}z)$ and λ_1, λ_2, λ_3 can be chosen arbitrarily but $\kappa\lambda_4=\lambda_1+\lambda_2+\lambda_3$.

2. Solve the classical wave equation by the method of separation of variables in x, y, z, t; and show that $\psi=\exp\pm i\omega_1\,(x-ct)$ and hence $\psi=\sin\,\omega_1\,(x-ct)$ are particular cases.

16.3. Legendre functions

We have just seen that in cartesian coordinates Laplace's equation separates into three elementary equations 16.2 (3) the solutions of which are the simple harmonic functions or their hyperbolic analogues.

In the next system of coordinates that we shall discuss, the spherical polars, two of the equations are elementary, the other is a modification of Legendre's equation. It is shown in 9.13 (ex.) and 17.73 that in spherical polars

$$\nabla^2V=\frac{1}{r}\frac{\partial^2}{\partial r^2}(rV)+\frac{1}{r^2\sin\theta}\frac{\partial}{\partial\theta}\left(\sin\theta\,\frac{\partial V}{\partial\theta}\right)+\frac{1}{r^2\sin^2\theta}\frac{\partial^2 V}{\partial\phi^2} \tag{1}$$

Substituting $V = \mathrm{R}(r)\Theta(\theta)\Phi(\phi)$ into $\nabla^2 V = 0$ and dividing throughout by $R\Theta\Phi$, we obtain

$$\frac{1}{Rr}\frac{\mathrm{d}^2}{\mathrm{d}r^2}(rR) + \frac{1}{r^2\Theta\sin\theta}\frac{\mathrm{d}}{\mathrm{d}\theta}\left(\sin\theta\frac{\mathrm{d}\Theta}{\mathrm{d}\theta}\right) + \frac{1}{\Phi}\frac{1}{r^2\sin^2\theta}\frac{\mathrm{d}^2\Phi}{\mathrm{d}\phi^2} = 0 \quad (2)$$

Multiplying by $r^2 \sin^2\theta$, we find that the first two terms are independent of ϕ and that the third is independent of both r and θ; the first separation therefore gives the two equations

$$\frac{1}{\Phi}\frac{\mathrm{d}^2\Phi}{\mathrm{d}\phi^2} = \lambda_1 = -m^2, \quad \text{say}, \quad (3)$$

and $$\frac{r\sin^2\theta}{R}\frac{\mathrm{d}^2}{\mathrm{d}r^2}(rR) + \frac{\sin\theta}{\Theta}\frac{\mathrm{d}}{\mathrm{d}\theta}\left(\sin\theta\frac{\mathrm{d}\Theta}{\mathrm{d}\theta}\right) - m^2 = 0 \quad (4)$$

The separation constant λ_1 can be given an unequivocal sign because, if V is to be a single-valued function of position in space, we must ensure that $\Phi(\phi + 2\pi) = \Phi(\phi)$. This condition also requires that m shall be an integer; there is no loss of generality in taking $m \geqslant 0$.

To separate R and Θ, divide (4) by $\sin^2\theta$; we obtain

$$\frac{r}{R}\frac{\mathrm{d}^2}{\mathrm{d}r^2}(rR) = \lambda_2 = \nu(\nu+1), \quad \text{say} \quad (5)$$

$$\frac{1}{\Theta}\frac{1}{\sin\theta}\frac{\mathrm{d}}{\mathrm{d}\theta}\left(\sin\theta\frac{\mathrm{d}\Theta}{\mathrm{d}\theta}\right) - \frac{m^2}{\sin^2\theta} = -\lambda_2 = -\nu(\nu+1) \quad (6)$$

It is convenient for later work to write this separation constant λ_2 in the form $\nu(\nu+1)$; this involves no loss of generality since for any value of λ_2, the equation $\nu(\nu+1) = \lambda_2$ can always be solved for ν.

The equation (5) in r is straightforward and has an elementary solution. On multiplication by R/r it becomes

$$\frac{\mathrm{d}^2}{\mathrm{d}r^2}(rR) = \nu(\nu+1)\frac{rR}{r^2} \quad (7)$$

an equation for (rR), homogeneous in r, which is a type considered in 11.53. Use of the trial solution $R = r^s$ shows that this is a solution if $s = +\nu$ or $s = -(\nu+1)$. Thus r^ν and $r^{-(\nu+1)}$ are two independent solutions of (7) [unless $\nu = -\frac{1}{2}$], and the general solution is $\mathrm{R}(\nu) = Ar^\nu + Br^{-(\nu+1)}$ where A and B are arbitrary constants. The case $\nu = n =$ integer is of particular importance for reasons which will appear in the next section;

for $\nu = n$, $\lambda_2 = n(n+1)$, and the general solution of equation (5) is $R(r) = Ar^n + Br^{-(n+1)}$.

The remaining equation (6) for Θ is more conveniently handled if we write $\cos\theta = x$ and $\Theta = y$. It then takes the form,

$$(1-x^2)\frac{d^2y}{dx^2} - 2x\frac{dy}{dx} + \left[\nu(\nu+1) - \frac{m^2}{1-x^2}\right]y = 0 \tag{8}$$

which is called the *associated Legendre equation.*

If V is independent of ϕ, $m = 0$ and equation (8) reduces to Legendre's equation

$$(1-x^2)\,d^2y/dx^2 - 2x\,dy/dx + \nu(\nu+1)y = 0 \tag{9}$$

This, being a linear differential equation of the second order, has two independent solutions : if the initial conditions are suitably chosen these are the functions $P_\nu(x)$, $Q_\nu(x)$ which are known as Legendre functions of the first and second kinds respectively. The general solution of (9) can then be written $AP_\nu(x) + BQ_\nu(x)$ where A, B are arbitrarily constants. We defer the full specification of $P_\nu(x)$, $Q_\nu(x)$ until 16.36.

16.31. *Legendre polynomials*

The importance of the solutions of Legendre's equation for integral values n of ν lies in this. In contexts in which the separation of variables expressed by (5) and (6) of 16.3 is used, a usual requirement is that the function Θ should be finite over the whole range of θ, including $\theta = 0$ and $\theta = \pi$, that is over the whole range of $x = \cos\theta$, including the values $x = \pm 1$. Now it has been shown in 12.15 that Legendre's equation 16.3 (9) has a solution which is finite both at $x = +1$ and at $x = -1$ if, and only if, ν has an integral value. This finiteness at both end-points is the important property of these solutions ; that the solutions which have this property happen to be polynomials in x is a convenient but relatively unimportant feature of them.

Since equation 16.3 (9) is homogeneous, any constant multiple of a solution is also a solution. If the constant multiplier in a polynomial solution with $\nu = n$ is taken so that this solution has the value 1 at $x = 1$, the solution is written $P_n(x)$ and is called the ' Legendre polynomial ' of order n. The first few such polynomials are

$$\left.\begin{array}{ll} P_0(x)=1 & P_1(x)=x \\ P_2(x)=\tfrac{1}{2}(3x^2-1) & P_3(x)=\tfrac{1}{2}(5x^3-3x) \\ P_4(x)=\tfrac{1}{8}(35x^4-30x^2+3) & P_5(x)=\tfrac{1}{8}(63x^5-70x^3+15x) \end{array}\right\} \quad (1)$$

In general $P_n(x)$ is a sum of even powers of x when n is even, and of odd powers when n is odd, the later coefficients being given in terms of the first coefficient in either case by formula 12.15 (6).

From what we have said it follows that

$$[Ar^n+Br^{-(n+1)}]P_n(\cos\theta)$$

satisfies Laplace's equation except at $r=0$ and at infinity where the expression becomes infinite. If we require a solution of Laplace's equation which is finite at $r=0$ we can obtain it by putting $B=0$, $Ar^nP_n(\cos\theta)$ being such a solution. Clearly the sum of two solutions of $\nabla^2V=0$ also satisfies the same equation, and in fact any finite sum $\sum_n A_nr^nP_n(\cos\theta)$ is a solution of $\nabla^2V=0$ within any sphere $(r<\infty)$ and is also independent of ϕ.

16.32. *Properties of the Legendre polynomials*

A convenient form for a polynomial solution, of degree n, of Legendre's equation is $D^n[(x^2-1)^n]$, where $D=d/dx$. That this is a solution can be verified as follows. Let $z=(x^2-1)^n$; then

$$dz/dx=n(x^2-1)^{n-1}\,.\,2x=2nxz/(x^2-1)$$

so that

$$(x^2-1)\,dz/dx=2nxz$$

Differentiating both sides of this identity $(n+1)$ times by means of Leibnitz's theorem, we obtain

$$(x^2-1)D^{n+2}z+(n+1)2xD^{n+1}z+(n+1)nD^nz$$
$$=2n[xD^{n+1}z+(n+1)D^nz]$$

which simplifies to

$$(x^2-1)D^{n+2}z+2xD^{n+1}z-n(n+1)D^nz=0$$

This is Legendre's equation in the form

$$(x^2-1)y''+2xy'-n(n+1)y=0 \qquad (1)$$

with D^nz in place of y. It follows that $D^nz\equiv D^n[(x^2-1)^n]$ is a solution of Legendre's equation (1); moreover, it is a polynomial of degree n. It must therefore be a multiple of $P_n(x)$, since the second solution $Q_n(x)$ of this equation is not a polynomial. Further, putting $x=1+u$, we have

$$(x^2-1)^n=u^n(2+u)^n=2^n u^n(1+\tfrac{1}{2}u)^n$$

so that
$$[D^n(x^2-1)^n]_{x=1}=2^n n!(1+\text{polynomial in } u)_{u=0}$$
$$=2^n n!$$

whereas $P_n(1)=1$; hence the multiplying constant relating $P_n(x)$ and $D^n[(x^2-1)^n]$ is such that

$$P_n(x)=\frac{1}{2^n n!}\frac{d^n}{dx^n}[(x^2-1)]^n \tag{2}$$

This formula is known as Rodrigues' formula.

16.321. *Polynomial as a linear combination of Legendre's polynomials*

Any polynomial of degree n can be expressed as a linear combination of Legendre polynomials of orders up to n. This can be established by induction as follows.

A first-degree polynomial $p_1(x)=a_0x+a_1$ is a linear combination of $P_0(x)=1$ and $P_1(x)=x$. Now suppose that any polynomial $p_{n-1}(x)$ of degree $n-1$ can be expressed as a linear combination of $P_m(x)$'s with $m \leqslant n-1$. Let the leading term in a polynomial $p_n(x)$ of degree n be a_0x^n, and let that in $P_n(x)$ be b_0x^n ($b_0 \neq 0$ since $P_n(x)$ is of degree n). Then $p_n(x)-(a_0/b_0)P_n(x)$ is a polynomial of degree $n-1$, so, by hypothesis, is a linear combination of $P_m(x)$'s with $m \leqslant n-1$. Hence

$$p_n(x)=(a_0/b_0)P_n(x)+(\text{linear combination of } P_m(x)\text{'s}, m \leqslant n-1)$$

and hence is a linear combination of $P_m(x)$'s with $m \leqslant n$. Hence the induction succeeds, giving the result stated.

One method of finding the coefficients in such a linear combination is considered in 16.33.

16.322. *Recurrence relations*

In this sub-section we deduce a number of formulae, mainly for reference.

Differentiation of Rodrigues' formula gives

$$2^n n!\,P'_n(x)=D^{n+1}(x^2-1)^n=D^n[D(x^2-1)^n]=D^n[2nx(x^2-1)^{n-1}]$$
$$=2n[xD^n(x^2-1)^{n-1}+nD^{n-1}(x^2-1)^{n-1}] \tag{1}$$

Now from Rodrigues' formula 16.32(2) with n replaced by

$(n-1)$, $D^{n-1}(x^2-1)^{n-1}=2^{n-1}(n-1)!\,P_{n-1}(x)$, and substitution in formula (1) gives

$$P'_n(x)=xP'_{n-1}(x)+nP_{n-1}(x) \tag{2}$$

one of a set of formulae relating Legendre polynomials of different orders n; such relations are called *recurrence relations.*

Three other useful relations can be derived from (2) and the differential equation (1) of 16.32 satisfied by $P_n(x)$. Differentiation of (2) gives

$$P''_n(x)=xP''_{n-1}(x)+(n+1)P'_{n-1}(x)$$

and from this relation and (2),

$$\begin{aligned}(x^2-1)P''_n(x)+2xP'_n(x)&=x[(x^2-1)P''_{n-1}(x)+2xP'_{n-1}(x)]\\&\quad+(n+1)(x^2-1)P'_{n-1}(x)+2nxP_{n-1}(x)\end{aligned} \tag{3}$$

since $y=P_n(x)$ satisfies equation 16.32(1), the left-hand side of (3) is $n(n+1)P_n(x)$, and the expression in the square bracket on the right-hand side of (3) is $(n-1)nP_{n-1}(x)$. Making these substitutions we find, after a little reduction,

$$nP_n(x)=nxP_{n-1}(x)+(x^2-1)P'_{n-1}(x) \tag{4}$$

$$=x[nP_{n-1}(x)+xP'_{n-1}(x)]-P'_{n-1}(x)$$

$$=xP'_n(x)-P'_{n-1}(x) \tag{5}$$

on using (2).

Another formula, required later, is obtained by replacing n by $(n+1)$ in (2) and using the result to eliminate $xP'_n(x)$ from (5). This gives

$$P'_{n+1}(x)=(2n+1)P_n(x)+P'_{n-1}(x) \tag{6}$$

Formulae (2), (4), (5) and (6) relate two Legendre polynomials, of degrees differing by unity, and their derivatives. A relation between three such functions, not involving derivatives, can be obtained as follows. From (4)

$$(x^2-1)P'_{n-1}(x)=n[P_n(x)-xP_{n-1}(x)] \tag{7}$$

and, by replacing n by $(n+1)$

$$(x^2-1)P'_n(x)=(n+1)[P_{n+1}(x)-xP_n(x)] \tag{8}$$

Now multiply (2) by (x^2-1) and substitute for $(x^2-1)P'_n(x)$ and $(x^2-1)P'_{n-1}(x)$ from (6), (7). This gives the required relation

$$(n+1)P_{n+1}(x)-(2n+1)xP_n(x)+nP_{n-1}(x)=0 \tag{9}$$

16.323. *Orthogonality*

Another important property of the Legendre polynomials is the orthogonality relation

$$\int_{-1}^{1} P_m(x)P_n(x)\,dx = 0 \quad \text{if } m \neq n \tag{1}$$

Proof of this follows the general lines of 12.32. The equation satisfied by $P_n(x)$ can be written

$$\frac{d}{dx}[(x^2-1)P_n'(x)] = n(n+1)P_n(x)$$

From this and the corresponding equation for $P_m(x)$ it follows that

$$P_m(x)\frac{d}{dx}[(x^2-1)P_n'(x)] - P_n(x)\frac{d}{dx}[(x^2-1)P_m'(x)]$$
$$= [n(n+1) - m(m+1)]P_m(x)P_n(x)$$

The left-hand side is $\frac{d}{dx}[(x^2-1)\{P_m(x)P_n'(x) - P_m'(x)P_n(x)\}]$, so integration from $x = -1$ to $x = +1$ gives

$$\Big[(x^2-1)\{P_m(x)P_n'(x) - P_m'(x)P_n(x)\}\Big]_{-1}^{+1}$$
$$= (n-m)(n+m+1)\int_{-1}^{1} P_m(x)P_n(x)\,dx$$

Now $P_m(x)$ and $P_n(x)$ are polynomials, so $[P_mP_n' - P_m'P_n]$ is finite at both limits, so the left-hand side vanishes; and the result (1) follows.

16.324. *Normalisation*

The integral $\int_{-1}^{1}[P_n(x)]^2\,dx$ is called the 'normalisation integral' for the Legendre polynomials; its value is required if we want to express a function as a linear combination of such polynomials. Its value can be obtained from formula 16.322 (5). Multiplying both sides of this formula by $2P_n(x)$ and integrating from $x = -1$ to $+1$, we have

$$2n\int_{-1}^{1}[P_n(x)]^2\,dx = 2\int_{-1}^{1} xP_n(x)P_n'(x)\,dx$$
$$- 2\int_{-1}^{1} P_n(x)P_{n-1}'(x)\,dx \tag{1}$$

Now $P'_{n-1}(x)$ is a polynomial of degree $(n-2)$, so is expressible as a linear combination of P_m's with $m \leqslant n-2$ (see 16.321), each of which is orthogonal to P_n; hence the second integral in (1) vanishes. The first integral is $\int_{-1}^{1} x \frac{d}{dx}[P_n(x)]^2 \, dx$, and integration by parts gives

$$2n \int_{-1}^{1} [P_n(x)]^2 \, dx = \Big[x\{P_n(x)\}^2 \Big]_{-1}^{1} - \int_{-1}^{1} [P_n(x)]^2 \, dx \qquad (2)$$

Now $[P_n(\pm 1)]^2 = 1$ for all n, so the first term on the right-hand side of (2) has the value 2; hence

$$\int_{-1}^{1} [P_n(x)]^2 \, dx = 2/(2n+1) \qquad (3)$$

16.33. *Expansions in Legendre polynomials*

If a function $f(x)$ is expressible over the range $-1 \leqslant x \leqslant 1$ as a linear combination of Legendre polynomials:

$$f(x) = a_0 P_0(x) + a_1 P_1(x) + \ldots + a_m P_m(x) + \ldots = \sum_m a_m P_m(x) \quad (1)$$

the coefficients can be determined by multiplying each side by $P_n(x)$ and integrating from $x = -1$ to $+1$. From the orthogonal relations between the $P_m(x)$'s it follows that the only term in the series which gives a non-zero contribution is that with $m = n$, so

$$\int_{-1}^{1} f(x) P_n(x) \, dx = a_n \int_{-1}^{1} [P_n(x)]^2 \, dx = [2/(2n+1)] a_n$$

whence

$$a_n = \tfrac{1}{2}(2n+1) \int_{-1}^{1} f(x) P_n(x) \, dx \qquad (2)$$

Example

Express x^3 as $\sum_m a_m P_m(x)$

From 16.321 we know that only P_m's with $m \leqslant 3$ will occur, further since x^3 is an odd function of x and $P_m(x)$ is even for m even, the integrals (2) for n even will vanish. We need only evaluate

$$a_1 = \frac{3}{2} \int_{-1}^{1} x^3 \, . \, x \, dx = 3/5$$

$$a_3 = \frac{7}{2} \int_{-1}^{1} x^3 \, . \, \tfrac{1}{2}(5x^3 - 3x) \, dx = 2/5$$

Hence $$x^3 = a_1 P_1(x) + a_3 P_3(x) = \tfrac{3}{5} P_1(x) + \tfrac{2}{5} P_3(x)$$
as can be verified by substitution of the polynomial forms for $P_1(x)$ and $P_3(x)$.

The question of the conditions under which a function $f(x)$, other than a polynomial, can be expanded in Legendre polynomials is a much deeper one, and will not be examined in detail here. We quote the result that in $-1<x<1$ it is sufficient that $f(x)$ should be a well-behaved continuous function (cf. 12.34).

16.34. *Generating function for Legendre polynomials*

If a unit charge is placed at the point with spherical polar coordinates $(a, 0, 0)$, the potential at any other point (r, θ, ϕ) is given by

$$V = 1/R = 1/(r^2 + a^2 - 2ar \cos \theta)^{\frac{1}{2}} \tag{1}$$

and is independent of ϕ. This function, as is to be expected from its physical interpretation, is a solution of Laplace's equation at all points except the point $(a, 0, 0)$ which is occupied by the charge. In particular Laplace's equation is satisfied at all points inside a sphere of radius a surrounding the origin. Now let us consider the expansion of V in powers of r. The equation $z^2 - 2az \cos \theta + a^2 = 0$ in a complex variable z has roots $z = a(\cos \theta \pm i \sin \theta)$, therefore the expression

$$1/\sqrt{(z^2 + a^2 - 2az \cos \theta)}$$

can be expanded as a power series in z which converges for $|z| < a$. Therefore, on replacing the complex variable z by the real variable r we see that V can be expanded as a power series in r provided that $r<a$. The coefficients will be functions of $\cos \theta$, thus

$$V = \sum_{n=0}^{\infty} r^n f_n(\cos \theta) \tag{2}$$

This series can be differentiated term by term provided that the resulting series is uniformly convergent. With this proviso we see that $\nabla^2 V = 0$ can be written

$$\sum_{n=0}^{\infty} \nabla^2 \{r^n f_n(\cos \theta)\} = 0$$

But the operation ∇^2 reduces the power of r in each term by two, except that

$$\nabla^2 f_0(\cos \theta) = \nabla^2 (1/a) = 0, \text{ and } \nabla^2 [r f_1(\cos \theta)] = \nabla^2 (r \cos \theta / a^2) = 0$$

so the series on the left is a series of linearly independent terms.

Hence each of the terms $\nabla^2\{r^n f_n(\cos\theta)\}$ must vanish separately. Now $r^n f_n(\cos\theta)$ is of the form $R(r)\Theta(\theta)$ of 15.3 with $m=0$, $\nu=n=$integer, so each $f_n(\cos\theta)$ is a constant multiple of $P_n(\cos\theta)$,

$$f_n(\cos\theta)=A_n P_n(\cos\theta) \tag{3}$$

The numbers A_n can be evaluated from the particular case $\theta=0$. From (2) and (3) we have

$$V(r, 0)=\sum_n A_n r^n P_n(1)$$

whereas from (1), $V(r, 0)=1/(a-r) \quad (r<a)$

So $$\sum_n A_n r^n=\frac{1}{a}\left(1+\frac{r}{a}+\frac{r^2}{a^2}+\ldots\right) \quad (r>a)$$

giving $$A_n=1/a^{n+1}$$

and hence, in general

$$V(r, \theta)\equiv\frac{1}{\surd(r^2+a^2-2ar\cos\theta)}=\frac{1}{a}\sum_n\frac{r^n}{a^n}P_n(\cos\theta) \tag{4}$$

We observe that $\frac{1}{a}\sum\nabla^2\left\{\frac{r^n}{a^n}P_n(\cos\theta)\right\}=\frac{1}{a}\sum 0$ is certainly convergent, so the assumptions of our proof are justified and equation (4) established for all θ and all $r<a$.

Putting $x=\cos\theta$ and $r/a=t$, we have the identity

$$1/(1-2tx+t^2)^{1/2}=\sum_n P_n(x)t^n \tag{5}$$

This formula provides an alternative starting point from which Legendre's polynomials can be defined. For we can also expand $(1-2tx+t^2)^{-1/2}$ by means of the binomial theorem

$$\begin{aligned}(1-2tx+t^2)^{-1/2}&=1+\tfrac{1}{2}(2tx-t^2)+\tfrac{3}{8}(2tx-t^2)^2+\ldots\\&=1+xt+\tfrac{1}{2}(3x^2-1)t^2+\ldots\end{aligned}$$

from which we have

$$P_0(x)=1,\ P_1(x)=x,\ P_2(x)=\tfrac{1}{2}(3x^2-1)$$

in agreement with formulae (1) of 16.31.

Formula (5) expresses the function of two variables on the left-hand side as a series in one variable (t) with coefficients which are functions of the other variable (x). That these functions of x are the Legendre polynomials is expressed by calling the function on the left the 'generating function' for the Legendre polynomials.

Use of the generating function provides an alternative method of deriving the recurrence relations of 16.322. For example differentiation of (5) with respect to t gives

$$(x-t)/(1-2tx+t^2)^{3/2}=\sum_n nt^{n-1}\mathrm{P}_n(x) \tag{6}$$

Then multiplying by $(1-2tx+t^2)$ and using (5) on the left-hand side we get

$$(x-t)\sum_n t^n\mathrm{P}_n(x)=(1-2tx+t^2)\sum_n nt^{n-1}\mathrm{P}_n(x)$$

and comparison of the coefficient of t^n on both sides gives

$$x\mathrm{P}_n(x)-\mathrm{P}_{n-1}(x)=(n+1)\mathrm{P}_{n+1}(x)-2nx\mathrm{P}_n(x)+(n-1)\mathrm{P}_{n-1}(x)$$

which on rearrangement gives formula (9) of 16.322.

Also differentiation of (5) with respect to x gives

$$t/(1-2tx+t^2)^{3/2}=\sum_n t^n\mathrm{P}_n'(x)$$

multiplication by $(x-t)$ and substitution from (6) gives

$$(x-t)\sum_n t^n\mathrm{P}_n'(x)=\sum_n nt^n\mathrm{P}_n(x)$$

and comparison of the coefficients of t^n on both sides gives

$$x\mathrm{P}_n'(x)-\mathrm{P}_{n-1}'(x)=n\mathrm{P}_n(x)$$

which is formula (5) of 16.322.

16.35. *Contour integral for the Legendre polynomials*

We now obtain a contour integral for the Legendre polynomials.

Consider the integral

$$\mathrm{S}_n(x)=\frac{1}{2\pi i}\int_C \frac{(t^2-1)^n}{2^n(t-x)^{n+1}}\,\mathrm{d}t \tag{1}$$

taken round a contour C, in the complex t-plane, encircling the point $t=x$ once in an anti-clockwise direction. Such an integral is called a ‘ Schläfli integral ’. We see that

$$\mathrm{S}_n(x)=\text{residue of } [(t^2-1)^n/2^n(t-x)^{n+1}] \text{ at } t=x$$

Bearing in mind that t (not x) is the variable in the integral (1) and that the residue is the coefficient of $(t-x)^{-1}$ in the Laurent expansion of the integrand in powers of $(t-x)$, it follows that

$$\mathrm{S}_n(x)=(1/2^n)\times[\text{coefficient of } (t-x)^n \text{ in expansion of } (t^2-1)^n \text{ in powers of } (t-x)]$$

$$=\frac{1}{2^n}\cdot\frac{1}{n!}\cdot\frac{\mathrm{d}^n}{\mathrm{d}x^n}(x^2-1)^n$$

which is Rodrigues' formula for $P_n(x)$. Thus the right-hand side of (1) is a contour integral for $P_n(x)$.

16.36. *Solutions of Legendre's equation for ν not integral*

Legendre's equation (9) of 16.3 with ν not integral is of far less frequent occurrence in applications, and of much less importance than with $\nu = n$, but it occurs occasionally. The main importance of the Schläfli integral 16.35 equation (1) is that it can be extended to provide a solution, in the form of a contour integral, to Legendre's equation for non-integral values of ν; it is applicable both when the independent variable is real ($=x$) and when it is complex ($=z$).

Let C be a contour in the complex t-plane (Fig 16.5) enclosing $t=z$ and $t=1$ and not intersecting the negative axis between $t=-1$ and $-\infty$; also let $\arg t$ have at A the value 0 (not a multiple of 2π). Then it can be shown (see Whittaker and Watson, *Modern Analysis*, §15.21) that the function defined by the Schläfli-integral

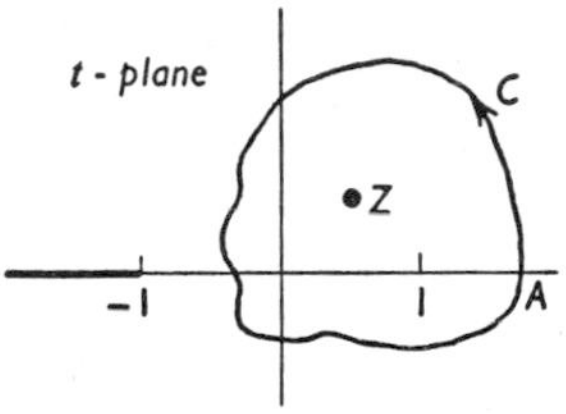

FIG. 16.5

$$S_\nu(z) = \frac{1}{2\pi i} \int_C \frac{(t^2-1)^\nu}{2^\nu (t-z)^{\nu+1}} \, dt$$

satisfies Legendre's equation 16.3(9) for a general value of ν. Further it is identical with $P_n(x)$ when $z=x$ and ν is an integer n. It is taken over as the *definition* of $P_\nu(x)$ when ν is non-integral; thus

$$P_\nu(x) = \frac{1}{2\pi i \,.\, 2^\nu} \int_C \frac{(t^2-1)^\nu}{(t-x)^{\nu+1}} \, dt$$

is the Legendre function of the first kind. Legendre functions $Q_\nu(x)$ of the second kind are similarly defined by a contour integral; for details see Whittaker and Watson, *Modern Analysis*, §15.3.

The second solution Q_ν of Legendre's equation is of interest only when the polar directions in our spherical polar coordinate system are excluded from the region in which a solution of Laplace's equation is to be found. As an example of such a problem, suppose that two halves of a conducting cone of semi-angle θ_1, are slightly separated and then charged to different potentials (Fig. 16.6). The region external to the conductor corresponds to

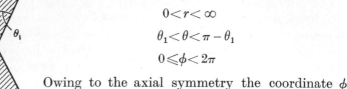

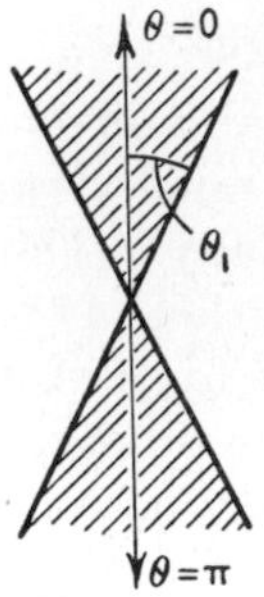

FIG. 16.6

$$0<r<\infty$$
$$\theta_1<\theta<\pi-\theta_1$$
$$0\leqslant\phi<2\pi$$

Owing to the axial symmetry the coordinate ϕ will not appear in the expression for the potential. The singularities of the function Q_n along the axes $\theta=0, \pi$ do not in this case exclude it from the problem, since these directions lie outside the region in which a solution of $\nabla^2 V=0$ is to be found. The solution may therefore involve contributions from terms like

$$V_\nu=r^{-(\nu+1)}[A_\nu \mathrm{P}_\nu(\cos\theta)+B_\nu \mathrm{Q}_\nu(\cos\theta)]$$

The second term is not merely ' not excluded ' but is necessary to satisfy the boundary conditions.

16.4. The associated Legendre equation

It has already been pointed out in § 16.31 that in most contexts in which the separation of variables is used, the function Θ is required to be finite over the whole range $0\leqslant\theta\leqslant\pi$, including the poles $\theta=0$, $\theta=\pi$; and, for the case of axial symmetry ($m=0$ in equations 16.3 (3) and (6)) this leads to the restriction of the parameter ν in equations (5) and (9) of 16.31 to integral values n. We shall now consider, more shortly, the corresponding results for functions which are not axially symmetrical, i.e. $m\neq 0$. The relevant equation is now 16.31 (8), namely

$$(1-x^2)\frac{\mathrm{d}^2y}{\mathrm{d}x^2}-2x\frac{\mathrm{d}y}{\mathrm{d}x}+\left[\nu(\nu+1)-\frac{m^2}{1-x^2}\right]y=0 \tag{1}$$

where $x=\cos\theta$.

It is first convenient to make the substitution

$$y=(1-x^2)^{\frac{1}{2}m}z \tag{2}$$

then z has to satisfy the equation

$$(1-x^2)\frac{\mathrm{d}^2z}{\mathrm{d}x^2}-2(m+1)x\frac{\mathrm{d}z}{\mathrm{d}x}+[\nu(\nu+1)-m(m+1)]z=0 \tag{3}$$

At $x=1$ the indicial equation for equation (3) has roots 0 and $-m$, so that this equation has one solution which is regular and one which is singular at $x=1$; and similarly at $x=-1$. Moreover a solution in which z is singular at $x=+1$ or -1 is also one in which y is singular, for near $x=1$, y is of order $(1-x)^{\frac{1}{2}m}z$ whereas a solution of (3) which is singular at $x=1$ is of order $(1-x)^{-m}$ near $x=1$, so that the corresponding function y is of order $(1-x)^{-\frac{1}{2}m}$.

Now let w be a solution of Legendre's equation (not necessarily a Legendre polynomial), so that

$$(1-x^2)\mathrm{D}^2w-2x\mathrm{D}w+\nu(\nu+1)w=0 \tag{4}$$

The result of differentiating this equation m times, using Leibnitz's theorem on the product terms, is

$$(1-x^2)\mathrm{D}^{m+2}w-2mx\mathrm{D}^{m+1}w-m(m-1)\mathrm{D}^m w$$
$$-2x\mathrm{D}^{m+1}w-2m\mathrm{D}^m w+\nu(\nu+1)\mathrm{D}^m w=0$$

This reduces to

$$(1-x^2)\mathrm{D}^{m+2}w-2(m+1)x\mathrm{D}^{m+1}w+[\nu(\nu+1)-m(m+1)]\mathrm{D}^m w=0$$

which is equation (3) with $\mathrm{D}^m w$ in place of z. Hence if w is a solution of Legendre's equation (4), then $\mathrm{D}^m w$, if not identically zero, is a solution of equation (3).

If ν is *not* integral, then we know that Legendre's equation (4) has one solution w_1 which is finite at $x=+1$ and singular at $x=-1$, and another solution w_2 which is finite at $x=-1$ and singular at $x=+1$. $\mathrm{D}^m w_1$ and $\mathrm{D}^m w_2$ are independent solutions of equation (3): hence there are no solutions of equation (3) for non-integral ν which are finite over the whole range $-1\leqslant x\leqslant 1$.

If ν is an integer n, then equation (4) has the polynomial solution $w=\mathrm{P}_n(x)$; and since any derivative of a polynomial is itself a polynomial and so is finite at $x=\pm 1$, it follows that for integral values n of ν, and $m\leqslant n$, equation (3) has solutions which are finite over the whole range $-1\leqslant x\leqslant 1$, and that these are

$$z=\left(\frac{\mathrm{d}}{\mathrm{d}x}\right)^m \mathrm{P}_n(x) \tag{5}$$

or, on expressing $P_n(x)$ by Rodrigues' formula,

$$z=\frac{1}{2^n\,.\,n!}\left(\frac{d}{dx}\right)^{m+n}(x^2-1)^n \tag{6}$$

Such solutions exist only for $m \leqslant n$. The corresponding solutions y of equation (1) are

$$y=\frac{1}{2^n\,.\,n!}(1-x^2)^{\frac{1}{2}m}\left(\frac{d}{dx}\right)^{m+n}(x^2-1)^n \tag{7}$$

The functions (7) are known as *Associated Legendre Functions*† ; they are themselves polynomials when m is even ; when m is odd they contain a factor $(1-x^2)^{\frac{1}{2}}$. They are denoted by $P_n^m(x)$; $P_n^0(x)$ is identical with the Legendre polynomial $P_n(x)$ and is usually so written. Other such functions, for values of n up to 4, are given in the following table :

n	$m=1$	$m=2$	$m=3$	$m=4$
1	$(1-x^2)^{\frac{1}{2}}$			
2	$3(1-x^2)^{\frac{1}{2}}x$	$3(1-x^2)$		
3	$\frac{3}{2}(1-x^2)^{\frac{1}{2}}(5x^2-1)$	$15(1-x^2)x$	$15(1-x^2)^{3/2}$	
4	$\frac{5}{2}(1-x^2)^{\frac{1}{2}}(7x^3-3x)$	$\frac{15}{2}(1-x^2)(7x^2-1)$	$105x(1-x^2)^{3/2}$	$105(1-x^2)^2$

Thus for $m \leqslant n$, the functions

$$P_n^m(x)=(1-x^2)^{\frac{1}{2}m}\left(\frac{d}{dx}\right)^m P_n(x) \tag{8}$$

provide a set of solutions of equation (1) with $\nu=n$.

Correspondingly, the functions

$$Q_n^m(x)=(1-x^2)^{\frac{1}{2}m}\left(\frac{d}{dx}\right)^m Q_n(x) \tag{9}$$

are also solutions of equations (1) for $\nu=n$. They are called *associated Legendre functions of the second kind.*

In the original notation of 16.3, $x=\cos\theta$. We note that $P_1'(\cos\theta)=\sin\theta$, $P_2'(\cos\theta)=3\sin\theta\cos\theta$; and so on.

16.41. *Orthogonality and normalisation*

The orthogonality of the functions $P_n^m(x)$ with the same value of m and different values of n can be established by an argument on the same lines as that used to establish the

† Or, Ferrers' associated Legendre functions to distinguish them from the functions $p_n^m(x)$ used by some authors (e.g. Jeffreys and Jeffreys), in which the arbitrary coefficients are differently defined. $p_n^m(x)=\frac{(n-m)!}{n!}P_n^m(x)$.

orthogonality of the $P_n(x)$'s. Applying this argument to the equation (1) of 16.4 which is satisfied by the $P_n^m(x)$ functions, we obtain

$$\int_{-1}^{1} P_l^m(x) P_n^m(x)\, dx = 0 \quad \text{if } l \neq n$$

The normalisation integral $\int_{-1}^{1} [P_n^m(x)]^2\, dx$ can also be evaluated formally (see Whittaker and Watson, *Modern Analysis*, §15.51) and is found to have the value

$$\int_{-1}^{1} [P_n^m(x)]^2\, dx = \frac{2}{2n+1} \frac{(n+m)!}{(n-m)!}$$

There is also an orthogonal relation between functions $P_n^m(x)$ with the same value of n and different values of m, namely

$$\int_{-1}^{1} [P_n^m(x) P_n^\mu(x)/(1-x^2)]\, dx = 0 \quad \text{if } \mu \neq m$$

(μ, m and n all integral and $\mu \leqslant n$, $m \leqslant n$). This result is obtained by taking equation 16.4 (1) and the corresponding equation with m replaced by μ, with $\nu = n$ in both equations, multiplying the former by $P_n^\mu(x)$, the latter by $P_n^m(x)$, subtracting, and integrating from $x = -1$ to $+1$.

16.42. *Recurrence relations for the functions* $P_n^m(x)$

Recurrence relations for the associated Legendre functions $P_n^m(x)$ can be deduced from those for the Legendre polynomials $P_n(x)$ (see 16.322) and the relation 16.4 (8). For example, from formulae (6) of 16.322,

$$P'_{n+1}(x) = (2n+1) P_n(x) + P'_{n-1}(x) \tag{1}$$

Hence from 16.4 (8)

$$\begin{aligned} P_{n+1}^m(x) &= (1-x^2)^{\frac{1}{2}m} D^{m-1} D P_{n+1}(x) \\ &= (1-x^2)^{\frac{1}{2}m} D^{m-1} [(2n+1) P_n(x) + D P_{n-1}(x)] \\ &\qquad\qquad\qquad\qquad [\text{from (1)}] \\ &= (2n+1)(1-x^2)^{\frac{1}{2}} P_n^{m-1}(x) + P_{n-1}^m(x) \qquad (2) \end{aligned}$$

by a second use of 16.4 (8). Similar methods lead to the derivation of numerous similar relationships. Elimination of terms involving upper indices other than m leads to the relation

$$(n-m+1) P_{n+1}^m(x) = (2n+1) x P_n^m(x) - (n+m) P_{n-1}^m(x) \tag{3}$$

while elimination of terms involving lower indices other than n gives

$$(1-x^2)^{\frac{1}{2}}\mathrm{P}_n^{m+1}(x) - 2mx\mathrm{P}_n^m(x) + (n+m)(n-m+1)(1-x^2)^{\frac{1}{2}}\mathrm{P}_n^{m-1}(x) = 0 \tag{4}$$

The relation

$$(1-x^2)\frac{\mathrm{d}}{\mathrm{d}x}\mathrm{P}_n^m(x) = (n+1)x\mathrm{P}_n^m(x) - (n-m+1)\mathrm{P}_{n+1}^m(x) \tag{5}$$

is also sometimes useful.

The recurrence formulae (3) and (4) allow us to extend the table of P_n^m's given in 16.41 to higher values of m, n.

The functions Q_n^m satisfy the same recurrence relations as the P_n^m's.

16.5. Bessel functions

After cartesian and spherical coordinate systems we consider the equations that arise from the separation of the variables when Laplace's equation is expressed in cylindrical coordinates r, θ, z (where, we recall, the symbols r, θ denote different quantities from the r, θ of spherical polar coordinates ; see 9.45). This system of coordinates is particularly well adapted to problems in which there is an axis of cylindrical symmetry.

The expansion of the Laplacian operator in cylindrical polars is (see 9.13, ex. and 17.73)

$$\nabla^2 V = \frac{\partial^2 V}{\partial r^2} + \frac{1}{r}\frac{\partial V}{\partial r} + \frac{1}{r^2}\frac{\partial^2 V}{\partial \theta^2} + \frac{\partial^2 V}{\partial z^2} \tag{1}$$

To solve Laplace's equation in this system by the method of separation of variables we look for solutions of the form

$$V = \mathrm{R}(r)\Theta(\theta)\mathrm{Z}(z)$$

Substituting this into (1) and dividing by $R\Theta Z$ we obtain

$$\frac{1}{R}\left[\frac{\mathrm{d}^2 R}{\mathrm{d}r^2} + \frac{1}{r}\frac{\mathrm{d}R}{\mathrm{d}r}\right] + \frac{1}{r^2\Theta}\frac{\mathrm{d}^2\Theta}{\mathrm{d}\theta^2} + \frac{1}{Z}\frac{\mathrm{d}^2 Z}{\mathrm{d}z^2} = 0$$

By arguments similar to those used in 16.2, 16.3 we are led to the equations,

$$\frac{1}{Z}\frac{d^2Z}{dz^2}=\lambda \tag{2}$$

$$\frac{1}{\Theta}\frac{d^2\Theta}{d\theta^2}=-n^2 \tag{3}$$

$$\frac{r^2}{R}\left[\frac{d^2R}{dr^2}+\frac{1}{r}\frac{dR}{dr}\right]=n^2-\lambda r^2 \tag{4}$$

where λ and n^2 are separation constants.

The first two equations are similar in form and have elementary circular or exponential functions as solutions. If V, and hence Θ, is known to be a continuous function of θ over the whole range $0\leqslant\theta\leqslant 2\pi$, and if V is a single-valued function of θ, so that $\Theta(\theta+2\pi)=\Theta(\theta)$, then the separation constant in (3) must be minus the square of an integer, that is, n is integral; and if it is non-zero, there is no restriction in taking it positive. In what follows, however, we shall not restrict ourselves to integral values of n.

The boundary conditions on Z may require either positive or negative values of λ; for example if it is required that $V\to 0$ at $z\to+\infty$, λ must be positive so as to admit an exponential solution; if $V=0$ at $z=0$ and $z=a$, then λ must be negative of the form $\lambda=-(m\pi/a)^2$ where m is an integer. With this value of λ, equation (2) has eigen-solutions of the form $Z=\sin m\pi z/a$.

The radial equation (4) is not elementary. If λ is positive the real substitutions

$$R=y,\ r=\lambda^{-\frac{1}{2}}x$$

reduce it to the form

$$x^2\frac{d^2y}{dx^2}+x\frac{dy}{dx}+(x^2-n^2)y=0 \tag{5}$$

This is Bessel's equation of order n. If λ is negative the real substitutions

$$R=y\,;\quad r=(-\lambda)^{-\frac{1}{2}}x$$

reduce the equation to the so-called ‘modified’ form

$$x^2\frac{d^2y}{dx^2}+x\frac{dy}{dx}-(x^2+n^2)y=0 \tag{6}$$

We now consider the solutions of these equations.

16.51. *Series solutions*

The Bessel equation was examined in 12.16 where it was found that the equation has a regular singularity at the origin; it has an irregular singularity (12.14) at infinity, i.e. the equation obtained by writing $\mathbf{x}=1/x$ has such a singularity at $\mathbf{x}=0$.

The indicial equation at $x=0$ is

$$c^2=n^2$$

The root $c=+n$ gives a series solution starting with x^n; if the multiplying constant in this solution is such that the leading term is $(\frac{1}{2}x)^n/n!$, this solution is written $J_n(x)$ and is called the Bessel function (sometimes with the qualification ' of the first kind ') of order n. Its series expansion is

$$J_n(x)=\frac{1}{n!}(\tfrac{1}{2}x)^n\left[1-\frac{1}{1\,.\,(n+1)}(\tfrac{1}{2}x)^2+\frac{1}{1\,.\,2\,(n+1)(n+2)}(\tfrac{1}{2}x)^4-\ldots\right]$$

$$=\sum_{r=0}^{\infty}\frac{(-1)^r(\frac{1}{2}x)^{n+2r}}{r!\,(n+r)!} \qquad (1)$$

In particular

$$J_0(x)=1-\frac{1}{(1!)^2}(\tfrac{1}{2}x)^2+\frac{1}{(2!)^2}(\tfrac{1}{2}x)^4-\frac{1}{(3!)^2}(\tfrac{1}{2}x)^6+\ldots \qquad (2)$$

and

$$J_1(x)=\tfrac{1}{2}x\left[1-\frac{1}{1!\,2!}(\tfrac{1}{2}x)^2+\frac{1}{2!\,3!}(\tfrac{1}{2}x)^4-\frac{1}{3!\,4!}(\tfrac{1}{2}x)^6+\ldots\right] \qquad (3)$$

For n integral, the rth positive root of $J_n(x)=0$ is usually denoted by $j_{n,r}$.

When n is non-integral, there is a second, independent, solution, given by the root $c=-n$ of the indicial equation, written $J_{-n}(x)$, whose series expansion is obtained by replacing n by $-n$ in (1),

$$J_{-n}(x)=\sum_{r=0}^{\infty}\frac{(-1)^r(\frac{1}{2}x)^{-n+2r}}{r!\,(-n+r)!}.$$

For an integral value of n the terms in this series with $r<n$ vanish on account of the factorials of negative integers in the denominator. If we take the series which remains as the definition of $J_{-n}(x)$ for positive integral n, we find

$$J_{-n}(x)=(-1)^nJ_n(x) \quad (n=\text{integer}) \qquad (4)$$

We have seen in 12.18 how a second *independent* solution of the differential equation can be obtained, and shall return to the matter in 16.61.

16.52. *Integral representation*

At first sight the integral transform method does not appear to be well adapted to the solution of Bessel's equation; the application of a Laplace Transformation merely produces another second-order differential equation. However, on examining this new equation it is found to be soluble in terms of elementary functions.

We make the substitution

$$y(x)=\int_\alpha^\beta e^{xt}g(t)\,dt$$

where g(t) and the range of integration are to be determined. Then a differentiation with respect to x and an integration by parts once with respect to t give

$$x\frac{dy}{dx}=\int_\alpha^\beta e^{xt}xtg(t)\,dt$$

$$=\Big[e^{xt}tg(t)\Big]_\alpha^\beta-\int_\alpha^\beta e^{xt}[tg'(t)+g(t)]\,dt$$

Similarly by differentiating twice with respect to x and integrating by parts twice with respect to t

$$x^2\frac{d^2y}{dx^2}=\int_\alpha^\beta e^{xt}x^2t^2g(t)\,dt$$

$$=\Big[e^{xt}xt^2g(t)\Big]_\alpha^\beta-\Big[e^{xt}\{2tg(t)+t^2g'(t)\}\Big]_\alpha^\beta$$

$$+\int_\alpha^\beta e^{xt}\{2g(t)+4tg'(t)+t^2g''(t)\}\,dt$$

so that

$$x^2\frac{d^2y}{dx^2}+x\frac{dy}{dx}+(x^2-n^2)y=\Big[e^{xt}\{xt^2g-t^2g'-tg+(xg-g')\}\Big]_\alpha^\beta$$

$$+\int_\alpha^\beta e^{xt}[(t^2+1)g''+3tg'+(1-n^2)g]\,dt \qquad (1)$$

We first determine the function g(t) so that the integrand vanishes; i.e. so that

$$(t^2+1)g''+3tg'+(1-n^2)g=0 \qquad (2)$$

This does not look much better than the original Bessel equation. However it has elementary solutions which become more apparent if we make the substitution

$$t = \sinh u$$

Then equation (2) becomes

$$d^2g/du^2 + 2 \tanh u \, dg/du + (1 - n^2)g = 0$$

whence $$\frac{d^2}{du^2}(g \cosh u) = n^2 (g \cosh u)$$

of which two solutions are

$$g \cosh u = e^{\pm nu}$$

or, in terms of t as independent variable,

$$g = 1/(1+t^2)^{\frac{1}{2}}\{(1+t^2)^{\frac{1}{2}} + t\}^{\mp n} \tag{3}$$

Hence an integral of the kind required is

$$\int_\alpha^\beta \frac{e^{xt}}{(1+t^2)^{\frac{1}{2}}[(1+t^2)^{\frac{1}{2}}+t]^n} \, dt \tag{4}$$

Nothing of value is gained by retaining both signs in $\pm n$, so in (4) we have discarded the alternative $-n$. This is a matter of convenience not of necessity : the form (4) could be used for n positive or negative, integral or fractional.

The path of integration must now be chosen so as to make the integrated terms in formula (1) vanish ; that is, so that

$$\Big[e^{xt}\{x(t^2+1)g - tg - (t^2+1)g'\} \Big]_\alpha^\beta = 0 \tag{5}$$

Now from (3) we see that the function $g(t)$ has branch points at $t = \pm i$, and that for $|t|$ large, $g(t)$ behaves like $1/2^n t^{n+1}$, so that if n is not integral, the point at infinity is also a branch point. A suitable set of barriers in the t-plane is shown by the heavy lines in Fig. 16.7, while the line marked with arrows indicates a contour M satisfying the relation (5). The left-hand side of the expression (5) vanishes at both limits, provided x is positive, since at the ends A, B of the contour $t \to -\infty$. This is true for positive or negative n.

(If we restrict ourselves to values of $n \geqslant 0$ the path of integration can be opened out as shown in Fig. 16.8 ; further the arc at infinity does not contribute to the integral if n, or more generally the real part of n, is greater than zero ; the

Bromwich contour, namely the straight line from $\gamma - i\infty$ to $\gamma + i\infty$ $(\gamma > 0)$, therefore becomes a suitable path of integration. With the negative sign however the integral along such a line does not even converge.)

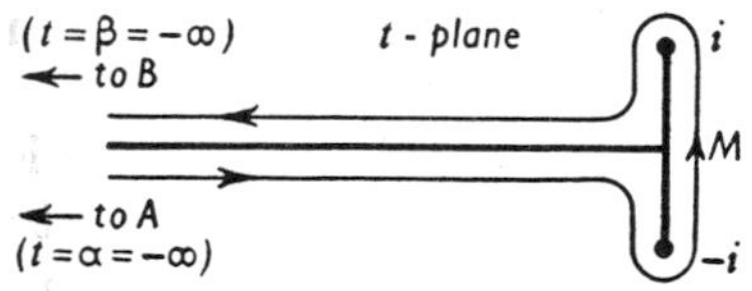

FIG. 16.7

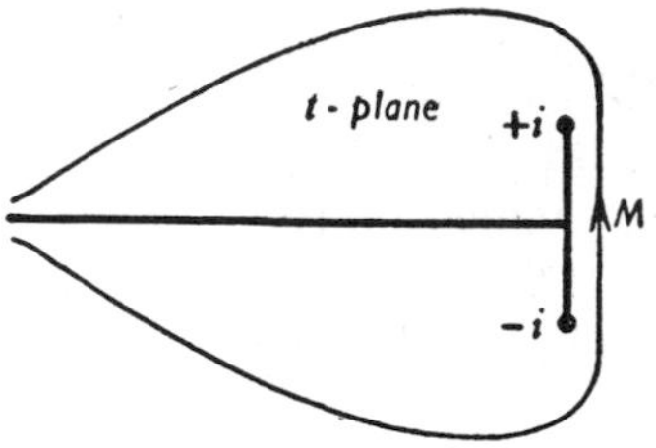

FIG. 16.8

16.53. *Contour integrals for* $J_n(x)$

From the argument of the previous section it follows that the integral 16.52(4), taken along the contour M of Fig. 16.7, is a solution of Bessel's equation. We shall shortly show that it behaves like x^n for small $|x|$, and so is a multiple of $J_n(x)$ as defined in 16.51, and, to anticipate, that the multiplying constant is such that

$$J_n(x) = \frac{1}{2\pi i} \int_M \frac{e^{xt}\,dt}{(1+t^2)^{\frac{1}{2}}[(1+t^2)^{\frac{1}{2}}+t]^n} \tag{1}$$

In contrast to the definition of $J_n(x)$ by series, where negative integers had to be treated as an exceptional case (cf. 16.51) the integral representation can be used for all n.

A number of more easily manageable integrals can be found by changing the variable as follows. First put

$$s = (1+t^2)^{\frac{1}{2}} + t, \text{ then } 1/s = (1+t^2)^{\frac{1}{2}} - t$$

and hence $t = \frac{1}{2}(s - 1/s)$, $(1+t^2)^{\frac{1}{2}} = \frac{1}{2}(s + 1/s)$ and $dt/(1+t^2)^{\frac{1}{2}} = ds/s$ Further, the path of integration M in Fig. 16.7 transforms into an essentially similar path in the s-plane, and we obtain Schläfli's integral for $J_n(x)$, namely,

$$J_n(x) = \frac{1}{2\pi i} \int_M s^{-(n+1)} \exp\left[\tfrac{1}{2}x(s - 1/s)\right] ds \tag{2}$$

A third form can be derived by the substitution $u = \frac{1}{2}xs$ which, for positive x, gives

$$J_n(x) = \frac{1}{2\pi i} \left(\tfrac{1}{2}x\right)^n \int_M u^{-(n+1)} \exp\left(u - x^2/4u\right) du \tag{3}$$

It follows that, for small x, $J_n(x)$ as given by the integral (1) is proportional to x^n; further, from (3)

$$[J_n(x)/(\tfrac{1}{2}x)^n] \to \frac{1}{2\pi i}\int_M u^{-(n+1)} \exp u \, du = \frac{1}{n!} \quad \text{by 16.14 (2)}$$

this completes the identification of the integral on the right-hand side of (1) with the solution $J_n(x)$ of Bessel's equation as defined in 16.51 (n not a negative integer).

If we now restrict n to integral values, the point at infinity is no longer a branch point and the contour M can be allowed to close. Further in formula (2) the integrand is analytic at all points except the origin $s=0$ which is an essential singularity. The contour can therefore be deformed into the unit circle (Fig. 16.9). Putting $s=e^{i\theta}$, the factor $\exp[\tfrac{1}{2}x(s-1/s)]$ in the integrand of (2) becomes $\exp[\tfrac{1}{2}x(e^{i\theta}-e^{-i\theta})]$, that is, $e^{ix\sin\theta}$, so this formula becomes

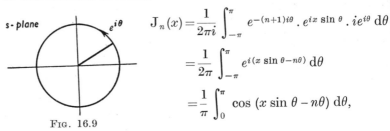

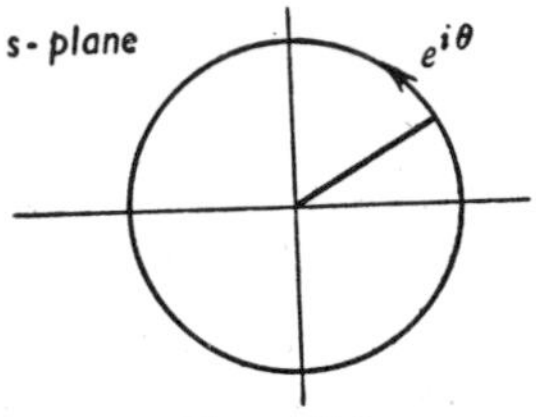

FIG. 16.9

$$J_n(x) = \frac{1}{2\pi i}\int_{-\pi}^{\pi} e^{-(n+1)i\theta} \,.\, e^{ix\sin\theta} \,.\, ie^{i\theta} \, d\theta$$

$$= \frac{1}{2\pi}\int_{-\pi}^{\pi} e^{i(x\sin\theta - n\theta)} \, d\theta$$

$$= \frac{1}{\pi}\int_0^{\pi} \cos(x\sin\theta - n\theta) \, d\theta,$$

which is known as Bessel's integral. (Note:

$$\int_{-\pi}^{\pi} \sin(x\sin\theta - n\theta) \, d\theta = 0$$

because the integrand is an odd function of θ, compare footnote to 14.32). Replacing n by $-n$, we find that

$$J_{-n}(x) = \frac{1}{\pi}\int_0^{\pi} \cos(x\sin\theta + n\theta) \, d\theta$$

In this replace θ by $\pi-\phi$; then

$$J_{-n}(x) = \frac{1}{\pi}\int_0^{\pi} \cos(x\sin\phi - n\phi + n\pi) \, d\phi$$

$$= (-1)^n J_{+n}(x)$$

in agreement with 16.51(6).

16.54. *Generating function*

Again considering only integral values of n we see from formula (2) of 16.53 and Cauchy's residue theorem (13.78) that if the function of two variables $\exp\left[\frac{1}{2}x(s-1/s)\right]$ is expanded in powers of s with coefficients functions of x, then the coefficient of s^n in this expansion is $J_n(x)$, that is

$$\exp\left[\tfrac{1}{2}x(s-1/s)\right]=\sum_{-\infty}^{\infty} J_n(x)s^n$$

The function $\exp\left[\frac{1}{2}x(s-1/s)\right]$ is therefore a generating function for Bessel functions of integral order, analogous to the generating function for the Legendre polynomials (16.34). We have

$$\exp\left[\tfrac{1}{2}x(s-1/s)\right]=1+\frac{x}{2}\left(s-\frac{1}{s}\right)+\ldots+\frac{1}{r!}\left(\frac{x}{2}\right)^r\left(s-\frac{1}{s}\right)^r+\ldots$$

Expanding by the binomial theorem we find

$$\exp\left[\tfrac{1}{2}x(s-1/s)\right]$$

$$=1+\frac{x}{2}\left(s-\frac{1}{s}\right)+\ldots+\frac{1}{r!}\left(\frac{x}{2}\right)^r\sum_{t=0}^{\infty}\frac{r!(-1)^t}{(r-t)!t!}s^{r-2t}+\ldots$$

and putting $r-2t=n$, we obtain as the coefficient of s^n

$$J_n(x)=(\tfrac{1}{2}x)^n\sum_{t=0}^{\infty}\frac{(-1)^t}{(n+t)!t!}(\tfrac{1}{2}x)^{2t}$$

in agreement with 16.51(1).

16.6. The Hankel functions

There are two other paths in the t-plane for which the integral (4) of 16.52 gives important solutions of Bessel's equation. These are the paths S and I shown in Fig. 16.10. Both begin and end at minus infinity, thereby satisfying equation (5) of 16.52; each encloses a branch point of the integrand, $+i$ and $-i$ respectively, and is therefore non-trivial. The

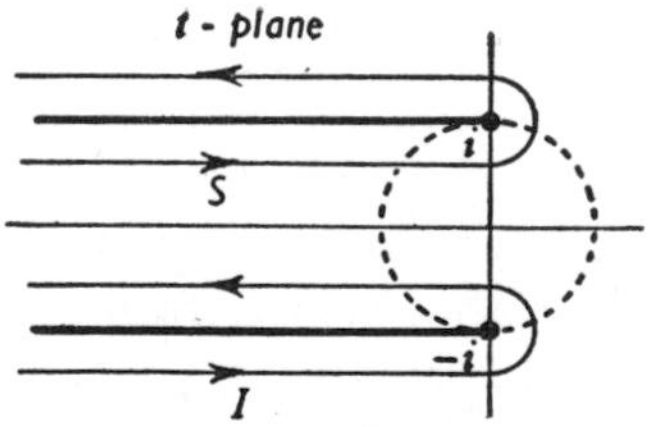

FIG. 16.10

integrals 16.52 (4) along these paths, with a suitable factor, are called the Hankel functions and written $\mathrm{Hs}_n(x)$, $\mathrm{Hi}_n(x)$†

$$\mathrm{Hs}_n(x) = \frac{1}{\pi i}\int_S \frac{e^{xt}\,dt}{(1+t^2)^{\frac{1}{2}}\{t+(1+t^2)^{\frac{1}{2}}\}^n} \tag{1}$$

$$\mathrm{Hi}_n(x) = \frac{1}{\pi i}\int_I \frac{e^{xt}\,dt}{(1+t^2)^{\frac{1}{2}}\{t+(1+t^2)^{\frac{1}{2}}\}^n} \tag{2}$$

The letters s, S and i, I denote the ‘ superior ’ and ‘ inferior ’ paths respectively.

Making the substitution $t = \frac{1}{2}(s - 1/s)$, we obtain integrals of the Schläfli form,

$$\mathrm{Hs}_n(x) = \frac{1}{\pi i}\int_S s^{-(n+1)} \exp\left[\tfrac{1}{2}x(s - 1/s)\right] ds \tag{3}$$

$$\mathrm{Hi}_n(x) = \frac{1}{\pi i}\int_I s^{-(n+1)} \exp\left[\tfrac{1}{2}x(s - 1/s)\right] ds \tag{4}$$

where the paths S and I in the s-plane are as shown in Fig. 16.11 ; each path has one terminus at the origin.

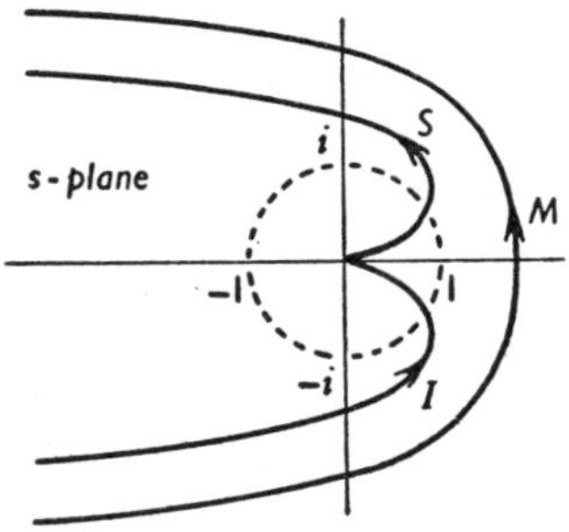

FIG. 16.11

The vanishing of the factor $s^{-(n+1)}$ in the integrand of the integrals (3), (4) does not lead to difficulty provided that the origin, which is an essential singularity of the integrand because of the factor $e^{-x/2s}$, is approached from a suitable direction.

† Other symbols in use are $H_n^{(1)}$, $H_n^{(2)}$. The present notation is due to Jeffreys, *Mathematical Physics*, p. 544.

The paths shown in Fig. 16.11 are appropriate to a positive value of x. Since the contribution to the integral from the neighbourhood of the origin is small, and since the integrand is an analytic function of s at all other points, the paths S and I taken together can be deformed into the curve M, which is effectively the same as the path taken to define $J_n(x)$ (see 16.53). Hence from (1) and (2)

$$\begin{aligned} \mathrm{Hs}_n(x) + \mathrm{Hi}_n(x) &= 2 \cdot \frac{1}{2\pi i} \int_M \frac{e^{xt}\,dt}{(1+t^2)^{\frac{1}{2}}\{t+(1+t^2)^{\frac{1}{2}}\}^n} \\ &= 2J_n(x) \qquad (5) \end{aligned}$$

One consequence of formulae (3) and (4) is that for real values of x the function $\mathrm{Hi}_n(x)$ is the conjugate complex of $\mathrm{Hs}_n(x)$. For let S be a path of integration for $\mathrm{Hs}_n(x)$ and S^* its reflection in the real axis (see Fig. 16.12); then the path S^* described in

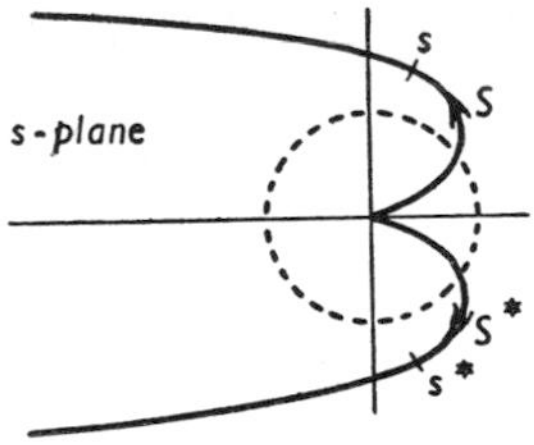

FIG. 16.12

the opposite direction is a path I. Now the result of taking the complex conjugate of equation (3) is

$$[\mathrm{Hs}_n(x)]^* = -\frac{1}{\pi i} \int_{S^*} (s^*)^{-(n+1)} \exp\left[\tfrac{1}{2}x(s^* - 1/s^*)\right] ds^*$$

and since the path I is the path S^* described in the opposite direction, $\int_{S^*} \phi(s^*)\, ds^* = -\int_I \phi(s^*)\, ds^*$. Hence

$$[\mathrm{Hs}_n(x)]^* = +\frac{1}{\pi i} \int_I (s^*)^{-(n+1)} \exp\left[\tfrac{1}{2}x(s^* - 1/s^*)\right] ds^*$$

The right-hand side in this formula is the same as that in formula (4) (but with the variable of integration now written s^*). Hence

$$[\mathrm{Hs}_n(x)]^* = \mathrm{Hi}_n(x) \qquad (6)$$

16.61. *The solution* $Y_n(x)$ *of Bessel's equation*

It follows from the result 16.6 (6), just obtained, that for real x the function $\mathrm{Hs}_n(x)+\mathrm{Hi}_n(x)$ is real, as is already implied by formula 16.6 (5), and that $\mathrm{Hs}_n(x)-\mathrm{Hi}_n(x)$ is pure imaginary. Hence for real x the function

$$Y_n(x)=[\mathrm{Hs}_n(x)-\mathrm{Hi}_n(x)]/2i \tag{1}$$

is real. It can be shown, for example from its behaviour for large x (see 16.71 (3) and (4)) that it is not a constant multiple of $J_n(x)$, hence it is a second solution of Bessel's equation, real for real x. It is sometimes called a ' Bessel function of the second kind '; the Hankel functions, which are complex for real x, are sometimes called ' Bessel functions of the third kind '. For integral values of n, $Y_n(x)$ is usually taken as the standard second solution of Bessel's equation. Any linear combination of $J_n(x)$ and $Y_n(x)$ is a solution of Bessel's equation, and is called a ' cylinder function '.

For non-integral values of n, $J_{-n}(x)$ is also a solution of Bessel's equation and must therefore be a linear combination of $J_n(x)$ and $Y_n(x)$; it can be shown† that this relation is

$$J_{-n}(x)=J_n(x)\cos n\pi-Y_n(x)\sin n\pi \tag{2}$$

16.62. *Orthogonality relation for cylinder functions*

The Bessel-type equation

$$x^2\frac{d^2y}{dx^2}+x\frac{dy}{dx}+(\lambda^2x^2-n^2)y=0 \tag{1}$$

can be put into the form, (called the *self-adjoint* form)

$$\frac{d}{dx}\left(x\frac{dy}{dx}\right)+(\lambda^2x-n^2/x)y=0$$

This equation with a pair of homogeneous boundary conditions such as

$$\left.\begin{aligned}\alpha_1y(a)+\alpha_2y'(a)=0\\ \beta_1y(b)+\beta_2y'(b)=0\end{aligned}\right\} \tag{2}$$

† See, for example G. N. Watson, *Theory of Bessel Functions*, §3.61.

gives a Sturm-Liouville system. Now the general solution of (1) is a cylinder function (see 16.61)

$$y = A\mathrm{J}_n(\lambda x) + B\mathrm{Y}_n(\lambda x) \tag{3}$$

One of the arbitrary constants A, B in (3) is, in effect, a scale factor and it is not in general possible to satisfy the two-point boundary conditions (2). The general discussion of 12.3–12.33 is applicable however, and shows that solutions will be found for certain discrete values of λ, namely the eigenvalues λ_1, λ_2 ... etc.

If λ_r, λ_s are different eigenvalues and y_r and y_s the corresponding eigensolutions, we find as in 12.32

$$(\lambda_r^2 - \lambda_s^2)\int_a^b xy_ry_s\,\mathrm{d}x = \int_a^b \left[y_r\frac{\mathrm{d}}{\mathrm{d}x}\left(x\frac{\mathrm{d}y_s}{\mathrm{d}x}\right) - y_s\frac{\mathrm{d}}{\mathrm{d}x}\left(x\frac{\mathrm{d}y_r}{\mathrm{d}s}\right)\right]\mathrm{d}x$$

$$= x\Big[y_ry_s' - y_sy_r'\Big]_a^b$$

The term on the right vanishes because of the boundary conditions ; since $\lambda_r \neq \lambda_s$ we therefore obtain

$$\int_a^b xy_ry_s\,\mathrm{d}x = 0 \tag{4}$$

The eigenfunctions y_r for any fixed n form a complete set (12.34) and any well-behaved function $\mathrm{f}(x)$ satisfying the same boundary conditions can therefore be expressed, in the range $a<x<b$, as an expansion of the form

$$\mathrm{f}(x) = \sum_r c_ry_r \tag{5}$$

The coefficient c_r can be calculated by multiplying both sides by xy_r and integrating from a to b.

16.7. Recurrence relations

The Bessel functions and their derivatives, like the Legendre functions, satisfy a number of recurrence relations. These are easily deduced from the generating function but the proof then applies to integral values of n only. To establish the relations in the general case, we use the Schläfli integral

$$\mathrm{J}_n(x) = \frac{1}{2\pi i}\int_M s^{-(n+1)}\exp\left[\tfrac{1}{2}x(s - 1/s)\right]\mathrm{d}s \tag{1}$$

integrating by parts we find

$$J_n(x) = \frac{1}{2\pi i}\left[-\frac{1}{ns^n}\exp\{\tfrac{1}{2}x(s-1/s)\}\right]_\alpha^\beta$$

$$+\frac{1}{2\pi i}\frac{x}{2n}\int_M s^{-n}(1+1/s^2)\exp[\tfrac{1}{2}x(s-1/s)]\,ds$$

The first term vanishes at both limits ; and the second can be re-expressed to give the three term recurrence relation

$$(2n/x)J_n(x) = J_{n-1}(x) + J_{n+1}(x) \tag{2}$$

Also differentiating (1) with respect to x we find

$$J'_n(x) = \frac{1}{2\pi i}\int_M \tfrac{1}{2}s^{-(n+1)}(s-1/s)\exp[\tfrac{1}{2}x(s-1/s)]\,ds$$

$$= \tfrac{1}{2}[J_{n-1}(x) - J_{n+1}(x)] \tag{3}$$

Eliminating J_{n-1} and J_{n+1} successively between (2) and (3) we obtain two more relations

$$J'_n(x) = \frac{n}{x}J_n(x) - J_{n+1}(x) \tag{4}$$

and

$$J'_n(x) = J_{n-1}(x) - \frac{n}{x}J_n(x) \tag{5}$$

The functions Hs_n, Hi_n and Y_n can be written as integrals of the same form as (1) differing only in the path of integration. It follows that all these functions satisfy the same recurrence relations.

16.71. *Asymptotic expansions for Bessel functions*

The general behaviour of $J_n(x)$, $Hs_n(x)$ and $Hi_n(x)$ for large values of x is conveniently investigated by the method of steepest descent ; and at the same time a good illustration of that important method is provided.

We start from the Schläfli integral for $Hs_n(x)$ (see 16.6 (3)) namely

$$Hs_n(x) = \frac{1}{\pi i}\int_S s^{-(n+1)}\exp\{\tfrac{1}{2}x(s-1/s)\}\,ds$$

The general behaviour of the function $\exp\{\tfrac{1}{2}x(s-1/s)\}$ for real, positive values of x is shown in Figs. 16.13 and 16.14 (drawn for the particular value $x=2$). Fig. 16.14 shows the behaviour on the real axis. Fig 16.13 shows contours of constant modulus. Put $s = \rho e^{i\phi}$; then on the unit circle $\rho = 1$, the quantity $(s - 1/s)$ is pure imaginary, so the function has modulus unity. In the first quadrant $\cos\phi > 0$ and $(s - 1/s) = (\rho - 1/\rho)\cos\phi + i(\rho + 1/\rho)\sin\phi$, so the

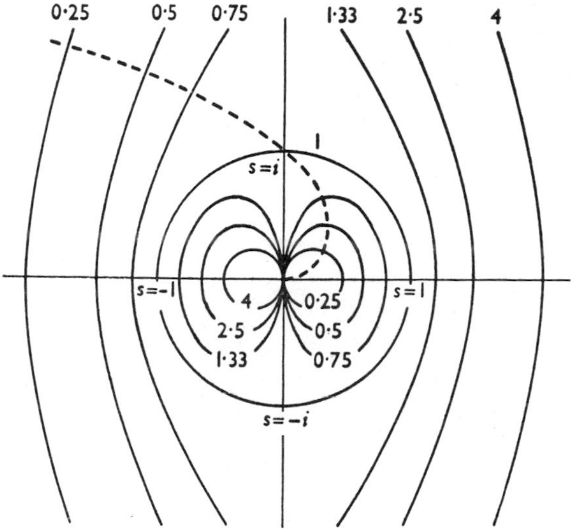

FIG. 16.13

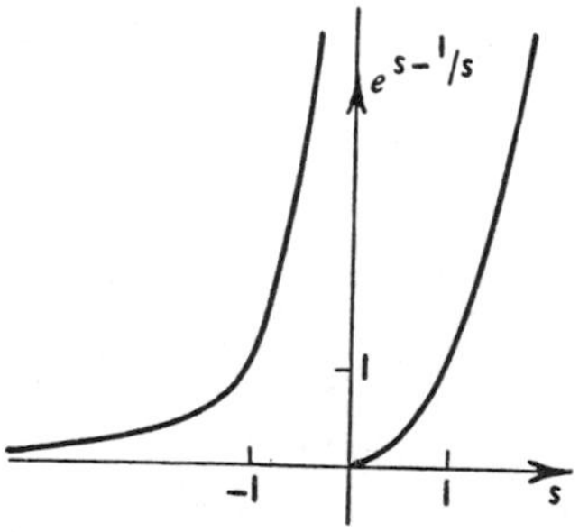

FIG. 16.14

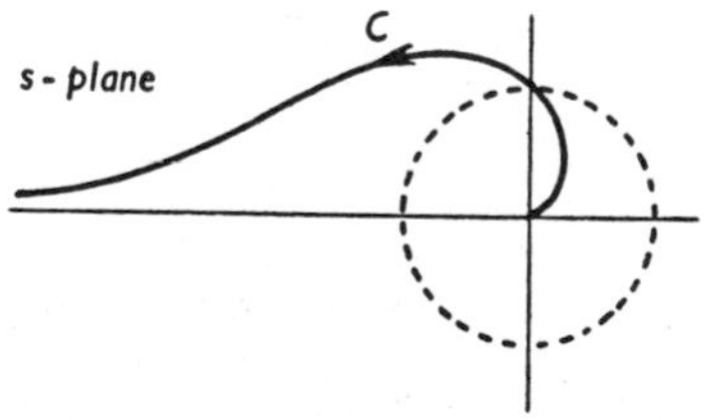

FIG. 16.15

function has modulus $\lessgtr 1$ according as $(\rho - 1/\rho) \lessgtr 0$, i.e. according as s lies inside or outside the unit circle. Similarly in the second quadrant the function has modulus less than one outside the unit circle, and modulus greater than one inside. The surface representing $|\exp\{\frac{1}{2}x(s - 1/s)\}|$ may be pictured as consisting, in the first and second quadrants, of a saddle point at $s = i$, with ridges to the north-east and south-west, and valleys to the north-west and south-east. The integrand $[\exp\{\frac{1}{2}x(s-1/s)\}]/s^{n+1}$ has no singularities in the finite part of the plane except at the origin, so we may choose a contour C of integration for $\mathrm{Hs}_n(x)$ which passes through the saddle point $s=i$ and is directed from south-east to north-west at this point (Fig. 16.15).

At all points on this path, except at $s=i$, the modulus of the integrand can be made as small as desired by taking x sufficiently large, since at all such points $\mathscr{R}(s-1/s)$ is negative. Hence for large x the main contribution to the integral is from the neighbourhood of $s=i$.

Putting $s=i+r\exp(3\pi i/4)$ we have,

$$(s-i)^2=r^2\exp(3\pi i/2)=-ir^2$$

But $(s-i)^2=s^2-2is-1$, so, for $r\ll 1$

$$s-1/s=(s^2-1)/s=(2is-ir^2)/s=2i-r^2+O(r^3) \tag{1}$$

Substitution in the Schläfli integral 16.6 (3) gives

$$\mathrm{Hs}_n(x)\approx\frac{\exp(3\pi i/4)}{\pi i^{n+2}}\int_C \exp\tfrac{1}{2}x(2i-r^2)\,dr$$

$$=(1/\pi)\exp i(x-\tfrac{1}{2}n\pi-\tfrac{1}{4}\pi)\int_C \exp(-\tfrac{1}{2}xr^2)\,dr \tag{2}$$

The approximation (1) is valid only for small r, but since in the integral (2) the integrand is not appreciable for large r we may in fact integrate over the range $(-\infty,\infty)$ and obtain the first term of an asymptotic expansion

$$\mathrm{Hs}_n(x)\sim(2/\pi x)^{\frac{1}{2}}\exp[i(x-\tfrac{1}{2}n\pi-\tfrac{1}{4}\pi)]$$

Taking complex conjugates and using the relation 16.6 (6) we have

$$\mathrm{Hi}_n(x)\sim(2/\pi x)^{\frac{1}{2}}\exp[-i(x-\tfrac{1}{2}n\pi-\tfrac{1}{4}\pi)]$$

and hence, from 16.6 (5) and 16.61 (1),

$$\mathrm{J}_n(x)\sim(2/\pi x)^{\frac{1}{2}}\cos(x-\tfrac{1}{2}n\pi-\tfrac{1}{4}\pi) \tag{3}$$

$$\mathrm{Y}_n(x)\sim(2/\pi x)^{\frac{1}{2}}\sin(x-\tfrac{1}{2}n\pi-\tfrac{1}{4}\pi) \tag{4}$$

Notice as a useful analogy that $\mathrm{Hs}_n(x)$, $\mathrm{Hi}_n(x)$, $\mathrm{J}_n(x)$ and $\mathrm{Y}_n(x)$ are related in the same kind of way as e^{ix}, e^{-ix}, $\cos x$ and $\sin x$.

Further terms of the series can be found by the use of higher order approximations to the integrand in the Schläfli integral

16.6 (3). It is however much more convenient to assume that there is an asymptotic series

$$\mathrm{Hs}_n(x) = \left(\frac{2}{\pi x}\right)^{\frac{1}{2}} \exp\left[i\left(x - \tfrac{1}{2}n\pi - \tfrac{1}{4}\pi\right)\right]\left(1 + \frac{a_1}{x} + \frac{a_2}{x^2} \cdots\right)$$

and to determine the other coefficients directly by substitution in the differential equation. It is found that

$$\mathrm{Hs}_n(x) = (2/\pi x)^{\frac{1}{2}} \exp\left[i(x - \tfrac{1}{2}n\pi - \tfrac{1}{4}\pi)\right]\left[\mathrm{P}(x) - i\mathrm{Q}(x)\right] \qquad (5)$$

where

$$\mathrm{P}(x) \sim \left[1 - \frac{(1^2 - 4n^2)(3^2 - 4n^2)}{2!\,(8x)^2} + \frac{(1^2 - 4n^2)(3^2 - 4n^2)(5^2 - 4n^2)(7^2 - 4n^2)}{4!\,(8x)^4} \cdots\right]$$

$$\mathrm{Q}(x) \sim \frac{1^2 - 4n^2}{8x} - \frac{(1^2 - 4n^2)(3^2 - 4n^2)(5^2 - 4n^2)}{3!\,(8x)^3} + \cdots$$

and, with the same notation,

$$\mathrm{Hi}_n(x) = (2/\pi x)^{\frac{1}{2}} \exp\left[-i(x - \tfrac{1}{2}n\pi - \tfrac{1}{4}\pi)\right]\left[\mathrm{P}(x) + i\mathrm{Q}(x)\right] \qquad (6)$$

$$\mathrm{J}_n(x) = (2/\pi x)^{\frac{1}{2}}\left[\mathrm{P}(x)\cos(x - \tfrac{1}{2}n\pi - \tfrac{1}{4}\pi) - \mathrm{Q}(x)\sin(x - \tfrac{1}{2}n\pi - \tfrac{1}{4}\pi)\right] \qquad (7)$$

$$\mathrm{Y}_n(x) = (2/\pi x)^{\frac{1}{2}}\left[\mathrm{P}(x)\sin(x - \tfrac{1}{2}n\pi - \tfrac{1}{4}\pi) + \mathrm{Q}(x)\cos(x - \tfrac{1}{2}n\pi - \tfrac{1}{4}\pi)\right] \qquad (8)$$

Although the first approximation (2) was obtained on the supposition that x is real and positive, the forms (5)–(8) can be obtained by the substitution of trial series in Bessel's equation. They are therefore asymptotic solutions of Bessel's equation for complex as well as real values of x. However, for real x the identification of these solutions with $\mathrm{Hs}_n(x)$, $\mathrm{Hi}_n(x)$, $\mathrm{J}_n(x)$, $\mathrm{Y}_n(x)$ depended on a contour integral argument about saddle points and steepest descents which cannot be taken over unchanged for complex x. Deeper investigation shows that the asymptotic forms (5)–(8) for $\mathrm{Hs}_n(x)$ etc. are valid provided that $-\pi < \arg x < \pi$.

16.8. The modified Bessel equation

The modified Bessel equation is

$$x^2 \frac{d^2y}{dx^2} + x\frac{dy}{dx} - (x^2 + n^2)y = 0 \qquad (1)$$

This can be derived from Bessel's equation

$$x^2 \frac{d^2y}{dx^2} + x \frac{dy}{dx} + (x^2 - n^2)y = 0$$

by replacing x by ix ; its solutions can therefore be regarded as Bessel functions of a pure imaginary argument.

Series solutions are easily found as in 16.51 for Bessel's equation. For non-integral n, two independent solutions are

$$I_n(x) = (\tfrac{1}{2}x)^n \sum_{r=0}^{\infty} \frac{1}{r!\,(n+r)!} (\tfrac{1}{2}x)^{2r} = i^{-n} J_n(ix) \tag{2}$$

$$I_{-n}(x) = (\tfrac{1}{2}x)^{-n} \sum_{r=0}^{\infty} \frac{1}{r!\,(-n+r)!} (\tfrac{1}{2}x)^{2r} = i^n J_{-n}(ix) \tag{3}$$

For n integral (and positive), $I_n(x)$ as given by (2) is a solution, but as for the (unmodified) Bessel functions, there is not a second solution expressible as a series. The solution $I_n(x)$ increases exponentially for large x ; it is convenient to adopt as a second standard solution one which tends to 0 for large x ; the standard function adopted is that with limiting behaviour $(\pi/2x)^{\frac{1}{2}} e^{-x}$ as $x \to \infty$, and is written $K_n(x)$. The asymptotic expansions of $I_n(x)$ and $K_n(x)$ for large x are

$$I_n(x) \sim e^x/(2\pi x)^{\frac{1}{2}} \left[1 + \frac{1^2 - 4n^2}{1!\,(x)} + \frac{(1^2 - 4n^2)(3^2 - 4n^2)}{2!\,(8x)^2} + \ldots\right]$$

$$K_n(x) \sim (\pi/2x)^{\frac{1}{2}} e^{-x} \left[1 - \frac{1^2 - 4n^2}{1!\,(8x)} + \frac{(1^2 - 4n^2)(3^2 - 4n^2)}{2!\,(8x)^2} - \ldots\right]$$

Tables of these functions, up to $n = 20$ and $x = 20$, and a large number of useful formulae concerning them, are given in the *B.A. Mathematical Tables*, Vols. VI and IX.

16.9. Bessel functions of order (integer $+\frac{1}{2}$)

We have seen in 16.5 how Bessel functions of integral order commonly occur as a result of separation of variables in cylindrical coordinates. Bessel functions, but now of order (integer $+\frac{1}{2}$), also occur as a result of separation of variables in *spherical* polar coordinates in the wave equation in three dimensions, $\nabla^2 u = (1/c^2)\partial^2 u/\partial t^2$. If we consider solutions of this equation which are simple-harmonic in time with frequency $kc/2\pi$, the space variation of u is given by

$$\nabla^2 u = -k^2 u \tag{1}$$

If we try to find a solution of this equation separable in r on the one hand and (θ, ϕ) on the other, $u = \mathrm{R}(r)\mathrm{Y}(\theta, \phi)$, we find that the functions $\mathrm{R}(r)$ and $\mathrm{Y}(\theta, \phi)$ must satisfy the equations

$$\frac{\mathrm{d}^2}{\mathrm{d}r^2}(rR) = -[k^2 - \lambda/r^2](rR) \tag{2}$$

$$\frac{1}{\sin\theta}\frac{\partial}{\partial\theta}\left(\sin\theta\frac{\partial \mathrm{Y}}{\partial\theta}\right) + \frac{\partial^2 \mathrm{Y}}{\partial\phi^2} = -\lambda \mathrm{Y} \tag{3}$$

λ being a separation constant.

The second of these equations is the same as for $k^2 = 0$, and this case has been considered in 16.3 and subsequent sections. It was there shown that equation (3) has solutions, finite and single valued over a complete sphere, only if λ has one of the values $n(n+1)$ where n is integral. Hence if, as is usual, we require such a solution, we can put $\lambda = n(n+1)$ in equation (2), which then becomes

$$\frac{\mathrm{d}^2}{\mathrm{d}r^2}(rR) + \left[k^2 - \frac{n(n+1)}{r^2}\right](rR) = 0 \tag{4}$$

If we now put $rR = r^{\frac{1}{2}}y$, $kr = x$, in (4), it becomes

$$\frac{\mathrm{d}^2 y}{\mathrm{d}x^2} + \frac{1}{x}\frac{\mathrm{d}y}{\mathrm{d}x} + \left[1 - \frac{(n+\frac{1}{2})^2}{x^2}\right]y = 0$$

which is the equation for the Bessel functions of order $\pm(n+\frac{1}{2})$.

Thus the general solution of equation (4) is

$$R = r^{-\frac{1}{2}}[A\mathrm{J}_{n+\frac{1}{2}}(kr) + B\mathrm{Y}_{n+\frac{1}{2}}(kr)]$$

or alternatively

$$R = r^{-\frac{1}{2}}[A\mathrm{J}_{n+\frac{1}{2}}(kr) + B\mathrm{J}_{-(n+\frac{1}{2})}(kr)]$$

The solution which is finite at the origin is $r^{-\frac{1}{2}}\mathrm{J}_{n+\frac{1}{2}}(kr)$. Because of their occurrence in this context, the functions $(\pi/2x)^{\frac{1}{2}}\mathrm{J}_{\pm(n+\frac{1}{2})}(x)$ are termed ‘ spherical Bessel functions ’ of order n ; the function $(\pi/2x)^{\frac{1}{2}}\mathrm{J}_{n+\frac{1}{2}}(x)$ is sometimes written† $\mathrm{j}_n(x)$, (not to be confused with the notation for the r'th zero $j_{n,r}$ of $\mathrm{J}_n(x)$). These functions have been extensively tabulated.‡

For $n = 0$, equation (4) becomes just

† See, for example, Stratton, *Electromagnetic Theory* (McGraw-Hill, 1941), §7.4.

‡ *Tables of Spherical Bessel Functions* (Columbia University Press, New York, 1947).

$$\frac{d^2}{dr^2}(rR) + k^2(rR) = 0$$

so that $R = (\sin kr)/kr$ and $R = (\cos kr)/kr$ are two solutions. The corresponding Bessel functions of order $\pm\frac{1}{2}$ are $(2/\pi x)^{\frac{1}{2}}$ $\sin x$ and $(2/\pi x)^{\frac{1}{2}} \cos x$ respectively, and the spherical Bessel function $j_0(x)$ is $(\sin x)/x$. From these results and the recurrence relations for the Bessel functions (16.61), it follows that all the Bessel functions of order $(n+\frac{1}{2})$ (n integral) can be expressed in terms of elementary functions ; for example

$$J_{3/2}(x) = \left(\frac{2}{\pi x}\right)^{\frac{1}{2}} \left(\frac{\sin x}{x} - \cos x\right)$$

$$J_{5/2}(x) = \left(\frac{2}{\pi x}\right)^{\frac{1}{2}} \left[\frac{3 - x^2}{x^2} \sin x - \frac{3}{x} \cos x\right]$$

the corresponding spherical Bessel functions are

$$j_1(x) = (\sin x - x \cos x)/x^2$$

$$j_2(x) = [3(\sin x - x \cos x) - x^2 \sin x]/x^3$$

CHAPTER SEVENTEEN

VECTOR ALGEBRA AND ANALYSIS

17.1. Introduction

Many physical quantities, for example temperature, volume, potential, are conveniently specified by numbers. Any such number needs to be supplemented by information about the units and often also about the zero of the scale of measurement before it can be interpreted or correctly inserted in formulae. The number, in short, embodies important but partial information about the physical quantity to which it refers.

Vectors are entities, analogous to numbers, which embody important but still only partial information about physical quantities such as forces, displacements, electric fields and so on. In elementary three-dimensional applications the advantage of using vectors can be ascribed to the fact that, by definition, a vector carries information about the direction as well as the magnitude of the physical quantity to which it refers. A vector representation gives no information about the point of application of a force or the initial point of a displacement, so information of this kind as well as a knowledge of the units used is necessary to supplement the specification of a force or a displacement by a vector : on the other hand the angular velocity of a rigid body is not associated with a particular 'point of application' or line of action, and the specification of an angular velocity by a vector together with a statement of the units used is complete in the same degree that the specification of a volume by a number and statement of units is complete. To distinguish them from vector entities, quantities of the latter kind, independent of direction, are called scalars.

The laws of vector algebra are defined so that 'addition' corresponds to the law of composition of two forces or of two displacements (it is an experimental observation that the same law covers both cases), 'multiplication' corresponds to the rule for finding the moment of a force or the work done by a force (here two different definitions are needed to cover the two cases), and so on.

Most of the properties of three-dimensional vectors have natural analogues in the four-dimensional space of relativity, but the concept of ' direction ' has no direct physical interpretation, and the two definitions of products of vectors may well be allowed to drop out of the picture, the notions of tensor calculus being introduced in their stead. The uses of tensor calculus are not, of course, restricted to relativity : they are equally applicable and equally important in three-dimensional work, notably the theory of elasticity.

Finally the algebraic laws for handling vectors may be used formally for vectors in n-dimensions or even an infinite number of dimensions. The ' vectors ' in these cases have no longer any pictorial correspondence with the physical quantities they may represent, but are an algebraic device for writing out calculations involving n variables at a time, when there is an element of choice as to which set of n variables will be used to specify the physical (or mathematical) situation. This use of vectors occurs in connection with matrices and in quantum mechanics.

17.2. Definition and graphical representation of a vector

A vector is defined by its magnitude and its direction : we use the word direction to connote not only orientation but also sense. Thus two entities which are equal in magnitude and parallel in direction would be specified by the same vector ; in particular any two straight lines which are parallel and equal correspond to one and the same vector. Hence the two straight lines AB and CD in Fig. 17.1 are vectorially indistinguishable : we may label either impartially by the vector symbol $\mathbf{a}$; and either may be regarded as the graphical representation of $\mathbf{a}$.

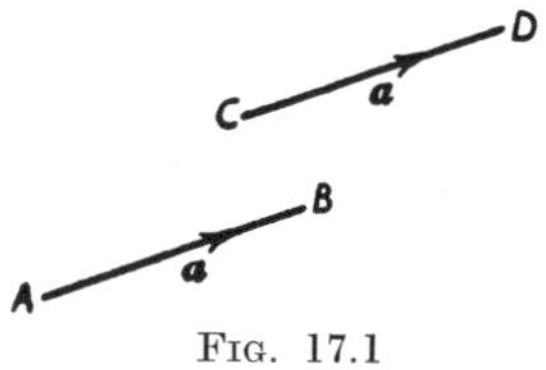

FIG. 17.1

If k is a positive constant, $k\mathbf{a}$ denotes a vector parallel to $\mathbf{a}$ and of magnitude k times that of $\mathbf{a}$. A negative sign denotes a reversal of the sense of the vector ; thus $-\mathbf{a}$ is a vector equal in magnitude to $\mathbf{a}$ but with the opposite direction.

Although the above description defines the entity ' a vector ', the term vector is normally used only when the individual entities can be combined according to the rules which are set out in the following paragraphs.

17.21. *Addition and subtraction of vectors*

For many of the purposes of mechanics the two forces represented by the line segments $\overrightarrow{PQ}$ and $\overrightarrow{PS}$ in Fig. 17.2 can be regarded as equivalent to the single force represented by $\overrightarrow{PR}$. It is customary to say that the latter force is the 'sum' of the two former forces. To reflect this property in the algebra of vectors we define the sum of two vectors **a** and **b** by the parallelogram rule of composition. Owing to the fact that if $\overrightarrow{PS}$ represents the vector **b** so also does $\overrightarrow{QR}$, the parallelogram rule $\overrightarrow{PQ}+\overrightarrow{PS}=\overrightarrow{PR}$ and the triangle rule $\overrightarrow{PQ}+\overrightarrow{QR}=\overrightarrow{PR}$ are two equivalent graphical expressions of the rule of addition of vectors $\mathbf{a}+\mathbf{b}=\mathbf{c}$.

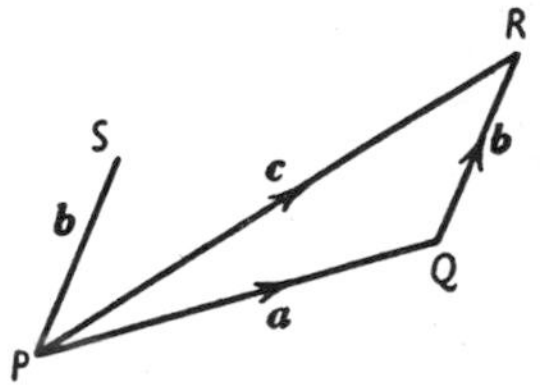

FIG. 17.2

Subtraction : from the triangle description it is clear that $\mathbf{a}+(-\mathbf{a})=0$; no inconsistency arises if we write $-\mathbf{a}$ instead of $+(-\mathbf{a})$, and we proceed to define subtraction by the equation

$$\mathbf{a}-\mathbf{b}=\mathbf{a}+(-\mathbf{b})$$

17.22. *Basic laws of vector algebra*

The following formal laws are direct consequences of the triangle law of addition :

$$\mathbf{a}+\mathbf{b}=\mathbf{b}+\mathbf{a}$$

$$k(\mathbf{a}+\mathbf{b})=k\mathbf{a}+k\mathbf{b}$$

$$k(l\mathbf{a})=kl\mathbf{a}$$

$$(k+l)\mathbf{a}=k\mathbf{a}+l\mathbf{a}$$

where **a**, **b** are vectors, and k, l are scalars. These laws, together with the definition of subtraction previously given, are sufficient to establish that all the processes of ordinary algebra which involve only repeated additions and subtractions in any order can be applied without alteration to vector algebra.

The following conventions of notation are also worth noting: the magnitude of a vector denoted by a single symbol such as $\mathbf{a}$ is usually represented by the corresponding italic letter a; the modulus notation $|\mathbf{a}|$ can also be used, thus $|\mathbf{a}|=a$. For the magnitude of a vector denoted by a combination of symbols e.g. $\mathbf{a}+\mathbf{b}$ the modulus notation $|\mathbf{a}+\mathbf{b}|$ must be used (unless we introduce the auxiliary vector $\mathbf{c}=\mathbf{a}+\mathbf{b}$ say, in which case the magnitude of $\mathbf{a}+\mathbf{b}$ is c). We note that in general $|\mathbf{a}+\mathbf{b}|$ is *not* equal to $a+b$.

The reader should also know that in manuscript and typescript, as opposed to printing, vectors are distinguished by underlining; thus the printed symbol $\mathbf{a}$ would appear in manuscript as $\underline{a}$.

17.23. *Unit vectors*

The following simple theorems are of considerable importance.
(1*a*) If $\mathbf{i}$ is a unit vector, that is, a vector whose magnitude is unity, any vector $\mathbf{v}$ parallel to $\mathbf{i}$ is expressible as a multiple of $\mathbf{i}$. For, if the magnitude of $\mathbf{v}$ is v, $v\mathbf{i}$ is equal to $\mathbf{v}$ in magnitude and direction.
(1*b*) If $\mathbf{a}$ and $\mathbf{b}$ are two non-zero vectors and $k_1\mathbf{a}=k_2\mathbf{b}$, then, either $\mathbf{a}$ is parallel to $\mathbf{b}$, or $k_1=k_2=0$. For, if $k_1\neq 0$, $k_1\mathbf{a}$ is a non-zero vector parallel to $\mathbf{a}$, i.e. $k_2\mathbf{b}$ is a non-zero vector parallel to $\mathbf{a}$. Since the magnitude of $k_2\mathbf{b}$ is not zero, $k_2\neq 0$, so $k_2\mathbf{b}$ must also be a vector parallel to $\mathbf{b}$; therefore $\mathbf{a}$ is parallel to $\mathbf{b}$.

If $\mathbf{a}$ is not parallel to $\mathbf{b}$ the premise $k_1\neq 0$ cannot hold, i.e. if $\mathbf{a}$ is not parallel to $\mathbf{b}$, then $k_1=0$, and consequently also $k_2=0$.

As a particular case of (1*b*) we note that if $\mathbf{i}_1$ and $\mathbf{i}_2$ are two unit vectors and $k_1\mathbf{i}_1=k_2\mathbf{i}_2$, then either $k_1=k_2=0$ or $k_1=\pm k_2$ and $\mathbf{i}_1=\pm\mathbf{i}_2$.

Definition. Any three vectors which *can* be represented by three lines in the same plane are said to be coplanar. The most obvious plane representation of three coplanar vectors is one in which the three lines all start from the same point.

Let $\mathbf{i}_1$ and $\mathbf{i}_2$ be any two non-parallel unit vectors. Then,
(2*a*) Any vector $\mathbf{v}$ coplanar with $\mathbf{i}_1$ and $\mathbf{i}_2$ can be expressed in the form $k_1\mathbf{i}_1+k_2\mathbf{i}_2$ (see Fig. 17.3).
(2*b*) If $\mathbf{v}=k_1\mathbf{i}_1+k_2\mathbf{i}_2$ and either k_1 or k_2 is non-zero, then $\mathbf{v}$ is coplanar with $\mathbf{i}_1$ and $\mathbf{i}_2$. Hence, if $k_1\mathbf{i}_1+k_2\mathbf{i}_2=k_3\mathbf{i}_3$, then either $\mathbf{i}_1$, $\mathbf{i}_2$ and $\mathbf{i}_3$ are coplanar or $k_1=k_2=k_3=0$.

(3*a*) Let $\mathbf{i}_1$, $\mathbf{i}_2$, $\mathbf{i}_3$ be any three non-coplanar unit vectors. Then any vector $\mathbf{v}$ can be expressed in the form $\mathbf{v}=k_1\mathbf{i}_1+k_2\mathbf{i}_2+k_3\mathbf{i}_3$ (cf. Fig. 17.4). The vectors $k_1\mathbf{i}_1$, $k_2\mathbf{i}_2$, $k_3\mathbf{i}_3$, or more loosely, the numbers k_1, k_2, k_3, are called the components of the vector $\mathbf{v}$ relative to oblique axes through O parallel to $\mathbf{i}_1$, $\mathbf{i}_2$, $\mathbf{i}_3$.

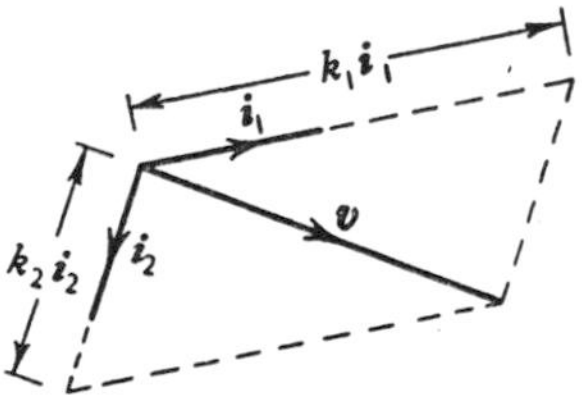

FIG. 17.3

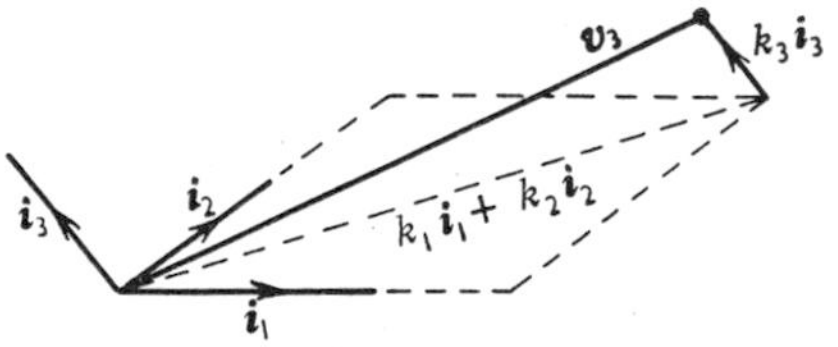

FIG. 17.4

(3*b*) The resolution of any vector $\mathbf{v}$ into three components parallel to $\mathbf{i}_1$, $\mathbf{i}_2$, $\mathbf{i}_3$, is unique. For, suppose

$$\mathbf{v}=k_1\mathbf{i}_1+k_2\mathbf{i}_2+k_3\mathbf{i}_3=l_1\mathbf{i}_1+l_2\mathbf{i}_2+l_3\mathbf{i}_3$$

hence

$$(k_1-l_1)\mathbf{i}_1+(k_2-l_2)\mathbf{i}_2=(l_3-k_3)\mathbf{i}_3$$

But $\mathbf{i}_1$, $\mathbf{i}_2$, $\mathbf{i}_3$ are not coplanar, so, by (2*b*), $k_1-l_1=0$, $k_2-l_2=0$ and $l_3-k_3=0$, i.e. $k_1=l_1$, $k_2=l_2$, $k_3=l_3$, i.e., only one resolution is possible.

When rectangular cartesian axes are used it is conventional to denote the three unit vectors parallel to the x, y, z directions respectively by the symbols $\mathbf{i}$, $\mathbf{j}$, $\mathbf{k}$. We shall sometimes also use $\mathbf{I}$, $\mathbf{J}$ to stand for two perpendicular unit vectors which are not necessarily parallel to fixed cartesian axes.

17.3. Differentiation of a vector function of a scalar variable

Quantities like force, velocity etc. are often functions of time : if vectors are to serve us in the description of these time variable quantities, we must admit the concept of variable vectors into our scheme of vector algebra, and the idea of differentiation. In what follows the vector $\mathbf{v}$ will be a function of t where t is a scalar variable, commonly, but not necessarily, the time. The variation of $\mathbf{v}$ may be an alteration of its magnitude, an alteration of its direction, or both.

The formation of the quantity

$$[\mathbf{v}(t+\delta t)-\mathbf{v}(t)]/\delta t$$

requires only a subtraction of two vectors, followed by a multiplication by the scalar quantity $1/\delta t$. Since the expression can be evaluated for a sequence of decreasing values of δt there is no obstacle to defining the derivative of $\mathbf{v}$ as the limit

$$\frac{d\mathbf{v}}{dt} = \lim_{\delta t \to 0} \frac{\mathbf{v}(t+\delta t) - \mathbf{v}(t)}{\delta t}$$

From this definition, together with the algebraic laws, certain of the laws of differentiation of composite functions follow as for scalar variables. Thus

$$\frac{d}{dt}(\mathbf{v}_1 + \mathbf{v}_2) = \frac{d\mathbf{v}_1}{dt} + \frac{d\mathbf{v}_2}{dt}$$

$$\frac{d}{dt}(k\mathbf{v}) = \frac{dk}{dt}\mathbf{v} + k\frac{d}{dt}\mathbf{v}$$

$\frac{d\mathbf{v}}{dt} = 0$ if and only if $\mathbf{v} =$ constant with respect to variations of t.

17.31. *Graphical representation of the derivative of a vector*

The two vectors $\mathbf{v}(t+\delta t)$ and $\mathbf{v}(t)$ may be represented by two straight lines $\overrightarrow{OQ}$, $\overrightarrow{OP}$ starting at any chosen origin O (Fig. 17.5): the difference $\mathbf{v}(t+\delta t) - \mathbf{v}(t)$ is then represented by $\overrightarrow{PQ}$. Now if as $\delta t \to 0$, Q approaches P steadily along some arc QP, of length δs say, the vector represented by $\overrightarrow{PQ}$ is almost equal to δs in magnitude, and in direction is nearly parallel to the tangent at P: thus if $\mathbf{i}_T$ is unit vector parallel to the tangent at P to the curve traced out by Q,

$$\mathbf{v}(t+\delta t) - \mathbf{v}(t) = \delta s\, \mathbf{i}_T + O(\delta s^2)$$

and

$$\frac{d\mathbf{v}}{dt} = \lim_{\delta t \to 0} \frac{\mathbf{v}(t+\delta t) - \mathbf{v}(t)}{\delta t} = \lim_{\delta t \to 0} \frac{\delta s\, \mathbf{i}_T}{\delta t}$$

$$= \frac{ds}{dt}\mathbf{i}_T \qquad (1)$$

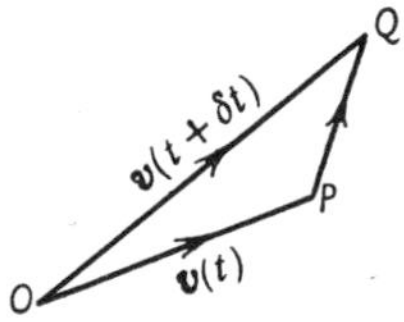

FIG. 17.5

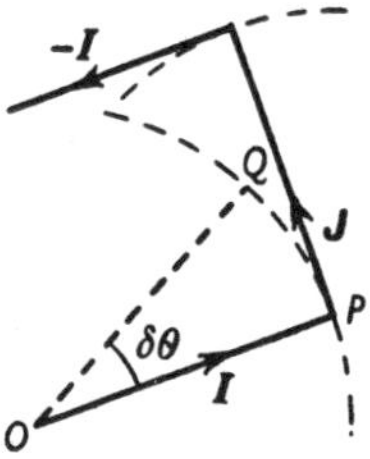

FIG. 17.6

A particularly useful case of this result occurs when the vector **v** is itself a unit vector, i.e. of constant (unit) magnitude but variable direction in a plane, $\mathbf{v}=\mathbf{I}$ say. In this case the arc PQ is part of a circle of unit radius, so $\delta s=\delta\theta$ where $\angle POQ=\delta\theta$; and the tangent at P is perpendicular to OP. Thus

$$\frac{\mathrm{d}\mathbf{I}}{\mathrm{d}t}=\frac{\mathrm{d}\theta}{\mathrm{d}t}\,.\,\mathbf{J}=\dot{\theta}\mathbf{J} \tag{2}$$

where **J** is unit vector perpendicular to **I** as shown in Fig. 17.6. Note that to turn from the positive direction of **I** into the positive direction of **J** requires a rotation of $\frac{1}{2}\pi$ in the direction of θ increasing, that is, in the same sense as a positive increment $\delta\theta$.

The same argument as that which led to (2) shows that

$$\frac{\mathrm{d}\mathbf{J}}{\mathrm{d}t}=\dot{\theta}\mathbf{I}'=-\dot{\theta}\mathbf{I} \tag{3}$$

where $\mathbf{I}'=-\mathbf{I}$ is unit vector in a direction $\frac{1}{2}\pi$ in advance of **J**.

17.32. *Applications in dynamics*

If O is a fixed point and P a moving point, and if the displacement OP is represented by the vector **r**, then, by definition, the velocity of point P is $\dfrac{\mathrm{d}\mathbf{r}}{\mathrm{d}t}$, and its acceleration is $\dfrac{\mathrm{d}^2\mathbf{r}}{\mathrm{d}t^2}$

In rectangular cartesian coordinates

$$\mathbf{r}=x\mathbf{i}+y\mathbf{j}+z\mathbf{k}$$

$$\frac{\mathrm{d}\mathbf{r}}{\mathrm{d}t}=\dot{x}\mathbf{i}+\dot{y}\mathbf{j}+\dot{z}\mathbf{k}$$

since **i**, **j** and **k** are *fixed* vectors, and similarly

$$\frac{\mathrm{d}^2\mathbf{r}}{\mathrm{d}t^2}=\ddot{x}\mathbf{i}+\ddot{y}\mathbf{j}+\ddot{z}\mathbf{k}$$

i.e. the components of velocity are $(\dot{x}, \dot{y}, \dot{z})$ and the components of acceleration are $(\ddot{x}, \ddot{y}, \ddot{z})$. (Dots denote differentiation with respect to time, thus $\ddot{x}=\mathrm{d}^2x/\mathrm{d}t^2$.)

In polar coordinates in two dimensions

$$\mathbf{r}=r\mathbf{I}$$

where r is the magnitude of $\mathbf{r}$ and $\mathbf{I}$ is unit vector in the radial direction (Fig. 17.7).

$$\frac{\mathrm{d}\mathbf{r}}{\mathrm{d}t}=\dot{r}\mathbf{I}+r\frac{\mathrm{d}\mathbf{I}}{\mathrm{d}t}$$

$$=\dot{r}\mathbf{I}+r\dot{\theta}\mathbf{J}$$

where $\mathbf{J}$ is unit vector in the transverse direction, i.e. perpendicular to $\mathbf{I}$ and $\frac{1}{2}\pi$ in advance of $\mathbf{I}$ in the sense of θ increasing.

$$\frac{\mathrm{d}^2\mathbf{r}}{\mathrm{d}t^2}=\ddot{r}\mathbf{I}+\dot{r}\frac{\mathrm{d}\mathbf{I}}{\mathrm{d}t}+(\dot{r}\dot{\theta}+r\ddot{\theta})\mathbf{J}+r\dot{\theta}\frac{\mathrm{d}\mathbf{J}}{\mathrm{d}t}$$

$$=\ddot{r}\mathbf{I}+\dot{r}\dot{\theta}\mathbf{J}+(\dot{r}\dot{\theta}+r\ddot{\theta})\mathbf{J}+r\dot{\theta}(-\dot{\theta}\mathbf{I})$$

$$=(\ddot{r}-r\dot{\theta}^2)\mathbf{I}+(2\dot{r}\dot{\theta}+r\ddot{\theta})\mathbf{J}$$

i.e. the radial and transverse components of velocity are $(\dot{r},\ r\dot{\theta})$, and those of acceleration are $(\ddot{r}-r\dot{\theta}^2,\ 2\dot{r}\dot{\theta}+r\ddot{\theta})$.

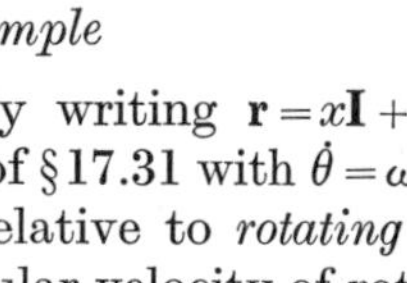

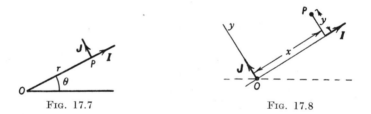

FIG. 17.7

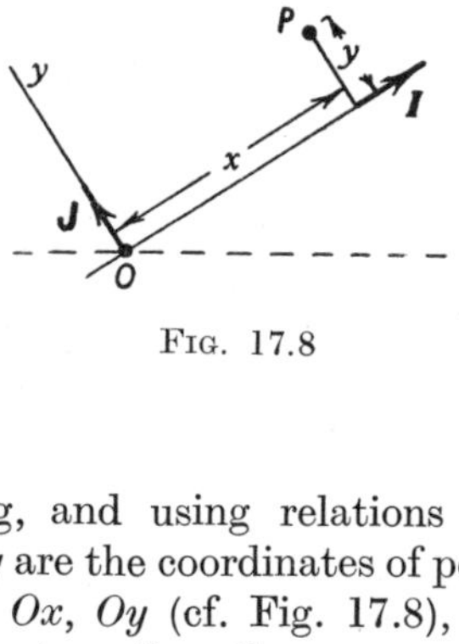

FIG. 17.8

Example

By writing $\mathbf{r}=x\mathbf{I}+y\mathbf{J}$, differentiating, and using relations (2), (3) of §17.31 with $\dot{\theta}=\omega$, prove that if x, y are the coordinates of point P relative to *rotating* rectangular axes Ox, Oy (cf. Fig. 17.8), the angular velocity of rotation being constant, ω, then the components of velocity in the instantaneous directions of the Ox, Oy axes are $(\dot{x}-\omega y,\ \dot{y}+\omega x)$ and of acceleration $(\ddot{x}-2\omega\dot{y}-\omega^2 x,\ \ddot{y}+2\omega\dot{x}-\omega^2 y)$.

For motion under no forces the acceleration components will be zero, so that $\ddot{x}=\omega^2 x+2\omega\dot{y}$ and $\ddot{y}=\omega^2 y-2\omega\dot{x}$. Just as the terms $\omega^2 x$, $\omega^2 y$ are attributed to a fictitious 'centrifugal force' (per unit mass), so the terms $2\omega\dot{y}$, $-2\omega\dot{x}$ can be regarded as components of a fictitious force (per unit mass) known as the 'Coriolis force'.

17.4. Scalar and vector products

17.41. *Definitions*

The scalar product of two vectors is defined in such a way that the scalar product of a vector **P** representing a constant force and a vector **r** representing a displacement of the point of application of the force, is equal to the work done by the force, (Fig. 17.9). The scalar product is written **P** . **r**.

$$\text{Thus } \mathbf{P} . \mathbf{r} = Pr \cos \theta$$

where θ is the angle between the positive directions of the vectors **r** and **P**.

Similarly for any two vectors **a** and **b**. The scalar product **a** . **b** is defined by

$$\mathbf{a} . \mathbf{b} = ab \cos \theta$$

where a, b are the magnitudes of **a**, **b** and θ is the angle between them.

It follows directly from the definition that **b** . **a** = **a** . **b** and (k**a**) . **b** = k(**a** . **b**).

Vector product : The vector product of two vectors is defined in such a way that if **r** represents the displacement from a chosen point O to a point on the line of action of a force **P**, then the vector product of **r** and **P** represents the moment of **P** about an axis through O perpendicular to the plane of **r** and **P** (Fig. 17.10).

The magnitude of the vector product $\mathbf{r} \wedge \mathbf{P}$ (read **r** cross **P**) is thus $rP \sin \theta$ where θ is the angle measured from the positive direction of **r** to that of **P**. It will be noted, however, that as well as the magnitude of the moment, the direction of its axis

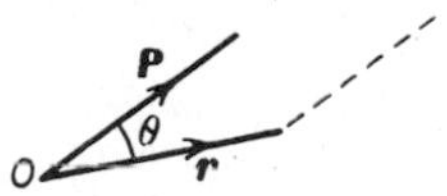

FIG. 17.9

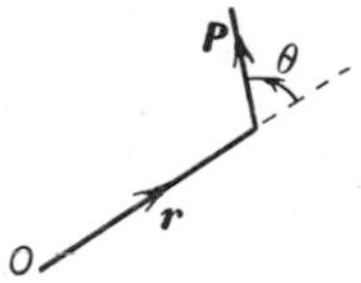

FIG. 17.10

in space is of physical interest. The scalar magnitude $rP \sin \theta$ would therefore be a less adequate representation than the vector quantity which is actually specified for the definition of a vector product, namely

$$\mathbf{r} \wedge \mathbf{P} = rP \sin \theta \mathbf{I}_n$$

where $\mathbf{I}_n$ is unit vector perpendicular to the plane of $\mathbf{r}$ and $\mathbf{P}$ and in the sense determined by a right-handed screw motion when the rotation of the screw is in the direction of θ increasing.

Similarly for any two vectors $\mathbf{a}$, $\mathbf{b}$ (Fig. 17.11)

$$\mathbf{a} \wedge \mathbf{b} = ab \sin \theta \mathbf{I}_n$$

We notice that if it is required to evaluate $\mathbf{b} \wedge \mathbf{a}$, the angle must be measured from $\mathbf{b}$ to $\mathbf{a}$. We can either redefine the positive direction as in Fig. 17.12, so that

$$\begin{aligned} \mathbf{b} \wedge \mathbf{a} &= ba \sin \theta \mathbf{I}_n' \text{ where } \mathbf{I}_n' = -\mathbf{I}_n \\ &= -ab \sin \theta \mathbf{I}_n \end{aligned}$$

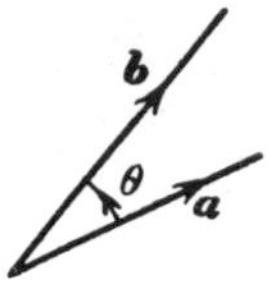

Fig. 17.11

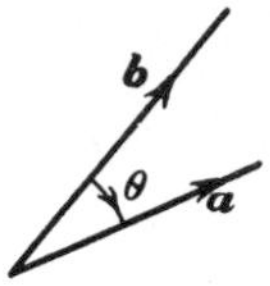

Fig. 17.12

Or, we may retain the original definition of the direction of θ increasing (Fig. 17.11) and note that the angle measured from the positive direction of $\mathbf{b}$ to the positive direction of $\mathbf{a}$ is $2\pi - \theta$, whence

$$\begin{aligned} \mathbf{b} \wedge \mathbf{a} &= ba \sin (2\pi - \theta) \mathbf{I}_n \\ &= -ab \sin \theta \mathbf{I}_n \quad \text{as before} \end{aligned}$$

In either case we have established that

$$\mathbf{b} \wedge \mathbf{a} = -\mathbf{a} \wedge \mathbf{b}$$

It also follows directly from the definition that $(k\mathbf{a}) \wedge \mathbf{b} = k(\mathbf{a} \wedge \mathbf{b})$. Other notations in use for the vector product $\mathbf{a} \wedge \mathbf{b}$ are $\mathbf{a} \times \mathbf{b}$ and $[\mathbf{a}\,\mathbf{b}]$.

17.42. *Scalar and vector products in terms of components*

The elegance and economy of vector methods are primarily due to the freedom of the notation (and the concepts) from reference to particular coordinate systems. We are, nevertheless, virtually compelled to discuss the expression of vector functions in terms of components both because such expression often simplifies the translation of physical results into or out of the vector notation, and because it simplifies the derivation and checking of formulae (e.g. those of 17.44).

First consider components in the common plane of two vectors **a** and **b**. Let us specify two perpendicular directions OX, OY with unit vectors **I**, **J**. We use capital **I**, **J** etc. to indicate that the axes are not necessarily fixed cartesian axes, but may refer to radial and transverse or any other pair of orthogonal directions.

Let **a** make angle θ_1 with OX, and put $a \cos \theta_1 = a_x$, $a \sin \theta_1 = a_y$: and let **b** make angle θ_2 with OX, putting $b \cos \theta_2 = b_x$, $b \sin \theta_2 = b_y$.

Then
$$\begin{aligned}\mathbf{a} \cdot \mathbf{b} &= ab \cos(\theta_2 - \theta_1)\\ &= ab(\cos\theta_2 \cos\theta_1 + \sin\theta_2 \sin\theta_1)\\ &= a_x b_x + a_y b_y \qquad (1)\\ \mathbf{a} \wedge \mathbf{b} &= ab \sin(\theta_2 - \theta_1)\mathbf{I}_n\\ &= ab(\sin\theta_2 \cos\theta_1 - \cos\theta_2 \sin\theta_1)\mathbf{I}_n\\ &= (a_x b_y - a_y b_x)\mathbf{I}_n \qquad (2)\end{aligned}$$

which may also be written $(a_x b_y - a_y b_x)\mathbf{K}$ where **K** is unit vector parallel to the direction OZ which makes a right-handed set of mutually perpendicular axes with OX, OY.

We note that $ab \sin(\theta_2 - \theta_1)$ is equal to the area of the parallelogram with sides **a**, **b** and that $\mathbf{I}_n$ is unit vector in the direction of the normal to the parallelogram. The product $\mathbf{a} \wedge \mathbf{b}$ can be regarded as a vector representation of the area.

Example 1

a has cartesian components (3, 4)

b ,, ,, ,, (2, −1)

then $\mathbf{a} \cdot \mathbf{b} = 3 \times 2 + 4 \times (-1) = 6 - 4 = 2$

$\mathbf{a} \wedge \mathbf{b} = [3 \times (-1) - 4 \times 2]\mathbf{k} = (-3 - 8)\mathbf{k} = -11\mathbf{k}$.

Example 2

The angular momentum of a mass m whose position relative to the fixed point O is specified by the vector **r** and whose velocity is **v** is defined $= m\mathbf{r} \wedge \mathbf{v}$. Express the angular momentum in terms of (i) rectangular cartesian (ii) polar coordinates and their derivatives.

(i) the components of **r** are (x, y)

of **v** are $(\dot{x}, \dot{y})$

hence angular momentum $m\mathbf{r} \wedge \mathbf{v} = m(x\dot{y} - y\dot{x})\mathbf{k}$

(ii) the components in the r and θ directions of **r** are $(r, 0)$

of **v** are $(\dot{r}, r\dot{\theta})$

hence angular momentum $= mr^2\dot{\theta}\mathbf{K}$

Now proceeding to the general, three-dimensional case, if **a** has direction cosines l_1, m_1, n_1 relative to three mutually perpendicular directions OX, OY, OZ, and if **b** has direction cosines l_2, m_2, n_2, we put

$$al_1 = a_x\,; \quad am_1 = a_y\,; \quad an_1 = a_z$$

$$bl_2 = b_x\,; \quad bm_2 = b_y\,; \quad bn_2 = b_z$$

If θ is the angle between the directions of **a** and **b**,

$$\cos\theta = l_1 l_2 + m_1 m_2 + n_1 n_2,$$

$$\mathbf{a}\,.\,\mathbf{b} = ab\,(l_1 l_2 + m_1 m_2 + n_1 n_2)$$

$$= a_x b_x + a_y b_y + a_z b_z \tag{3}$$

In particular

$$\mathbf{a}\,.\,\mathbf{I} = a_x\,; \quad \mathbf{a}\,.\,\mathbf{J} = a_y\,; \quad \mathbf{a}\,.\,\mathbf{K} = a_z$$

We also note that $a^2 = \mathbf{a}\,.\,\mathbf{a} = a^2(l_1^2 + m_1^2 + n_1^2) = a_x^2 + a_y^2 + a_z^2$ or, since a is by definition the (positive) magnitude of the vector, $a = \surd(a_x^2 + a_y^2 + a_z^2)$; similarly $b = \surd(b_x^2 + b_y^2 + b_z^2)$.

For the general expression of the vector product in terms of the components in any orthogonal axis system OX, OY, OZ, unit vectors **I**, **J**, **K**, we shall show that

$$\mathbf{a} \wedge \mathbf{b} = (a_y b_z - a_z b_y)\mathbf{I} + (a_z b_x - a_x b_z)\mathbf{J} + (a_x b_y - a_y b_x)\mathbf{K} \tag{4}$$

Denoting the right-hand side by the vector symbol **v** we have to prove that $\mathbf{v} = ab \sin\theta \mathbf{I}_n$ in magnitude and direction.

The magnitude of **v** is given by

$$\begin{aligned} v &= \surd[v_x^2 + v_y^2 + v_z^2] \\ &= \surd[(a_y b_z - a_z b_y)^2 + (a_z b_x - a_x b_z)^2 + (a_x b_y - a_y b_x)^2] \\ &= \surd[(a_x^2 + a_y^2 + a_z^2)(b_x^2 + b_y^2 + b_z^2) - (a_x b_x + a_y b_y + a_z b_z)^2] \\ &= \surd[a^2 b^2 - a^2 b^2 \cos^2\theta] \\ &= ab \sin\theta \end{aligned}$$

The direction of **v** is perpendicular to the plane of **a** and **b**, for, from (3)

$$\mathbf{v}\,.\,\mathbf{a} = (a_y b_z - a_z b_y)a_x + (a_z b_x - a_x b_z)a_y + (a_x b_y - a_y b_x)a_z = 0$$

and similarly $\mathbf{v}\,.\,\mathbf{b} = 0$. Hence **v** has the same magnitude as

$\mathbf{a} \wedge \mathbf{b}$ and either the same direction or the opposite direction; that is

$$\mathbf{v} = k\mathbf{a} \wedge \mathbf{b} \tag{5}$$

where $k = +1$ or $k = -1$.

Now k is $+1$ in the special 'two-dimensional' case (2) above, and it follows that it must be $+1$ always. For suppose the set of vectors **a**, **b**, and **v**, remaining rigidly connected together, is rotated continuously until **v** is parallel to the z-axis so that the relation (2) applies. In this process, the values of (a_x, a_y, a_z) and (b_x, b_y, b_z) will change, but their change will be continuous. Hence k in the relation (5) will change continuously, if at all. But since it can only take the values $+1$ or -1, it cannot change continuously. Hence it does not change, but retains the value $+1$ which it has in formula (2). Hence $\mathbf{v} = \mathbf{a} \wedge \mathbf{b}$, which is formula (5) with $k = +1$.

Although vectors are primarily useful as an algebraical or geometrical rather than as an arithmetical tool, a few numerical examples will help to familiarise the formulae.

Example 1

a, **b** have rectangular cartesian components $(1, 3, -2)$ and $(2, 0, 5)$ respectively. For these vectors

$$\mathbf{a} \cdot \mathbf{b} = 1 \cdot 2 + 3 \cdot 0 + (-2) \cdot 5 = -8$$

$$\mathbf{a} \wedge \mathbf{b} = [3 \cdot 5 - (-2) \cdot 0]\,\mathbf{i} + [(-2) \cdot 2 - 1 \cdot 5]\mathbf{j} + [1 \cdot 0 - 3 \cdot 2]\mathbf{k}$$

$$= 15\mathbf{i} - 9\mathbf{j} - 6\mathbf{k}$$

Example 2

$$\mathbf{a} = 2\mathbf{i} - \mathbf{k}\,; \quad \mathbf{b} = 4\mathbf{i} + 2\mathbf{j} + \mathbf{k}\,; \quad \mathbf{c} = \mathbf{i} + \mathbf{j} + \mathbf{k}$$

Find $(\mathbf{a} + 2\mathbf{b}) \cdot (\mathbf{c} + 3\mathbf{b} \wedge \mathbf{a})$

$$\mathbf{a} + 2\mathbf{b} = 10\mathbf{i} + 4\mathbf{j} + \mathbf{k}$$

$$\mathbf{b} \wedge \mathbf{a} = -2\mathbf{i} + 6\mathbf{j} + (-4\mathbf{k})\,; \quad \therefore \ \mathbf{c} + 3\mathbf{b} \wedge \mathbf{a} = -5\mathbf{i} + 19\mathbf{j} - 11\mathbf{k}$$

$$\therefore \ (\mathbf{a} + 2\mathbf{b}) \cdot (\mathbf{c} + 3\mathbf{b} \wedge \mathbf{a}) = -50 + 76 - 11 = 15$$

Example 3

With **a**, **b**, **c** as in question 2, evaluate

(i) $\mathbf{a} \cdot \mathbf{b}$ (ii) $\mathbf{b} \wedge \mathbf{c}$ (iii) $\mathbf{b} \cdot (\mathbf{c} \wedge \mathbf{a})$ (iv $(\mathbf{b} - 2\mathbf{c}) \wedge (3\mathbf{a} + 2\mathbf{b})$

(v) $(\mathbf{b} \cdot \mathbf{c})\mathbf{a} + (\mathbf{c} \cdot \mathbf{a})\mathbf{c}$ (vi) $(\mathbf{b} \wedge \mathbf{c}) \wedge (\mathbf{c} \wedge \mathbf{a})$

Answers: 7; $\mathbf{i} - 3\mathbf{j} + 2\mathbf{k}$; 0; $4\mathbf{i} - 12\mathbf{j} + 8\mathbf{k}$; $15\mathbf{i} + \mathbf{j} - 6\mathbf{k}$; $\mathbf{0}$.

17.43. *Scalar and vector products of unit vectors*

The reader should verify the following useful results, (only about four of which are essentially different). For any right-handed triad of mutually orthogonal unit vectors **I**, **J**, **K**.

$$\mathbf{I}\,.\,\mathbf{I} = \mathbf{J}\,.\,\mathbf{J} = \mathbf{K}\,.\,\mathbf{K} = 1$$
$$\mathbf{I}\,.\,\mathbf{J} = \mathbf{J}\,.\,\mathbf{I} = \mathbf{J}\,.\,\mathbf{K} = \mathbf{K}\,.\,\mathbf{J} = \mathbf{K}\,.\,\mathbf{I} = \mathbf{I}\,.\,\mathbf{K} = 0$$
$$\mathbf{I}\wedge\mathbf{I} = \mathbf{J}\wedge\mathbf{J} = \mathbf{K}\wedge\mathbf{K} = 0$$
$$\mathbf{I}\wedge\mathbf{J} = \mathbf{K} = -\mathbf{J}\wedge\mathbf{I}$$
$$\mathbf{J}\wedge\mathbf{K} = \mathbf{I} = -\mathbf{K}\wedge\mathbf{J}$$
$$\mathbf{K}\wedge\mathbf{I} = \mathbf{J} = -\mathbf{I}\wedge\mathbf{K}$$

17.44. *Rules for algebraic manipulation of scalar and vector products*

$$\begin{aligned}\mathbf{a}\,.\,(\mathbf{b}+\mathbf{c}) &= a_x(b_x+c_x)+a_y(b_y+c_y)+a_z(b_z+c_z)\\ &= (a_xb_x+a_yb_y+a_zb_z)+(a_xc_x+a_yc_y+a_zc_z)\\ &= \mathbf{a}\,.\,\mathbf{b}+\mathbf{a}\,.\,\mathbf{c} \qquad (1)\end{aligned}$$

The reader may similarly verify by expansion in terms of rectangular components that :

$$\mathbf{a}\wedge(\mathbf{b}+\mathbf{c}) = \mathbf{a}\wedge\mathbf{b}+\mathbf{a}\wedge\mathbf{c} \qquad (2)$$

It follows from these distributive properties of the scalar and vector products, and from the properties already mentioned in 17.41, that expressions like $(k_1\mathbf{a}+k_2\mathbf{b})\wedge(k_3\mathbf{c}+k_4\mathbf{d})$ can be expanded as in ordinary algebra, provided only that the order of factors in each vector product is maintained.

Examples

1. Prove that $(\mathbf{a}+\mathbf{b})\,.\,(\mathbf{a}-\mathbf{b}) = a^2 - b^2$
2. Prove that $(\mathbf{a}+\mathbf{b})\wedge(\mathbf{a}-\mathbf{b}) = 2\mathbf{b}\wedge\mathbf{a}$
3. Prove by explicit expansion in terms of components
$$\mathbf{a}\,.\,(\mathbf{b}\wedge\mathbf{c}) = \mathbf{b}\,.\,(\mathbf{c}\wedge\mathbf{a}) = \mathbf{c}\,.\,(\mathbf{a}\wedge\mathbf{b})$$
4. Prove that $\mathbf{a}\,.\,(\mathbf{b}\wedge\mathbf{c}) = (\mathbf{a}\wedge\mathbf{b})\,.\,\mathbf{c}$
5. Prove by expanding in terms of components that
$$\mathbf{a}\wedge(\mathbf{b}\wedge\mathbf{c}) = (\mathbf{a}\,.\,\mathbf{c})\mathbf{b} - (\mathbf{a}\,.\,\mathbf{b})\mathbf{c}$$
6. Show that $\mathbf{a}\wedge(\mathbf{b}\wedge\mathbf{c})$ and $(\mathbf{a}\wedge\mathbf{b})\wedge\mathbf{c}$ are in general unequal, and find the condition that they should be equal.

The results of Examples 3 and 5 are useful forms to be able to quote from memory.

Although two kinds of multiplication of vectors have been defined, it is not necessary or advantageous to define any form of division by a vector: we shall never use or write down any expression with a vector occurring in the denominator. A consequence of the fact that division by a vector is not defined, is that differentiation with respect to a vector cannot be defined through a limit of a quotient (both $\delta k/\delta \mathbf{v}$ and $\delta \mathbf{a}/\delta \mathbf{v}$ are meaningless in the absence of a definition of division). The quantities of the next sections to some extent fill this gap.

17.5. Gradient, divergence, curl and the operator ∇

17.51. *Gradient*

Consider a differentiable scalar function of position. If the position coordinates are restricted to the points of a plane, the magnitude of the function at any point may be represented by a perpendicular distance or height above the plane, and the graph of the function will have the form of a surface. If the position coordinates are unrestricted, the scalar function, $h(x, y, z)$ say, can no longer in actual fact be represented in this way, but we may conveniently talk of its magnitude as a 'height' in a hypothetical, four-dimensional space.

Starting from a given point (x, y, z) a small displacement will in general result in a change of height of the surface representing $h(x, y, z)$. The rate of increase of height with distance in the x, y, z 'plane' will depend on the direction of the displacement; the rate of increase $=\left(\frac{dh}{ds}\right)_{\mathbf{u}}$ say, where the unit vector $\mathbf{u}$ is used to specify the direction along which the displacement δs takes place, ($\delta s^2 = \delta x^2 + \delta y^2 + \delta z^2$ if x, y, z are rectangular cartesian coordinates).

Usually there will be one choice of the direction $\mathbf{u}$ for which the rate of increase of height will be greatest, $\mathbf{u} = \mathbf{U}$, say; then $(dh/ds)_{\mathbf{U}}$ is the magnitude of the greatest rate of increase of height, and $\mathbf{U}$ is its direction. The vector $(dh/ds)_{\mathbf{u}}\,\mathbf{U}$ is called the gradient of the function $h(x, y, z)$.

$$\text{grad } h = (dh/ds)_{\mathbf{u}}\,\mathbf{U}$$

If $(dh/ds)_{\mathbf{u}} = 0$ in all directions $\mathbf{u}$, then grad $h = 0$; in all other cases where the definition of grad h given above is inapplicable (for example if there are two distinct directions $\mathbf{u}_1$ and $\mathbf{u}_2$ for which $(\mathrm{d}h/\mathrm{d}s)_{\mathbf{u}}$ attains its greatest value), grad h is undefined.

17.52. *Divergence*

Consider a region occupied by fluid, and let the density and velocity of the fluid at any point be $\rho(x, y, z)$ and $\mathbf{v}(x, y, z)$. Let S be any fixed closed surface drawn in the fluid, and consider the rate at which fluid escapes out of the surface S. If $\mathbf{n}$ is unit outward normal to the element δS of surface, $\mathbf{v} \,.\, \mathbf{n}$ = velocity with which fluid of density ρ escapes across δS. Therefore the total mass of liquid escaping per second

$$=\int_S \rho\mathbf{v} \,.\, \mathbf{n}\, \mathrm{d}S$$

The loss of mass will mean that the density of fluid inside S is decreasing (unless fluid is being created by some means inside the region). The average rate of decrease of density will be equal to the rate of escape divided by the volume τ enclosed by the surface S. If we take the surface S sufficiently small, i.e. let $S \to 0$ and $\tau \to 0$, this quotient will be equal to the rate of change of density at the point into which the surface S shrinks. We call $\lim_{\tau\to 0}\left[\frac{1}{\tau}\int_S \rho\mathbf{v} \,.\, \mathbf{n}\, \mathrm{d}S\right]$ the divergence of $\rho\mathbf{v}$; and in general for any differentiable vector function of position $\mathbf{a}(x, y, z)$

$$\operatorname{div} \mathbf{a} = \lim_{\tau\to 0}\left[\frac{1}{\tau}\int_S \mathbf{a} \,.\, \mathbf{n}\, \mathrm{d}S\right] \tag{1}$$

where S is a closed surface about the point x, y, z at which div $\mathbf{a}$ is to be defined, and τ is the volume enclosed by S. If the right-hand side of equation (1) is not defined, as is the case for example if different shapes of the enclosing surface S or different ways of evaluating the integral lead to different answers (cf. 9.41–9.46), the quantity div $\mathbf{a}$ is not defined (does not exist). When div $\mathbf{a}$ does exist it is therefore a function of position only, and not dependent in any way on τ or S.

If the vector we are concerned with is the electrostatic field vector $\mathbf{E}$ in a matter-free region, we note that $\int_S \mathbf{E} \,.\, \mathbf{n}\, \mathrm{d}S$ is, by Gauss' theorem, 4π times the electric charge within the surface S, so $\int_S \mathbf{E} \,.\, \mathbf{n}\, \mathrm{d}S \Big/ 4\pi\tau$ is the average density of charge within this surface. Thus, in the limit, the density of charge at any point is $(1/4\pi)$ times div **E** at that point (or div $\mathbf{D}/4\pi$ in the presence of matter, **D** being the electric displacement).

17.53. *The curl of a vector*

The increase in the magnetic scalar potential due to a single circuit round a conductor carrying electric current is proportional to the magnitude of the current. The change in potential is evaluated as (minus) the line integral of the magnetic field vector in the circuit, $\oint \mathbf{H} \, . \, \mathrm{ds}$. Thus the total current crossing an area S bounded by a plane curve which encircles the current is proportional to $\oint \mathbf{H} \, . \, \mathrm{ds}$, and the mean current per unit area is $(1/S) \oint \mathbf{H} \, . \, \mathrm{ds}$. When the area S is perpendicular to the direction of the current, the mean current per unit area will be greatest. Conversely if we are given a differentiable vector function of position **H** we can find the orientation of a plane area S for which $\oint \mathbf{H} \, . \, \mathrm{ds}$ is greatest; the magnitude of the current density is then proportional to $\lim_{S \to 0} \left[\frac{1}{S} \oint \mathbf{H} \, . \, \mathrm{ds} \right]$, and its direction is that of the normal to the limiting position of the area S, unit normal $\mathbf{i}_n$ say.

This suggests the following definition of a quantity which is called curl **H**:

$$\mathrm{curl}\, \mathbf{H} = \lim_{S \to 0} \left[\frac{1}{S} \oint \mathbf{H} \, . \, \mathrm{ds} \right] \mathbf{i}_n$$

where the orientation of the plane area S is such that the limit has its greatest magnitude. Curl **H** is independent of the area S and contour elements ds in the same way, and for the same reason that div **a** is independent of τ and S, viz. the entity curl **H** is only defined when the limit is independent of the shape of S. These reservations about the existence of div **a** and curl **H** help to explain why certain physical laws e.g. charge density = div $\mathbf{E}/4\pi$ have to be expressed in a different form at an abrupt interface e.g. on a charged surface.

Those more interested in fluid dynamics than electricity may prefer to restate the above definition of the curl of a vector, replacing **H** by the velocity vector **v**. Then $\oint \mathbf{v} \, . \, \mathrm{d}\mathbf{s}$ is the circulation of fluid round a closed path, and $\boldsymbol{\omega}=\frac{1}{2}$ curl **v** is the vorticity.

17.6. Expressions for grad, div, and curl in terms of rectangular cartesian coordinates

The definitions we have given in the preceding paragraphs are conspicuously inconvenient for handling algebraically. We shall now find alternative expressions.

17.61. *Grad* ϕ

Let l, m, n be the direction cosines of the (variable) unit vector **u** referred to in the definition of the gradient of a function. Then if $\mathrm{d}x$, $\mathrm{d}y$, $\mathrm{d}z$, are the components of the displacement **u** $\mathrm{d}s$

$$(\mathrm{d}x/\mathrm{d}s)_{\mathbf{u}}=l,\ (\mathrm{d}y/\mathrm{d}s)_{\mathbf{u}}=m,\ (\mathrm{d}z/\mathrm{d}s)_{\mathbf{u}}=n$$

and
$$\left(\frac{\mathrm{d}\phi}{\mathrm{d}s}\right)_{\mathbf{u}}=\left(\frac{\partial\phi}{\partial x}\right)_{y,z}\left(\frac{\mathrm{d}x}{\mathrm{d}s}\right)_{\mathbf{u}}+\left(\frac{\partial\phi}{\partial y}\right)_{z,x}\left(\frac{\mathrm{d}y}{\mathrm{d}s}\right)_{\mathbf{u}}+\left(\frac{\partial\phi}{\partial z}\right)_{x,y}\left(\frac{\mathrm{d}z}{\mathrm{d}s}\right)_{\mathbf{u}}$$
$$=\frac{\partial\phi}{\partial x}\,.\,l+\frac{\partial\phi}{\partial y}\,.\,m+\frac{\partial\phi}{\partial z}\,.\,n=\mathbf{v}\,.\,\mathbf{u} \qquad (1)$$

where **v** is the vector with components $(\partial\phi/\partial x,\ \partial\phi/\partial y,\ \partial\phi/\partial z)$. Now we must choose the direction $\mathbf{u}=\mathbf{U}$ for which the quantity (1) is biggest. As $\mathbf{v}\,.\,\mathbf{u}=v\cos\theta$, where θ is the angle between **u** and **v**, **v** . **u** is greatest when **u** is parallel to **v**, and is then equal in magnitude to v. Hence the magnitude of grad ϕ is v, and the direction of grad ϕ is **U** parallel to **v**, hence

$$\text{grad}\ \phi=\mathbf{v}=\mathbf{i}(\partial\phi/\partial x)+\mathbf{j}(\partial\phi/\partial y)+\mathbf{k}(\partial\phi/\partial z)$$

Thus the cartesian components of the vector grad ϕ are

$$(\text{grad}\ \phi)_x=\partial\phi/\partial x\ ;\ \ (\text{grad}\ \phi)_y=\partial\phi/\partial y\ ;\ \ (\text{grad}\ \phi)_z=\partial\phi/\partial z \qquad (2)$$

Similarly if **I** is any unit vector, and δI is a length increment parallel to **I**,

$$\mathbf{I}\,.\,\text{grad}\ \phi=\partial\phi/\partial I \qquad (3)$$

17.62. *Div* **a**

To evaluate div **a** in a rectangular cartesian system we consider $\int_S \mathbf{a}\,.\,\mathbf{n}\,\mathrm{d}S$ (where **n** is written for unit vector perpendicular to area element δS, drawn outwards from the volume τ enclosed by S) over the surface of a rectangular block with centre at x_0, y_0, z_0 and sides parallel to the cartesian axes.

We suppose the (y, z) faces of the block are at $x_0 \pm \delta x$, the (z, x) faces at $y_0 \pm \delta y$ and the (x, y) faces at $z_0 \pm \delta z$, where δx, δy and δz are of similar order of magnitude, as in Fig. 17.13. The

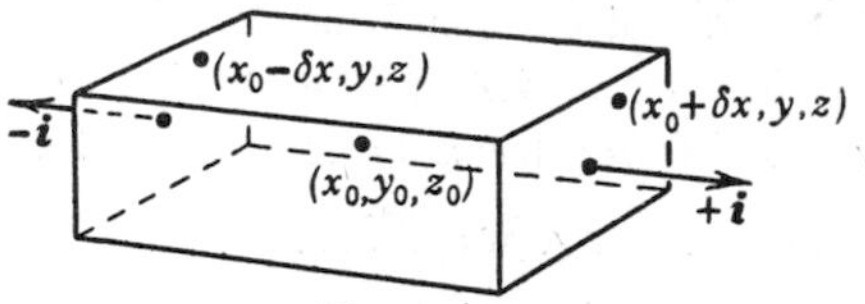

FIG. 17.13

outward normal to the (y, z) face at $x_0 - \delta x$ is the negative unit vector $-\mathbf{i}$, while the outward normal to the y, z face at $x + \delta x$ is $+\mathbf{i}$. Thus the contribution to $\int \mathbf{a} \cdot \mathbf{n}\, dS$ from these two faces is

$$\int_{z_0-\delta z}^{z_0+\delta z} \int_{y_0-\delta y}^{y_0+\delta y} \{-a_x(x_0 - \delta x, y, z) + a_x(x_0 + \delta x, y, z)\}\, dy\, dz$$

$$= \left(2\,\delta x \frac{\partial a_x}{\partial x}\right) . 4\,\delta y\,\delta z \quad + \quad \text{higher order terms}$$

$$= (\partial a_x/\partial x) . 8\,\delta x\,\delta y\,\delta z \quad + \quad ,, \quad ,, \quad ,,$$

$$= (\partial a_x/\partial x) . \tau \quad + \quad ,, \quad ,, \quad ,,$$

To the same order the contribution from the two (z, x) faces is $(\partial a_y/\partial y) . \tau$ and that from the two (x, y) faces $(\partial a_z/\partial z) . \tau$

Hence $$\int_S \mathbf{a} \cdot \mathbf{n}\, dS = \left(\frac{\partial a_x}{\partial x} + \frac{\partial a_y}{\partial y} + \frac{\partial a_z}{\partial z}\right) . \tau + \text{higher order terms}$$

and $$\operatorname{div} \mathbf{a} = \lim_{\tau \to 0} \left[\frac{1}{\tau} \int_S \mathbf{a} \cdot \mathbf{n}\, dS\right]$$

$$= \frac{\partial a_x}{\partial x} + \frac{\partial a_y}{\partial y} + \frac{\partial a_z}{\partial z}$$

which is the required expression for div **a** in the chosen cartesian system.

17.63. *Curl* **b**

The result (5) below and its corollary are the most important parts of this section; their derivation is given for the sake of completeness.

We first require a vector expression for a plane element of area. For an elementary triangle, sides $\mathbf{r}$ and $\mathbf{r}+\delta\mathbf{r}$ inclined at an angle $\delta\theta$,

$$|\mathbf{r}\wedge(\mathbf{r}+\delta\mathbf{r})|=|\mathbf{r}|\,|\mathbf{r}+\delta\mathbf{r}|\sin\delta\theta=2(\text{area of }\triangle)=2\,\delta S,$$

and the direction of $\mathbf{r}\wedge(\mathbf{r}+\delta\mathbf{r})$ is that of the unit vector $\mathbf{I}_n$ normal to the plane of the triangle, drawn in such a direction that a right-handed rotation about $\mathbf{I}_n$ through an angle $\delta\theta$ turns the direction of $\mathbf{r}$ to the direction of $\mathbf{r}+\delta\mathbf{r}$. Also $\mathbf{r}\wedge(\mathbf{r}+\delta\mathbf{r})=\mathbf{r}\wedge\delta\mathbf{r}$. Hence for an elementary triangle

$$\mathbf{r}\wedge\delta\mathbf{r}=2\,\delta S\,\mathbf{I}_n$$

Any plane area can be divided up into triangles with a common vertex in its plane ; $\mathbf{I}_n$ is the same for each, hence

$$S\mathbf{I}_n=\tfrac{1}{2}\oint\mathbf{r}\wedge d\mathbf{r} \tag{1}$$

the integral being taken, right-handedly about $\mathbf{I}_n$, round the perimeter of S. Expressing the vector product in terms of components, this gives

$$S\mathbf{I}_n=\tfrac{1}{2}\Big[\oint(y\,dz-z\,dy)\mathbf{i}+\oint(z\,dx-x\,dz)\mathbf{j}$$
$$+\oint(x\,dy-y\,dx)\mathbf{k}\Big]$$

and since $\oint(y\,dz+z\,dy)=\oint d(zy)=0$, and similarly for the other integrals, this gives

$$S\mathbf{I}_n=\left(\oint y\,dz\right)\mathbf{i}+\left(\oint z\,dx\right)\mathbf{j}+\left(\oint x\,dy\right)\mathbf{k} \tag{2}$$

If (l, m, n) are the direction cosines of $\mathbf{I}_n$, resolution into components gives

$$\oint y\,dz=-\oint z\,dy=lS,\quad \oint z\,dx=-\oint x\,dz=mS,$$
$$\oint x\,dy=-\oint y\,dx=nS \tag{3}$$

Now consider $\oint \mathbf{b}\,.\,d\mathbf{r}=\oint(b_x\,dx+b_y\,dy+b_z\,dz)$ taken round the perimeter of a small plane area S in the neighbourhood of a point O (x_0, y_0, z_0). Let suffix 0 denote the value of a quantity at O and let δs be the greatest distance from O to a point on the perimeter of S. Consider first the integral $\oint b_x\,\mathrm{d}x$. We have

$$b_x = (b_x)_0 + \left(\frac{\partial b_x}{\partial x}\right)_0 (x - x_0) + \left(\frac{\partial b_x}{\partial y}\right)_0 (y - y_0) + \left(\frac{\partial b_x}{\partial z}\right)_0 (z - z_0) + O(\delta s)^2$$

Now $\oint \mathrm{d}x = 0$, $\oint (x - x_0)\,\mathrm{d}x = \oint \mathrm{d}[\frac{1}{2}(x - x_0)^2] = 0$, and, from (3),

$$\oint (y - y_0)\,\mathrm{d}x = -nS, \quad \oint (z - z_0)\,\mathrm{d}x = +mS,$$

so $$\oint b_x\,\mathrm{d}x = [-n(\partial b_x/\partial y)_0 + m(\partial b_x/\partial z)_0]S + O(\delta s)^3$$

and similarly for $\oint b_y\,\mathrm{d}y$ and $\oint b_z\,\mathrm{d}z$. Also S is $O(\delta s)^2$, so

$$\lim_{S\to 0}\left[\frac{1}{S}\oint \mathbf{b}\,.\,\mathrm{d}\mathbf{r}\right] = l\left(\frac{\partial b_z}{\partial y} - \frac{\partial b_y}{\partial z}\right) + m\left(\frac{\partial b_x}{\partial z} - \frac{\partial b_z}{\partial x}\right) + n\left(\frac{\partial b_y}{\partial x} - \frac{\partial b_x}{\partial y}\right) \tag{4}$$

Of all possible directions (l, m, n), the greatest value of the right-hand side of (4) occurs when (l, m, n) is in the direction of the vector whose components are

$$\left(\frac{\partial b_z}{\partial y} - \frac{\partial b_y}{\partial z},\quad \frac{\partial b_x}{\partial z} - \frac{\partial b_z}{\partial x},\quad \frac{\partial b_y}{\partial x} - \frac{\partial b_x}{\partial y}\right)$$

and the value of the right-hand side is then equal to the magnitude of this vector (compare the argument of §15.61). Hence

$$\operatorname{curl}\mathbf{b} = \mathbf{i}\left(\frac{\partial b_z}{\partial y} - \frac{\partial b_y}{\partial z}\right) + \mathbf{j}\left(\frac{\partial b_x}{\partial z} - \frac{\partial b_z}{\partial x}\right) + \mathbf{k}\left(\frac{\partial b_y}{\partial x} - \frac{\partial b_x}{\partial y}\right) \tag{5}$$

Corollary: Equation (4) can also be expressed in the form

$$\lim_{S\to 0}\left[\frac{1}{S}\oint \mathbf{b}\,.\,\mathrm{d}\mathbf{r}\right] = \operatorname{curl}\mathbf{b}\,.\,\mathbf{n}$$

where S is any small area and $\mathbf{n}$ unit vector normal to S.

17.64. *The Operator* ∇

The cartesian expressions for grad, div and curl can be very easily expressed and remembered in terms of the differential operator $\mathbf{i}(\partial/\partial x)+\mathbf{j}(\partial/\partial y)+\mathbf{k}(\partial/\partial z)$ which we denote by the symbol ∇ (del). For

$$\nabla\phi=\left(\mathbf{i}\frac{\partial}{\partial x}+\mathbf{j}\frac{\partial}{\partial y}+\mathbf{k}\frac{\partial}{\partial z}\right)\phi=\mathbf{i}\frac{\partial\phi}{\partial x}+\mathbf{j}\frac{\partial\phi}{\partial y}+\mathbf{k}\frac{\partial\phi}{\partial z}$$

$$=\text{grad}\,\phi$$

$$\nabla\,.\,\mathbf{a}=\left(\mathbf{i}\frac{\partial}{\partial x}+\mathbf{j}\frac{\partial}{\partial y}+\mathbf{k}\frac{\partial}{\partial z}\right)\,.\,\left(\mathbf{i}a_x+\mathbf{j}a_y+\mathbf{k}a_z\right)$$

$$=\frac{\partial}{\partial x}a_x+\frac{\partial}{\partial y}a_y+\frac{\partial}{\partial z}a_z=\text{div}\,\mathbf{a}$$

and

$$\nabla\wedge\mathbf{b}=\left(\mathbf{i}\frac{\partial}{\partial x}+\mathbf{j}\frac{\partial}{\partial y}+\mathbf{k}\frac{\partial}{\partial z}\right)\wedge(\mathbf{i}b_x+\mathbf{j}b_y+\mathbf{k}b_z)$$

$$=\mathbf{i}\left(\frac{\partial}{\partial y}b_z-\frac{\partial}{\partial z}b_y\right)+\mathbf{j}\left(\frac{\partial}{\partial z}b_x-\frac{\partial}{\partial x}b_z\right)+\mathbf{k}\left(\frac{\partial}{\partial x}b_y-\frac{\partial}{\partial y}b_x\right)$$

$$=\text{curl}\,\mathbf{b}$$

∇ often behaves very much like an ordinary vector quantity (it is actually a vector differential *operator*), thus $\nabla\,.\,(\mathbf{a}+\mathbf{b})=\nabla\,.\,\mathbf{a}+\nabla\,.\,\mathbf{b}$, $\nabla\wedge(k\mathbf{a})=k(\nabla\wedge\mathbf{a})$ and so on (these results follow at once when the expressions are written out in full). The most important exception to the general rule that ∇ behaves algebraically in the same way as a true vector is that, since it is a differential operator, the *order* of any product containing ∇ must be strictly preserved. Thus while $\mathbf{a}\,.\,\mathbf{b}=\mathbf{b}\,.\,\mathbf{a}$ and $\mathbf{a}\phi=\phi\mathbf{a}$,

$$\nabla\,.\,\mathbf{b}\neq\mathbf{b}\,.\,\nabla \qquad (1)$$

and

$$\nabla\phi\neq\phi\nabla \qquad (2)$$

In fact the right-hand sides of (1) and (2) do not represent vector *quantities* of any kind, but are new differential operators, namely $b_x\dfrac{\partial}{\partial x}+b_y\dfrac{\partial}{\partial y}+b_z\dfrac{\partial}{\partial z}$ and $\mathbf{i}\phi(\partial/\partial x)+\mathbf{j}\phi(\partial/\partial y)+\mathbf{k}\phi(\partial/\partial z)$ respectively.

The usefulness of introducing the special symbols div, grad, curl, ∇, is dependent on our ability to manipulate them without continually harking back to the original definitions. We proceed to discuss such matters.

17.7. Analytic and algebraic properties of grad, div, curl and ∇

17.71. *Invariance properties*

The work of 17.6 showing that grad ϕ, div $\mathbf{a}$ and curl $\mathbf{b}$ are equal to $\mathbf{i}\,\partial\phi/\partial x+\mathbf{j}\,\partial\phi/\partial y+\mathbf{k}\,\partial\phi/\partial z$ etc. can equally well be applied using a different set of cartesian axes, with coordinates x', y', z' say and unit vectors $\mathbf{i}', \mathbf{j}', \mathbf{k}'$. Then grad ϕ will also be equal to $\mathbf{i}'(\partial\phi/\partial x')+\mathbf{j}'(\partial\phi/\partial y')+\mathbf{k}'(\partial\phi/\partial z')$. Thus, if grad ϕ exists it is necessarily true that

$$\mathbf{i}'\frac{\partial\phi}{\partial x'}+\mathbf{j}'\frac{\partial\phi}{\partial y'}+\mathbf{k}'\frac{\partial\phi}{\partial z'}=\mathbf{i}\frac{\partial\phi}{\partial x}+\mathbf{j}\frac{\partial\phi}{\partial y}+\mathbf{k}\frac{\partial\phi}{\partial z} \tag{1}$$

and, in a similar way, if div $\mathbf{a}$ exists,

$$\frac{\partial}{\partial x'}a_{x'}+\frac{\partial}{\partial y'}a_{y'}+\frac{\partial}{\partial z'}a_{z'}=\frac{\partial}{\partial x}a_x+\frac{\partial}{\partial y}a_y+\frac{\partial}{\partial z}a_z \tag{2}$$

and similarly for curl $\mathbf{b}$.

These relations can be deduced without mention of div, grad, curl, provided the derivatives occurring on both sides exist. For, suppose the unit vectors $\mathbf{i}', \mathbf{j}', \mathbf{k}'$ (mutually orthogonal) have components, that is, direction cosines l_1, m_1, n_1; l_2, m_2, n_2; l_3, m_3, n_3 respectively relative to the original x, y, z axes,

$$\left.\begin{aligned}\mathbf{i}'&=l_1\mathbf{i}+m_1\mathbf{j}+n_1\mathbf{k}\\ \mathbf{j}'&=l_2\mathbf{i}+m_2\mathbf{j}+n_2\mathbf{k}\\ \mathbf{k}'&=l_3\mathbf{i}+m_3\mathbf{j}+n_3\mathbf{k}\end{aligned}\right\} \tag{3}$$

and by solving these equations for $\mathbf{i}, \mathbf{j}, \mathbf{k}$ we find

$$\left.\begin{aligned}\mathbf{i}&=l_1\mathbf{i}'+l_2\mathbf{j}'+l_3\mathbf{k}'\\ \mathbf{j}&=m_1\mathbf{i}'+m_2\mathbf{j}'+m_3\mathbf{k}'\\ \mathbf{k}&=n_1\mathbf{i}'+n_2\mathbf{j}'+n_3\mathbf{k}'\end{aligned}\right\} \tag{4}$$

Since $\mathbf{i}\,.\,\mathbf{i}=\mathbf{j}\,.\,\mathbf{j}=\mathbf{k}\,.\,\mathbf{k}=1$ and $\mathbf{i}\,.\,\mathbf{j}=\mathbf{j}\,.\,\mathbf{k}=\mathbf{k}\,.\,\mathbf{i}=0$, it follows that

$$\left.\begin{aligned}&l_1^2+l_2^2+l_3^2=m_1^2+m_2^2+m_3^2=n_1^2+n_2^2+n_3^2=1\\ &l_1m_1+l_2m_2+l_3m_3=m_1n_1+m_2n_2+m_3n_3=n_1l_1+n_2l_2+n_3l_3=0\end{aligned}\right\} \tag{5}$$

Using (3) we see that for any vector,

$$\begin{aligned}x'\mathbf{i}'+y'\mathbf{j}'+z'\mathbf{k}'=(l_1x'+l_2y'+l_3z')\mathbf{i}&\\ +(m_1x'+m_2y'+m_3z')\mathbf{j}+(n_1x'+n_2y'+n_3z')\mathbf{k}&\end{aligned}$$

so, if $x\mathbf{i}+y\mathbf{j}+z\mathbf{k}=x'\mathbf{i}'+y'\mathbf{j}'+z'\mathbf{k}'$,

$$\left.\begin{aligned} x&=l_1x'+l_2y'+l_3z' \\ y&=m_1x'+m_2y'+m_3z' \\ z&=n_1x'+n_2y'+n_3z' \end{aligned}\right\} \tag{6}$$

From (6) it follows that

$$\frac{\partial}{\partial x'}=\frac{\partial x}{\partial x'}\frac{\partial}{\partial x}+\frac{\partial y}{\partial x'}\frac{\partial}{\partial y}+\frac{\partial z}{\partial x'}\frac{\partial}{\partial z}=l_1\frac{\partial}{\partial x}+m_1\frac{\partial}{\partial y}+n_1\frac{\partial}{\partial z}$$

and similarly
$$\frac{\partial}{\partial y'}=l_2\frac{\partial}{\partial x}+m_2\frac{\partial}{\partial y}+n_2\frac{\partial}{\partial z} \tag{7}$$

$$\frac{\partial}{\partial z'}=l_3\frac{\partial}{\partial x}+m_3\frac{\partial}{\partial y}+n_3\frac{\partial}{\partial z}$$

and
$$\left.\begin{aligned} a_{x'}&=l_1a_x+m_1a_y+n_1a_z \\ a_{y'}&=l_2a_x+m_2a_y+n_2a_z \\ a_{z'}&=l_3a_x+m_3a_y+n_3a_z \end{aligned}\right\} \tag{8}$$

so

$$\frac{\partial}{\partial x'}a_{x'}+\frac{\partial}{\partial y'}a_{y'}+\frac{\partial}{\partial z'}a_{z'}$$

$$=(l_1^2+l_2^2+l_3^2)\frac{\partial}{\partial x}a_x+(m_1^2+m_2^2+m_3^2)\frac{\partial}{\partial y}a_y$$

$$+(n_1^2+n_2^2+n_3^2)\frac{\partial}{\partial z}a_z+(l_1m_1+l_2m_2+l_3m_3)\left(\frac{\partial}{\partial x}a_y+\frac{\partial}{\partial y}a_x\right)$$

$$+(l_1n_1+l_2n_2+l_3n_3)\left(\frac{\partial}{\partial y}a_z+\frac{\partial}{\partial z}a_y\right)$$

$$+(m_1n_1+m_2n_2+m_3n_3)\left(\frac{\partial}{\partial z}a_x+\frac{\partial}{\partial x}a_z\right)$$

$$=\frac{\partial}{\partial x}a_x+\frac{\partial}{\partial y}a_y+\frac{\partial}{\partial z}a_z$$

So we have verified equation (2), that is, we have established that the form of div $\mathbf{a}$ is *invariant* for a change from any set of rectangular cartesian axes to any other set. The invariance of grad ϕ and curl $\mathbf{b}$ can be established in a similar way.

We may also mention here the invariance property of the operator

$$\nabla \cdot \nabla = \left(\mathbf{i}\frac{\partial}{\partial x}+\mathbf{j}\frac{\partial}{\partial y}+\mathbf{k}\frac{\partial}{\partial z}\right) \cdot \left(\mathbf{i}\frac{\partial}{\partial x}+\mathbf{j}\frac{\partial}{\partial y}+\mathbf{k}\frac{\partial}{\partial z}\right)$$
$$=\frac{\partial^2}{\partial x^2}+\frac{\partial^2}{\partial y^2}+\frac{\partial^2}{\partial z^2}$$

which is usually written ∇^2. The operator ∇^2 is invariant with respect to a change from one set of rectangular cartesian axes to another in the sense that if

$$(\nabla')^2=\frac{\partial^2}{(\partial x')^2}+\frac{\partial^2}{(\partial y')^2}+\frac{\partial^2}{(\partial z')^2}$$

and ϕ is any scalar function of position $\phi=\mathrm{f}(x, y, z)=\mathrm{g}(x', y', z')$ say, then $\nabla^2 f=(\nabla')^2 g$; or, we may write $\nabla^2\phi=(\nabla')^2\phi$ in which it is implied that ϕ is to be expressed in terms of the variables which appear in the corresponding operator, i.e. x, y, z on the L.H.S. and x', y', z' on the R.H.S.

17.72. *Rules of algebra for grad, div, curl and* $\boldsymbol{\nabla}$

In all cases where grad ϕ, div **a** or curl **b** exists, we are free to represent it by its cartesian expression, viz.

$$\mathbf{i}\,\partial\phi/\partial x+\mathbf{j}\,\partial\phi/\partial y+\mathbf{k}\,\partial\phi/\partial z,$$
$$\partial a_x/\partial x+\partial a_y/\partial y+\partial a_z/\partial z$$

or $\mathbf{i}(\partial b_z/\partial y-\partial b_y/\partial z)+\mathbf{j}(\partial b_x/\partial z-\partial b_z/\partial x)+\mathbf{k}(\partial b_y/\partial x-\partial b_x/\partial y)$

The following algebraic properties may then be established quite easily by writing the expressions out in full ; we leave this as an exercise for the reader.

(i) grad $(\phi_1+\phi_2)=$ grad ϕ_1+ grad ϕ_2 ;
i.e. $\boldsymbol{\nabla}(\phi_1+\phi_2)=\boldsymbol{\nabla}\phi_1+\boldsymbol{\nabla}\phi_2$

(ii) div $(\mathbf{a}_1+\mathbf{a}_2)=$ div $\mathbf{a}_1+$ div $\mathbf{a}_2$;
i.e. $\boldsymbol{\nabla}\cdot(\mathbf{a}_1+\mathbf{a}_2)=\boldsymbol{\nabla}\cdot\mathbf{a}_1+\boldsymbol{\nabla}\cdot\mathbf{a}_2$

(iii) curl $(\mathbf{b}_1+\mathbf{b}_2)=$ curl $\mathbf{b}_1+$ curl $\mathbf{b}_2$;
i.e. $\boldsymbol{\nabla}\wedge(\mathbf{b}_1+\mathbf{b}_2)=\boldsymbol{\nabla}\wedge\mathbf{b}_1+\boldsymbol{\nabla}\wedge\mathbf{b}_2$

(iv) div $(\phi\mathbf{a})=\phi$ div $\mathbf{a}+\mathbf{a}$. grad ϕ ;
i.e. $\boldsymbol{\nabla}\cdot(\phi\mathbf{a})=\phi\boldsymbol{\nabla}\cdot\mathbf{a}+(\boldsymbol{\nabla}\phi)\cdot\mathbf{a}$

(v) curl grad $\phi=0$
i.e. $\boldsymbol{\nabla}\wedge(\boldsymbol{\nabla}\phi)=0$

(vi) div curl $\mathbf{b}=0$;

i.e. $\nabla\,.\,(\nabla\wedge\mathbf{b})=0$

(vii) div grad $\phi=\nabla^2\phi$

i.e. $\nabla\,.\,(\nabla\phi)=\nabla^2\phi$

(viii) curl curl $\mathbf{b}=$ grad (div $\mathbf{b}$) $-\nabla^2\mathbf{b}$

i.e. $\nabla\wedge(\nabla\wedge\mathbf{b})=\nabla(\nabla\,.\,\mathbf{b})-\nabla^2\mathbf{b}$

(ix) curl $(\phi\mathbf{a})=$ grad $\phi\wedge\mathbf{a}+\phi$ curl $\mathbf{a}$

(x) div $(\mathbf{a}\wedge\mathbf{b})=\mathbf{b}\,.$ curl $\mathbf{a}-\mathbf{a}\,.$ curl $\mathbf{b}$

(xi) If ϕ, $\mathbf{a}$ and $\mathbf{b}$, as well as being functions of position are suitably differentiable functions of a scalar variable t, independent of x, y, z,

$$\frac{\partial}{\partial t}(\text{grad}\,\phi)=\text{grad}\,\frac{\partial\phi}{\partial t}\,;\quad \frac{\partial}{\partial t}(\text{div}\,\mathbf{a})=\text{div}\,\frac{\partial\mathbf{a}}{\partial t}\,;\quad \frac{\partial}{\partial t}(\text{curl}\,\mathbf{b})=\text{curl}\,\frac{\partial\mathbf{b}}{\partial t}\,,$$

The above formulae should be remembered, except that it is not necessary to memorise the ∇ notation forms in addition to the div, grad, curl forms.

17.73. *Expressions for div, grad, curl and ∇^2 in systems of coordinates other than rectangular cartesians*

Expressions for grad, div, curl and ∇^2 may be derived for other orthogonal coordinate systems in the same way as were the rectangular cartesian expressions, except that the derivation of the form for curl can be greatly simplified because the corollary of 17.63 is now available, and a similar short cut is possible in finding grad ϕ.

Distance elements in spherical polar coordinates are given by dr, r dθ, r sin θ dϕ not by dr, dθ, dϕ. Similarly in the case of cylindrical polar coordinates the distance elements are not dr, dθ, dz, but dr, r dθ, dz. These systems are particular examples of the general orthogonal coordinate system (u_1, u_2, u_3) say in which the distance elements are $h_1\,du_1$, $h_2\,du_2$, $h_3\,du_3$, where h_1, h_2, h_3 are in general functions of the coordinates u_1, u_2, u_3, and the elements $h_1\,du_1$, $h_2\,du_2$, $h_3\,du_3$ are mutually perpendicular.

In this system an area element drawn on the surface $u_1=$ constant with sides $h_2\,du_2$, $h_3\,du_3$ will be of magnitude $h_2h_3\,du_2\,du_3$, while the typical volume element is

$$h_1h_2h_3\,du_1\,du_2\,du_3$$

Grad ϕ. We have shown in 17.61 that the component of grad ϕ in the x-direction is $\partial\phi/\partial x$. Now $h_1\,\delta u_1$ takes the place of δx, $h_2\,\delta u_2$ that of δy, $h_3\,\delta u$, of δz : hence

$$\text{grad}\ \phi = \frac{1}{h_1}\frac{\partial\phi}{\partial u_1}\mathbf{I} + \frac{1}{h_2}\frac{\partial\phi}{\partial u_2}\mathbf{J} + \frac{1}{h_3}\frac{\partial\phi}{\partial u_3}\mathbf{K}$$

where **I**, **J**, **K** are unit vectors in the directions of the elements $h_1\,du_1$, $h_2\,du_2$, $h_3\,du_3$, respectively. So we have in spherical polars (r, θ, ψ) :

$$\text{grad}\ \phi = \frac{\partial\phi}{\partial r}\mathbf{I} + \frac{1}{r}\frac{\partial\phi}{\partial\theta}\mathbf{J} + \frac{1}{r\sin\theta}\frac{\partial\phi}{\partial\psi}\mathbf{K}$$

where **I**, **J**, **K** are unit vectors in the directions of δr, $\delta\theta$, $\delta\psi$ increasing, cf. Figs 9.4, 9.6. While in terms of cylindrical polar coordinates

$$\text{grad}\ \phi = \frac{\partial\phi}{\partial r}\mathbf{I}' + \frac{1}{r}\frac{\partial\phi}{\partial\theta}\mathbf{J}' + \frac{\partial\phi}{\partial z}\mathbf{K}'$$

where $\mathbf{I}'$, $\mathbf{J}'$, $\mathbf{K}'$ are unit vectors in the directions δr, $\delta\theta$, δz increasing, see Figs. 9.3, 9.5.

Div **a**. In evaluating div **a** and curl **b** it must be remembered that when an increment is given to curvilinear coordinates the directions of the axes change, and opposite faces of elementary blocks no longer have equal areas. Some of the simplifications available when finding the forms of div and curl in rectangular cartesian coordinates have no counterpart with curvilinear coordinates, so mere replacement of δx by $h_1\,\delta u_1$ etc. in the final formula is inadmissible, and we must go back to the original definitions, i.e. we evaluate div **a** as $\lim\limits_{\tau\to 0}\dfrac{1}{\tau}\displaystyle\int_S \mathbf{a}\,.\,\mathbf{n}\,\mathrm{d}S$ where S is the surface of the approximately rectangular box of length $h_1\,\delta u_1$ (between surfaces u_1 and $u_1+\delta u_1$), breadth $h_2\,\delta u_2$ (between u_2 and $u_2+\delta u_2$) and height $h_3\,\delta u_3$ (between u_3 and $u_3+\delta u_3$).

The outgoing contribution to $\int \mathbf{a}\,.\,\mathbf{n}\,\mathrm{d}S$ from the u_1 face

$$= -a_1 \times h_2 h_3\,\delta u_2\,\delta u_3 - \text{higher order terms},$$

and from the $u_1+\delta u_1$ face

$$= (a_1 h_2 h_3\,\delta u_2\,\delta u_3 + \text{the same higher order terms})$$

$$+ \frac{\partial}{\partial u_1}(a_1 h_2 h_3\,\delta u_2\,\delta u_3 + \text{the same higher order terms})\,\delta u_1$$

i.e. from these two faces together the contribution is

$$\frac{\partial}{\partial u_1}(a_1 h_2 h_3)\,\delta u_1\,\delta u_2\,\delta u_3 + \text{higher order terms}$$

and similarly for the other two pairs of faces, giving

$$\int \mathbf{a}\,.\,\mathbf{n}\,\mathrm{d}S = \left[\frac{\partial}{\partial u_1}(a_1 h_2 h_3) + \frac{\partial}{\partial u_2}(a_2 h_3 h_1) + \frac{\partial}{\partial u_3}(a_3 h_1 h_2)\right]\delta u_1\,\delta u_2\,\delta u_3 + \text{higher order terms}$$

Also $\tau = h_1 h_2 h_3\,\delta u_1\,\delta u_2\,\delta u_3 + \text{higher order terms}$

Whence $\operatorname{div}\mathbf{a} = \lim_{\tau\to 0}\left[\frac{1}{\tau}\int \mathbf{a}\,.\,\mathbf{n}\,\mathrm{d}S\right]$

$$= \frac{1}{h_1 h_2 h_3}\left[\frac{\partial}{\partial u_1}(a_1 h_2 h_3) + \frac{\partial}{\partial u_2}(a_2 h_3 h_1) + \frac{\partial}{\partial u_3}(a_3 h_1 h_2)\right]$$

Thus for spherical polar coordinates

$$\operatorname{div}\mathbf{a} = \frac{1}{r^2 \sin\theta}\left[\frac{\partial}{\partial r}(a_r r \ \sin\ \theta) + \frac{\partial}{\partial\theta}(a_\theta r \sin\theta) + \frac{\partial}{\partial\psi}(a_\psi r)\right]$$

while in terms of cylindrical polars

$$\operatorname{div}\mathbf{a} = \frac{1}{r}\left[\frac{\partial}{\partial r}(a_r r) + \frac{\partial}{\partial\theta}a_\theta + \frac{\partial}{\partial z}(a_z r)\right]$$

$\nabla^2\phi$. Since $\nabla^2\phi = \operatorname{div}\operatorname{grad}\phi$ we can deduce the curvilinear forms of ∇^2 from these of div and grad. Thus grad ϕ has components $(1/h_1)\partial\phi/\partial u_1$, $(1/h_2)\partial\phi/\partial u_2$, $(1/h_3)\partial\phi/\partial u_3$. Hence

$\nabla^2\phi = \operatorname{div}\operatorname{grad}\phi$

$$= \frac{1}{h_1 h_2 h_3}\left[\frac{\partial}{\partial u_1}\left(\frac{h_2 h_3}{h_1}\frac{\partial\phi}{\partial u_1}\right) + \frac{\partial}{\partial u_2}\left(\frac{h_3 h_1}{h_2}\frac{\partial\phi}{\partial u_2}\right) + \frac{\partial}{\partial u_3}\left(\frac{h_1 h_2}{h_3}\frac{\partial\phi}{\partial u_3}\right)\right]$$

In terms of spherical polar coordinates this becomes

$$\nabla^2\phi = \frac{1}{r^2\sin\theta}\left[\frac{\partial}{\partial r}\left(r^2\sin\theta\,\frac{\partial\phi}{\partial r}\right) + \frac{\partial}{\partial\theta}\left(\sin\theta\,\frac{\partial\phi}{\partial\theta}\right) + \frac{\partial}{\partial\psi}\left(\frac{1}{\sin\theta}\frac{\partial\phi}{\partial\psi}\right)\right]$$

$$= \frac{\partial^2\phi}{\partial r^2} + \frac{2}{r}\frac{\partial\phi}{\partial r} + \frac{1}{r^2}\frac{\partial^2\phi}{\partial\theta^2} + \frac{\cot\theta}{r^2}\frac{\partial\phi}{\partial\theta} + \frac{1}{r^2\sin^2\theta}\frac{\partial^2\phi}{\partial\psi^2}$$

and in cylindrical polars

$$\nabla^2\phi = \frac{1}{r}\left[\frac{\partial}{\partial r}\left(r\frac{\partial\phi}{\partial r}\right) + \frac{\partial}{\partial\theta}\left(\frac{1}{r}\frac{\partial\phi}{\partial\theta}\right) + \frac{\partial}{\partial z}\left(r\frac{\partial\phi}{\partial z}\right)\right]$$

$$= \frac{\partial^2\phi}{\partial r^2} + \frac{1}{r}\frac{\partial\phi}{\partial r} + \frac{1}{r^2}\frac{\partial^2\phi}{\partial\theta^2} + \frac{\partial^2\phi}{\partial z^2}$$

Curl **b**. The component of curl **b** in the u_1 direction can be found (cf. 17.63 corollary) by evaluating $\lim_{S\to 0}\left[\frac{1}{S}\oint \mathbf{b}\,.\,d\mathbf{r}\right]$ where S is an element of area perpendicular to the u_1 direction, i.e. S lies in the plane $u_1=$ constant, and may be represented by $h_2h_3\,\delta u_2\,\delta u_3$, bounded by the contours corresponding to u_2, $u_2+\delta u_2$, u_3, $u_3+\delta u_3$. For a right-handed system of axes circulating round the u_1 direction, we shall, in forming the u_1 component of $\oint \mathbf{b}\,.\,d\mathbf{s}$, travel along $u_2+\delta u_2$ in the direction of u_3 increasing, and return along u_2 in the direction of u_3 decreasing. The contribution from these two sections is thus

$$+\frac{\partial}{\partial u_2}(b_3h_3\,\delta u_3)\,\delta u_2+o(\delta u_2\,\delta u_3)$$

and we note that δu_3 is independent of u_2 so $\frac{\partial}{\partial u_2}(b_3h_3\,\delta u_3)=\frac{\partial}{\partial u_2}(b_3\,h_3)\,\delta u_3$. On the other hand the circuit goes along $u_3+\delta u_3$ in the direction of u_2 decreasing and along u_3 in the increasing direction of u_2; the corresponding term is

$$-\frac{\partial}{\partial u_3}(b_2h_2)\,\delta u_2\,\delta u_3\quad+o(\delta u_2,\,\delta u_3)$$

Hence

$$(\text{curl }\mathbf{b})_1=\lim\left\{\frac{1}{h_2h_3\,\delta u_2\,\delta u_3}\left[\frac{\partial}{\partial u_2}(b_3h_3)-\frac{\partial}{\partial u_3}(b_2h_2)\right]\delta u_2\,\delta u_3\right.$$
$$\left.+\text{higher order terms}\right\}$$

$$=\frac{1}{h_2h_3}\left[\frac{\partial}{\partial u_2}(b_3h_3)-\frac{\partial}{\partial u_3}(b_2h_2)\right]$$

and similarly for the other two components of curl **b**. The spherical polar expression for curl **b** is therefore

$$\text{curl }\mathbf{b}=\frac{1}{r^2\sin\theta}\left[\frac{\partial}{\partial\theta}(b_\psi r\sin\theta)-\frac{\partial}{\partial\psi}(b_\theta r)\right]\mathbf{I}$$
$$+\frac{1}{r\sin\theta}\left[\frac{\partial}{\partial\psi}b_r-\frac{\partial}{\partial r}(b_\psi r\sin\theta)\right]\mathbf{J}+\frac{1}{r}\left[\frac{\partial}{\partial r}(b_\theta r)-\frac{\partial}{\partial\theta}b_r\right]\mathbf{K}$$

I, **J**, **K** being unit vectors in the r, θ, ψ directions respectively. In cylindrical polars

$$\text{curl } \mathbf{b} = \frac{1}{r}\left[\frac{\partial}{\partial\theta}b_z - \frac{\partial}{\partial z}(b_\theta r)\right]\mathbf{I}' + \left[\frac{\partial}{\partial z}b_r - \frac{\partial}{\partial r}b_z\right]\mathbf{J}'$$
$$+\frac{1}{r}\left[\frac{\partial}{\partial r}(b_\theta r) - \frac{\partial}{\partial\theta}b_r\right]\mathbf{K}'$$

I$'$, **J**$'$, **K**$'$ being unit vectors in the r, θ, z directions respectively.

Example 1

Prove that each of the following expressions for ϕ satisfies Laplace's equation $\nabla^2\phi = 0$

(i) $1/r$ (r of spherical polars)

(ii) $2x^2 - y^2 - z^2$

(iii) $r\cos\theta$ (cylindrical polars)

Example 2

If r is a distance measured from a point O, find (i) the cartesian (ii) the spherical polar components of grad $(1/r)$ and verify in each case that curl grad $(1/r) = 0$.

17.8. Theorems of Gauss, Green, and Stokes

17.81. *Gauss's divergence theorem*

This theorem states that

$$\int_\tau \text{div } \mathbf{a} \, d\tau = \int_S \mathbf{a} \cdot \mathbf{n} \, dS \tag{1}$$

where τ denotes a finite volume bounded by the surface S (which may consist of a single closed surface or of a number of non-intersecting closed surfaces), **n** is unit vector normal to the area element dS and directed outwards from the region τ, and **a** is a vector function of position for which div **a** is finite and continuous in the region τ.

The theorem is in fact merely an integrated form of our original definition of div **a** : but since in practice we usually work with one of the alternative expressions for div **a**, such as $\partial a_x/\partial x + \partial a_y/\partial y + \partial a_z/\partial z$ or the spherical polar or cylindrical polar forms of 17.72, the equation (1) embodies a relation which is far from trivial.

To establish the theorem we first note that if S_1 and S_2 are two closed surfaces which have the portion S_{12} in common, but S_1 and S_2 enclose regions on opposite sides of S_{12}, then

$$\int_{S_1} \mathbf{a} \cdot \mathbf{n}_1 \, \mathrm{d}S_1 + \int_{S_2} \mathbf{a} \cdot \mathbf{n}_2 \, \mathrm{d}S_2 = \int_{S_3} \mathbf{a} \cdot \mathbf{n} \, \mathrm{d}S_3 \qquad (2)$$

where S_3 is the surface formed by the non-overlapping parts of S_1 and S_2, i.e. is the surface bounding the volume $\tau_1 + \tau_2$. This is true because on S_{12}, $\mathbf{n}_1 = -\mathbf{n}_2$ i.e. the outgoing normal to S_1 is ingoing to the surface S_2, so we find

$$\int_{S_{12}} \mathbf{a} \cdot \mathbf{n}_1 \, \mathrm{d}S_1 = -\int_{S_{12}} \mathbf{a} \cdot \mathbf{n}_2 \, \mathrm{d}S_2$$

and hence the result (2).

Now let the volume τ which appears in the statement of the theorem (1) be divided into small volumes $\delta\tau_1, \delta\tau_2, \ldots, \delta\tau_i, \ldots$ with surfaces $S_1, S_2, \ldots, S_i, \ldots$, and let $\mathbf{a}_i$ be used to denote the vector $\mathbf{a}$ at points inside S_i, then

$$\operatorname{div} \mathbf{a}_i = (1/\delta\tau_i) \int_{S_i} \mathbf{a} \cdot \mathbf{n}_i \, \mathrm{d}S_i + \epsilon_i$$

where $\epsilon_i \to 0$ as $\delta\tau_i \to 0$. (This follows immediately from the definition of div $\mathbf{a}$.) So, using (2)

$$\begin{aligned}\int_S \mathbf{a} \cdot \mathbf{n} \, \mathrm{d}S &= \int_{S_1} \mathbf{a} \cdot \mathbf{n}_1 \, \mathrm{d}S_1 + \int_{S_2} \mathbf{a} \cdot \mathbf{n}_2 \, \mathrm{d}S_2 + \ldots + \int_{S_i} \mathbf{a} \cdot \mathbf{n}_i \, \mathrm{d}S_i + \ldots \\ &= \operatorname{div} \mathbf{a}_1 \, \delta\tau_1 + \operatorname{div} \mathbf{a}_2 \, \delta\tau_2 + \ldots + \operatorname{div} \mathbf{a}_i \, \delta\tau_i + \ldots \\ &\qquad - \epsilon_1 \, \delta\tau_1 - \epsilon_2 \, \delta\tau_2 - \ldots - \epsilon_i \, \delta\tau_i - \ldots\end{aligned}$$

Now, let each of the volumes $\delta\tau_i \to 0$. We note that $\sum \delta\tau_i = \tau$ is finite, so $\sum \epsilon_i \, \delta\tau_i \to 0$, and we have the result

$$\int_S \mathbf{a} \cdot \mathbf{n} \, \mathrm{d}S = \int_\tau \operatorname{div} \mathbf{a} \, \mathrm{d}\tau$$

17.82. *Green's theorems*

If ϕ_1 and ϕ_2 are scalar functions of position, $\phi_1 \operatorname{grad} \phi_2$ is a vector function of position, and we can put $\mathbf{a} = \phi_1 \operatorname{grad} \phi_2$ in Gauss's divergence theorem.

We have
$$\begin{aligned}\mathbf{a} \cdot \mathbf{n} &= \phi_1 \mathbf{n} \cdot \operatorname{grad} \phi_2 \\ &= \phi_1 \, \partial\phi_2/\partial n\end{aligned}$$

(compare §17.61, equation (3)), and

$$\begin{aligned}\operatorname{div} \mathbf{a} &= \operatorname{div} (\phi_1 \operatorname{grad} \phi_2) \\ &= \phi_1 \nabla^2 \phi_2 + \operatorname{grad} \phi_1 \cdot \operatorname{grad} \phi_2\end{aligned}$$

(from (iv) of 17.72). Hence

$$\int_S \phi_1 \frac{\partial \phi_2}{\partial n} \, \mathrm{d}S = \int_\tau [\phi_1 \nabla^2 \phi_2 + (\operatorname{grad} \phi_1) \cdot (\operatorname{grad} \phi_2)] \, \mathrm{d}\tau \qquad (1)$$

This is the first form of Green's theorem. We note that $(\operatorname{grad} \phi_1) \cdot (\operatorname{grad} \phi_2)$ is symmetrical in ϕ_1 and ϕ_2 and can therefore be eliminated by interchanging ϕ_1 and ϕ_2 and subtracting the result from (1). Thus

$$\int_S \left(\phi_1 \frac{\partial \phi_2}{\partial n} - \phi_2 \frac{\partial \phi_1}{\partial n} \right) \mathrm{d}S = \int_\tau (\phi_1 \nabla^2 \phi_2 - \phi_2 \nabla^2 \phi_1) \, \mathrm{d}\tau \qquad (2)$$

This is the second form of Green's theorem.

17.83. *Stokes' theorem*

If $\mathbf{b}$ is a vector function of position and curl $\mathbf{b}$ is finite and continuous over a surface S whose boundary is the closed curve C, then

$$\begin{aligned}\oint \mathbf{b} \cdot \mathrm{d}\mathbf{s} &= \int_S (\operatorname{curl} \mathbf{b}) \cdot \mathbf{n} \, \mathrm{d}S \\ &= \int_S (\operatorname{curl} b)_n \, \mathrm{d}S\end{aligned}$$

where $\mathrm{d}\mathbf{s}$ is an element of the curve C, $\oint$ denotes the integral round C, and $\mathbf{n}$ is unit normal to the area element $\mathrm{d}S$ in the sense defined by the direction of circulation round C and the right-handed screw convention.

Suppose the area S is divided up into smaller areas δS_1, $\delta S_2, \ldots, \delta S_i, \ldots$ whose boundaries are $C_1, C_2, \ldots, C_i \ldots$ (Fig. 17.14). We can assign directions of circulation as shown so that the edge elements, round C, are described just once and in the same sense as the prescribed path C; while all internal elements are described once in each direction. If we now evaluate

$$\int_{C_1} \mathbf{b} \cdot \mathrm{d}\mathbf{s} + \int_{C_2} \mathbf{b} \cdot \mathrm{d}\mathbf{s} + \ldots$$

we find that the contributions of all internal elements cancel out, so

$$\oint \mathbf{b} \,.\, \mathrm{d}\mathbf{s} = \int_{C_1} \mathbf{b} \,.\, \mathrm{d}\mathbf{s} + \int_{C_2} \mathbf{b} \,.\, \mathrm{d}\mathbf{s} + \ldots + \int_{C_i} \mathbf{b} \,.\, \mathrm{d}\mathbf{s}$$

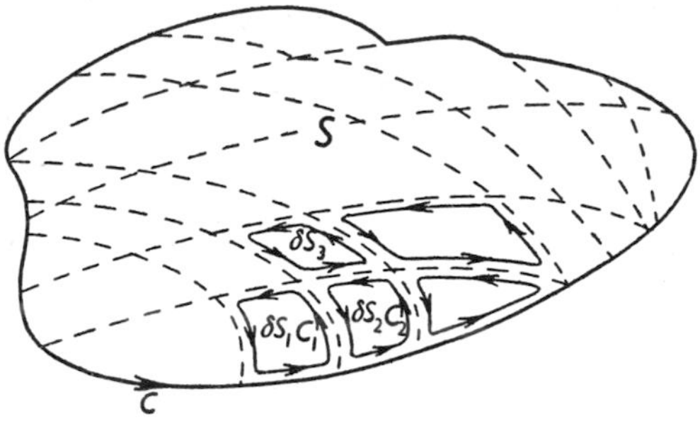

FIG. 17.14

But (cf. 17.53)

$$\int_{C_i} \mathbf{b} \,.\, \mathrm{d}\mathbf{s} = [(\text{curl } \mathbf{b})_i \,.\, \mathbf{n}_i] \, \delta S_i + \epsilon_i \, \delta S_i$$

Hence $$\oint \mathbf{b} \,.\, \mathrm{d}\mathbf{s} = \sum (\text{curl } \mathbf{b})_i \,.\, \mathbf{n}_i \, \delta S_i + \sum \epsilon_i \, \delta S_i$$

As the $\delta S_i \to 0$, $\quad \sum \delta S_i = S \quad$ but $\quad \max |\epsilon_i| \to 0$

Hence $$\oint \mathbf{b} \,.\, \mathrm{d}\mathbf{s} = \oint \text{curl } \mathbf{b} \,.\, \mathbf{n} \, \mathrm{d}S$$

Example 1

By putting $\mathbf{a} = \text{grad } \phi$ in Gauss's divergence theorem prove that $\int_S (\partial\phi/\partial n) \, \mathrm{d}S = \int_\tau \nabla^2\phi \, \mathrm{d}\tau$. (This result is often of use, and may be regarded as a second way of stating the divergence theorem.)

Example 2

By putting $\mathbf{a} = \text{curl } \mathbf{b}$ in the divergence theorem, and invoking Stokes' theorem, verify that $\int \text{div curl } \mathbf{b} \, \mathrm{d}\tau = 0$.

17.9. Vectors in four or more dimensions

In so far as the rules governing the use of vectors can be expressed algebraically we can extend them readily to four or more ' dimensions '. Thus although there can be no geometrical representation of four unit vectors $\mathbf{I}_1$, $\mathbf{I}_2$, $\mathbf{I}_3$, $\mathbf{I}_4$ such that $\mathbf{I}_4$

cannot be expressed in terms of $\mathbf{I}_1$, $\mathbf{I}_2$, $\mathbf{I}_3$, if the algebraic concept of four such vectors is accepted, we can readily define other vectors,

$$\mathbf{a}=a_1\mathbf{I}_1+a_2\mathbf{I}_2+a_3\mathbf{I}_3+a_4\mathbf{I}_4$$

$$\mathbf{b}=b_1\mathbf{I}_1+b_2\mathbf{I}_2+b_3\mathbf{I}_3+b_4\mathbf{I}_4$$

etc. which obey the laws of algebraic manipulation

$$\left.\begin{aligned}\mathbf{a}+\mathbf{b}&=\mathbf{b}+\mathbf{a}\\(\mathbf{a}+\mathbf{b})+\mathbf{c}&=\mathbf{a}+(\mathbf{b}+\mathbf{c})\\k(\mathbf{a}+\mathbf{b})&=k\mathbf{a}+k\mathbf{b}\end{aligned}\right\}\tag{1}$$

and so on.

If $\mathbf{I}_1$, $\mathbf{I}_2$, $\mathbf{I}_3$, $\mathbf{I}_4$ are in some sense 'mutually perpendicular' it is further possible to define the scalar product

$$\mathbf{a}\,.\,\mathbf{b}=a_1b_1+a_2b_2+a_3b_3+a_4b_4\dagger$$

which has the familiar algebraic properties

$$\left.\begin{aligned}\mathbf{a}\,.\,k\mathbf{b}&=k(\mathbf{a}\,.\,\mathbf{b})\\\mathbf{a}\,.\,(\mathbf{b}+\mathbf{c})&=\mathbf{a}\,.\,\mathbf{b}+\mathbf{a}\,.\,\mathbf{c}\quad\text{etc.}\end{aligned}\right\}\tag{2}$$

An analogue to the vector product does not readily suggest itself, and such a quantity will not be used.

The operator $\nabla=\mathbf{i}\,\partial/\partial x+\mathbf{j}\,\partial/\partial y+\mathbf{k}\,\partial/\partial z$ is naturally extended into the four-dimensional operator

$$\Box=\mathbf{I}_1\,\partial/\partial x_1+\mathbf{I}_2\,\partial/\partial x_2+\mathbf{I}_3\,\partial/\partial x_3+\mathbf{I}_4\,\partial/\partial x_4.$$

Then if Φ is a scalar function of (x_1, x_2, x_3, x_4) and $\mathbf{A}$ is a vector function of the same variables we can form

$$\Box\Phi=\mathbf{I}_1\,\partial\Phi/\partial x_1+\mathbf{I}_2\,\partial\Phi/\partial x_2+\mathbf{I}_3\,\partial\Phi/\partial x_3+\mathbf{I}_4\,\partial\Phi/\partial x_4$$

$$\Box\,.\,\mathbf{A}=\partial A_1/\partial x_1+\partial A_2/\partial x_2+\partial A_3/\partial x_3+\partial A_4/\partial x_4$$

$$\Box^2\Phi\equiv\Box\,.\,(\Box\Phi)=\partial^2\Phi/\partial x_1^2+\partial^2\Phi/\partial x_2^2+\partial^2\Phi/\partial x_3^2+\partial^2\Phi/\partial x_4^2$$

However, more is implied by the word vector than the properties of linear combination given in (1) and (2) and the

† This definition of the scalar product is not always the most useful in more than three dimensions. In the four-dimensional space of relativity it is appropriate if imaginary coordinates are admitted in the fourth (time) dimension. If coordinates are restricted to real numbers a more useful definition of scalar product—one which better reflects the geometrical nature of the 'space'—is $\mathbf{a}\,.\,\mathbf{b}=a_1b_1+a_2b_2+a_3b_3-a_4b_4$. However the definition is modified, it is required to satisfy the relations (2) if the name 'scalar product' is to be retained.

possibility of writing down a symbol $\square$: the word vector is normally reserved for an entity which can be described equally well in any number of different systems of reference, i.e. with different sets of unit vectors. This in turn implies the existence of laws of transformation from one set of axes to another.

The structure of the four dimensional space of relativity is expressed by a transformation law of the form,

$$\left.\begin{aligned} x' &= l_1 x + m_1 y + n_1 z + p_1 t \\ y' &= l_2 x + m_2 y + n_2 z + p_2 t \\ z' &= l_3 x + m_3 y + n_3 z + p_3 t \\ t' &= l_4 x + m_4 y + n_4 z + p_4 t \end{aligned}\right\} \qquad (3)$$

In relativity a velocity has the same nature as has a slope in three dimensions (compare dy/dt and dy/dx) ; it is therefore natural that the coefficients l_i, m_i, n_i, p_i in (3) are dependent on the velocities as well as on the inclinations of the new axes relative to the old. The general form of the coefficients in (1) is rather clumsy, but its essence is contained in the ordinary three-dimensional formulae for rotation of axes together with the Lorentz transformation in the simple form

$$\begin{aligned} x' &= \frac{1}{\sqrt{1-v^2/c^2}} \cdot x - \frac{v}{\sqrt{1-v^2/c^2}} \cdot t \\ y' &= y \\ z' &= z \\ t' &= \frac{-v}{c^2\sqrt{1-v^2/c^2}} \cdot x + \frac{1}{\sqrt{1-v^2/c^2}} \cdot t \end{aligned}$$

which is appropriate in the particular case when the x', y', z' axes are parallel to and have a velocity $(v, 0, 0)$ relative to the x, y, z axes.

The vector notation can usefully be retained, too, for problems in the n-dimensional and infinite-dimensional ‘ function spaces ’ of 12.5. The sets of equations (1), (2), (3) above each have their analogues in many-dimensional space ; equations (1) are taken over unchanged ; equations (2) are valid with a suitable redefinition of the scalar product ; and expansion laws such as (1) of 12.34 or (2) of 12.41 provide a means of deducing laws of transformation similar in form to (3).

CHAPTER EIGHTEEN

MATRICES AND DETERMINANTS

18.1. Linear simultaneous equations and linear transformations

A problem encountered early in elementary algebra is that of finding solutions of simultaneous linear equations such as

$$\left.\begin{aligned} a_1x+b_1y+c_1z&=h_1\\ a_2x+b_2y+c_2z&=h_2\\ a_3x+b_3y+c_3z&=h_3 \end{aligned}\right\} \tag{1}$$

Solution can always be attempted by the method of elimination ; this is in fact the basis of some of the numerical processes that are used in practice.

Problems such as the solution of (1) might not seem to merit very intensive study; but in fact, two important ideas in theoretical physics, namely the linear transformation from one set of quantities to another, and the linear dependence of one vector on another, provide equations similar in form to (1); the set of relations

$$\left.\begin{aligned} x_1'&=a_{11}x_1+a_{12}x_2+a_{13}x_3+\dots\\ x_2'&=a_{21}x_1+a_{22}x_2+a_{23}x_3+\dots\\ x_3'&=a_{31}x_1+a_{32}x_2+a_{33}x_3+\dots\\ &\text{etc.} \end{aligned}\right\} \tag{2}$$

with constant coefficients a_{ij} is a typical linear transformation by which one set of numbers $(x_1, x_2, x_3 \dots)$ is transformed into a second set $(x_1', x_2', x_3' \dots)$. In physical applications, the set of numbers $(x_1, x_2, x_3 \dots)$ may represent a composite physical variable of some kind ; the transformation may then indicate how these numbers change when the viewpoint of the observer is changed in some specific way.

For example, if we use two sets of fixed cartesian axes with the same origin but differently oriented in space the coordinates

(x, y, z) and (x', y', z') of a given point P in the two systems are related by

$$\left.\begin{aligned} x' &= l_{11}x + l_{12}y + l_{13}z \\ y' &= l_{21}x + l_{22}y + l_{23}z \\ z' &= l_{31}x + l_{32}y + l_{33}z \end{aligned}\right\} \qquad (3)$$

For another example, suppose that an observer O chooses a set of axes with himself at the origin, and determines, relative to these axes, the coordinates of a certain point P. A second observer O' who is moving with constant velocity relative to O also determines the coordinates of P relative to his own set of axes ; these axes are supposed taken parallel to the ones used by O but moving so that O' is always at the origin. It is supposed that O and O' coincide at time $t=0$ and that the measurements on P are made at a subsequent time which O records as t and O' as t'. Then if the velocity of O' relative to O is small compared with the velocity of light, the relations between the measurements made by O and O' on the coordinates of P are given by the so-called ‘ Galilean transformation ’

$$\left.\begin{aligned} x' &= x - ut \\ y' &= y - vt \\ z' &= z - wt \\ t' &= t \end{aligned}\right\} \qquad (4)$$

where u, v and w are constants, actually the velocity components of O' relative to O's system of axes. If the velocity of O' relative to O is comparable to the velocity of light, the Galilean transformation becomes inaccurate and must be replaced by another linear transformation, the ‘ Lorentz transformation ’ of the special theory of relativity. If the directions of the axes are chosen so that $v=w=0$ this transformation is :

$$\left.\begin{aligned} x' &= \frac{x - ut}{\sqrt{(1 - u^2/c^2)}} \\ y' &= y \\ z' &= z \\ t' &= \frac{t - ux/c^2}{\sqrt{(1 - u^2/c^2)}} \end{aligned}\right\} \qquad (5)$$

where c is the velocity of light.

The variables involved in a linear transformation need not be coordinates of a point. The components A_x, A_y, A_z of a vector **A** also transform under rotation of axes according to a scheme similar to (3). Thus

$$\left.\begin{aligned} A_x' &= l_{11}A_x + l_{12}A_y + l_{13}A_z \\ A_y' &= l_{21}A_x + l_{22}A_y + l_{23}A_z \\ A_z' &= l_{31}A_x + l_{32}A_y + l_{33}A_z \end{aligned}\right\} \qquad (6)$$

An important part is played in quantum theory by linear transformations of the type (6). Suppose that an arbitrary function f(x) can be represented by a series such as

$$\mathrm{f}(x) = a_1\phi_1(x) + a_2\phi_2(x) + a_3\phi_3(x) + \ldots$$

where the ϕ's are a given set of standard functions of some kind. Then the set of coefficients represented by the symbol $(a_1, a_2, a_3, \ldots)$ may be considered to represent the function f(x). If now the basic functions $\phi(x)$ are replaced by a new set $\phi'(x)$, the new expansion of f becomes

$$f = a_1'\phi_1'(x) + a_2'\phi_2'(x) + \ldots$$

and the symbol representing f(x) becomes $(a_1', a_2', a_3' \ldots)$. Under certain conditions, the relation between the numbers a' and the numbers a is given by a scheme analogous to (6), and the transformation from one set of basic functions to another is analogous to a rotation of cartesian axes in function space (see 12.5); an infinite number of dimensions is required in general.

A second class of example leading to similar relations arises when one vector is linearly dependent on another. Thus the components of electric polarisation **P** in a crystalline dielectric are related to those of the electric field **E** by

$$\left.\begin{aligned} P_1 &= a_{11}E_1 + a_{12}E_2 + a_{13}E_3 \\ P_2 &= a_{21}E_1 + a_{22}E_2 + a_{23}E_3 \\ P_3 &= a_{31}E_1 + a_{32}E_2 + a_{33}E_3 \end{aligned}\right\} \qquad (7)$$

The nine coefficients a_{11}, a_{12}, a_{13} etc. take the place of the single constant α that suffices in the corresponding relation $\mathbf{P} = \alpha\mathbf{E}$ for an isotropic dielectric.

A third class of example is encountered in network analysis in alternating current theory. If the inputs to a given network are voltages or currents x_1, x_2, x_3 etc. and the outputs are y_1, y_2, y_3 etc., then under certain conditions the outputs y_i are related to the inputs x_i by a set of relations

$$\left.\begin{aligned} y_1 &= a_{11}x_1 + a_{12}x_2 + \ldots + a_{1n}x_n \\ y_2 &= a_{21}x_1 + a_{22}x_2 + \ldots + a_{2n}x_n \\ y_3 &= a_{31}x_1 + a_{32}x_2 + \ldots + a_{3n}x_n \end{aligned}\right\} \tag{8}$$

where the numbers a_{ij} are determined by the values of the resistances, inductances etc. of the various elements in the circuit.

This example illustrates incidentally that the number of equations need not be equal to the number of variables. For example there may be more input than output terminals ; if so the equations will not be soluble uniquely for the x_i in terms of the y_i; a given output, i.e. set of y_i, can be realised by more than one set of inputs. If however there are more output than input terminals, the y_i's will not all be independent; in this case one cannot choose a set of inputs x_i to produce an arbitrary set of outputs y_i.

18.2. Matrices

We now consider a typical transformation such as

$$\left.\begin{aligned} y_1 &= a_{11}x_1 + a_{12}x_2 + a_{13}x_3 \\ y_2 &= a_{21}x_1 + a_{22}x_2 + a_{23}x_3 \\ y_3 &= a_{31}x_1 + a_{32}x_2 + a_{33}x_3 \end{aligned}\right\} \tag{1}$$

We shall adopt initially the point of view that the x's are a given set of numbers specifying a given input into a circuit and that the y's specify the resulting output. The set of coefficients a_{ij} specifies the circuit and does not depend on the input or the output. The other kinds of application mentioned above (changes of axes and relations between vectors) can also be regarded from this point of view. Thus, the coordinates of the point (x_1, x_2, x_3) in equations (2) of 18.1 become the input data, the numbers (x_1', x_2', x_3') the output data, and the numbers a_{ij} specify the transformation. [If the set of equations arises in the process of calculating points of intersection of lines or planes, or from the solution of a set of simultaneous equations such as (1) of 18.1 the description of the x's as input data and the h's as output data becomes a somewhat formal analogy.]

In equations (1) the variables and coefficients have been distinguished by numerical suffixes, rather than by different letters. This may be an unfamiliar notation ; (x, y, z) for example is more familiar than (x_1, x_2, x_3) for the coordinates of a point. However, the advantages of the numerical suffix notation are very considerable ; it imposes no restriction on the number of variables, and enables summation over the values of the suffix to be indicated compactly by means of a summation sign ($\sum$). The usual convention is that in a coefficient a_{ij} the *first* suffix refers to the *row* and the *second* letter to the *column*, i.e. a_{23} is the coefficient in the second row and third column on the right hand side of equation (1).

We now consider the possibility of abbreviating equation (1) into the single statement

$$\mathbf{y} = \mathbf{A}\mathbf{x} \tag{2}$$

The single letters **x** and **y** represent symbolically the whole of the input and output data, and are not single numbers as they are in ordinary algebra. Similarly **A** represents the whole set of coefficients a_{ij}. Equation (2) implies that the result of operating on the input numbers **x** by the coefficients in **A** (according to the detailed instructions specified by equation (1)), gives the output **y**.

This step would appear to be nothing more than an abbreviated notation were it not for the very remarkable discovery that the quantities **x**, **y**, **A** are found to obey an algebra very similar to ordinary algebra in all but a few respects. An essential feature of this algebra is that the entity symbolised by **A** has an existence apart from the symbol **x** ; it can be treated as a separate entity and can be added and multiplied by other symbols representing other transformations. In this algebra the right hand of equation (2) is a simple product of the two quantities **A** and **x**.

These quantities **A**, **x** and **y** are examples of matrices. Thus **x** and **y** are column matrices of order 3×1 (3 rows and 1 column)

$$\mathbf{x} = \begin{pmatrix} x_1 \\ x_2 \\ x_3 \end{pmatrix} \qquad \mathbf{y} = \begin{pmatrix} y_1 \\ y_2 \\ y_3 \end{pmatrix} \tag{3}$$

and A is a square matrix of order 3×3 (3 rows and 3 columns)

$$\mathbf{A}=\begin{pmatrix} a_{11} & a_{12} & a_{13} \\ a_{21} & a_{22} & a_{23} \\ a_{31} & a_{32} & a_{33} \end{pmatrix} \tag{4}$$

A matrix, in the general case, is a set of $m \times n$ numbers, the 'elements' of the matrix, arranged in a rectangular array of m rows and n columns

$$\mathbf{A}=\begin{pmatrix} a_{11} & a_{12} & \cdots & a_{1n} \\ a_{21} & a_{22} & \cdots & a_{2n} \\ \cdots & \cdots & \cdots & \cdots \\ a_{m1} & a_{m2} & \cdots & a_{mn} \end{pmatrix} \tag{5}$$

Matrices such as (4) and (5) are sometimes denoted by the abbreviated form (a_{ij}).

The numbers m, n of rows and columns, respectively, in a matrix need not be equal, but apart from column matrices ($n=1$), far the most important kind of matrix in applications is that for which $m=n$; such a matrix is called 'square' or 'n by n'; many of the properties with which we will be concerned later are restricted to square matrices.

We must now set up an algebra of matrices, in which the symbols stand for rectangular arrays such as (5). The rules of the algebra of matrices—that is the definitions of what is meant by addition and multiplication as applied to them—have been adopted as being the most convenient for the manipulation of linear transformations and the solution of linear equations. We take the electrical network application as an illustration of some of these rules; in this application the column matrices represent inputs or outputs, and a rectangular matrix of m rows and n columns represents a network with n inputs and m outputs.

Two $m \times n$ matrices **A** and **B** are called *equal* if each element a_{ij} of **A** is equal to the corresponding element b_{ij} of **B**. In terms of the network application, for any specified input, the outputs of networks **A** and **B** are the same.

The sum of $m \times n$ such matrices is defined as the matrix for which each element is the sum of the corresponding elements of **A** and **B**; that is if $\mathbf{A}=(a_{ij})$, $\mathbf{B}=(b_{ij})$, then $\mathbf{A}+\mathbf{B}$ is the matrix $(a_{ij}+b_{ij})$. It follows from this definition that

$$\mathbf{Ax}+\mathbf{Bx}=(\mathbf{A}+\mathbf{B})\mathbf{x}$$
$$\mathbf{A}+\mathbf{B}=\mathbf{B}+\mathbf{A}$$
$$(\mathbf{A}+\mathbf{B})+\mathbf{C}=\mathbf{A}+(\mathbf{B}+\mathbf{C})$$

18.21. *Multiplication of matrices*

To consider the product of two matrices, suppose the output from network A is applied to a network B having the same number of *input* terminals as the number of *output* terminals of A (see Fig. 18.1); and suppose B has a high input impedance, so that the currents in the wires connecting A to B are negligibly small and the output potentials y_j from A are not affected by the connection to B.

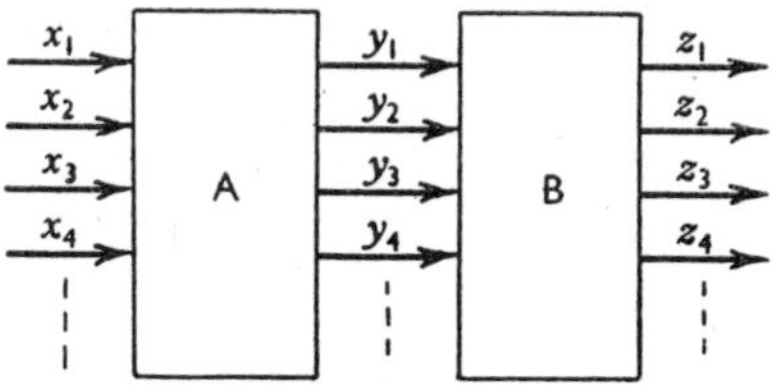

FIG. 18.1

Let **z** be the final result i.e. the set of output currents from B, then

$$\mathbf{y}=\mathbf{Ax}$$
$$\mathbf{z}=\mathbf{By}$$

Formal elimination of **y** gives

$$\mathbf{z}=\mathbf{B}(\mathbf{Ax})$$

Written out in full, this expresses the elements z_i of **z** as homogeneous linear functions of the elements x_j of **x**; hence there is a matrix **C** such that $\mathbf{z}=\mathbf{Cx}$. This matrix **C** is called the ' product ' **BA** (in this order) of the matrices **A** and **B**; in the

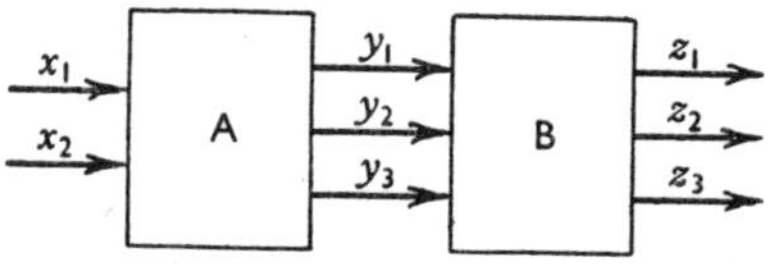

FIG. 18.2

network application it is the matrix of the network formed by putting the networks A and B in series, with the input applied to A.

The elements of this product matrix can now be found by direct calculation from those of **A** and **B**. Suppose for example that the matrix **A** is of order 3×2 and **B** of order 3×3 (Fig. 18.2) Then

$$\left.\begin{aligned} y_1 &= a_{11}x_1 + a_{12}x_2 \\ y_2 &= a_{21}x_1 + a_{22}x_2 \\ y_3 &= a_{31}x_1 + a_{32}x_2 \end{aligned}\right\} \tag{1}$$

and

$$\left.\begin{aligned} z_1 &= b_{11}y_1 + b_{12}y_2 + b_{13}y_3 \\ z_2 &= b_{21}y_1 + b_{22}y_2 + b_{23}y_3 \\ z_3 &= b_{31}y_1 + b_{32}y_2 + b_{33}y_3 \end{aligned}\right\} \tag{2}$$

Eliminating the y's from (2) and (1), gives (z_1, z_2, z_3) in terms of (x_1, x_2) ; expressed in matrix form, the result is

$$\begin{pmatrix} z_1 \\ z_2 \\ z_3 \end{pmatrix} = \begin{pmatrix} b_{11}a_{11} + b_{12}a_{21} + b_{13}a_{31} & b_{11}a_{12} + b_{12}a_{22} + b_{13}a_{32} \\ b_{21}a_{11} + b_{22}a_{21} + b_{23}a_{31} & b_{21}a_{12} + b_{22}a_{22} + b_{23}a_{32} \\ b_{31}a_{11} + b_{32}a_{21} + b_{32}a_{31} & b_{31}a_{12} + b_{32}a_{22} + b_{33}a_{32} \end{pmatrix} \begin{pmatrix} x_1 \\ x_2 \end{pmatrix} \tag{3}$$

The 3×2 matrix in (3) is the product **BA**, of the matrices

$$\mathbf{A} = \begin{pmatrix} a_{11} & a_{12} \\ a_{21} & a_{22} \\ a_{31} & a_{32} \end{pmatrix} \quad \text{and} \quad \mathbf{B} = \begin{pmatrix} b_{11} & b_{12} & b_{13} \\ b_{21} & b_{22} & b_{23} \\ b_{31} & b_{32} & b_{33} \end{pmatrix}$$

Each element of the matrix $\mathbf{C} = \mathbf{BA}$ is constructed according to the formula

$$\begin{aligned} c_{ij} &= b_{i1}a_{1j} + b_{i2}a_{2j} + b_{i3}a_{3j} \\ &= \sum_{k=1}^{3} b_{ik}a_{kj} \end{aligned} \tag{4}$$

The condition that the number of output terminals on network A is equal to the number of inputs to network B implies that the number of rows in matrix **A** must equal the number of columns of **B**. Thus if **A** is of order $m \times n$, **B** must be of order $l \times m$; and **BA** is then of order $l \times n$.

As an aid to remembering the product rule of equation (4) notice that the element $(\mathbf{BA})_{ij}$ is formed entirely from elements of the form $b_{ik}a_{kj}$ and that the adjacent suffices (represented by k) are equal and summed over all possible values, thus

$$(\mathbf{BA})_{ij} = b_{i1}a_{1j} + b_{i2}a_{2j} + b_{i3}a_{3j}$$

We have been led to this product rule by considerations of a partly physical nature. These considerations can now be abandoned and we define the product of two matrices $\mathbf{A} = (a_{ij})$ of order $m \times n$, $\mathbf{B} = (b_{ij})$ of order $l \times m$ by the rule : **BA** is a matrix of order $l \times n$ with elements given by

$$(\mathbf{BA})_{ij} = \sum_{k=1}^{m} b_{ik}a_{kj} \tag{5}$$

Notice that the letter (here k) used on the right to indicate the suffix over which summations are carried does not appear when the sum is written out in full; any letter, other than i or j, would serve. Such a suffix is sometimes called a ‘ dummy suffix ’ (cf. dummy variable in 5.9).

An important point now appears which distinguishes matrix algebra from ordinary algebra, namely the matrix **AB** is not generally equal to **BA**. To begin with unless **A** and **B** are square matrices of the same order, **AB** and **BA** do not both exist. If however **A** and **B** are both of order $m \times m$ say, then

$$(\mathbf{AB})_{ij} = \sum_{k=1}^{m} a_{ik}b_{kj}$$

and

$$(\mathbf{BA})_{ij} = \sum_{k=1}^{m} b_{ik}a_{kj};$$

these two sets of numbers are not in general equal. For example taking $m = 3$ we have

$$(\mathbf{AB})_{21} = a_{21}b_{11} + a_{22}b_{21} + a_{23}b_{31}$$

and

$$(\mathbf{BA})_{21} = b_{21}a_{11} + b_{22}a_{21} + b_{23}a_{31}$$

These are not equal if the a's and b's are given arbitrary values, although, of course, they may be in special cases. Matrix multiplication is therefore non-commutative apart from special cases. If $\mathbf{AB} = \mathbf{BA}$ we say that the matrices **A**, **B** commute.

From the network analogy we can expect that multiplication will be associative, i.e. that the product of three or more matrices is the same no matter how the factors are associated : thus

$$\mathbf{A}(\mathbf{BC}) = (\mathbf{AB})\mathbf{C}$$

Physically, the network corresponding to $\mathbf{A}(\mathbf{BC})$ is obtained by joining $\mathbf{B}$ and $\mathbf{C}$ together into a single network and then joining $\mathbf{A}$ on to this combination whereas $(\mathbf{AB})\mathbf{C}$ is obtained by joining $\mathbf{A}$ to $\mathbf{B}$ and then the combination on to $\mathbf{C}$. There is of course no difference in the result. Obviously the only point that matters is the order of $\mathbf{A}$, $\mathbf{B}$ and $\mathbf{C}$ in the final product. This can be proved formally by writing out the full expression for the (i, j)th element of each of the matrices.

Matrix multiplication is also distributive; this can also be proved formally by writing out the full expression for the (i, j)th element of $\mathbf{A}(\mathbf{B}+\mathbf{C})$.

Since multiplication of matrices is not in general commutative, it is necessary to distinguish between the processes of forming, from matrices $\mathbf{A}$ and $\mathbf{B}$, the matrices $\mathbf{AB}$ and $\mathbf{BA}$. Multiplication to produce $\mathbf{BA}$ is called ‘ premultiplication ’ of $\mathbf{A}$ by $\mathbf{B}$ and multiplication to produce $\mathbf{AB}$ is called ‘ post-multiplication ’ of $\mathbf{A}$ by $\mathbf{B}$.

Example 1

If the equation

$$\mathbf{y} = \mathbf{A}\mathbf{x}$$

is written out in full, as follows

$$\begin{pmatrix} y_1 \\ y_2 \\ y_3 \end{pmatrix} = \begin{pmatrix} a_{11} & a_{12} & a_{13} \\ a_{21} & a_{22} & a_{23} \\ a_{31} & a_{32} & a_{33} \end{pmatrix} \begin{pmatrix} x_1 \\ x_2 \\ x_3 \end{pmatrix}$$

it will be noticed that the expansion of the product on the right, according to the multiplication rule gives

$$\begin{pmatrix} y_1 \\ y_2 \\ y_3 \end{pmatrix} = \begin{pmatrix} a_{11}x_1 + a_{12}x_2 + a_{13}x_3 \\ a_{21}x_1 + a_{22}x_2 + a_{23}x_3 \\ a_{31}x_1 + a_{32}x_2 + a_{33}x_3 \end{pmatrix}$$

Example 2

The unit matrix. Networks that simply reproduce the input (possibly at a higher power level) are often used. The matrix of such a network is easily verified to be square with elements unity along the principal diagonal and zero elsewhere, i.e. $a_{ij} = 1$ if $i = j$ and 0 if $i \neq j$. A matrix of this kind is called a unit matrix and is denoted by $\mathbf{I}$. The unit matrix of order 3×3 is

$$\mathbf{I} = \begin{pmatrix} 1 & 0 & 0 \\ 0 & 1 & 0 \\ 0 & 0 & 1 \end{pmatrix}$$

Example 3

The null matrix. A matrix, all of whose elements are zero, is called a null matrix, and is denoted usually by **0**. The unit and null matrices take the place of unity and zero in ordinary algebra.

Example 4

Factors of zero. The product of two matrices may be a null matrix although neither factor is null. Thus if

$$\mathbf{A}=\begin{pmatrix}1 & 0\\ 0 & 0\end{pmatrix},\ \mathbf{B}=\begin{pmatrix}0 & 0\\ 0 & 1\end{pmatrix}\quad \text{then}\quad \mathbf{BA}=\mathbf{AB}=\begin{pmatrix}0 & 0\\ 0 & 0\end{pmatrix}$$

A simple pair of networks illustrating this situation is indicated in Fig. 18.3. A passes an input on its first terminal and suppresses the input on its second. B does the opposite. When A and B are connected in series there is no output on either terminal, whatever the input is.

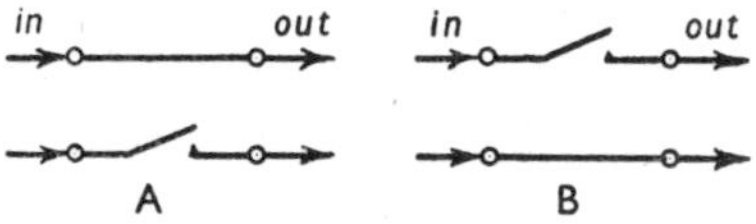

FIG. 18.3

The last example serves to show that the analogy between matrix and ordinary algebra, although very close, is not complete; consequently some care must be used especially in applying familiar algebraic formulae. For example, exactly as in ordinary algebra, one finds that

$$(\mathbf{A}+\mathbf{B})^2=\mathbf{A}^2+\mathbf{AB}+\mathbf{BA}+\mathbf{B}^2$$

but the further reduction of the right-hand side to $\mathbf{A}^2+2\mathbf{AB}+\mathbf{B}^2$, automatic in the algebra of numbers, is not permissible in matrix algebra, unless **A** and **B** happen to commute.

18.3. The solution of simultaneous equations, and the inverse matrix

The matrix equation

$$\mathbf{Ax}=\mathbf{h} \tag{1}$$

where **A** is a square matrix of order $n\times n$, represents n simultaneous equations of the form

$$a_{i1}x_1+a_{i2}x_2+\ldots+a_{in}x_n=h_i \tag{2}$$

Unless there is a particular relation between the coefficients a_{ij} (see 18.62) these n equations can be solved to give $(x_1, x_2, \ldots)$

in terms of $(h_1, h_2, \ldots)$. This solution can be expressed in matrix form as follows. Suppose that there is a matrix $\mathbf{B}$ such that $\mathbf{BA}=\mathbf{I}$, the unit $n \times n$ matrix. The premultiplication of (1) by $\mathbf{B}$ gives

$$\mathbf{x}=\mathbf{Bh} \tag{3}$$

since

$$\mathbf{BAx}=\mathbf{Ix}=\mathbf{x}$$

$\mathbf{B}$ is called the 'inverse' (sometimes the 'reciprocal') of the matrix $\mathbf{A}$ and is written $\mathbf{A}^{-1}$ so that (3) is written $\mathbf{x}=\mathbf{A}^{-1}\mathbf{h}$. It follows that the solution of simultaneous equations and the inversion of a square matrix are different aspects of a single problem. In the solution of this problem an important part is played by a quantity called the determinant of the coefficients a_{ij}. The next section contains a discussion of this quantity; we return to the reciprocal matrix and the solution of simultaneous equations in 18.6.

18.4. The determinant of a square matrix

We begin by giving a set of rules for calculating a certain number from the elements of a square matrix. The point of this calculation will not appear until 18.5 and until then the whole procedure may seem somewhat artificial.

Let $\mathbf{A}$ be a square matrix of order $n \times n$:

$$\mathbf{A}=\begin{pmatrix} a_{11} & a_{12} & \cdots & a_{1n} \\ a_{21} & a_{22} & \cdots & a_{2n} \\ \cdots & \cdots & \cdots & \cdots \\ a_{n1} & a_{n2} & \cdots & a_{nn} \end{pmatrix} \tag{1}$$

The determinant of the matrix is a sum of products of elements of the matrix, formed in the following way.

Let

$$a_{1\alpha}a_{2\beta}a_{3\gamma}\ldots a_{n\nu} \tag{2}$$

be a product of elements of which no two belong to the same row (so that the row suffixes $1, 2, 3, \ldots, n$ are all unequal) and no two belong to the same column (so that the column suffixes $\alpha, \beta, \ldots, \nu$ are all unequal); and let the factors be arranged with the row suffixes in their natural order. There are $n!$ such products in all, for the column suffix α may have any value from 1 to n; for each value of α, β may have any of the $(n-1)$ values not equal to the value of α, and so on.

The column suffixes in the order $(\alpha, \beta, \dots, \nu)$ are a permutation of the numbers $(1, 2, \dots, n)$ in their natural order; such a permutation is called 'even' or 'odd' according as an even or odd number of interchanges of pairs of numbers is required to bring the ordered set of integers $(\alpha, \beta, \dots, \nu)$ into the natural order $(1, 2 \dots, n)$; two permutations are called 'of the same parity' if they are both even or both odd. The parity of a permutation is independent of the steps of the rearrangement.

The *determinant* of the matrix $\mathbf{A}$ is defined as the sum

$$\sum \pm a_{1\alpha} a_{2\beta} a_{3\gamma} \dots a_{n\nu} \tag{3}$$

of $n!$ terms of the type (2), in each of which $(\alpha, \beta, \dots, \nu)$ is a different one of the $n!$ permutations of the numbers $(1, 2, \dots, n)$, and the products are taken with a $+$ or a $-$ sign according as the permutation is even or odd. Note that if the values of the a_{ij} are known, the determinant is a single number.

The notations used for the determinant of matrix $\mathbf{A}$, include det $\mathbf{A}$, $|\mathbf{A}|$, $|a_{ij}|$ and, if the elements are to be shown in full,

$$\begin{vmatrix} a_{11} & a_{12} & \dots & a_{1n} \\ a_{21} & a_{22} & \dots & a_{2n} \\ a_{n1} & a_{n2} & \dots & a_{nn} \end{vmatrix}$$

Although the determinant of a square matrix is *defined* as the sum (3), it is seldom necessary, or advisable, to write out this sum in full in handling determinants. For determinants of even moderate size this becomes impracticable (a determinant of order 8 has over 40,000 terms). In most cases it is advisable to use other properties derived from the definition. Almost the only case which it is often convenient to write out in full is a determinant of order 2, for which there are 2! terms, namely $a_{11}a_{22}$ and $a_{12}a_{21}$. In the first term the column suffixes are 1, 2 which is in the natural order and is therefore an even permutation. In the second the column suffixes are 21 which requires one interchange to give the natural order. Hence

$$\begin{vmatrix} a_{11} & a_{12} \\ a_{21} & a_{22} \end{vmatrix} = a_{11}a_{22} - a_{12}a_{21}$$

18.41. *Properties of determinants*

The following are the more important general properties of determinants.

(i) If two columns of a determinant are interchanged, the

determinant changes sign. To see this let $|\mathbf{A}|$ be a determinant and let $|\mathbf{A}'|$ be the result of interchanging columns ρ and σ. In the expansion of $|\mathbf{A}|$, there will be a term

$$a_{1\alpha}a_{2\beta} \dots a_{r\rho} \dots a_{s\sigma} \dots a_{n\nu} \tag{1}$$

and also a term

$$a_{1\alpha}a_{2\beta} \dots a_{r\sigma} \dots a_{s\rho} \dots a_{n\nu} \tag{2}$$

with the same values of $(\alpha, \beta, \dots, \nu)$. In the expansion of $|\mathbf{A}'|$ there will be a term

$$a'_{1\alpha}a'_{2\beta} \dots a'_{r\rho} \dots a'_{s\sigma} \dots a'_{n\nu} \tag{3}$$

Now (1) and (2) will be given opposite signs since there is one interchange of column suffixes, whereas (1) and (3) will have the same sign. (2) and (3) will therefore have opposite signs. But (2) is identically equal to (3), since $a'_{r\rho}=a_{r\sigma}$, $a_{s\sigma}'=a'_{s\rho}$ and the other elements are unchanged. Hence to every term (2) in the expansion of $|\mathbf{A}|$ there is an equal and opposite term in that of $|\mathbf{A}'|$. Hence $|\mathbf{A}'| = -|\mathbf{A}|$.

A similar proof shows that the determinant also changes sign when two rows are interchanged.

(ii) An important consequence is that if two rows are identical, the determinant must vanish.

(iii) The determinant is unaltered when rows and columns are interchanged. By definition the value of the determinant before interchange is

$$|a_{ij}| = \sum \pm a_{1\alpha}a_{2\beta} \dots a_{n\nu} \tag{4}$$

Now interchange rows and columns and let the new elements be denoted by a'_{ij} where

$$a'_{ij} = a_{ji} \tag{5}$$

Then the new determinant $|\mathbf{A}'|$ will by definition be a sum similar to (1):

$$|\mathbf{A}'| = \sum \pm a'_{1\alpha}a'_{2\beta} \dots a'_{n\nu} \tag{6}$$

$$= \sum \pm a_{\alpha 1}a_{\beta 2} \dots a_{\nu n} \tag{7}$$

using (5).

Now rearrange the factors in each product in (7) so that the row suffixes for the determinant $|\mathbf{A}'|$ revert to the natural order. In the process let the column suffixes become permuted to $\alpha'\beta' \dots \nu'$. Then (7) becomes

$$|\mathbf{A}'| = \sum \pm a_{1\alpha'}a_{2\beta'} \dots a_{n\nu} \tag{8}$$

Now expansion (8) consists of the same terms as expansion (4), apart, possibly, from the question of signs ; there remains the question whether the parity of $\alpha\beta\ldots\nu$ is the same as that of $\alpha'\beta'\ldots\nu'$. However, by comparing (7) and (8) we see that the same rearrangement which permutes $\alpha, \beta, \ldots, \nu$ to $1, 2 \ldots, n$, also permutes $1, 2, \ldots, n$, to $\alpha', \beta' \ldots, \nu'$. Hence $\alpha, \beta, \ldots, \nu$ and $\alpha', \beta', \ldots, \nu'$ are of the same parity and therefore the terms in (4) and (7) are not only of the same magnitude but have the same sign. Hence a determinant is unaffected by transposition of rows and columns. The transposed *matrix* on the other hand is in general a new matrix.

18.42. *The co-factors of the elements of a determinant*

In the expansion of a determinant of order $n \times n$ there are $n!$ terms of the form

$$\pm a_{1\alpha} a_{2\beta} \ldots a_{n\nu} \tag{1}$$

Each of these terms contains one and only one of the elements a_{1k} with row suffix 1. If all those containing a_{11} are grouped together, then all those containing a_{12}, and so on, the result is an expression of the form

$$| a_{ij} | = a_{11}A_{11} + a_{12}A_{12} + a_{13}A_{13} + \ldots = \sum_k a_{1k}A_{1k} \tag{2}$$

The quantities A_{1k} in this expansion are called the ' co-factors ' of the respective matrix elements a_{1k}. Similarly, if the term involving any particular matrix element, say a_{rs} with specified values of r and s, is $a_{rs}A_{rs}$, then A_{rs} is called the ' co-factor ' of a_{rs}, and the determinant can be expressed in terms of the elements of any row and their co-factors :

$$| a_{ij} | = \sum_s a_{rs}A_{rs} \tag{3}$$

(r being the same in all terms of the sum).

An important result now appears ; namely, each of these co-factors is itself a determinant of a subset of elements of the matrix a_{ij}. For example, consider the term involving a_{11} in (2). This is

$$a_{11} \sum \pm a_{2\beta} a_{3\gamma} \ldots a_{n\nu} \tag{4}$$

In this sum there are $(n-1)!$ terms, obtained by permuting the $(n-1)$ column suffixes $(\beta, \ldots, \nu)$. The sum here contains elements properly selected from the reduced determinant obtained by deleting the first row and column from the original determinant $| a_{ij} |$. There remains the question of sign. This is the sign which is determined in equation (1), and therefore in (4) also, by the parity of the permutation $1, \beta, \gamma, \ldots, \nu$ but, since the initial column suffix is already in its natural position, the parity of $1, \beta, \gamma, \ldots, \nu$ is the same as the parity of $\beta, \gamma, \ldots, \nu$ in (4). Hence equation (3) is a correct expansion in accordance with the rules of 18.4 of this reduced determinant ; hence

$$A_{11} = \begin{vmatrix} a_{22} & \cdots & a_{2n} \\ \cdot & \cdots & \cdot \\ \cdot & \cdots & \cdot \\ \cdot & \cdots & \cdot \\ \cdot & \cdots & \cdot \\ a_{n2} & \cdots & a_{nn} \end{vmatrix} \tag{5}$$

The co-factor of any other element a_{ij} is also a determinant, obtained (apart from sign) by deleting the ith row and jth column in $| \mathbf{A} |$. To establish the sign it is simplest to bring the element a_{ij} into the leading position (i.e. first row and first column) without changing the order of the other rows and columns ; this involves $i+j-2$ interchanges, so the determinant is multiplied by $(-1)^{i+j}$. Deletion of the first row and column in the determinant as rearranged has the same result as deleting the ith row and jth column in the original determinant. Hence

$$A_{ij} = (-1)^{i+j} \times [\text{determinant formed by deleting } i\text{th row and } j\text{th column from det } \mathbf{A}] \tag{6}$$

The determinant formed by deleting the ith row and jth column from det $\mathbf{A}$ is called the 'minor' of a_{ij}; in most contexts, co-factors are more convenient to use than minors.

Instead of expressing the determinant $| a_{ij} |$ as the sum of multiples of elements of a single *row*, as in (3), it can be expressed in terms of elements of a column :

$$| a_{ij} | = \sum_r a_{rs} A_{rs} \tag{7}$$

For any particular values of r and s, the contribution to the determinant from the terms involving a_{rs} is $a_{rs}A_{rs}$, whether this term occurs as part of a sum over column suffixes as in (3) or over row suffixes as in (7).

18.43. *Sum of products with 'alien co-factors'*

An important result is obtained if we form a sum of products of elements of one row of a determinant with co-factors of elements of another row. Consider for example the expression

$$a_{21}A_{11}+a_{22}A_{12}+a_{23}A_{13}+\dots \tag{1}$$

where the elements are those of the second row and the co-factors are those of the elements of the first row. This can be recognised as the expansion not of $|\,\mathbf{A}\,|$ but of the determinant

$$\begin{vmatrix} a_{21} & a_{22} & \dots & a_{2n} \\ a_{21} & a_{22} & \dots & a_{2n} \\ a_{31} & a_{32} & \dots & a_{3n} \\ \dots & \dots & \dots & \dots \\ a_{n1} & a_{n2} & \dots & a_{nn} \end{vmatrix} \tag{2}$$

for (2) is obtained from (2) of 18.42 by replacing each a_{1k} by the corresponding a_{2k}. This determinant (2), which is another way of writing the expression (1), has two rows equal and therefore vanishes. Similarly

$$\sum_k a_{ik}A_{jk}=0 \quad \text{for } j\neq i \tag{3}$$

Whereas from (2) of 18.42

$$\sum_k a_{ik}A_{ik}=|\,\mathbf{A}\,| \tag{4}$$

Similarly an expression like

$$a_{12}A_{11}+a_{22}A_{21}+a_{32}A_{31}+\dots=a_{k2}A_{k1} \tag{5}$$

consisting of the sum of products of elements of one *column* with the co-factors of corresponding elements of another *column* is zero, and in general

$$\sum_k a_{ki}A_{kj}=0 \quad \text{for } j\neq i \tag{6}$$

whereas from (7) of 18.42

$$\sum_k a_{ki}A_{ki}=|\,\mathbf{A}\,| \tag{7}$$

An expression like (1) and (5), or more generally, the left-hand sides of (3) and (6), is sometimes called a sum of products with (or 'expansion by') 'alien co-factors'; such expressions always vanish, because they represent determinants with two equal rows or two equal columns.

Example

If

$$|a_{ij}| = \begin{vmatrix} 1 & 0 & 3 \\ 2 & 1 & 4 \\ 0 & 1 & 3 \end{vmatrix}, \quad A_{11} = \begin{vmatrix} 1 & 4 \\ 1 & 3 \end{vmatrix} = -1, \quad A_{12} = -\begin{vmatrix} 2 & 4 \\ 0 & 3 \end{vmatrix} = -6,$$

$$A_{13} = \begin{vmatrix} 2 & 1 \\ 0 & 1 \end{vmatrix} = +2$$

$$a_{21}A_{11} + a_{22}A_{12} + a_{23}A_{13} = 2 \times (-1) + 1 \times (-6) + 4 \times (+2) = 0$$

The reader should verify that the other sum of products with alien co-factors also vanish.

18.44. *A further property of determinants*

The addition of a multiple of the jth row (or jth column) to the ith row (or ith column) does not alter a determinant. For example let

$$|\mathbf{A}| = \begin{vmatrix} a_{11} & a_{12} & a_{13} \\ a_{21} & a_{22} & a_{23} \\ a_{31} & a_{32} & a_{33} \end{vmatrix}$$

and consider

$$|\mathbf{A}'| = \begin{vmatrix} a_{11} + Ka_{21}, & a_{12} + Ka_{22}, & a_{13} + Ka_{23} \\ a_{21} & a_{22} & a_{23} \\ a_{31} & a_{32} & a_{33} \end{vmatrix}$$

obtained by adding a multiple of the second row to the first. Expand $|\mathbf{A}'|$ by elements and co-factors of the first row : we have

$$|\mathbf{A}'| = (a_{11} + Ka_{21})A_{11} + (a_{12} + Ka_{22})A_{12} + (a_{13} + Ka_{23})A_{13}$$

The co-factors of the first row are clearly the same in $|\mathbf{A}|$ and $|\mathbf{A}'|$. Then

$$\begin{aligned} |\mathbf{A}'| = {} & a_{11}A_{11} + a_{12}A_{12} + a_{13}A_{13} \\ & + K[a_{21}A_{11} + a_{22}A_{12} + a_{23}A_{13}] \\ = {} & |\mathbf{A}| \end{aligned}$$

The terms in brackets are an expansion by elements of the second row and alien co-factors from the first row and therefore their sum vanishes. Similarly the determinant is unaltered by addition of a multiple of one column to another.

18.5. The inverse of a matrix

The properties of determinants described above now provide a means of obtaining a formal expression for the inverse of a square matrix. Let **A** be the matrix with elements a_{ij} and determinant $|\mathbf{A}|$ which we suppose is not zero. Then the problem is to find a matrix $\mathbf{B}=\mathbf{A}^{-1}$ with elements b_{ij} such that

$$\mathbf{BA}=\mathbf{I} \tag{1}$$

Relations (6) and (7) of 18.43 have a close resemblance to the formula (5) of 18.21 which defines the elements of a product of two matrices. This resemblance becomes closer if we form from the matrix **A** a second matrix by first replacing each element a_{ij} by its co-factor in the determinant $|\mathbf{A}|$, and then transposing rows and columns. The resulting matrix is called the matrix adjugate to **A** and is written adj **A**; its (jk)th element is

$$(\text{adj } \mathbf{A})_{jk}=A_{kj}\,; \tag{2}$$

and relations (6) and (7) of 18.43, written in terms of the matrix (adj **A**), are

$$\sum_k (\text{adj } \mathbf{A})_{jk}a_{ki}=0 \qquad \text{if } j\neq i$$

$$=|\mathbf{A}| \text{ if } j=i,$$

that is, from the definition of the unit matrix **I**,

$$\sum_k (\text{adj } \mathbf{A})_{jk}a_{ki}=|\mathbf{A}|I_{ji} \tag{3}$$

for all values of i and j.

Now by formula (5) of 18.21, the sum on the left-hand side of (3) is the (ji)th element of the matrix product (adj **A**) . **A**; hence each element of this product is equal to $|\mathbf{A}|$ times the corresponding element of **I**; so we can write (3) as a relation between matrices:

$$(\text{adj } \mathbf{A})\,.\,\mathbf{A}=|\mathbf{A}|\mathbf{I}$$

Thus the matrix

$$\mathbf{B}=(1/|\mathbf{A}|)\text{ adj }\mathbf{A}=(1/|\mathbf{A}|)\begin{pmatrix} A_{11} & A_{21} & \dots & A_{n1} \\ A_{12} & A_{22} & \dots & A_{n2} \\ \dots & \dots & \dots & \dots \\ A_{1n} & A_{2n} & \dots & A_{nn} \end{pmatrix}$$

with elements $b_{ij}=A_{ji}/|\mathbf{A}|$, is a matrix satisfying relation (1), and as we shall see shortly, it is unique.

By a similar argument it follows from (3) and (4) of 18.43 that,

$$\mathbf{A} \,.\, (\text{adj } \mathbf{A}) = |\,\mathbf{A}\,|\,\mathbf{I} \tag{4}$$

so that the matrices **A** and (adj **A**) commute.

Example

Let
$$\mathbf{A} = \begin{pmatrix} 1 & 0 & 3 \\ 2 & 1 & 4 \\ 0 & 1 & 3 \end{pmatrix}$$

The determinant of **A** is found to be 5. On replacing elements by their co-factors, and transposing rows and columns, we obtain the matrix

$$\text{adj } \mathbf{A} = \begin{pmatrix} -1 & 3 & -3 \\ -6 & 3 & 2 \\ 2 & -1 & 1 \end{pmatrix}$$

From equation (4) we have

$$\mathbf{A}^{-1} = (1/|\,\mathbf{A}\,|) \text{ adj } \mathbf{A} = \tfrac{1}{5}\begin{pmatrix} -1 & 3 & -3 \\ -6 & 3 & 2 \\ 2 & -1 & 1 \end{pmatrix}$$

It is easily verified by multiplying out that this gives the required result $\mathbf{A}^{-1}\mathbf{A} = \mathbf{I}$. It can also be verified that $\mathbf{A}\mathbf{A}^{-1} = \mathbf{I}$.

18.51. *Uniqueness of the inverse*

We have shown that a correct solution of both equations $\mathbf{BA} = \mathbf{I}$ and $\mathbf{AB} = \mathbf{I}$ is

$$\mathbf{B} = \mathbf{A}^{-1} \equiv (1/|\,\mathbf{A}\,|) \text{ adj } \mathbf{A}$$

It is easily proved that there is no other solution. For if **C** is a second matrix satisfying $\mathbf{CA} = \mathbf{I}$, we have by postmultiplication by $\mathbf{A}^{-1}$, $\mathbf{CAA}^{-1} = \mathbf{A}^{-1}$ and hence $\mathbf{C} = \mathbf{A}^{-1}$. Similarly if **C** satisfies $\mathbf{AC} = \mathbf{I}$ we find by premultiplying by $\mathbf{A}^{-1}$, that $\mathbf{C} = \mathbf{A}^{-1}$ again. Thus there is only one matrix inverse to **A**.

Multiplication by an inverse matrix takes the place in matrix algebra of division in the algebra of numbers.

18.52. *Inverse of a product*

Let **A** and **B** be two square matrices of order n with reciprocals $\mathbf{A}^{-1}$ and $\mathbf{B}^{-1}$. Then the reciprocal of **AB** is not $\mathbf{A}^{-1}\mathbf{B}^{-1}$ as in algebra, but $\mathbf{B}^{-1}\mathbf{A}^{-1}$. For

$$(\mathbf{B}^{-1}\mathbf{A}^{-1})(\mathbf{AB}) = \mathbf{B}^{-1}\mathbf{A}^{-1}\mathbf{AB} = \mathbf{B}^{-1}\mathbf{IB} = \mathbf{B}^{-1}\mathbf{B} = \mathbf{I}$$

whereas $\mathbf{A}^{-1}\mathbf{B}^{-1}\mathbf{AB}$ does not reduce further unless **A** and **B** happen to commute.

18.6. Solution of simultaneous equations

We have seen in 18.3 that the solution of the system of n equations represented by the matrix equation

$$\mathbf{Ax}=\mathbf{h} \tag{1}$$

(where **h**, like **x**, is an $(n \times 1)$ column matrix) is

$$\mathbf{x}=\mathbf{A}^{-1}\mathbf{h} \tag{2}$$

Example

$$\begin{aligned} x+3z&=7\\ 2x+y+4z&=13\\ y+3z&=9 \end{aligned}$$

These equations are equivalent to the matrix equation

$$\begin{pmatrix} 1 & 0 & 3\\ 2 & 1 & 4\\ 0 & 1 & 3 \end{pmatrix}\begin{pmatrix} x\\ y\\ z \end{pmatrix}=\begin{pmatrix} 7\\ 13\\ 9 \end{pmatrix}$$

The reciprocal of the matrix of the coefficients has been obtained in 18.5 ; we find

$$\begin{pmatrix} x\\ y\\ z \end{pmatrix}=\tfrac{1}{5}\begin{pmatrix} -1 & 3 & -3\\ -6 & 3 & 2\\ 2 & -1 & 1 \end{pmatrix}\begin{pmatrix} 7\\ 13\\ 9 \end{pmatrix}$$

$$=\tfrac{1}{5}\begin{pmatrix} 5\\ 15\\ 10 \end{pmatrix}=\begin{pmatrix} 1\\ 3\\ 2 \end{pmatrix}$$

Hence

$x=1$, $y=3$, $z=2$ is the required solution.

18.61. *Second form of solution : Cramer's formula*

An explicit formula for the solution in terms of determinants can be obtained, and is occasionally useful in theoretical work, though evaluation of the solution in this form is seldom if ever the best way to obtain a numerical answer in a particular case.

The formula is easily obtained from the expression for the reciprocal matrix $\mathbf{A}^{-1}$ in terms of the matrix adjugate to **A**. The solution of (2) of 18.6 is

$$\begin{aligned} \mathbf{x}&=\mathbf{A}^{-1}\mathbf{h}\\ &=(1/|\mathbf{A}|)(\text{adj}\,\mathbf{A})\,.\,\mathbf{h} \end{aligned} \tag{1}$$

Using the definition of (adj **A**) (see 18.5) and writing out equation (1) more fully we have explicit solutions for $x_1, \dots, x_n$, thus

$$x_1 = (1/|\mathbf{A}|)(h_1A_{11} + h_2A_{21} + \dots + h_nA_{n1}) \tag{2}$$

and generally

$$x_r = (1/|\mathbf{A}|)(h_1A_{1r} + h_2A_{2r} + \dots + h_nA_{nr}) \tag{3}$$

The bracketed terms on the right of (3) can be recognised as the expansion of a determinant ; they are in fact the expansion by elements of the rth column of the determinant formed by replacing the rth column of **A** by the elements $h_1, \dots, h_n$. Hence we can rewrite (3) as the ratio of two determinants :

$$x_r = \begin{vmatrix} a_{11} & a_{12} & \dots & h_1 & \dots & a_{1n} \\ a_{21} & a_{22} & \dots & h_2 & \dots & a_{2n} \\ \dots & \dots & \dots & \dots & \dots & \dots \\ a_{n1} & a_{n2} & \dots & h_n & \dots & a_{nn} \end{vmatrix} \Bigg/ \begin{vmatrix} a_{11} & a_{12} & \dots & a_{1r} & \dots & a_{1n} \\ a_{21} & a_{22} & \dots & a_{2r} & \dots & a_{2n} \\ \dots & \dots & \dots & \dots & \dots & \dots \\ a_{n1} & a_{n2} & \dots & a_{nr} & \dots & a_{nn} \end{vmatrix} \tag{4}$$

This is called Cramer's formula.

18.62. *Singular matrices*

We have so far supposed that the determinant $|\mathbf{A}|$ is not zero. This has been necessary because the elements of $\mathbf{A}^{-1}$ contain the factor $1/|\mathbf{A}|$, which reappears in equation (4) of 18.61. If $|\mathbf{A}| = 0$ the matrix **A** is said to be singular and its inverse does not exist.

The solution of the equations

$$\mathbf{Ax} = \mathbf{h}$$

in this case requires further consideration. To get an informal picture of the possibilities that arise, let us suppose that the elements are slightly altered so that $|\mathbf{A}|$ is small but not zero. Cramer's formula then applies, and explicit values can be obtained for the x_r's. If the elements are now allowed to tend to their original values, there are two possibilities : the numerator in (4) of 18.61 either remains finite or else tends to zero like the denominator. In the first case x_r tends to infinity and the equations have no finite solution. In the second case the equations may have a solution, in fact will frequently have an infinite number of solutions.

The two possibilities are illustrated in their simplest form by the equations

$$\left.\begin{aligned} ax+by&=c \\ ax+by&=d \end{aligned}\right\} \qquad (1)$$

and

$$\left.\begin{aligned} ax+by&=c \\ 3ax+3by&=3c \end{aligned}\right\} \qquad (2)$$

Equations (1) with $c \neq d$ are incompatible ; there is clearly no finite solution. (The geometer prefers to say in such a case that there is a solution, which he calls a point at infinity ; this point of view is useful in abolishing various provisos and exceptions, but we shall not adopt it.) Equations (2) on the other hand are perfectly compatible, but the second is simply a restatement of the first. Any solution of one automatically satisfies the other, and there are obviously an infinite number of solutions. The geometrical significance of the pairs of equations (1) and (2) should also be noted ; (1) represents two parallel lines which have no intersection (or alternatively meet at infinity) ; (2) represents two coincident lines and any point on either line satisfies both equations.

With matrices of higher order, entirely analogous situations arise. Consider, for example, the equations

$$\begin{aligned} x+2y-z&=4 \\ 2x+3y-2z&=7 \\ x+3y-z&=2 \end{aligned}$$

The determinant of the coefficients is again zero. The equations are actually incompatible, for the sum of the last pair of equations gives

$$3x+6y-3z=9$$

i.e.

$$x+2y-z=3$$

which is incompatible with the first. There is therefore no solution.

In the equations

$$\begin{aligned} x+2y-2z&=3 \\ 2x+3y-2z&=7 \\ x+3y-4z&=2 \end{aligned}$$

the matrix of coefficients is again singular. In this case the equations are interdependent. For by forming the sum of the last pair and dividing by 3, we reproduce the first. The equations therefore give essentially two pieces of information, and this is not sufficient to determine x, y and z separately. The most that can be done is to put

$$x = 5 - 2k$$
$$y = 2k - 1$$
$$z = k$$

All three equations are then satisfied for any value of k.

To summarise the present section we may say that if the matrix $\mathbf{A}$ is singular, the equations

$$\mathbf{Ax} = \mathbf{h}$$

are either incompatible with no solution, or else they are not independent. In the latter case the information supplied is not sufficient to determine all the unknowns; one, or possibly more, of the variables can be given an arbitrary value, and the equations can still be solved for the other variables.

18.63. *Ill-conditioned equations*

If $|\mathbf{A}|$ is not exactly zero but is merely small compared to the coefficients themselves then there may still be some difficulty in solving the equations. If the numbers are exact then there is a unique exact solution and nothing further need be said about it. If, however, the coefficients a_{ij} and numbers h_i are determined from experiment and therefore not exact, it may be that the final solution is very sensitive to any small errors that may be present. For example the solution of the equations

$$1{\cdot}53x + 3{\cdot}24y - 4{\cdot}18z = 20{\cdot}55$$
$$3{\cdot}41x - 1{\cdot}62y - 0{\cdot}41z = 1{\cdot}40$$
$$0{\cdot}88x + 19{\cdot}44y - 20{\cdot}08z = 100{\cdot}00$$

is $x = 1, y = 2, z = -3$ exactly, as is easily verified by substitution. If however the number 100·00 on the right-hand side of the third equation is increased by only 0·05% to 100·05 the solution is altered to

$$x = 2{\cdot}00, \quad y = 3{\cdot}68, \quad z = -1{\cdot}33$$

From the experimental point of view the equations are useless and might just as well be incompatible; at best they give the order of magnitude of the unknowns. The reason is that the determinant of the coefficients is only $-0{\cdot}405$, whereas in its expansion there are individual terms of magnitude over 200.

Thus although algebraically a matrix is either singular or non-singular, in numerical applications this classification is too rigid and there is an intermediate class such as that of the above example, called ‘ ill-conditioned ’.

Part of the skill in the design of experiments is to avoid getting results in the form of ill-conditioned equations. The general rule to follow is to make sure that each equation represents a distinctly new piece of information. The above equations fail in this respect because the information in the third equation is not very different from that obtained by subtracting twice the second equation from five times the first ; sufficiently different to make an algebraic solution possible but not sufficiently different to define a firm solution in the presence of small errors.

18.7. Linear homogeneous equations

In the present section we consider a system of n homogeneous linear algebraic equations in n variables $x_1, x_2, \ldots, x_n$, of the type

$$a_{11}x_1 + a_{12}x_2 + \ldots + a_{1n}x_n = 0 \tag{1}$$

In matrix notation the whole set is represented by

$$\mathbf{Ax} = 0 \tag{2}$$

The feature in which these differ from the equations of 18.3 is that now all the h's are zero, and in contexts in which such equations arise in applications, the interest is in the conditions under which solutions *other than* the identically zero solution $\mathbf{x} = 0$ can occur.

Whatever the properties of the matrix $\mathbf{A}$, $\mathbf{x} = 0$ is a solution. If the matrix $\mathbf{A}$ is non-singular then this solution is unique. Hence a necessary condition that there should be a solution not identically zero is that the matrix $\mathbf{A}$ should be singular ; this condition is also sufficient.

18.71. *Linear dependence*

n algebraic quantities $\psi_1, \psi_2, \ldots, \psi_n$ are said to be linearly dependent if there is an identical relation between them of the form

$$c_1\psi_1 + c_2\psi_2 + \ldots + c_n\psi_n = 0 \tag{1}$$

where the constants $c_1, c_2, \ldots, c_n$ are not all zero. Thus the functions

$$\psi_1=\cos^2 x, \quad \psi_2=\sin^2 x, \quad \psi_3=\tfrac{1}{2}\cos 2x$$

are linearly dependent because, for all x,

$$\psi_1-\psi_2-2\psi_3=0$$

On the other hand $\sin x$, $\cos x$, and $\cos 2x$ are not linearly dependent since if

$$c_1 \sin x+c_2 \cos x+c_3 \cos 2x=0$$

for all x then $c_1=c_2=c_3=0$, as it is easy to prove, by inserting special values for x. Similarly the vectors

$$\begin{aligned}\psi_1&=(3,\ 2,\ -4)\\ \psi_2&=(2,\ 1,\ -3)\\ \psi_3&=(1,\ 3,\ \ \ 1)\end{aligned}$$

are linearly dependent since

$$5\psi_1-7\psi_2-\psi_3=0$$

On the other hand the vectors $\psi_1=(1, 0, 0)$, $\psi_2=(0, 1, 0)$, $\psi_3=(0, 0, 1)$ are linearly independent. In three dimensions linearly dependent vectors are coplanar.

A useful restatement of the results of 18.41 (ii) and 18.44 can be made in terms of this definition as follows. The determinant $|\mathbf{A}|$ vanishes if and only if its rows or columns are linearly dependent. For the equations

$$\mathbf{Ac}=0 \tag{2}$$

have a non zero solution $\mathbf{c}$ if and only if $|\mathbf{A}|=0$. But equation (2) is of the form (1), thus :

$$\begin{pmatrix}a_{11}\\ a_{21}\\ \vdots\\ a_{n1}\end{pmatrix}c_1+\begin{pmatrix}a_{12}\\ a_{22}\\ \vdots\\ a_{n2}\end{pmatrix}c_2+\ldots+\begin{pmatrix}a_{1n}\\ a_{2n}\\ \vdots\\ a_{nn}\end{pmatrix}c_n=0$$

and hence the columns of $|\mathbf{A}|$ are linearly dependent. A similar result holds for the rows of $|\mathbf{A}|$ since the rows and columns of the determinant can be transposed.

If $\mathbf{x}_j$ $(1 \leqslant j \leqslant n)$ is a set of n linearly independent column matrices of order $n \times 1$, then any column matrix $\mathbf{y}$ can be expressed as a linear combination of the $\mathbf{x}_j$'s ; that is, coefficients $c_1, c_2, \ldots, c_n$ exist such that

$$\mathbf{y}=c_1\mathbf{x}_1+c_2\mathbf{x}_2+\ldots+c_n\mathbf{x}_n \tag{3}$$

To prove this let us assemble the n column matrices

$$\mathbf{x}_j = \begin{pmatrix} x_{1j} \\ x_{2j} \\ \vdots \\ x_{nj} \end{pmatrix} \quad j = 1 \text{ to } n$$

into a square matrix $\mathbf{X}$ defined by

$$\mathbf{X} = \begin{pmatrix} x_{11} & x_{12} & \cdots & x_{1n} \\ x_{21} & x_{22} & \cdots & x_{2n} \\ \cdot & \cdot & \cdots & \cdot \\ \cdot & \cdot & \cdots & \cdot \\ \cdot & \cdot & \cdots & \cdot \\ x_{n1} & x_{n2} & \cdots & x_{nn} \end{pmatrix} \tag{4}$$

Then since the columns of the matrix $\mathbf{X}$ are linearly independent, this matrix $\mathbf{X}$ is non-singular. It follows that any column matrix $\mathbf{y}$ of order n can be expressed in the form (3) or its equivalent

$$\mathbf{y} = \mathbf{X}\mathbf{c}$$

In fact, the required values of c_j are given by

$$\mathbf{c} = \mathbf{X}^{-1}\mathbf{y}$$

The reader should note the formal resemblance of this result to corresponding theorems in vector algebra. An arbitrary vector in n dimensions can always be expressed as a linear combination of n basic vectors provided these are linearly independent. There are an infinite number of possible sets of basic vectors in n dimensions. Similarly there are an infinite number of basic column matrices of order $n \times 1$.

Similar ideas have been met in Chapter 12. It is there stated that an arbitrary well-behaved function can be expanded in terms of certain basic functions. Further, just as the latent solutions of a matrix provide an acceptable set of basic matrices, so the eigen-solutions of certain differential equations provide an acceptable set of basic functions.

18.72. *The latent roots of a matrix*

A problem of particular importance in the theory of vibrations, in quantum theory and in other contexts is the calculation of certain special column matrices $\mathbf{x}$ and numbers λ associated with a given square matrix $\mathbf{A}$ by the equation

$$\mathbf{Ax} = \lambda\mathbf{x}, \text{ or } (\mathbf{A} - \lambda\mathbf{I})\mathbf{x} = 0 \tag{1}$$

The solution $\mathbf{x} = 0$ is excluded. There may be several different column matrices $\mathbf{x}$, each with a different value of λ, and each satisfying (1). The numbers λ are called the latent roots of the matrix $\mathbf{A}$, or, especially in quantum theory, the eigenvalues of $\mathbf{A}$. The matrices $\mathbf{x}$ are the latent solutions or eigen-solutions of $\mathbf{A}$. This equation (1), written out in full, is a homogeneous system of linear equations, and will have a solution, other than $\mathbf{x} = 0$, if and only if

$$\begin{vmatrix} a_{11} - \lambda & a_{12} & \cdots & a_{1n} \\ a_{21} & a_{22} - \lambda & \cdots & a_{2n} \\ \cdot & \cdot & \cdots & \cdot \\ \cdot & \cdot & \cdots & \cdot \\ \cdot & \cdot & \cdots & \cdot \\ a_{n1} & a_{n2} & \cdots & a_{nn} - \lambda \end{vmatrix} = 0 \tag{2}$$

This is an algebraic equation in λ of degree n and will have n roots $\lambda_1, \lambda_2, \ldots, \lambda_n$ (possibly including repeated and complex roots). To each value of λ there will correspond in general a distinct solution $\mathbf{x}$ of equations (1). Let $\mathbf{x}_{(1)}, \ldots \mathbf{x}_{(n)}$ correspond to $\lambda_1, \lambda_2 \ldots \lambda_n$ then

$$\left.\begin{aligned} \mathbf{Ax}_{(1)} &= \lambda_1\mathbf{x}_{(1)} \\ \mathbf{Ax}_{(2)} &= \lambda_2\mathbf{x}_{(2)} \\ \vdots\quad & \quad\vdots \\ \mathbf{Ax}_{(n)} &= \lambda_n\mathbf{x}_{(n)} \end{aligned}\right\} \tag{3}$$

These solutions will not be unique; for example, if $\mathbf{x}_{(1)}$ is a solution of $\mathbf{Ax}_{(1)} = \lambda\mathbf{x}_{(1)}$, then $k\mathbf{x}_{(1)}$ is also a solution.

Example 1

Determine the latent roots and latent solutions of the matrix

$$\mathbf{A} = \begin{pmatrix} 21 & 7 & -26 \\ 36 & 10 & -42 \\ 28 & 8 & -33 \end{pmatrix}$$

The required roots are the solution of the cubic

$$\begin{vmatrix} 21 - \lambda & 7 & -26 \\ 36 & 10 - \lambda & -42 \\ 28 & 8 & -33 - \lambda \end{vmatrix} = 0$$

which reduces to

$$\lambda^3 + 2\lambda^2 - \lambda - 2 = 0$$

i.e.

$$(\lambda + 2)(\lambda - 1)(\lambda + 1) = 0$$

The latent roots of $\mathbf{A}$ are therefore $\lambda = -1$, $\lambda = -2$ and $\lambda = +1$. The three latent solutions $\mathbf{x}_{(1)}$, $\mathbf{x}_{(2)}$ and $\mathbf{x}_{(3)}$ satisfy $\mathbf{Ax} = \lambda\mathbf{x}$, with the corresponding values of λ.

If $\mathbf{x}_{(1)} = \begin{pmatrix} x_{1(1)} \\ x_{2(1)} \\ x_{3(1)} \end{pmatrix}$, then, putting $\lambda = -1$ in $(\mathbf{A} - \lambda\mathbf{I})\mathbf{x}_{(1)} = 0$

$$22x_{1(1)} + 7x_{2(1)} - 26x_{3(1)} = 0$$

$$36x_{1(1)} + 11x_{2(1)} - 42x_{3(1)} = 0$$

$$28x_{1(1)} + 8x_{2(1)} - 32x_{3(1)} = 0$$

Solution of the first two of these equations for $x_{1(1)}/x_{3(1)}$ and $x_{2(1)}/x_{3(1)}$ gives

$$x_{1(1)}/x_{3(1)} = 4/5, \; x_{2(1)}/x_{3(1)} = 6/5$$

and substitution into the third equation verifies these values. Hence the latent solution corresponding to $\lambda = -1$ is, apart from an arbitrary factor,

$$\mathbf{x}_{(1)} = \begin{pmatrix} x_{1(1)} \\ x_{2(1)} \\ x_{3(1)} \end{pmatrix} = \begin{pmatrix} 4 \\ 6 \\ 5 \end{pmatrix}$$

Similarly putting $\lambda = -2$ and $+1$ in turn we find the solutions

$$\mathbf{x}_{(2)} = \begin{pmatrix} x_{1(2)} \\ x_{2(2)} \\ x_{3(2)} \end{pmatrix} = \begin{pmatrix} 3 \\ 5 \\ 4 \end{pmatrix}$$

and

$$\mathbf{x}_{(3)} = \begin{pmatrix} x_{1(3)} \\ x_{2(3)} \\ x_{3(3)} \end{pmatrix} = \begin{pmatrix} 5 \\ 8 \\ 6 \end{pmatrix}$$

Example 2

Show that the latent roots of the matrix

$$\begin{pmatrix} 3 & -2 & 2 \\ -4 & 1 & 4 \\ 4 & 4 & 1 \end{pmatrix}$$

are $+5$, $+5$, -5 and that three latent solutions are the columns of the non-singular matrix :

$$\begin{pmatrix} 1 & 0 & 1 \\ 1 & -1 & 2 \\ 2 & -1 & -2 \end{pmatrix}$$

It should be mentioned that the method illustrated in example 1, involving the expansion of the determinant (2) and solution of the resulting nth degree polynomial equation, is seldom the best practical method for evaluating latent roots and latent solutions except for matrices of order 2 or 3, and for matrices of higher order constructed to have simple latent roots (for other procedures see L. F. Richardson, *Phil. Trans. Roy. Soc.*, **242**, 439 (1950), and J. H. Wilkinson, *Proc. Camb. Phil. Soc.*, **50**, 536 (1954).

If $\mathbf{x}_{(1)}, \mathbf{x}_{(2)}, \ldots, \mathbf{x}_{(k)}$ are latent solutions corresponding to the distinct latent roots $\lambda_1, \lambda_2, \ldots, \lambda_k$ of the matrix **A**, then $\mathbf{x}_{(1)}, \mathbf{x}_{(2)}, \ldots, \mathbf{x}_{(k)}$ are linearly independent. For suppose there is a linear relation

$$c_1\mathbf{x}_{(1)} + c_2\mathbf{x}_{(2)} + c_3\mathbf{x}_{(3)} + \ldots + c_k\mathbf{x}_{(k)} = \mathbf{0} \tag{4}$$

between the latent solutions **x**. From equations (3)

$$(\mathbf{A} - \lambda_i\mathbf{I})\mathbf{x}_{(j)} = (\lambda_j - \lambda_i)\mathbf{x}_{(j)}$$

so that multiplication of (4) by any matrix $(\mathbf{A} - \lambda_i\mathbf{I})$ gives another linear combination of the $\mathbf{x}_{(j)}$'s with $\mathbf{x}_{(i)}$ missing. Hence we can eliminate $\mathbf{x}_{(2)}, \mathbf{x}_{(3)}, \ldots, \mathbf{x}_{(k)}$ by multiplying in succession by $(\mathbf{A} - \lambda_2\mathbf{I}), (\mathbf{A} - \lambda_3\mathbf{I}), \ldots, (\mathbf{A} - \lambda_k\mathbf{I})$. The result is

$$c_1(\lambda_1 - \lambda_2)(\lambda_1 - \lambda_3)\ldots(\lambda_1 - \lambda_k)\mathbf{x}_{(1)} = 0 \tag{5}$$

and, if all the λ's are unequal, as supposed, it follows that $c_1 = 0$. Similarly, each of the other c_j's in (4) is zero ; that is, there is no such relation (4) (except with $c_1 = c_2 = c_3 = \ldots = c_k = 0$).

It follows that if **A** has n distinct latent roots the n corresponding solutions provide a set of basic vectors in the sense of 18.71. If, however, any two of the latent roots λ are equal, the corresponding coefficients c in (4) need not be zero (though they may be) so that then the latent solutions, which are not normally unique for the repeated root, may or may not be independent.

18.73. *Reduction of a matrix to diagonal form*

A matrix is said to be of diagonal form when its elements are zero except along the principal diagonal. It is usually an advantage to work if possible with diagonal matrices, if only because of the smaller number of elements involved. On the other hand the reduction of a matrix to diagonal form may itself be a lengthy process.

A matrix **A** can formally be *reduced to diagonal form* as follows. Suppose that the n latent solutions $\mathbf{x}_{(i)}$ of **A** are the n columns of a matrix **X** i.e. $\mathbf{x}_{i(j)} = x_{ij}$ and that the latent roots of **A** are $\lambda_1, \lambda_2 \ldots, \lambda_n$. Then

$$\mathbf{AX} = \begin{pmatrix} a_{11} & a_{12} & \ldots & a_{1n} \\ a_{21} & a_{22} & \ldots & a_{2n} \\ \multicolumn{4}{c}{\dotfill} \\ a_{n1} & a_{n2} & \ldots & a_{nn} \end{pmatrix} \begin{pmatrix} x_{11} & x_{12} & \ldots & x_{1n} \\ x_{21} & x_{22} & \ldots & x_{2n} \\ \multicolumn{4}{c}{\dotfill} \\ x_{n1} & x_{n2} & \ldots & x_{nn} \end{pmatrix}$$

$$= \begin{pmatrix} \lambda_1 x_{11} & \lambda_2 x_{12} & \ldots & \lambda_n x_{1n} \\ \lambda_1 x_{21} & \lambda_2 x_{22} & \ldots & \lambda_n x_{2n} \\ \multicolumn{4}{c}{\dotfill} \\ \lambda_1 x_{n1} & \lambda_2 x_{n2} & \ldots & \lambda_n x_{nn} \end{pmatrix}$$

$$= \begin{pmatrix} x_{11} & x_{12} & \ldots & x_{1n} \\ x_{21} & x_{22} & \ldots & x_{2n} \\ \multicolumn{4}{c}{\dotfill} \\ x_{n1} & x_{n2} & \ldots & x_{nn} \end{pmatrix} \begin{pmatrix} \lambda_1 & 0 & \ldots & 0 \\ 0 & \lambda_2 & \ldots & 0 \\ \multicolumn{4}{c}{\dotfill} \\ 0 & 0 & \ldots & \lambda_n \end{pmatrix}$$

$$= \mathbf{XA'} \tag{1}$$

where $\mathbf{A'}$ is a diagonal matrix, whose elements are the latent roots of **A**.

If now **X** is non-singular (a sufficient but not necessary condition for which is that the latent roots are all distinct) then the matrix $\mathbf{X}^{-1}$ exists : therefore premultiplying by $\mathbf{X}^{-1}$

$$\mathbf{X}^{-1}\mathbf{AX} = \mathbf{A'} \tag{2}$$

Using the same **X** we can also define the transformation

$$\mathbf{B'} = \mathbf{X}^{-1}\mathbf{BX} \tag{3}$$

of any other $(n \times n)$ matrix **B**, but $\mathbf{B'}$ will not in general be diagonal.

Any transformation of the form (3), that is, any transformation which consists of postmultiplication by a non-singular matrix (**X**) and premultiplication by the inverse ($\mathbf{X}^{-1}$) of the same matrix has the important property that any equation satisfied by the matrices **A**, **B**, **C**, **D**, ... is satisfied by the transformed matrices $\mathbf{A'}$, $\mathbf{B'}$, $\mathbf{C'}$, $\mathbf{D'}$, ... whether or not they become diagonal in the process. For the equation

$$\mathbf{ABC}=\mathbf{D} \tag{4}$$

for example, can be written

$$\mathbf{XABCX}^{-1}=\mathbf{XDX}^{-1} \tag{5}$$

Since $\mathbf{XX}^{-1}=\mathbf{X}^{-1}\mathbf{X}=\mathbf{I}$, the matrix on the left-hand side of (5) can be written

$$\mathbf{XAX}^{-1}\mathbf{XBX}^{-1}\mathbf{XCX}^{-1}$$

and since matrix multiplication is associative, this is $\mathbf{A'B'C'}$; hence

$$\mathbf{A'B'C'}=\mathbf{D'} \tag{6}$$

Similarly if $\mathbf{A'B'C'}=\mathbf{D'}$, then

$$\mathbf{ABC}=\mathbf{D}. \tag{7}$$

In particular if, in addition to **A**, some other matrix **B** also becomes diagonal after the transformation, that is, if $\mathbf{A}'=\mathbf{XAX}^{-1}$ and $\mathbf{B}'=\mathbf{XBX}^{-1}$ are both diagonal, then **A** and **B** commute. For any two diagonal matrices of the same order commute, as becomes evident on writing out their product. So $\mathbf{A'B'}=\mathbf{B'A'}$, and hence, by the result (7), $\mathbf{AB}=\mathbf{BA}$.

18.8. Geometrical significance of determinant

Consider a square matrix **A** of order $n\times n$ and a column matrix **x** of order n. The numbers x_j may represent a set of voltages, or moments or indeed any physical variable whatever but can always be represented by the coordinates of a point in n-dimensional space. The position of this point is determined by the coordinates $x_1, x_2, \ldots, x_n$ which together define the column matrix **x**. We suppose for simplicity that the coordinates are rectangular cartesians.

If $X=(x_1, x_2 \ldots x_n)$, $Y=(y_1, y_2 \ldots y_n)$ …, $W=(w_1, w_2 \ldots w_n)$ are points in this space, the quantity $(x_1{}^2+x_2{}^2+\ldots+x_n{}^2)^{1/2}$ is called the 'distance' of X from the origin (and similarly for the other points) and the relation

$$x_1y_1+x_2y_2+\ldots+x_ny_n=0 \tag{1}$$

is expressed by saying that OX, OY are 'orthogonal'. Also it can be shown that the value of the determinant

$$\begin{vmatrix} x_1 & y_1 & \cdots & w_1 \\ x_2 & y_2 & \cdots & w_2 \\ \cdots & \cdots & \cdots & \cdots \\ x_n & y_n & \cdots & w_n \end{vmatrix}$$

is equal to the volume or 'hypervolume' of the 'hyperparallelepiped' of which $OX, OY, \ldots, OW$ are concurrent edges. These are extensions of the corresponding relations in two and three dimensions.

The equation $\mathbf{x}' = \mathbf{A}\mathbf{x}$ serves to define for every point $X = (x_1, \ldots, x_n)$ a second point X' with coordinates $(x_1', \ldots, x_n')$ given by

$$x_1' = a_{11}x_1 + \ldots + a_{1n}x_n$$
$$x_2' = a_{21}x_1 + \ldots + a_{2n}x_n \quad \text{etc.}$$

In particular if we take the n points $X_1 = (1, 0, 0, \ldots, 0)$ $X_2 = (0, 1, 0, 0, \ldots, 0) \ldots X_n = (0, 0, 0, \ldots, 1)$ in succession we obtain n points $X_1', \ldots, X_n'$ whose coordinates are given by the column matrices

$$\mathbf{x}_1' = \begin{pmatrix} a_{11} \\ a_{21} \\ \cdot \\ \cdot \\ a_{n1} \end{pmatrix}, \quad \mathbf{x}_2' = \begin{pmatrix} a_{21} \\ a_{22} \\ \cdot \\ \cdot \\ a_{2n} \end{pmatrix} \quad \ldots \quad \mathbf{x}_n' = \begin{pmatrix} a_{n1} \\ a_{n2} \\ \cdot \\ \cdot \\ a_{nn} \end{pmatrix}$$

Hence the determinant of the matrix $\mathbf{A}$,

$$|\mathbf{A}| = \begin{vmatrix} a_{11} & a_{12} & \ldots & a_{1n} \\ a_{21} & a_{22} & \ldots & a_{2n} \\ \cdot & \cdot & & \cdot \\ \cdot & \cdot & & \cdot \\ a_{n1} & a_{n2} & \ldots & a_{nn} \end{vmatrix}$$

is the hypervolume of an n-dimensional parallelepiped having one vertex at the origin and the others at the points $X_1', \ldots, X_n'$.

For example with $n = 2$, the matrix equation

$$\mathbf{x}' = \begin{pmatrix} 3 & 2 \\ 2 & 4 \end{pmatrix} \mathbf{x} \qquad (2)$$

transforms the points $X_1 = (1, 0)$ and $X_2 = (0, 1)$ to $(3, 2)$ and $(2, 4)$ respectively. The square of unit side is therefore transformed into a parallellogram as shown in Fig. 18.4; the area of this can be found in various ways, and is 8 units. The value of the determinant of the matrix in equation (2) is also 8.

The geometrical significance of singular matrices is easily illustrated. Consider for example the matrix

$$\mathbf{A} = \begin{pmatrix} 1 & 2 \\ 2 & 4 \end{pmatrix}$$

Then the points $X_1 = (1, 0)$ and $X_2 = (0, 1)$ transform to $X_1' = (1, 2)$ and $X_2' = (2, 4)$ (see Fig. 18.5). These do not define a parallelogram as in the previous example, being collinear with the origin. Alternatively we may say they define a degenerate parallelogram of zero area. Similarly in three dimensions the vertices of the unit cube are transformed by a singular matrix into points that are coplanar or even collinear, and so do not define a parallelepiped, or to express this in another way, the points define a degenerate parallelepiped of zero volume.

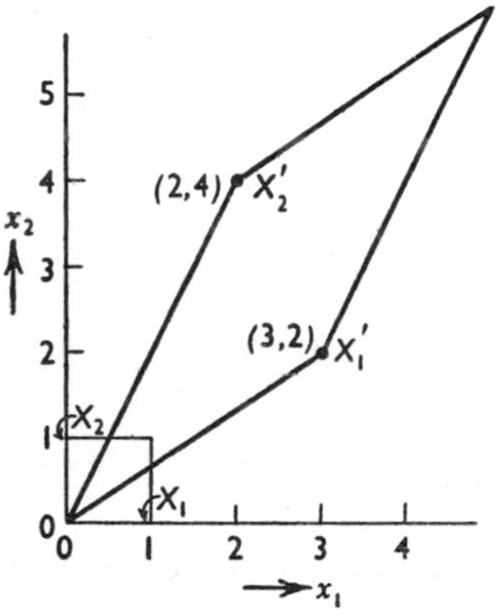

FIG. 18.4

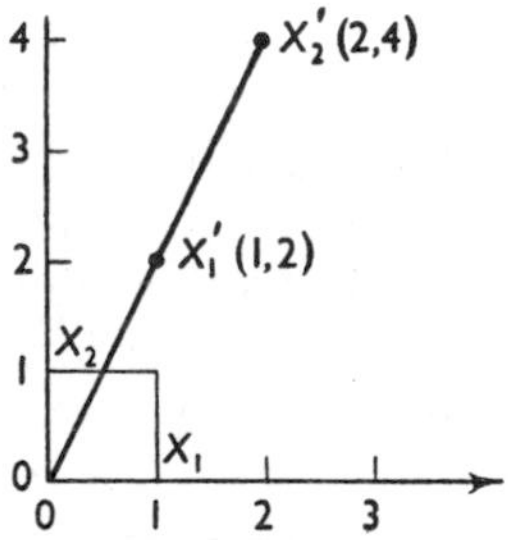

FIG. 18.5

It will be apparent that any unit cube irrespective of its position is transformed by a matrix $\mathbf{A}$ of order 3×3 into a parallelepiped of volume $|\mathbf{A}|$. Further a cube of side k is transformed into a parallelepiped of volume $k^3|\mathbf{A}|$. These are simple consequences of the distributive law of matrix multiplication and the commutability of a matrix and a numerical constant.

A further consequence is that since an arbitrary volume can be built up from infinitesimal cubes, any region of volume V is transformed by $\mathbf{A}$ into a region of volume $|\mathbf{A}|V$.

18.81. *Multiplication of determinants*

Let $\mathbf{A}$ and $\mathbf{B}$ be two square matrices of the same order. Then the matrix $\mathbf{A}$ will transform the unit hyper-cube in n dimensions into a hyper-parallelepiped of hyper-volume $|\mathbf{A}|$. If this is further transformed by $\mathbf{B}$, the final volume will be by the previous paragraph $|\mathbf{A}||\mathbf{B}|$. The same final state can also be reached by applying the single transformation **BA** to the hypercube. This gives a final volume of $|\mathbf{BA}|$. Hence

$$|\mathbf{A}|\,|\mathbf{B}|=|\mathbf{BA}|$$

In other words the product of two determinants can be written as a single determinant of the same order with elements formed by the rule of matrix multiplication. Actually since rows and columns of determinants can be interchanged, the multiplication may also be done row into row or column into column.

18.9. Some special kinds of matrices

In many physical applications, there is a relation of some kind between the elements of the matrices used. The following examples illustrate the more important special kinds of matrix.

18.91. *Symmetric matrix*

A matrix $\mathbf{A}=(a_{ik})$ is symmetrical if it is unchanged when rows and columns are transposed; this implies that $a_{ik}=a_{ki}$ or, in terms of the transposed matrix of **A** which is commonly denoted by $\tilde{\mathbf{A}}$ (**A** tilde),

$$\tilde{\mathbf{A}}=\mathbf{A}$$

18.92. *Antisymmetric matrix*

If $a_{ik}=-a_{ki}$ so that $\tilde{\mathbf{A}}=-\mathbf{A}$ then **A** is said to be antisymmetric. The elements on the principal diagonal are necessarily zero.

An arbitrary matrix **A** can always be expressed as the sum of a symmetric and an antisymmetric matrix; for

$$\mathbf{A}=\tfrac{1}{2}(\mathbf{A}+\tilde{\mathbf{A}})+\tfrac{1}{2}(\mathbf{A}-\tilde{\mathbf{A}})$$

and $\frac{1}{2}(\mathbf{A}+\tilde{\mathbf{A}})$ is symmetric whilst $\frac{1}{2}(\mathbf{A}-\tilde{\mathbf{A}})$ is antisymmetric.

18.93. *Hermitian and anti-hermitian matrices*

When the elements a_{ij} are complex quantities, as will often be the case when the physical variables are vibrations, (a.c. voltages, mechanical oscillations, waves and especially wave functions in quantum theory), the symmetry or anti-symmetry of the elements in the sense of the previous paragraph becomes unimportant, and is replaced by a more general concept. The matrix **A** is said to be hermitian if it is equal to the complex conjugate of $\tilde{\mathbf{A}}$, i.e. if

$$a_{ik} = a_{ki}{}^* = \tilde{a}_{ik}{}^*$$

or $\mathbf{A} = \tilde{\mathbf{A}}^*$

A single symbol † is frequently employed to denote the transposed complex conjugate, thus

$$\mathbf{A}^\dagger = \tilde{\mathbf{A}}^*$$

In this notation, **A** is hermitian if

$$\mathbf{A}^\dagger = \mathbf{A}$$

and is antihermitian if

$$\mathbf{A}^\dagger = -\mathbf{A}$$

If the elements of a hermitian matrix are real, then the matrix is also symmetrical.

Any matrix can be expressed as the sum of a hermitian and an antihermitian matrix, thus :

$$\mathbf{A} = \tfrac{1}{2}(\mathbf{A} + \mathbf{A}^\dagger) + \tfrac{1}{2}(\mathbf{A} - \mathbf{A}^\dagger)$$

18.94. *Orthogonal matrices*

A matrix **A** is said to be orthogonal if it satisfies

$$\mathbf{A}\tilde{\mathbf{A}} = \mathbf{I}$$

Since $|\mathbf{A}|\,|\tilde{\mathbf{A}}| = |\mathbf{A}|^2 = 1$, it follows that

$$|\mathbf{A}| = \pm 1$$

The positive sign is associated with rotations of axes and the negative sign with reflections.

18.95. *Unitary matrices*

A matrix **A** is unitary if

$$\mathbf{A}\mathbf{A}^\dagger = \mathbf{I}$$

A real unitary matrix is therefore orthogonal. If the elements are complex a unitary matrix has simpler properties than the orthogonal matrix.

Since $|\mathbf{A}|\,|\mathbf{A}^\dagger| = 1$ and $|\mathbf{A}|$, $|\mathbf{A}^\dagger|$ are conjugate complex, a unitary matrix is non-singular. Premultiplying by $\mathbf{A}^{-1}$ we therefore obtain a second definition of the unitary matrix, namely a matrix which has the property

$$\mathbf{A}^\dagger = \mathbf{A}^{-1}$$

18.96. *Orthogonal transformations*

The transformation effected by an orthogonal matrix is called an orthogonal transformation.

Let $\mathbf{A}$ be orthogonal of order $n \times n$ and let $\mathbf{x}$ be a column matrix, whose elements are the rectangular cartesian coordinates of a point X. Then the column matrix $\mathbf{x}'$ defined by

$$\mathbf{x}' = \mathbf{A}\mathbf{x}$$

represents a transformed point X'. Consider the n special points $X_1, X_2, \ldots, X_n$ with column matrices

$$\mathbf{x}_1 = \begin{pmatrix} 1 \\ 0 \\ \cdot \\ \cdot \\ 0 \end{pmatrix}, \quad \mathbf{x}_2 = \begin{pmatrix} 0 \\ 1 \\ \cdot \\ \cdot \\ 0 \end{pmatrix}, \quad \ldots, \quad \mathbf{x}_n = \begin{pmatrix} 0 \\ 0 \\ \cdot \\ \cdot \\ 1 \end{pmatrix}$$

respectively. These n column matrices are the successive columns of the unit matrix $\mathbf{I}$, i.e. in the notation of 18.71, $\mathbf{X} = \mathbf{I}$ and the transformed points are then represented in the same way by the square matrix $\mathbf{X}' = \mathbf{A}\mathbf{X} = \mathbf{A}\mathbf{I} = \mathbf{A}$. Thus the n columns of $\mathbf{A}$ give the n points $X_1', X_2', \ldots, X_n'$ to which $X_1, X_2, \ldots, X_n$ are transformed. Now using the fact that $\mathbf{A}$ is orthogonal we have

$$\mathbf{A}\tilde{\mathbf{A}} = \mathbf{I} \quad \text{and} \quad |\,\mathbf{A}\,| = \pm 1$$

Let us suppose first that $|\,\mathbf{A}\,| = +1$. Then

$$\tilde{\mathbf{A}} = \mathbf{A}^{-1} = (1/|\,\mathbf{A}\,|)(\text{adj } \mathbf{A}) = \text{adj } \mathbf{A} \tag{1}$$

that is,

$$a_{ij} = A_{ij} \tag{2}$$

in other words each element of $|\,\mathbf{A}\,|$ is equal to its co-factor.

Now expand $|\,\mathbf{A}\,|$ by elements of the ith column.

$$\begin{aligned} |\,\mathbf{A}\,| &= a_{1i}A_{1i} + a_{2i}A_{2i} + \ldots + a_{ni}A_{ni} \\ &= a_{1i}^2 + a_{2i}^2 + \ldots + a_{ni}^2 = 1 \end{aligned}$$

using (2). The ith column in $|\,\mathbf{A}\,|$ consists of the coordinates of $\mathbf{x}_i'$ and the equation is therefore a statement that every $\mathbf{x}_i'$ is at unit distance from the origin.

Further if we take any two columns of $|\,\mathbf{A}\,|$ we have

$$a_{1i}a_{1j} + a_{2i}a_{2j} + \ldots + a_{ni}a_{nj} = a_{1i}A_{1j} + a_{2i}A_{2j} + \ldots + a_{ni}A_{nj} = 0 \tag{3}$$

since it is the sum of products with alien co-factors (18.43). This is the relation described by saying that the lines OX_i' and OX_j' are perpendicular.

Hence the unit hypercube transforms not to a general hyper-parallelepiped but to a new unit hypercube, each side being of unit length and all sides mutually perpendicular. The orthogonal transformation therefore involves no change of shape or size and consists either of a pure rotation, as of a rigid body (in n dimensions) about the origin, or of reflections in one or more planes, or both.

If $|\mathbf{A}| = -1$ then exactly similar results are obtained. The negative sign implies an odd number of reflections in this case.

Example

Consider the restrictions to be placed on the general matrix of order 2×2 with real elements

$$\mathbf{A} = \begin{pmatrix} a & b \\ c & d \end{pmatrix}$$

if it is to be orthogonal. We have

$$\mathbf{A}\tilde{\mathbf{A}} = \begin{pmatrix} a & b \\ c & d \end{pmatrix} \begin{pmatrix} a & c \\ b & d \end{pmatrix} = \begin{pmatrix} a^2 + b^2 & ac + bd \\ ac + bd & c^2 + d^2 \end{pmatrix}$$

and this is to be the unit matrix $\mathbf{I}$. Hence

$$a^2 + b^2 = 1 \tag{4}$$

$$ac + bd = 0 \tag{5}$$

$$c^2 + d^2 = 1 \tag{6}$$

Since a and b are real, equation (4) shows that $-1 \leqslant a \leqslant 1$, so we can write

$$a = \cos\theta, \; b = \sin\theta. \tag{7}$$

and similarly from (6),

$$c = \cos\phi, \; d = \sin\phi.$$

Equation 5 then requires that $\cos(\theta - \phi) = 0$, and hence

$$\phi = \theta + \tfrac{1}{2}\pi \quad \text{or} \quad \phi = \theta + \tfrac{3}{2}\pi$$

hence $$c = \mp \sin\theta, \; d = \pm \cos\theta$$

Hence the only orthogonal matrices of order (2×2) are

$$\mathbf{A} = \begin{pmatrix} \cos\theta & \sin\theta \\ -\sin\theta & \cos\theta \end{pmatrix} \quad \text{and} \quad \mathbf{A}' = \begin{pmatrix} \cos\theta & \sin\theta \\ \sin\theta & -\cos\theta \end{pmatrix}$$

Notice that $|\mathbf{A}| = 1$ and $|\mathbf{A}'| = -1$.

The transformation $\mathbf{y} = \mathbf{A}\mathbf{x}$ transforms the points $(1, 0)$ and $(0, 1)$ to $(\cos\theta, -\sin\theta)$ and $(\sin\theta, \cos\theta)$ respectively, and therefore corresponds to a rotation through θ. The transformation $\mathbf{y} = \mathbf{A}'\mathbf{x}$ consists of a similar rotation followed by a reversal of the sign of the second coordinate, i.e. a rotation through θ followed by a reflection in OX_1.

CHAPTER NINETEEN

TENSORS

19.1. Oblique and curvilinear coordinate systems

Physical substances with a crystalline structure are often more easily described in terms of oblique cartesian axes than in a rectangular frame of reference. Even naturally isotropic materials, when subjected to distortion, may be more conveniently described relative to distorted e.g. oblique axes, than relative to an immovable rectangular frame. Electromagnetic theory and relativity are two other fields of study in which oblique frames of reference arise naturally : in special relativity, for example, the natural (four-dimensional) frame of reference of one observer would be described as oblique by a second observer relative to whom the first had a constant velocity. General relativity and the more complex problems of elasticity require the use of more general, curvilinear, coordinate systems.

The theory of tensors may be regarded as the theory of the use of distorted frames of reference in physical problems, and the rules of translation from one frame to another : the basic tensor properties are most simply introduced by a study of the use of oblique cartesian axes.

19.11. *Covariant and contravariant components of a vector*

The process of finding the rectangular cartesian components of a vector $\mathbf{a} = \overrightarrow{OP}$ (Fig. 19.1) can be described in either of two ways, either : draw lines QP, RP respectively parallel to OY,

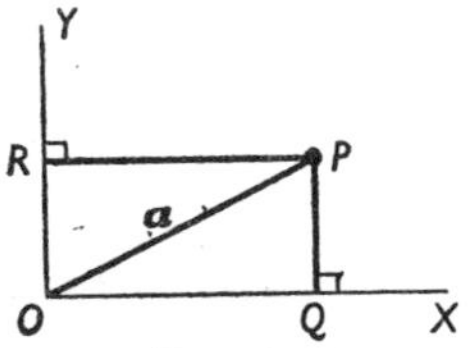

FIG. 19.1

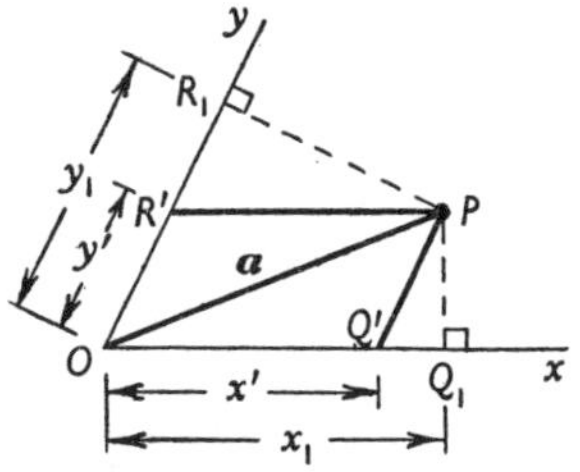

FIG. 19.2

OX, then the intercepts OQ, OR are the required components, or : drop perpendiculars PQ, PR from P on to OX, OY, then the components are OQ, OR. The two methods give the same components. With oblique axes on the other hand the two prescriptions are not equivalent ; the first gives the cartesian components $x' = OQ'$, $y' = OR'$ (Fig. 19.2) while the second prescription results in a new kind of coordinates, called the *covariant* coordinates of P, viz. $x_1 = OQ_1$, $y_1 = OR_1$. Similar definitions can be used in three dimensions, the covariant components being the projections of the given vector on the three coordinate axes. The standard notation for the three covariant components of a vector **a** obtained by dropping perpendiculars onto (oblique) cartesian axes Ox, Oy, Oz is (a_1, a_2, a_3). The standard notation for the (oblique) cartesian components, which are also known as *contravariant* components, is (a^1, a^2, a^3).

The vector **a** can equally well be specified by covariant or by contravariant components : we shall see later that each system has special advantages and disadvantages. Before either can be used as freely as rectangular components, however, it is necessary to know their algebraic properties, for example, how to find the covariant or contravariant components of $\mathbf{a}+\mathbf{b}$ if the covariant or contravariant components of **a** and **b** are given ; how to deduce the components in one frame of reference from those in another (transformation laws) ; how to express the length of a vector **a** or the magnitude of a scalar product $\mathbf{a} \,.\, \mathbf{b}$ in terms of their components, and so on.

The covariant component a_1 has the simple and useful property that it is identical with the X' component of **a** in any rectangular cartesian frame OX', OY', OZ' in which the OX' axis coincides with Ox. It follows that the covariant x-component of $\mathbf{a}+\mathbf{b}$ is equal to the OX' component, which, in turn is equal to the sum of the OX' components of **a** and **b**

$$(\mathbf{a}+\mathbf{b})_1 = a_1 + b_1$$

Similarly for the covariant y and z components,

$$(\mathbf{a}+\mathbf{b})_2 = a_2 + b_2 \,; \quad (\mathbf{a}+\mathbf{b})_3 = a_3 + b_3.$$

This is illustrated in Fig. 19.3 for the two-dimensional case. The three equations may be written in the condensed form

$$(\mathbf{a}+\mathbf{b})_i = a_i + b_i \qquad i = 1, 2, 3 \tag{1}$$

The parallelogram rule ensures that a similar law of addition is true for contravariant components,

$$(\mathbf{a}+\mathbf{b})^i = a^i + b^i \qquad i=1,\ 2,\ 3 \tag{2}$$

(compare Fig. 19.4).

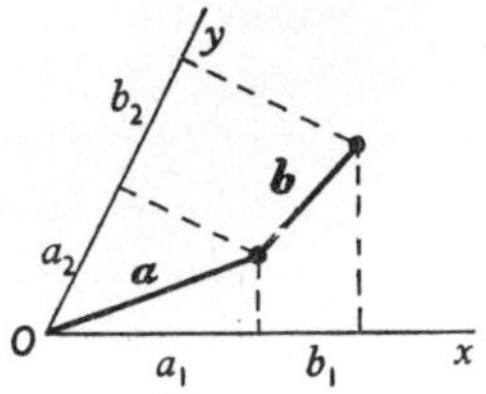

FIG. 19.3

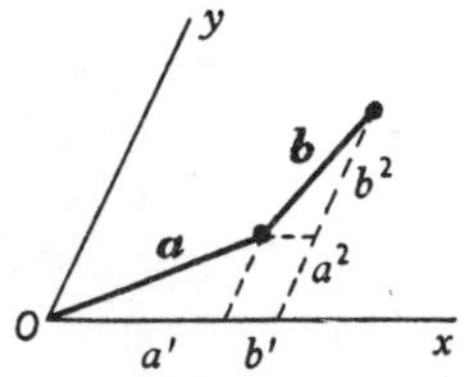

FIG. 19.4

19.12. *Transformation laws for covariant and contravariant components*

The use of separate symbols x, y, z for cartesian coordinates lends itself less easily to the neat presentation of formulae than does the notation x^1, x^2, x^3 or x^i ($i=1,\ 2,\ 3$). The latter forms also provide an explicit reminder that cartesian coordinates are contravariant.

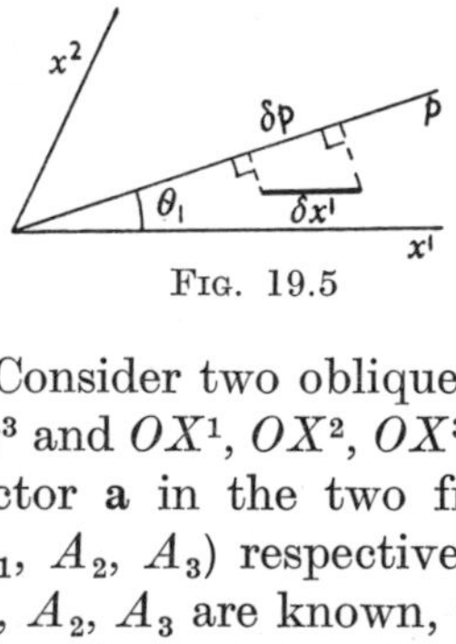

FIG. 19.5

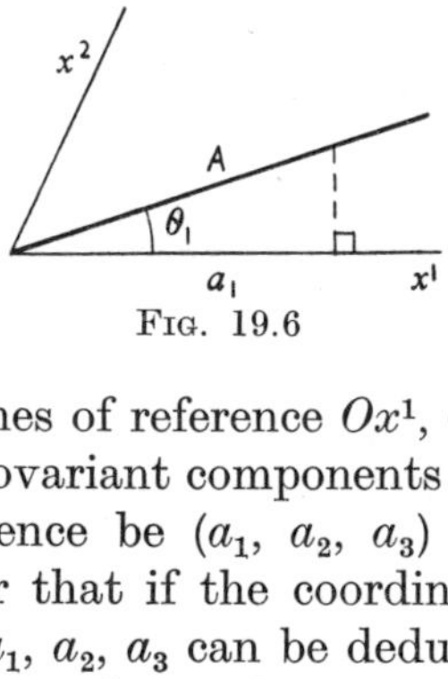

FIG. 19.6

Consider two oblique cartesian frames of reference Ox^1, Ox^2, Ox^3 and OX^1, OX^2, OX^3, and let the covariant components of a vector $\mathbf{a}$ in the two frames of reference be $(a_1,\ a_2,\ a_3)$ and $(A_1,\ A_2,\ A_3)$ respectively. It is clear that if the coordinates A_1, A_2, A_3 are known, the values of a_1, a_2, a_3 can be deduced. The rule for doing this is called the law of transformation for covariant components.

Let the length of $\mathbf{a}$ be denoted by A, and let the direction of $\mathbf{a}$ be taken as the axis of a new auxiliary covariant coordinate, p, say. We first note (compare Fig. 19.5) that if x^2 and x^3 are held constant and x^1 is allowed to increase by δx^1, the corresponding increase in p is $\cos\theta_1\,\delta x^1$ where θ_1 is the angle between the directions of p and of x^1; that is, $\partial p/\partial x^1 = \cos\theta_1$. Now

a_1 = projection of A on the x^1 direction $= A \cos \theta_1$ (Fig. 19.6)
$= A \, \partial p / \partial x^1$

Similarly $A_1 = A \, \partial p / \partial X^1$; $A_2 = A \, \partial p / \partial X^2$; $A_3 = A \, \partial p / \partial X^3$

But
$$A \frac{\partial p}{\partial x^1} = A \left\{ \frac{\partial X^1}{\partial x^1} \frac{\partial p}{\partial X^1} + \frac{\partial X^2}{\partial x^1} \frac{\partial p}{\partial X^2} + \frac{\partial X^3}{\partial x^1} \frac{\partial p}{\partial X^3} \right\}$$

i.e.
$$a_1 = \frac{\partial X^1}{\partial x^1} \cdot A_1 + \frac{\partial X^2}{\partial x^1} \cdot A_2 + \frac{\partial X^3}{\partial x^1} \cdot A_3 \qquad (1)$$
$$= \sum_{i=1}^{3} \frac{\partial X^i}{\partial x^1} A_i$$

Two similar equations can be written down for a_2 and a_3, and all three results can be condensed into the single equation,

(Covariant law)
$$a_k = \sum_{i=1}^{3} \frac{\partial X^i}{\partial x^k} A_i \qquad (k = 1, 2, 3) \qquad (2)$$

The student who, not necessarily unwisely, prefers at first to write all equations out fully, as in (1) with similar equations for a_2 and a_3, will soon tire of the labour and drop naturally into the use first of the summation notation, and then of the condensed form (2).

If X^1, X^2, X^3 happen to be *rectangular* cartesian coordinates, they may be regarded as either contravariant or covariant, and with the latter interpretation X^1, X^2, X^3 can each be substituted for p in Fig. 19.5; it follows that $\partial X^1 / \partial x^1 = \cos$ (angle between x^1 and X^1), etc. If Ox^1 has direction cosines l_1, m_1, n_1 relative to the rectangular cartesian axes OX^1, OX^2, OX^3, equation (1) therefore reduces to

$$a_1 = l_1 A_1 + m_1 A_2 + n_1 A_3 \qquad (3)$$

a relation of a form already familiar from § 17.7. Equation (1) is thus the generalisation of (3) which is appropriate when oblique axes are used. Because the geometry of oblique axes is more difficult to work out from scratch each time it is required, one must be able to quote equation (2) [or equation (1) and the two similar equations for a_2 and a_3] from memory.

[We have so far considered only cartesian frames of reference, and tacitly assumed that similar scales of length are used on each of the three coordinate axes. When different scales are admitted, it is simpler to substitute an algebraic definition of covariant components for the geometrical definition from which we started: if X^1, X^2, X^3 is any cartesian system (e.g. one with similar scales on the three axes), equation (2) defines the covariant components in any new system x^1, x^2, x^3 in terms of those in the original system. That this definition is independent of the particular X^1, X^2, X^3 system chosen can be seen fairly easily, for

$$\sum_i \frac{\partial X'^i}{\partial x^k} A'_i = \sum_i \left\{ \frac{\partial X'^i}{\partial x^k} \sum_j \left(\frac{\partial X^j}{\partial X'^i} A_j \right) \right\} = \sum_j \frac{\partial X^j}{\partial x^k} A_j.$$

Indeed, all transformations according to (2) are mutually consistent, regardless of scales etc. The only requirement is that the functions relating one set of coordinates to another should be differentiable.]

Equation (2) expresses the fundamental transformation property of the covariant components of a vector. Covariance is the property of transforming according to equations (2).

The transformation law for contravariant components may be derived in much the same way as that for covariant components. We first note (compare Fig. 19.7) that if the p

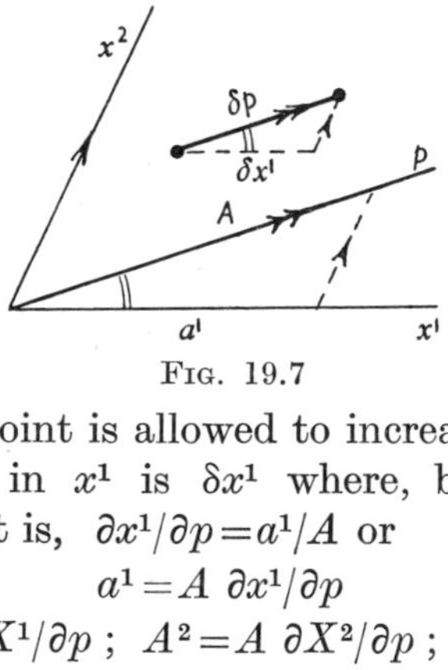

FIG. 19.7

coordinate of any point is allowed to increase by δp, the corresponding increase in x^1 is δx^1 where, by similar triangles, $\delta x^1/\delta p = a^1/A$; that is, $\partial x^1/\partial p = a^1/A$ or

$$a^1 = A\ \partial x^1/\partial p$$

Similarly $A^1 = A\ \partial X^1/\partial p$; $A^2 = A\ \partial X^2/\partial p$; $A^3 = A\ \partial X^3/\partial p$

But $$A\frac{\partial x^1}{\partial p} = A\left\{\frac{\partial x^1}{\partial X^1}\frac{\partial X^1}{\partial p} + \frac{\partial x^1}{\partial X^2}\frac{\partial X^2}{\partial p} + \frac{\partial x^1}{\partial X^3}\frac{\partial X^3}{\partial p}\right\}$$

i.e. $$a^1 = \frac{\partial x^1}{\partial X^1} A^1 + \frac{\partial x^1}{\partial X^2} A^2 + \frac{\partial x^1}{\partial X^3} A^3 \qquad (4)$$

$$= \sum_{i=1}^{3} \frac{\partial x^1}{\partial X^i} A^i$$

In the condensed notation the transformation of all three components is given by

$$\text{(Contravariant law)} \quad a^k = \sum_{i=1}^{3} \frac{\partial x^k}{\partial X^i} A^i \qquad (k=1, 2, 3) \tag{5}$$

Equation (5) expresses the fundamental transformation property of the contravariant components of a vector. Contravariance is the property of transforming according to the equations (5).

19.13. *Extension to more general coordinate systems*

When both the x^1, x^2, x^3 and the X^1, X^2, X^3 coordinate systems are rectilinear, that is, cartesian, the quantities $\partial x^k/\partial X^i$ and $\partial X^i/\partial x^k$ are ordinary constants whose value may be written down explicitly in terms of the (constant) angles made by one set of axes with the other set. We have refrained from so doing or even from introducing any shorthand abbreviation such as $c_{ki} = \partial x^k/\partial X^i$ which might suggest constants because equations (2) and (5) of 19.12 can be used even when x^1, x^2, x^3 and X^1, X^2, X^3 are non-cartesian i.e. when they are curvilinear coordinates of any kind. The values of $\partial x^k/\partial X^i$ etc. will then be functions of position.

19.14. *Examples of the application of the transformation law*

Example 1

Let us find the form taken by (*a*) the covariant, (*b*) the contravariant components of the vector grad ϕ, where ϕ is a scalar quantity. The components of $\mathbf{a} = \text{grad}\,\phi$ in a rectangular cartesian system OX^1, OX^2, OX^3 say, are $\partial\phi/\partial X^1$, $\partial\phi/\partial X^2$, $\partial\phi/\partial X^3$. The covariant components in any (in general oblique) frame Ox^1, Ox^2, Ox^3 are therefore

$$a_1 = \frac{\partial X^1}{\partial x^1}\frac{\partial \phi}{\partial X^1} + \frac{\partial X^2}{\partial x^1}\frac{\partial \phi}{\partial X^2} + \frac{\partial X^3}{\partial x^1}\frac{\partial \phi}{\partial X^3} \tag{1}$$

$$= \frac{\partial \phi}{\partial x^1}; \quad a_2 = \frac{\partial \phi}{\partial x^2}; \quad a_3 = \frac{\partial \phi}{\partial x^3}$$

By contrast, we find for the contravariant components,

$$a^1 = \frac{\partial x^1}{\partial X^1}\frac{\partial \phi}{\partial X^1} + \frac{\partial x^1}{\partial X^2}\frac{\partial \phi}{\partial X^2} + \frac{\partial x^1}{\partial X^3}\frac{\partial \phi}{\partial X^3}$$

and two similar expressions for a^2, a^3, and these, unlike (1) do not in general simplify to neater expressions. It is therefore clear that the specification of a gradient in terms of covariant components is likely to be a simpler matter than specification in terms of contravariant components when oblique or curvilinear coordinates are used.

Example 2

The components of an elementary displacement $\delta\mathbf{r}$ in a rectangular cartesian system are δX^1, δX^2, δX^3, which may also be written δX_1, δX_2, δX_3 since there is no distinction between covariant and contravariant in such a system. The contravariant components of $\delta\mathbf{r}$ in any other system are given by the transformation law,

$$(\delta x)^1 = \frac{\partial x^1}{\partial X^1}\,\delta X^1 + \frac{\partial x^1}{\partial X^2}\,\delta X^2 + \frac{\partial x^1}{\partial X^3}\,\delta X^3$$

$$= \delta x^1\,; \quad (\delta x)^2 = \delta x^2\,; \quad (\delta x)^3 = \delta x^3$$

This is evidently a simple and convenient form. By contrast the covariant components are

$$(\delta x)_1 = \frac{\partial X^1}{\partial x^1}\,\delta X_1 + \frac{\partial X^2}{\partial x^1}\,\delta X_2 + \frac{\partial X^3}{\partial x^1}\,\delta X_3 \tag{2}$$

and similarly for $(\delta x)_2$ and $(\delta x)_3$. For a general curvilinear system (2) does not simplify to any neater form.

19.2. Covariant, contravariant, and mixed tensors

Some physical quantities, like the stresses and strains in a distorted elastic medium, or the electromagnetic field experienced by a moving observer, are difficult to visualise precisely as entities. The usual way of discussing and relating such entities is to analyse each into components and thereafter to use algebraical transformation laws such as equations (2) and (5) of 19.12 to express the geometrical content of the physical problem. When the covariant and contravariant notation of components is employed, the resulting algebra is called tensor analysis. It is worth noting that whereas in vector analysis elegance is achieved by allowing direct geometrical apprehension to render the introduction of particular coordinate systems superfluous, tensor analysis comes into its own when the geometrical complexity is too great for ready pictorial apprehension, so that coordinate systems and algebraic laws must be used to remedy the deficiency.

We shall, in 19.21, give an illustrative example of a physical quantity, namely the stress in an elastic medium which is conveniently represented by a second-order tensor. However, each of the various tensors of physics presents a different appearance so the algebraical definition of a tensor perhaps merits priority over any particular illustration. The general algebraic definition of a tensor is, in fact, no more than an extension to several suffixes of the covariant and contravariant transformation laws of 19.12.

The covariant components of a vector define a covariant tensor of order one, e.g. a_i $(i=1, 2, 3)$†. The contravariant components of a vector define a contravariant tensor of order one, e.g. a^i $(i=1, 2, 3)$. Tensors of higher order have more indices, and these indices may be in either the covariant or the contravariant position e.g. $a_{ij}^{\cdot\cdot k}$ or $a_{\cdot i}^{j}$, and the corresponding transformation laws are built up from the covariant and contravariant laws (2) and (5) of § 19.12 in a fairly direct way (see below). The dots in the symbol $a_{ij}^{\cdot\cdot k}$ are inserted to indicate that k is the *third* index in order, so distinguishing it, for example, from $a_{i\cdot j}^{\cdot k \cdot}$. Some authors omit the dots and rely on accurate placing of the indices to denote their order, but this is not recommended. The tensor character i.e. the covariant and contravariant indices and the transformation laws are the same for $a_{ij}^{\cdot\cdot k}$ and for $a_{i\cdot j}^{\cdot k}$, or for $a_{\cdot i}^{j}$ and $a_{i}^{\cdot j}$, and in some particular cases where the order of the indices is known to be immaterial, the notation a_{ij}^{k} for either of the first pair or a_{i}^{j} for either of the second pair may be used.

Since in three-dimensional work three axes are involved, i.e. $i=1, 2, 3$ and similarly $j=1, 2, 3$ etc., a second order tensor a_{ij} or a_i^j has the same number of components as has the 3×3 matrix (a_{ij}) or (a_i^j), that is a second order tensor has nine components. Tensors of order one, two, three etc. can in fact be thought of as matrices with one, two, three etc. dimensions with special transformation laws corresponding to changes in coordinate systems.

The transformation law for a second order covariant tensor a_{kl} must relate the nine quantities a_{kl} $(k, l=1, 2, 3)$ to the corresponding nine quantities A_{ij} $(i, j=1, 2, 3)$ in any other coordinate system. Corresponding to the covariant transformation of the first index the symbols $\sum_{i=1}^{3} \dfrac{\partial X^i}{\partial x^k}$ must appear, and for the second

† Or $(i=1, 2, 3, 4)$ in relativity physics.

index the symbols $\sum_{i=1}^{3} \frac{\partial X^j}{\partial x^l}$: the transformation law is

$$a_{kl} = \sum_{i=1}^{3} \sum_{j=1}^{3} \frac{\partial X^i}{\partial x^k} \frac{\partial X^j}{\partial x^l} A_{ij} \tag{1}$$

Similarly for a contravariant second order tensor

$$a^{kl} = \sum_{i=1}^{3} \sum_{j=1}^{3} \frac{\partial x^k}{\partial X^i} \frac{\partial x^l}{\partial X^j} A^{ij} \tag{2}$$

For a mixed second order tensor

$$a^{l}_{\cdot k} = \sum_{i=1}^{3} \sum_{j=1}^{3} \frac{\partial X^j}{\partial x^k} \cdot \frac{\partial x^l}{\partial X^j} A^{j}_{\cdot i} \tag{3}$$

(or $a_k^{\cdot l}$ or a^l) (or $A_i^{\cdot j}$ or A_i^j)

For a covariant third order tensor

$$a_{lmn} = \sum_{i=1}^{3} \sum_{j=1}^{3} \sum_{k=1}^{3} \frac{\partial X^i}{\partial x^l} \frac{\partial X^j}{\partial x^m} \frac{\partial X^k}{\partial x^n} A_{ijk} \tag{4}$$

and so on.

19.21. *The stress tensor*

When a body composed of elastic material is held in a distorted configuration, the material of the interior, although at rest, is in a state of stress, that is, it transmits forces. If a small plane cut were made at a point Q in the interior, the material on either side of Q would generally experience a small shift of position owing to the absence of forces previously transmitted. Moreover, the amount and direction of the shift would depend on the orientation as well as on the area of the cut. This picture of a hypothetical cut should make the following axioms about the stresses in a continuous elastic material acceptable to the reader.

The resultant force $\mathbf{F}$ exerted *by* the material on one side of a plane face A *on* the material (with which it is continuously joined) on the other side of the face will usually have a shear component as well as a normal component. If two faces A, A' of different orientation pass through the same point Q, the corresponding forces $\mathbf{F}$, $\mathbf{F}'$ will in general differ in both magnitude and direction. To specify the stress at Q completely it is necessary to provide sufficient information to enable the force $\mathbf{F}'$ on a small face at Q of *any* orientation to be calculated.

We shall, as is usual in vector work, represent a plane area α by the vector $\boldsymbol{\alpha}$ whose magnitude is equal to α and whose direction is normal to the area (see 17.42). If the area is a face of an enclosed volume, the conventional sense for the vector is that of the *outward* normal.

Let us first consider the equilibrium of a tetrahedron whose dimensions are so small that variations in the force per unit area over any one face may be neglected. If the face areas are $\boldsymbol{\alpha}^1$, $\boldsymbol{\alpha}^2$, $\boldsymbol{\alpha}^3$, $\boldsymbol{\alpha}^4$ the forces on the faces can be written $\alpha^1\mathbf{s}_1$, $\alpha^2\mathbf{s}_2$, $\alpha^3\mathbf{s}_3$, $\alpha^4\mathbf{s}_4$ respectively. The indices 1, 2, 3, 4 in the above are, so far, to be regarded only as labels : we shall discuss possible covariant or contravariant behaviour later. In order that the tetrahedron may remain in equilibrium under the action of the forces on its faces it is necessary that

$$\alpha^1\mathbf{s}_1+\alpha^2\mathbf{s}_2+\alpha^3\mathbf{s}_3+\alpha^4\mathbf{s}_4=0 \tag{1}$$

If the directions of $\boldsymbol{\alpha}^1$, $\boldsymbol{\alpha}^2$, $\boldsymbol{\alpha}^3$ remain fixed, but that of $\boldsymbol{\alpha}^4$ is varied, we see, by writing (1) in the form

$$\alpha^4\mathbf{s}_4= -\alpha^1\mathbf{s}_1-\alpha^2\mathbf{s}_2-\alpha^3\mathbf{s}_3 \tag{2}$$

that the force on a plane $\boldsymbol{\alpha}^4$ in any direction can be deduced if the forces $\mathbf{s}_1$, $\mathbf{s}_2$, $\mathbf{s}_3$ on unit areas of planes in three standard directions are given. If we allow the orientation of $\boldsymbol{\alpha}^4$ to vary, the magnitudes but not the directions of $\boldsymbol{\alpha}^1$, $\boldsymbol{\alpha}^2$, $\boldsymbol{\alpha}^3$ will vary, so equation (3) will express the force per unit area on $\boldsymbol{\alpha}^4$ in terms of the same three vectors $\mathbf{s}_1$, $\mathbf{s}_2$, $\mathbf{s}_3$. We deduce that the state of stress at a point (which we can regard as the limiting position of the tetrahedron as its dimensions become indefinitely small) is completely specified if the values of the forces per unit area, $\mathbf{s}_1$, $\mathbf{s}_2$, $\mathbf{s}_3$, on three constant planes (which can be regarded as the limiting positions of the faces of the tetrahedron) through that point are given. Thus not more than nine components are required to specify the stress at a point.

To investigate the transformation properties of the nine components of stress, let Ox^1, Ox^2, Ox^3 and OX^1, OX^2, OX^3 be two sets of cartesian axes. Let four planes be drawn which are respectively normal to Ox^1, Ox^2, Ox^3, OX^1, and form a small tetrahedron about the point, Q say, at which the stress is to be

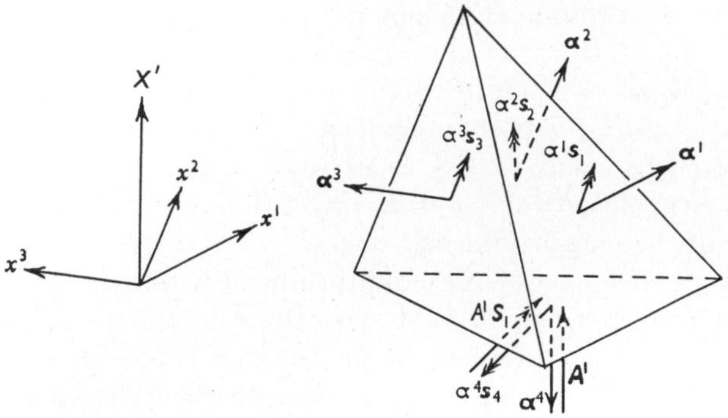

FIG. 19.8

investigated. If OX^1 has positive components in the directions of Ox^1, Ox^2, Ox^3, and if the senses of Ox^1, Ox^2, Ox^3 are the same as those of $\boldsymbol{\alpha}^1$, $\boldsymbol{\alpha}^2$, $\boldsymbol{\alpha}^3$, the sense of $\boldsymbol{\alpha}^4$ will be opposite to that of OX^1 (compare Fig. 19.8). To take this into account and to emphasize the association of $\boldsymbol{\alpha}^4$ with OX^1, we shall write $-\boldsymbol{\alpha}^4 = \mathbf{A}^1$. It is possible to establish that $\alpha^1/A^1 = \partial x^1/\partial X^1$ and two similar equations for α^2/A^1, α^3/A^1 either by geometry or by a physical argument as follows :

If all faces of the tetrahedron were subjected to the same pressure P i.e. if forces $-P\boldsymbol{\alpha}^1$, $-P\boldsymbol{\alpha}^2$, $-P\boldsymbol{\alpha}^3$, $-P\boldsymbol{\alpha}^4$ $(=P\mathbf{A}^1)$, were applied to its faces, it would be maintained in equilibrium. So,

$$-P\boldsymbol{\alpha}^1 - P\boldsymbol{\alpha}^2 - P\boldsymbol{\alpha}^3 + P\mathbf{A}^1 = 0$$

$$\mathbf{A}^1 = \boldsymbol{\alpha}^1 + \boldsymbol{\alpha}^2 + \boldsymbol{\alpha}^3 \tag{3}$$

But, in the x^1, x^2, x^3 frame of reference, the contravariant components of $\boldsymbol{\alpha}^1$ are $(\alpha^1, 0, 0)$, those of $\boldsymbol{\alpha}^2$ are $(0, \alpha^2, 0)$ and those of α^3 are $(0, 0, \alpha^3)$. Hence from (3) the contravariant components in the x^1, x^2, x^3 frame of $\mathbf{A}^1$ are $(\alpha^1, \alpha^2, \alpha^3)$. In the X^1, X^2, X^3 frame, the contravariant components of $\mathbf{A}^1$ are $(A^1, 0, 0)$. The law of contravariant transformation therefore gives,

$$\alpha^i = \frac{\partial x^i}{\partial X^1} \cdot A^1 + \frac{\partial x^i}{\partial X^2} \cdot 0 + \frac{\partial x^i}{\partial X^3} \cdot 0 = \frac{\partial x^i}{\partial X^1} A^1,$$

whence $\alpha^1/A^1 = \partial x^1/\partial X^1$; $\alpha^2/A^1 = \partial x^2/\partial X^1$; $\alpha^3/A^1 = \partial x^3/\partial X^1$ (4)

This result, in conjunction with equation (2) now enables us to establish the transformation law for the components of stress. For, if we write $-\mathbf{s}_4 = \mathbf{S}_1$ equation (2) takes the form

$$A^1\mathbf{S}_1 = \alpha^1\mathbf{s}_1 + \alpha^2\mathbf{s}_2 + \alpha^3\mathbf{s}_3$$

i.e., using (4)

$$\mathbf{S}_1 = \frac{\partial x^1}{\partial X^1}\,\mathbf{s}_1 + \frac{\partial x^2}{\partial X^1}\,\mathbf{s}_2 + \frac{\partial x^3}{\partial X^1}\cdot\mathbf{s}_3 \tag{5}$$

Now if the covariant components of $\mathbf{s}_1$ in the x^1, x^2, x^3 frame are s_{11}, s_{12}, s_{13}, the covariant component of $\mathbf{s}_1$ in the X^1 direction in the X^1, X^2, X^3 frame is $\sum_j \frac{\partial x^j}{\partial X^1} s_{1j}$ and similarly those of $\mathbf{s}_2$, $\mathbf{s}_3$ are $\sum_j \frac{\partial x^j}{\partial X^2} s_{2j}$, $\sum_j \frac{\partial x^j}{\partial X^3} s_{3j}$. The covariant X^1 component of equation (5) is then

$$S_{11} = \sum_{i,j} \frac{\partial x^i}{\partial X^1}\frac{\partial x^j}{\partial X^1}\,s_{ij}$$

The X^2 and X^3 components of (5) are similarly found, and all three equations derived from (5) are represented by

$$S_{1k} = \sum_{i,j} \frac{\partial x^i}{\partial X^1}\frac{\partial x^j}{\partial X^k}\,s_{ij} \qquad k=1,\,2,\,3 \tag{6}$$

By taking not OX^1 but OX^2 or OX^3 as the direction of the fourth face of our tetrahedron we get similar relations for S_{2k} and S_{3k}, and the whole collection of relations can be summarised :

$$S_{lk} = \sum_{i,j} \frac{\partial x^i}{\partial X^l}\frac{\partial x^j}{\partial X^k}\,s_{ij} \tag{7}$$

Equation (7) is the fundamental equation expressing the second order covariant transformation property, so we have established that the stress components s_{ij} form a covariant second order tensor. If, after (5) we had chosen to take contravariant components of $\mathbf{s}_1$ etc. we could equally well have established that these components, s^i_j were components of a mixed second order tensor.

It should perhaps be mentioned that the nine stress components are not in fact independent. For the equilibrium of the tetrahedron it is necessary not only that the resultant force shall be zero, as already considered, but also that the resultant couple shall be zero. This further condition is satisfied if and only if

$$s_{ij} = s_{ji} \qquad i,\,j=1,\,2,\,3 \tag{8}$$

The result (8) can be proved for the tetrahedron by vector methods. A much simpler method, which is left as an exercise for the reader, is to consider a small volume in the shape of a rectangular block; take rectangular cartesian axes OX^1, OX^2, OX^3 perpendicular to the faces of the block; establish by taking moments about OX^3 that $S_{12}=S_{21}$; and finally from this, the similar results for S_{23}, S_{31}, and the covariant transformation law, deduce that $s_{ij}=s_{ji}$ for any cartesian axes.

Any tensor s_{ij} satisfying (8) is called a symmetric tensor.

For completeness we state the sign convention for stress components explicitly: If the normal to area α^i lies in the direction Ox^i, the quantity $\alpha^i s_{ij}$ is the covariant component of the force on the material to the side of α^i where x^i is smaller in the sense tending to increase its x^j coordinate. Thus in a state of pure tension in the x^1 direction, s_{11} is positive.

The commonest applications of the stress tensor as we have defined it are to *rectangular* cartesian systems, when the distinction between covariant and contravariant components vanishes and, in fact, all the transformation quantities $\partial x^i/\partial X^j$ can be simply expressed as direction cosines.

The physical entity represented by the second order tensor s_{ij} is one in whose definition two separately directed quantities, viz. $\boldsymbol{\alpha}$ and $\mathbf{F}$ are involved. Third or higher order tensors are likely to be associated with entities whose definition involves three or more directed quantities.

One word of encouragement to the reader may not be out of place. The process of examining physical quantities and establishing their tensorial character is often admittedly indirect or involved†, but in most applications of tensor calculus this basic process has already been carried out by the founders of the subject, and the student is mainly concerned with the vastly more straightforward business of performing algebraic operations of the kind described in the remainder of this chapter.

19.22. *Products and sums of tensors*

Suppose a_i and b_i are two first order tensors. Let A_i and B_i be their representations in another coordinate system. We have

† For example, if curvilinear coordinates are introduced, the above treatment of the stress tensor is no longer adequate, and a much more complicated formulation has to be substituted.

$$a_k = \sum_i \frac{\partial X^i}{\partial x^k} A_i \,; \quad b_l = \sum_j \frac{\partial X^j}{\partial x^l} B_j$$

so

$$a_k b_l = \sum_i \frac{\partial X^i}{\partial x^k} A_i \,.\, \sum_j \frac{\partial X^j}{\partial x^l} B_j = \sum_i \sum_j \frac{\partial X^i}{\partial x^k} \frac{\partial X^j}{\partial x^l} A_i B_j \tag{1}$$

But (1) is the transformation law which characterises a second order covariant tensor, so the nine components $a_k b_l$ compose a second order tensor, c_{kl} say. This tensor is called the product of the tensors a_k and b_l. We note in passing that the tensor product $a_k b_l$ contains all possible combinations of the components, unlike the scalar product, $A_1B_1 + A_2B_2 + A_3B_3$, in rectangular cartesian coordinates, or the vector product $\mathbf{i}(A_2B_3 - A_3B_2) + \mathbf{j}(A_3B_1 - A_1B_3) + \mathbf{k}(A_1B_2 - A_2B_1)$, in which only particular combinations of components appear.

The multiplication of higher order tensors results in a tensor which has one covariant index for each covariant index in each of the factors, and similarly for the contravariant indices, for example

$$a^k_{ij} b^{kmno}_l = c^{kmno}_{ijl}$$

or

$$a^{j \cdot k}_{\cdot i} b_l = c^{j \cdot k}_{\cdot i \cdot l} \quad \text{or} \quad c^{\cdot j \cdot k}_{l \cdot i}$$

The order of the indices in the c's on the right-hand side is not determined by the transformation laws and is therefore a matter of choice: convenience however usually demands, or at least favours, an order closely related to that on the left-hand side.

If two tensors are of the same type i.e. if they have the same number of covariant indices and the same number of contravariant indices, the sum or difference of the tensors is the set of components formed by adding or subtracting corresponding terms of the two tensors (as in the sum or difference of matrices), and this resulting set of components constitutes another tensor of the same type. Thus

$$a^k_{ij} + b^k_{ij} \text{ is a tensor of type } c^k_{ij}$$

This follows immediately from the transformation laws.

19.23. *Conventions of notation*

(i). Since in 3-dimensional space the indices $i, j, k, l, \ldots$ all run through the values 1, 2, 3, the tensor a_{ij} may equally well be referred to as the tensor a_{kl}, for the same nine components are specified by the notation. However, in particular contexts the two notations may not be equally satisfactory : thus it would be confusing to write the sum $a_{ij}^k + b_{ij}^k$ of two tensors as $a_{ij}^k + b_{lm}^n$ since there is an association between the components which are to be added (and the resulting component in the sum) which is brought out by the first notation and obscured by the second. On the other hand, to use $a_i b_j$ on the left-hand side of equation (1) of 19.22 would cause immense confusion, and, in fact, the summation notation would have to be abandoned on the right-hand side. The dummy indices i, j etc. are thus arbitrary only subject to two important qualifications, namely that important associations are shown up, and that false associations, especially with regard to summations are not implied.

(ii). A tensor equation e.g. $a_{ij}^k = b_{ij}^k$ means that each of the $3 \times 3 \times 3 = 27$ components of a_{ij}^k is equal to the corresponding component of b_{ij}^k. The tensors on the two sides of a tensor equation must therefore be of the same type.

(iii). Tensor equations refer to tensor components in one and the same coordinate system. If a_{ij} and A_{ij} represent the same tensor in different coordinate systems, it is the transformation law which relates a_{ij} and A_{ij} (*not* an equation $a_{ij} = A_{ij}$).

(iv). In both (i.e. covariant and contravariant) laws of transformation one dummy index, i say, occurs in each of two factors on the right hand side, and summation over all values of i is prescribed. The process of summing over all values of a repeated index (a process by the way which has a marked resemblance to matrix multiplication) is so common in tensor analysis that to achieve compactness of notation the following *summation convention* is made : whenever an index is repeated in a single term, a $\sum$ sign is understood and need not be written down, thus

$$a_j b^j = a_1 b^1 + a_2 b^2 + a_3 b^3 \tag{1}$$

$$a_{ij\cdot i}^{\cdot\cdot k} = a_{1j\cdot 1}^{\cdot\cdot k} + a_{2j\cdot 2}^{\cdot\cdot k} + a_{3j\cdot 3}^{\cdot\cdot k}$$

The fundamental transformation laws (2) and (4) of 19.12 are, with this convention, written

$$\text{(Covariant)} \qquad a_k = \frac{\partial X^i}{\partial x^k} A_i \tag{2}$$

(Contravariant) $$a^k = \frac{\partial x^k}{\partial X^i} A^i \tag{3}$$

If one wishes to use the same index twice without implying the summation convention, capital letters may be used for indices. Thus, in contrast to (1),

$a_J b^J$ denotes either $a_1 b^1$ or $a_2 b^2$ or $a_3 b^3$

19.24. *Contraction*

Consider the sum a_i^i of the 'diagonal elements' of a mixed tensor a_i^j. We find that the transformation law for such a sum takes the form,

$$a_k^k = A_i^i \text{ ; that is } a_1^1 + a_2^2 + a_3^3 = A_1^1 + A_2^2 + A_3^3 \tag{1}$$

Thus the sum a_i^i is a number which is independent of the coordinate system, that is a constant with respect to transformations of axes. In the same way a_{ij}^{ki} is a tensor of type c_j^k, that is a_{ij}^{ki} is a tensor of order two less than is the tensor a_{ij}^{kl}. The process of making one contravariant index equal to a covariant index in a mixed tensor, and summing the components so obtained is called *contraction*, and the result is a tensor with one less covariant index and one less contravariant index than the original tensor.

Thus, if we had a tensor equation

$$a_{ij}^k = b_{ij}^k \tag{2}$$

we could, by contraction, deduce the equation

$$a_{ij}^j = b_{ij}^j \tag{3}$$

which is of the form $c_i = d_i$, or alternatively we could deduce

$$a_{ij}^i = b_{ij}^i \tag{4}$$

The contracted equations (3) and (4) give no information that was not implicitly contained in (2), but are often convenient for special purposes.

Examples

1. Verify the transformation law (1) above.

2. By expressing $a_i b^i$ as $A_i B^i$ where A_i, B^i are components in a rectangular cartesian frame, show that $a_i b^i$ is the scalar product of the two vectors represented by a_i and b^i respectively. (Note: $A^i = A_i$.)

19.25. *The 'quotient law'*

From the preceding paragraphs we can deduce the tensor character of any product of tensors, whether with distinct or with repeated indices, e.g.

$$a^{ij}b^k_l = c^{ijk}_l \tag{1}$$

$$a^i_j b_{ik} = c_{jk} \tag{2}$$

Our present enquiry takes the converse form : if we are given equations (or rather, sets of equations) of the form

$$a^{ij}(?) = c^{ijk}_l \tag{3}$$

or

$$a^i_j(?) = c_{jk} \tag{4}$$

can we deduce that the unknown quantities in brackets in (3) form the components of a tensor of type b^k_l and that those in (4) are components of a tensor of type b_{ik}?

We first note that each of the quantities in brackets in equation (3) is of the form c^{ijk}_l/a^{ij} (no summation) and that it therefore may depend on four indices i, j, k, l, and we shall write the unknown quantities as $b(i, j, k, l)$ i.e. equation (3) as

$$a^{ij}b(i, j, k, l) = c^{ijk}_l \tag{5}$$

with the reservation that the summation convention applies only to tensor indices i.e. the indices in brackets do not provoke summation. The quotient law can now be stated for this case as follows : if for *all* tensors of type a^{ij} the result of multiplying a^{ij} and $b(i, j, k, l)$ is a tensor of type c^{ijk}_l, then $b(i, j, k, l)$ is a tensor of type b^k_l. If (5) is known to be true only for a particular tensor a^{ij}, it is not possible to deduce that $b(i, j, k, l)$ is a tensor.

Proof : Consider the transformation between coordinate systems x^i $(i=1, 2, 3)$ and X^i $(i=1, 2, 3)$. We define $B(m, n, o, p)$ by analogy with (5),

$$A^{mn}B(m, n, o, p) = C^{mno}_p \tag{6}$$

Then

$$a^{ij} = \frac{\partial x^i}{\partial X^m}\frac{\partial x^j}{\partial X^n}A^{mn}$$

$$c^{ijk}_l = \frac{\partial x^i}{\partial X^m}\frac{\partial x^j}{\partial X^n}\frac{\partial x^k}{\partial X^o}\frac{\partial X^p}{\partial x^l}C^{mno}_p$$

Hence from (5)

$$\frac{\partial x^i}{\partial X^m}\frac{\partial x^j}{\partial X^n}\left\{A^{mn}b(i, j, k, l) - \frac{\partial x^k}{\partial X^o}\frac{\partial X^p}{\partial x^l}C^{mno}_p\right\} = 0$$

or, using (6)

$$\frac{\partial x^i}{\partial X^m}\frac{\partial x^j}{\partial X^n}A^{mn}\left\{b(i,j,k,l)-\frac{\partial x^k}{\partial X^o}\frac{\partial X^p}{\partial x^l}B(m,n,o,p)\right\}=0 \qquad (7)$$

Now equation (7) can be true for all coordinate systems and for all tensors a^{ij}, i.e. all tensors A^{mn}, only if the bracket vanishes identically, that is

$$b(i,j,k,l)=\frac{\partial x^k}{\partial X^o}\frac{\partial X^p}{\partial x^l}B(m,n,o,p) \qquad (8)$$

Equation (8) is the transformation law characterising a mixed second order tensor, i.e. we have

$$b(i,j,k,l)=b_l^k \qquad (9)$$

The quotient law corresponding to equation (3) has thus been established, and we note that the argument depends on a^{ij} being an arbitrary tensor of its type.

The quotient law corresponding to (4) can be stated : if for all tensors of type a_j^i the result of multiplying a_j^i and $b(i,j,k)$ is a tensor of type c_{jk}, then $b(i,j,k)$ is a tensor of type b_{ik}.

The proof follows the same lines as the proof of (9) and is recommended as an exercise for the reader.

From the two particular examples which we have given, the form of the quotient theorem for a wide range of cases with any number of distinct or repeated indices should be apparent to the reader. Its explicit statement in general terms would however be clumsy.

19.26. *The Kronecker delta and the epsilon tensors*

The quantities $\partial x^j/\partial x^i$ can be regarded as composing a mixed tensor, for

$$\frac{\partial x^l}{\partial x^k}=\sum_i\frac{\partial x^l}{\partial X^i}\frac{\partial X^i}{\partial x^k}=\sum_i\sum_j\frac{\partial x^l}{\partial X^i}\cdot\frac{\partial X^j}{\partial x^k}\cdot\frac{\partial X^i}{\partial X^j}$$

which is the law of transformation for a mixed tensor of order two. This tensor is written δ_k^l and is called the Kronecker delta. Its components are easily evaluated explicitly, for, since x^1, x^2, x^3 are independent variables,

$$\delta_i^j=\frac{\partial x^j}{\partial x^j}=1 \quad \text{if } i=j$$

$$=0 \quad \text{otherwise}$$

The Kronecker delta therefore has the peculiar property that although it is a tensor, its components have the same value no matter what coordinate system is chosen.

Two other tensors, the ϵ-tensors, can be defined by means of their particular values in rectangular cartesian systems. We define

$$
\begin{aligned}
e_{ijk} = e^{ijk} &= 0 \quad \text{when any two of the indices are equal} \\
&= +1 \quad \text{when } i, j, k \text{ is an even permutation of the numbers } 1, 2, 3 \\
&= -1 \quad \text{when } i, j, k \text{ is an odd permutation of the numbers } 1, 2, 3.
\end{aligned}
$$

It is not difficult to show that these components are invariant for any change to another rectangular cartesian system. In other types of coordinate system however the components are

$$\epsilon_{ijk} = f \,.\, e_{ijk}$$
$$\epsilon^{ijk} = e^{ijk}/f$$

where f is in general a scalar function of position.

19.3. Length, and the metric tensors

Let X^1, X^2, X^3 be rectangular cartesian coordinates: then an elementary displacement with components $\mathrm{d}X^1$, $\mathrm{d}X^2$, $\mathrm{d}X^3$ has length $\mathrm{d}s$ given by

$$\mathrm{d}s^2 = (\mathrm{d}X^1)^2 + (\mathrm{d}X^2)^2 + (\mathrm{d}X^3)^2$$

But
$$\mathrm{d}X^i = \frac{\partial X^i}{\partial x^j}\,\mathrm{d}x^j \tag{1}$$

so
$$\mathrm{d}s^2 = g_{mn}\,\mathrm{d}x^m\,\mathrm{d}x^n \tag{2}$$

where we have put

$$g_{mn} = \sum_{i=1}^{3} \frac{\partial X^i}{\partial x^m}\frac{\partial X^i}{\partial x^n} = \frac{\partial X^i}{\partial x^m}\frac{\partial X^i}{\partial x^n} \tag{3}$$

We are justified in writing g_{mn} as a covariant second order tensor for the following reasons: in equation (2), $\mathrm{d}x^m$, $\mathrm{d}x^n$ are arbitrary contravariant tensors while $\mathrm{d}s^2$, being the square of the length of the displacement is independent of coordinate system, and consequently has no tensor indices. It follows from (3) that g_{mn} is a covariant second order tensor. It is called the covariant metric tensor (or fundamental tensor).

By a similar argument the length of any vector **a** can be expressed first in terms of rectangular cartesian components and then, by use of the covariant transformation similar to (1),

$$a^2 = g_{mn} a^m a^n$$

that is,

$$a = (g_{mn} a^m a^n)^{\frac{1}{2}} \tag{4}$$

Next let us consider the magnitude of a vector **a** in terms of its covariant components a_i. If in a rectangular cartesian frame OX^1, OX^2, OX^3 the components of **a** are A_1, A_2, A_3 then

$$a^2 = A_1{}^2 + A_2{}^2 + A_3{}^2$$

But

$$A_i = \frac{\partial x^j}{\partial X^i} a_j$$

so

$$a^2 = g^{mn} a_m a_n \tag{5}$$

where

$$g^{mn} = \frac{\partial x^m}{\partial X^i} \cdot \frac{\partial x^n}{\partial X^j} \tag{6}$$

That is

$$a = (g^{mn} a_m a_n)^{\frac{1}{2}} \tag{7}$$

The quotient law allows us to deduce from equation (5) that g^{mn} is a second order contravariant tensor. It is called the contravariant metric tensor.

To complete the survey of the ways in which the length of a vector can be expressed, let us consider one covariant and one contravariant component in each term. We have already observed in 19.24 Example 2 that the scalar product of two vectors **a**, **b** is given by $\mathbf{a} . \mathbf{b} = a_i b^i$. Hence

$$a^2 = \mathbf{a} . \mathbf{a} = a_i a^i \tag{8}$$

To represent (8) in a notation similar to (4) and (7), we may write

$$a = (g_n^m a_m a^n)^{\frac{1}{2}} \tag{9}$$

where

$$g_n^m = 0 \quad m \neq n$$
$$= 1 \quad m = n$$

We see that g_n^m is identical with the Kronecker delta defined in 19.26,

$$g_n^m \equiv \delta_n^m, \tag{10}$$

and we have already established that δ_n^m is a mixed second order tensor. When this tensor is written as g_n^m or is used in equations similar to (9) it may be called the mixed metric tensor.

19.31. *Properties of the metric tensors*

From the definitions

$$g_{mn}=\frac{\partial X^i}{\partial x^m}\frac{\partial X^i}{\partial x^n}; \quad g^{mn}=\frac{\partial x^m}{\partial X^i}\cdot\frac{\partial x^n}{\partial X^i}; \quad g_n^m=\delta_n^m$$

we see that each of the metric tensors is symmetric, that is,

$$g_{nm}=g_{mn}; \quad g^{nm}=g^{mn}; \quad g_m^n=g_n^m$$

The following properties are also worthy of mention ; their proof is left as an exercise for the reader.

1. $g_{lm}g^{mn}=g^{lm}g_{mn}=\delta_l^n$
2. $g_{mn}g^{mn}=3$
3. In a rectangular cartesian frame $g_{mn}=g^{mn}=\delta_m^n$. The determinant of the elements g_{ij} is often of importance and is denoted by the symbol g,

$$g=|\, g_{ij}\,|$$

The value of the scalar quantity f mentioned in §19.26 is in fact equal to $\sqrt{g}$.

19.32. *Associated tensors : raising and lowering indices*

If we are given a covariant tensor of order one, a_j say, we can obtain an associated contravariant tensor by multiplying by the contravariant metric tensor and contracting,

$$g^{ij}a_j=b^i \quad \text{say}$$

Transforming to rectangular cartesian coordinates and using the result (3) of the last section,

$$\delta_i^j A_j=B^i$$

that is, since $\delta_i^j A_j=A_i$ and, in the rectangular frame $A_i=A^i$,

$$A^i=B^i, \quad \text{and hence} \quad a^i=b^i$$

Thus the associated contravariant tensor of a_j is

$$g^{ij}a_j=a^i \tag{1}$$

Similarly given the contravariant components of a vector, a^j, the covariant components are given by the associated covariant tensor,

$$g_{ij}a^j=a_i$$

With tensors of higher order than the first, associated tensors can be defined in the same way. Thus for a tensor a_{ij} we can define associated tensors

$$g^{li}a_{ij}=a_j^l; \quad g^{li}g^{mj}a_{ij}=a^{lm}. \tag{2}$$

If we have a tensor equation, for example

$$a_{ij}^{\cdot\cdot k} + b_{ij}^{\cdot\cdot k} = c_{ij}^{\cdot\cdot k} \tag{3}$$

it is clearly legitimate to multiply throughout by g_{lm} and then to pick out for summation those terms for which $m = k$ i.e. to contract with respect to the index $m = k$.

$$g_{lk} a_{ij}^{\cdot\cdot k} + g_{lk} b_{ij}^{\cdot\cdot k} = g_{lk} c_{ij}^{\cdot\cdot k}$$

i.e.

$$a_{ijl} + b_{ijl} = c_{ijl} \tag{4}$$

Equation (4) may equally well be written

$$a_{ijk} + b_{ijk} = c_{ijk} \tag{5}$$

Comparison of (5) and (3) shows why this algebraic procedure is often called ‘lowering the index k’. Raising an index can be justified in an exactly similar way, thus from equation (3) we could deduce the following relations between associated tensors,

$$a_{\cdot j}^{i \cdot k} + b_{\cdot j}^{i \cdot k} = c_{\cdot j}^{i \cdot k} \tag{6}$$

and

$$a^{ijk} + b^{ijk} = c^{ijk} \tag{7}$$

This completes our enumeration of the more important elementary definitions and techniques used in tensor analysis. For further information the student may refer to McConnell, *Applications of the Absolute Differential Calculus*, where applications of tensors in relativity, elasticity, geometry, dynamics and magnetism and electricity are discussed, as well as more advanced processes of manipulation, such as covariant differentiation of tensors.

Examples

Show that in a rectangular cartesian system, and hence in any system

1. $\epsilon^{rst}\epsilon_{ist} = 2\delta_i^r$
2. $\begin{cases} \epsilon^{rst} = g^{ri}g^{sj}g^{tk}\epsilon_{ijk} \\ \epsilon_{rst} = g_{ri}g_{sj}g_{tk}\epsilon^{ijk} \end{cases}$
3. $\epsilon^{rst}\epsilon^{ijk}g_{ri}g_{sj}g_{tk} = 6$
4. $\epsilon^{rst}\epsilon^{ijk}g_{sj}g_{tk} = 2g^{ri}$

CHAPTER TWENTY

UNITS AND DIMENSIONS

20.1. Introduction

It is perhaps as well to begin by warning the reader that the subject of the units and dimensions of physical quantities, especially those of electric and magnetic quantities, is one on which no two writers appear to agree. The present chapter therefore should be regarded as an expression of the personal opinion of the author—strongly held, certainly, but no more strongly than the widely different views held by others.

20.2. The need for units

The question of units appears as soon as we try to use symbols and equations to express physical quantities and laws : in other words as soon as we try to apply mathematical methods to scientific problems. There are two ways of making this first step : in the first the symbol is regarded as a direct representation of the physical quantity itself ; in the second the symbol denotes a number (or possibly a set of numbers) which is a measure of the physical quantity. There is something to be said for each of these points of view, but it is necessary, if muddled thinking is to be avoided, to adopt one and only one of them. The second, emphasising as it does the preoccupation of the scientist with quantities which can be measured on some kind of scale rather than with the qualitative concepts of philosophy such as truth, beauty, goodness and so on, seems by far the more preferable for present purposes and will be adopted here.

Consider now the measurement of a physical quantity such as length. The first step is to choose a unit of length ; in principle one takes a flat piece of material, draws a straight line on it and marks off two points on the line. This distance can then be defined as a unit length. In order to simplify the process of comparison with other lengths to be measured, one can now put other marks on the straight line labelled 0, 1, 2, etc.

These new marks are made systematically, by means of a divider for example, in such a way that the distance between 1 and 2 is equal to that between 0 and 1, and so on. Intermediate marks are also convenient ; for example the mark to be labelled p/q where p and q are integers, is located by setting the dividers to a distance such that q applications are required to span the distance between the marks 0 and p. In this way one obtains a scale of lengths. It will be noted that the marks on the scale are located in close analogy with the way in which rational numbers are defined ; the reader with a philosophical bent should try to decide whether the laws of addition of length are deductions from experiment or necessary consequences of this method of graduating the scale.

With appropriate variations in detail similar scales can be developed for other physical quantities, such as mass and time. Typical units of length are the centimetre, metre, inch, foot ; of mass, the gram, kilogram, pound, ton ; of time, the second, hour, day, year. It should be noticed that the units of mass, length and time are independent : one is not obliged to use the pound as the unit of mass when the chosen unit of length is the foot ; if it becomes expedient to change from say the pound to the ton, no alteration need be made in the units of length and time.

It is possible to go on in this way and choose independent units for all other physical variables, and in sufficiently specialised fields this is in fact done. The supreme example is that of gunnery in the British Army : horizontal distances from the gun are measured in yards, vertical distances in feet, distances between map points in metres, velocities in feet per second (for the projectile), or knots (for ship targets), or miles per hour (for aircraft targets) and so on. Lesser examples of a similar kind will be familiar to the engineer in particular, but also to the physicist (for example the current sensitivity of a galvanometer may be expressed in millimetres per microamp. per metre).

In theoretical work a different approach is preferred and a system of derived units related in some way to the fundamental units is used. Thus in the foot-pound-second (F.P.S.) system, a particle with unit velocity travels one foot every second ; and in general a particle with unit velocity travels unit distance in unit time. It is clear that when the units of length and time are altered the unit of velocity is also altered. This unit is therefore not a new independent unit but a derived unit. In the same way unit acceleration, unit power and in principle the unit of all physical quantities can be defined in terms of the three fundamental units. In practice one does not usually carry out the full programme; and some additional independent units are allowed to remain. Of these exceptions, the most important is the unit of temperature, but there are a number of others such as the units of heat energy and luminous flux: these exceptional cases will be discussed later (20.3).

20.21. *The dimensions of derived units*

The most familiar systems are those which employ basic units of mass, length and time. Thus the F.P.S. system is based on the foot, pound and second, the C.G.S. system on the centimetre, gram and second, and the M.K.S. system on the metre, kilogram and second.

The problem of transforming a derived unit from one of these systems to another can be handled by introducing the dimensions of the derived unit. A more mystical significance is often given to the concept of dimensions, but here we define the term in the following way. Consider any physical quantity, such as velocity, force, charge, etc., and denote it by X. The derived unit of X will depend on the chosen values of the three basic units of mass, length and time. Consider two such systems and let the units in the second system be greater or less than those in the first by numerical factors L, M, and T respectively. For example, if the first system is the C.G.S. system and the second is the F.P.S., then $L=30{\cdot}48$, $M=453{\cdot}6$, $T=1$. The derived unit of X will not be the same in the two systems (except by coincidence); if the basic units of the first system are altered one at a time, the derived unit will increase by factors L^a, M^b, T^c where a, b, c are numbers, usually integers, which we shall be able to determine for any given X. We now define the dimensions of X, written $[X]$, to be the set of symbols $L^aM^bT^c$, where a, b and c are given the values appropriate to X, but the general symbols L, M, T are retained.

For example consider the dimensions of velocity and acceleration. We first define the unit of velocity in terms of the basic units of a given system as a velocity such that unit length is travelled in unit time. Suppose now that the unit of length is increased by a factor L, while that of time is kept constant. The new unit of velocity must be correspondingly increased, since a greater distance must be covered in the same time. Now increase the unit of time by a factor T. The unit of velocity must now be decreased by the same factor. Finally, the unit of mass is clearly without influence; hence the dimensions of velocity are $L^1M^0T^{-1}$ or simply LT^{-1}. Similarly the unit of acceleration is defined in terms of the basic units, as an acceleration in which there is unit increase in velocity in unit time; it follows readily that the dimensions of acceleration are LT^{-2}.

20.22. *The calculation of dimensions*

The dimensions of other derived units can be found in the same way; but the process can be greatly simplified by dealing with symbols which represent the measures of physical quantities, and equations relating them, instead of the physical quantities themselves. Thus from the equations $s=vt, s=\frac{1}{2}ft^2$, the dimensions of velocity v and acceleration f follow by inspection.

Before drawing up a table of dimensions, it is as well to examine this process a little more closely. Consider first a system in which the unit of velocity is defined independently of those of mass, length and time. As we have seen there is nothing absurd in this; it is merely inconvenient. In this system the relation between velocity, distance travelled and time will be of the form

$$s=kvt \qquad (1)$$

where k is a dimensional constant, i.e. a number which takes different values in different systems. For example if the units of distance, time and velocity are the foot, second and mile-per-hour, k has the value 88/60; if the units are the mile, hour and knot, k has approximately the value 1·15.

Now return to systems in which the unit of velocity is a derived unit. The essential advantage of these systems is that they eliminate all dimensional constants such as k in equation (1) above. The unit of velocity is in fact chosen so that k is identically equal to unity and in all consistent systems the equation reduces to

$$s=vt$$

Now suppose that the motion of a certain object travelling at constant velocity is timed over the same given distance by two observers using different systems of units. The first observer finds that the distance is equal to s_1 units and the time taken is t_1 units. He concludes that in his system the particle has a velocity v_1 units where

$$v_1 = s_1/t_1$$

The second observer's units of length and time are greater than those of the first by factors L and T and his measurements are therefore $s_2 = s_1/L$ and $t_2 = t_1/T$. He concludes that in his system the velocity is

$$v_2 = s_2/t_2 = (T/L)v_1$$

Thus in the second system the measure of velocity is greater by a factor T/L and hence the unit of velocity is greater by a factor L/T. Thus the dimensions of velocity are LT^{-1}.

In practice one simply writes down the equation, $v = s/t$ and puts square brackets round each term, thus,

$$[v] = [s]/[t] = LT^{-1}$$

Similarly from $\quad f = 2s/t^2$

we find the dimensions of acceleration f to be

$$[f] = [s]/[t^2] = LT^{-2}$$

There is thus no difficulty in finding the dimensions of a quantity provided that one can find a formula connecting the quantity with others whose dimensions are known.

It will be noticed that strictly interpreted the symbols $[v]$, $[f]$ etc. represent the dimensions not of v and f but of the physical quantities of which v and f are the measures; the equation $[v] = LT^{-1}$ means that on increasing the units of length and time by factors L and T respectively, the derived unit of velocity increases by the factor LT^{-1}. Notice in particular that the actual numerical value of v for a given velocity also alters in going to the new system but the factor is $1/LT^{-1}$; a smaller number of larger units is sufficient to describe a given velocity.

20.3. Other independent units

There are a number of physical quantities such as temperature and candle power which do not seem to fit into the above scheme. We shall discuss temperature as a typical representative of this class of quantities.

The units of temperature, the degrees Celsius, Fahrenheit and Réaumur, are independent units ; they do not depend on the units of mass, length and time, but are arbitrarily chosen. This departure from the general programme of using only derived units is a matter of convenience only, and no fundamental issue is involved. The alternative scheme is to take one of the equations in which temperature appears, and so define the unit of temperature as to simplify the constant of proportionality. Perhaps the simplest is the equation of state of a perfect gas. For a mass of M gram-molecules, and in terms of an arbitrary unit of temperature, this equation is

$$pV = MR\theta \tag{1}$$

where p, V and θ are measures of pressure, volume and temperature, and R (the gas constant per gram-molecule) is independent of the nature of the gas. The quantity represented by M (the number of gram-molecules of gas present) is actually a mass, since the ‘ molecular weight ’ is defined in terms of ratios of masses and so is dimensionless.

Equation (1) is a very suitable starting point for defining a unit of temperature. The simplest choice is the one that makes $R=1$, irrespective of the value of the basic units. With this consistent unit of temperature, the perfect gas equation (for M moles of gas) is

$$pV = M\theta \tag{2}$$

In other words the temperature is equal to 1 unit if the pressure of 1 gram-molecule of gas contained in unit volume is equal to unity.

To illustrate the point more fully, let us find and compare the derived units of temperature on the C.G.S. and F.P.S. systems with the degree centigrade. On the C.G.S. systems the unit of pressure is one dyne per sq. cm. and the unit of volume is one cc. We require the temperature at which one gram-molecule of perfect gas occupies one cc. at a pressure of 1 dyne/cm.^{2} Knowing that one gram-molecule occupies 22·4 litres at N.T.P. (i.e. at 1 atmosphere and 273° absolute centigrade) we easily find that the required temperature is

$$273 \times \frac{1}{22400} \times \frac{1}{76 \times 13{\cdot}59 \times 981} = 1{\cdot}20 \times 10^{-8}$$

degrees absolute centigrade. Hence the C.G.S. derived unit of temperature is $1{\cdot}20 \times 10^{-8}$ °C.

To find the F.P.S. unit of temperature we can go through a similar calculation but knowing the dimensions of θ from equation (2), viz. $[\theta]=L^2T^{-2}$, we find immediately that the F.P.S. unit is $(30{\cdot}48)^2 \times 1{\cdot}2 \times 10^{-8}$ °C, i.e. $11{\cdot}15 \times 10^{-6}$ °C.

These are the consistent units of temperature. It is clear that the units employed in practice are defined in an entirely different way and are independent of the other basic units. The unit of temperature in practice is a fourth arbitrary unit, defined not by reference to the other three but in terms of the difference in temperature between the freezing and boiling points of water (under prescribed conditions).

To summarise this discussion we have shown that it is possible to define a consistent unit of temperature, but that in practice the unit used is an arbitrary one. This means that a dimensional constant R is retained in the gas equations with dimensions $L^2T^{-2}\theta^{-1}$.

An exactly similar situation exists in photometry. The unit of luminous intensity can be defined as the intensity of a monochromatic source which radiates unit amount of energy in unit time, but in practice, at least until recently, the unit chosen has been in fact an independent unit, such as the candle, based on some arbitrary material standard.

If such additional independent units are used, it should be borne in mind that the dimensions of derived physical quantities depend on these units as well as on those of mass, length and time; these systems have in fact more than three fundamental units.

20.31. *Systems with less than three fundamental units*

As we have seen in 20.3, systems with more than three arbitrary fundamental units are possible; we now consider the possibility of systems with two or one or none.

We may obtain an example of a system with two arbitrary units as follows. Choose independent units of mass and time as usual and then make the unit of length a derived unit; e.g. let the unit of length be the length of pendulum whose period of oscillation (at a particular point on the earth) is equal to the unit of time, or the distance travelled by light or sound under given conditions in unit time. Notice that the distance so defined is an ordinary length, and that measurement of length is still done by scales and not by clocks. The dimensions of length certainly involve those of time but there is nothing mystical in this ; it simply means that if the unit of time is altered, so also is that of length.

The number of independent units may be further reduced to one, e.g. by defining the unit of mass to be the mass of unit volume of water under given conditions. The unit of volume of course is defined in terms of the unit of length and hence depends on the unit of time. In this system the unit of time is the sole arbitrary unit, once this is defined the others follow.

Finally, if we define once and for all that the unit of time is, say, the period of rotation of the earth or the time taken by a radio pulse to travel to the moon and back, or the periodic time of a given oscillating system, we should have no arbitrary units left and no need for dimensions. In such a system a velocity of 60 would imply one particular velocity without further specif-cation. There are difficulties of course ; the electron-micro-scopist's millimicron and the astronomer's megaparsec cannot be squeezed into the same dimension-free convention without one or both spending a considerable part of his time counting up noughts. A further disadvantage will appear when we consider the ' method of dimensions '.

20.4. The agreement of dimensions in an equation

If an equation is to hold in any and every system of units, then apart from artificial examples, the dimensions of each term must be the same. For example Bernoulli's equation relates the pressure p, velocity v, density ρ and depth z in a perfect fluid in steady motion, as follows

$$(p/\rho)+\tfrac{1}{2}v^2-gz=gh \qquad (1)$$

where h is a constant of the motion (the effective head of fluid) and g is the acceleration due to gravity.

It will be found that each term has dimensions L^2T^{-2}. The importance of this is that the equation is not confined to one particular system of units. Provided the numbers p, ρ, v, g, z, h in one system of units satisfy equation (1), the corresponding values of p, ρ, etc., in any other system necessarily satisfy the same equation.

An equation such as

$$(p/\rho)+\tfrac{1}{2}v^2-32z=32h \qquad (2)$$

on the other hand, although correct in the F.P.S. system, is not generally correct: the dimensions of two of the terms now appear to be those of length only.

It is possible to construct equations which, although the dimensions of individual terms are not the same, yet remain true in all systems of units. Thus for a particle of mass m moving with constant acceleration f under a force P, the distance travelled in time t is

$$s=\tfrac{1}{2}ft^2 \qquad (3)$$

and the acceleration is given by

$$P=mf \qquad (4)$$

Adding (3) and (4) we obtain

$$P+s=f(\tfrac{1}{2}t^2+m) \qquad (5)$$

which, although of no immediate value, is a perfectly correct equation in any system of units.

Apart from equations of this type, differences in dimensions are a certain indication of mistakes in derivation.

20.41. *Dimensions as simple powers of M, L, and T*

The reader will possibly have wondered why the dimensions of a physical quantity are always of the form $M^aL^bT^c$, rather than say e^M or L^2+T^2. It is in fact impossible to construct permissible quantities having dimensions of the latter type, but it is not obvious from mere inspection why the functions of M, L and T should always be simple powers.

Let a derived quantity X be supposed to have dimensions $\mathrm{f}(M, L, T)$ where f is to be determined. This statement conveys the following information. Suppose that the derived unit of X is obtained in any given system of fundamental units, let the unit amount of X be represented by the length of the line in Fig. 20.1(*a*). Now go over to a new system of units greater than those of the first by numerical factors M_1, L_1 and T_1 respectively. Then the unit of X increases by a numerical factor $\mathrm{f}(M_1, L_1, T_1)$, and can be represented by Fig. 20.1(*b*).

Suppose that we now construct a further system with units increased yet again by numerical factors M_2, L_2 and T_2. Then the new unit of X will be increased by a numerical factor $\mathrm{f}(M_2, L_2, T_2)$ and hence will be greater than the first by a factor $\mathrm{f}(M_1, L_1, T_1) \times \mathrm{f}(M_2, L_2, T_2)$. Its value is represented in Fig. 20.1(c).

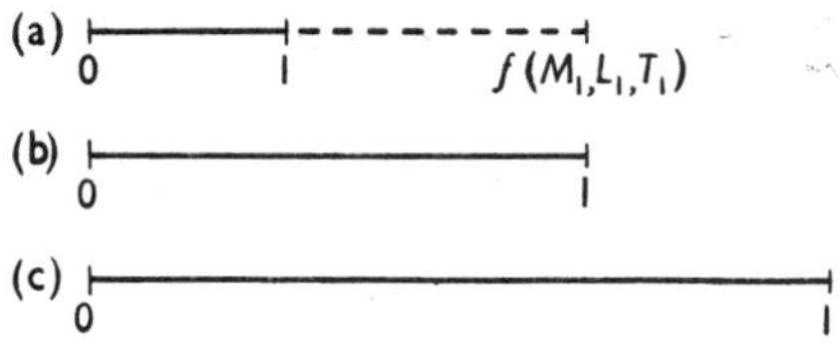

FIG. 20.1

Since we can also go direct from the first to the third system by using factors M_1M_2, L_1L_2 and T_1T_2, it follows that the final unit must be greater than the first by the factor

$$\mathrm{f}(M_1M_2, L_1L_2, T_1T_2)$$

We deduce that f must satisfy the functional equation.

$$\mathrm{f}(M_1, L_1, T_1) \times \mathrm{f}(M_2, L_2, T_2) = \mathrm{f}(M_1M_2, L_1L_2, T_1T_2)$$

To see what limitation this imposes on f, differentiate partially with respect to M_1 and M_2 in succession. For simplicity we omit the other arguments which are supposed held constant during the differentiation.

Then $$\mathrm{f}'(M_1M_2) \, . \, M_2 = \mathrm{f}'(M_1) \, . \, \mathrm{f}(M_2)$$

and $$\mathrm{f}'(M_1M_2) \, . \, M_1 = \mathrm{f}(M_1) \, . \, \mathrm{f}'(M_2)$$

Dividing and re-arranging

$$\frac{M_1\mathrm{f}'(M_1)}{\mathrm{f}(M_1)} = \frac{M_2\mathrm{f}'(M_2)}{\mathrm{f}(M_2)}$$

The L.H.S. is independent of M_2 and the R.H.S. is independent of M_1. Hence

$$\frac{M_1\mathrm{f}'(M_1)}{\mathrm{f}(M_1)} = a$$

where a is a constant. Solving this differential equation we find

$$\mathrm{f}(M_1) = KM_1^{a}$$

Further since $\mathrm{f}(1) = 1$, $K = 1$.

A similar proof holds for the remaining arguments L and T. We deduce that the most general form which f can take is

$$\mathrm{f}(M, L, T) = M^a L^b T^c$$

An important corollary of this is that any function, other than a power, that occurs in an equation having physical significance, must normally have a dimensionless argument. Examples are

Simple harmonic motion:

$y = y_0 \sin(\omega t + \phi)$, ω = frequency, $\omega t + \phi$ dimensionless.

Vapour pressure:

$P = P_0 e^{L/R\theta}$ L = Latent heat, and R, θ gas constant and temperature, $L/R\theta$ dimensionless.

This rule is not quite an absolute one, however, because apparent exceptions can be constructed. Thus the formula $V = V_0 + 2e \log(r_0/r)$ for the potential outside a cylindrical wire of radius r_0 and charge density e per unit length can equally well be written in the form

$$V = C - 2e \log r$$

in which form the argument of the log function is no longer dimensionless. It remains true however that the equation *can* be written, or rewritten, in a form conforming to the rule.

20.5. The method of dimensions

The most important application of dimensions is to the determination of the general form of the relation between physical quantities. A surprising amount of information can often be obtained, apparently without using any kind of physical picture or any detailed knowledge whatsoever of the phenomenon under investigation.

The usual example is the determination of the period of a simple pendulum. Let the length of the pendulum be l, the mass of the bob m, and the acceleration due to gravity g. We suppose for the moment that no other variables enter the calculation. Then let the formula connecting T with these variables be

$$T = K l^a m^b g^c$$

where K is dimensionless and a, b, c are constants to be determined.

The dimensions of the right-hand side must be those of time. Hence

$$l^a m^b g^c = T$$

i.e.

$$l^a m^b [LT^{-2}]^c = T$$

whence $a = \frac{1}{2}$, $b = 0$, $c = -\frac{1}{2}$ and therefore

$$T = K\surd(l/g) \tag{1}$$

where K is a dimensionless quantity.

A more elaborate example is the following. A spherical cannon ball of diameter d is travelling with velocity v, through air of density ρ and viscosity η. It will be supposed that the pressure and temperature of air enter only through the velocity of sound, a. It is required to calculate the resistance R exerted by the air on the projectile.

We assume a formula of the type

$$R = Kd^\alpha v^\beta \rho^\gamma \eta^\delta a^\epsilon \tag{2}$$

α, β, ... have to be chosen so that the dimensions of the right-hand side are those of force. Inserting the dimensions of r, v, ... , a, we have

$$L^\alpha [LT^{-1}]^\beta [ML^{-3}]^\gamma [ML^{-1}T^{-1}]^\delta [LT^{-1}]^\epsilon = MLT^{-2}$$

On comparing the indices of M, L, T we find

$$\gamma + \delta = 1$$

$$\alpha + \beta - 3\gamma - \delta + \epsilon = 1$$

$$\beta + \delta + \epsilon = 2$$

These equations have not a unique solution because there are now more unknowns than equations. The most that can be done is to express three of them in terms of the other two, for example

$$\alpha = 2 - \delta$$

$$\beta = 2 - \delta - \epsilon$$

$$\gamma = 1 - \delta$$

Hence

$$R = Kd^{2-\delta} v^{2-\delta-\epsilon} \rho^{1-\delta} \eta^\delta a^\epsilon$$

or more conveniently

$$R = Kd^2 \rho v^2 (\eta/d\rho v)^\delta (a/v)^\epsilon \tag{3}$$

The bracketed terms can be raised to an arbitrary power without affecting the dimensions only because they are dimensionless. This is clear enough in the case of the second bracket and can be easily verified in the first. These and other dimensionless combinations or quantities are of great importance and it is useful to have a systematic way of detecting them such as is given above. The quantity v/a is known as the Mach number and the quantity $d\rho v/\eta$ is the Reynolds' number. They are not of course absolute constants ; they are numbers simply in the sense that if $d\rho v/\eta$ has the value 1000 in the C.G.S. system then it also has the value 1000 in any other consistent system.

An immediate generalisation of (3) can now be made. Since $(d\rho v/\eta)$ and (v/a) are dimensionless we cannot assume that simple powers are the only permissible functions, and an arbitrary function of these quantities must be used. Hence we write

$$R = Kd^2\rho v^2 \mathrm{f}(d\rho v/\eta, v/a) \tag{4}$$

No further information on the form of the function f can be obtained from this argument.

It will be noticed that the method of dimensions will usually give an explicit formula (apart from an unknown constant) provided that the quantity to be found does not depend on more than three given quantities. If there are more than three, then a dimensionless combination can certainly be found and an arbitrary function appears in the resulting formula. It may be wondered whether it is possible to increase the precision of the method by using a system with more than three arbitrary units, but every increase in the number of dimensions adds an associated dimensional constant such as the gas constant which can be used with the other quantities to create dimensionless combinations. If a system of less than three arbitrary units is used, the method of dimensions becomes less valuable. Three therefore appears to be the optimum number of units from this point of view.

20.51. *Similitude*

The principle of similitude, or dynamical similarity, has been much used in scaling up the results from experiments on small models. The method will be illustrated by a short discussion of the use of the wind-tunnel to determine the drag on an aircraft as a function of velocity.

A model of the aircraft is made reduced in the ratio $k:1$ (linear dimensions). The model is then mounted in the wind-tunnel and the forces exerted on it by a moving air stream are measured for different velocities of flow. The problem is to interpret these results so that they can be applied to the full-scale aircraft.

Formula (4) of 20.5 was deduced originally for a sphere ; it can however be applied to any other shape by adding new dimensionless arguments in sufficient number to specify the ratios of all relevant dimensions to one particular dimension. Thus

$$R = Kd^2\rho v^2 \mathrm{f}(d\rho v/\eta,\ v/a,\ \sigma_1,\ \sigma_2,\ \ldots) \qquad (1)$$

where the σ's are shape factors, and d is now one particular dimension specifying the overall size of the aircraft or model. For speeds well below the speed of sound (say $v < 0{\cdot}7a$), it is known that the function f does not vary appreciably with the Mach number v/a ; this number is important only when the compressibility of the air becomes appreciable, i.e. at velocities in the neighbourhood of and greater than the velocity of sound.

Since a scale model is used, the various dimensionless shape factors σ_1, σ_2 etc. are the same for model and original ; hence equation (1) is effectively

$$R = \rho d^2 v^2 \mathrm{F}(d\rho v/\eta) \qquad (2)$$

where F is some function of the Reynolds' number only. The form of F can now be determined by experiments, as follows. Let the observed force on the model at velocity v be $R(v)$; instead of plotting $R(v)$ against v, however, exhibit the results in the form $R(v)/\rho v^2 d^2$ against $d\rho v/\eta$. This curve is then a graph of the function F against Reynolds' number. Having been determined from the model experiment the function F is now known for any body of the same shape as the model, whatever its size.

20.52. *Gravitational and inertial mass*

The reader will notice on looking through the dimensions listed in Table IV that some quantities such as velocity and acceleration are actually defined in terms of the fundamental quantities of mass, length and time. There are others, however, such as force whose dimensions are obtained essentially by taking an empirical equation, Newton's second law in this case, and reducing it to the simplest possible form.

It should be noted however that mass has *two* mechanical properties : it possesses inertia so that a force is required to change its velocity ; in addition, two separate masses exert a

TABLE IV

Dimensions of mechanical quantities

Quantity	*Dimensions*
Mass	M
Length	L
Time	T
Area	L^2
Volume	L^3
Velocity	LT^{-1}
Acceleration	LT^{-2}
Force	MLT^{-2}
Work, Energy	ML^2T^{-2}
Moment of Inertia	ML^2
Couple, Torque	ML^2T^{-2}
Angle	Dimensionless
Angular velocity	T^{-1}
Angular acceleration	T^{-2}
Gravitational constant	$M^{-1}L^3T^{-2}$

gravitational force on each other. The empirical law of force between two particles of masses m_1 and m_2 distant r apart is

$$F = Gm_1m_2/r^2$$

where G is the gravitational constant, with dimensions $M^{-1}L^3T^{-2}$.

It is quite feasible to choose a derived unit of force so as to simplify this equation rather than Newton's Second Law. Applying the usual method we should take the unit of force to be that between two unit masses unit distance apart ; in this scheme G is identically equal to unity in all consistent systems of units and hence the law of gravitation becomes

$$F = m_1m_2/r^2$$

and the dimensions of force become M^2L^{-2}.

This simplification of the law of gravity is obtained at the expense of Newton's law of motion which becomes

$$F = kmf$$

where k is a constant with dimensions $ML^{-3}T^2$.

20.6. The units of electric and magnetic quantities

The development of two parallel systems of mechanical units is therefore clearly possible ; it has not in fact occurred because of the comparatively infrequent use that is made of the law of gravitation.

In electricity and magnetism, however, a similar situation arises, and here there is no one system of units that can be regarded as the most obviously convenient.

The source of the multiplicity of systems lies again in the fact that electric charge and magnetic pole, like mass, each have two distinct basic properties. Thus electric charge has the property of exerting Coulomb forces on other charges and also the property of generating a magnetic field when in motion. Magnetic pole likewise has the property of exerting forces on other poles, and of generating an electric field when in motion. The experimental laws which are found to hold are (1) Coulomb's law : the force between two charges q_1 and q_2 distance r apart is proportional to q_1q_2/r^2, (2) the corresponding law in magnetism which gives the force between two poles m_1 and m_2 as proportional to m_1m_2/r^2, (3) Ampere's law : the work done in carrying unit pole round a path enclosing current i is proportional to $i\,(=\mathrm{d}q/\mathrm{d}t)$.

There are thus three constants of proportionality, any two of which may be given assigned values by appropriate definitions of the units of electric charge and magnetic pole. Thus in the electrostatic system charge is so defined that

(1) Coulomb's law takes the form

$$\text{Force} = q_1q_2/r^2$$

the constant of proportionality in the previous statement of the law being unity in free space by definition,

(2) Ampère's law has the form

$$\oint H \,.\, \mathrm{d}s = 4\pi\, \mathrm{d}q/\mathrm{d}t$$

the unit of magnetic pole strength being such that the constant of proportionality is 4π. The inverse square law of magnetism then becomes force $= m_1 m_2/\psi r^2$ where ψ is a dimensional constant. In the electromagnetic system of units on the other hand, ψ is defined to be 1 and a constant K appears in Coulomb's law.

In the Gaussian system both K and ψ are taken equal to unity but a dimensional constant c appears in Ampère's law; thus

$$\oint H \, . \, \mathrm{d}s = (4\pi/c)\, \mathrm{d}q/\mathrm{d}t$$

These and two other systems, the practical system and the M.K.S. coulomb system will now be discussed in more detail.

20.61. *The electrostatic system*

In this system the unit of charge is so defined that the inverse square law of electrostatics takes the form

$$F = q_1 q_2/r^2 \tag{1}$$

In free space F is the force between charges q_1 and q_2 at distance r. The dimensions of charge are therefore $[(Fr^2)^{1/2}]$ i.e. $M^{1/2}L^{3/2}T^{-1}$.

Fractional indices have not appeared previously and are often regarded as being in some way improper. This is mainly due to confusion between the use of M for a *number which is the measure* of a mass and for a mass itself. Only the former is involved here. To say that the dimensions of charge are $M^{1/2}L^{3/2}T^{-1}$ means one thing only, namely that if the unit of mass is increased by a factor of say 100 then the unit of charge is increased by a factor of $100^{1/2}$ i.e. 10. Otherwise, the inverse square law (1) would not hold in the new system. The concept of $(\text{mass})^{1/2}$ as a new kind of physical quantity is not involved. An attempt to remove fractional indices from the dimensions of electric quantities is often made and is in fact mistaken. It is founded on the fact that if the force between charges is measured not in free space, but in a dielectric medium, the law of force becomes

$$F = q_1 q_2/Kr^2$$

The argument then put forward is that the dielectric constant K perhaps has some dimensions of its own and that even in vacuo one should allow for the dimensions of K in calculating those of charge. Thus on this scheme the 'true' dimensions of charge are $[K^{1/2}]M^{1/2}L^{3/2}/T^{-1}$ and it is possible that if we knew what $[K^{1/2}]$ was, the dimensions of charge would become more reasonable. This however is fallacious for we do in fact know the dimensions of dielectric constant. It cannot be too strongly emphasised that on the electrostatic system dielectric constant is dimensionless. By this we mean as always that no matter how we choose the units of mass, length and time, $K=1$ for free space (and is a definite constant not equal to 1 for material media). The vague notion that K may have some dimensions of its own arises from the equally vague notion that the dimensions of a physical quantity have some connection with the intrinsic nature of that quantity ; in fact dimensions are much less elusive than this, and are concerned only with the way in which we measure it.

As an example consider the size of the unit charge on the F.P.S. electrostatic system. It is often thought incidentally that the electrostatic system is based entirely on C.G.S. units. This is not so ; any system of units in which the inverse square law of electrostatics is of the form (1) is an electrostatic system. The unit charge on the F.P.S. electrostatic system is thus that charge which placed at one foot (in vacuo) from an equal charge repels it with a force of one poundal.

Its relation to the C.G.S. electrostatic unit can be easily found by evaluating the numbers M, L, T for the two systems. We have $M=453{\cdot}6$, $L=30{\cdot}48$, $T=1$. Since the dimensions of charge are $M^{1/2}L^{3/2}T^{-1}$, the F.P.S. unit is equal to $(453{\cdot}6)^{1/2}(30{\cdot}48)^{3/2}$ i.e. about 3584 C.G.S. units. Similarly in going to the M.K.S. system we have $M=1000$, $L=100$, $T=1$ and hence

$$M^{1/2}L^{3/2}T^{-1}=31{,}620.$$

Thus the M.K.S. electrostatic unit of charge is equal to 31,620 C.G.S. units.

Having obtained the dimensions of charge we can now proceed to draw up a table of the dimensions of other electric quantities as in Table V. The reader should be able to verify the entries in this table without difficulty. Notice in particular that the dimensions of capacity are those of length. This is often described by saying that, in the electrostatic system, capacity is a length. A more correct statement is to say that the measure of the capacity of a given condenser transforms in the same way as the numerical measure of a given length. Thus a condenser of capacity 100 units in the C.G.S. system has a capacity of 1 unit in the M.K.S. system and about 3·3 units in the F.P.S. system.

To determine the units of magnetic quantities in the electrostatic system we bridge the gap between the two kinds of quantity by introducing some empirical relation concerning the phenomenon of electromagnetic induction. The simplest, perhaps, is the observed fact that the contribution to the field at a point due to a circuit element of length ds carrying current i and at distance r is proportional to $(i\,\mathrm{d}s \sin\theta)/r^2$ where θ is the angle between the vectors $\mathbf{ds}$ and $\mathbf{r}$. In accordance with the usual practice we choose the unit of magnetic field (on the electrostatic system) in such a way that this law assumes the simplest possible form, thus

$$H=(i\,\mathrm{d}s \sin\theta)/r^2$$

with the constant of proportionality set equal to unity. The dimensions of H follow and in due course those of all other magnetic quantities. The reader should verify the entries in Table V. Notice in particular that the inverse square law of magnetism cannot be written in the simple form

$$F=m_1m_2/r^2$$

but that a dimensional constant of proportionality must be inserted, thus

$$F=m_1m_2/\mu r^2$$

This quantity μ may be called the permeability of free space in the electrostatic system. Its value cannot be deduced from anything that we have so far discussed, but in the C.G.S. system is found to be $1/(9\times10^{20})$. The dimensions of permeability are those of $(\text{velocity})^{-2}$; so that its value in any other system can be found in the usual way.

20.62. *The electromagnetic system*

This system is entirely analogous to the electrostatic system except that the starting point is the inverse square law of

TABLE V

Quantity	Dimensions Electrostatic	Dimensions Electromagnetic	M.K.S. coulomb	Name of M.K.S. coulomb unit	Symbol
Charge	$M^{1/2}L^{3/2}T^{-1}$	$M^{1/2}L^{1/2}$	Q	Coulomb	q
Potential	$M^{1/2}L^{1/2}T^{-1}$	$M^{1/2}L^{3/2}T^{-2}$	$ML^2T^{-2}Q^{-1}$	Volt	V
Electric Field	$M^{1/2}L^{-1/2}T^{-1}$	$M^{1/2}L^{1/2}T^{-2}$	$MLT^{-2}Q^{-1}$	Volt/metre	E
Electric Induction	$M^{1/2}L^{-1/2}T^{-1}$	$M^{1/2}L^{-3/2}$	$L^{-2}Q$	coulomb/metre²	D
Current	$M^{1/2}L^{3/2}T^{-2}$	$M^{1/2}L^{1/2}T^{-1}$	$T^{-1}Q$	ampere	i
Resistance	$L^{-1}T$	LT^{-1}	$ML^2T^{-1}Q^{-2}$	Ohm	R
Capacity	L	$L^{-1}T^2$	$M^{-1}L^{-2}T^2Q^2$	Farad	C
Inductance	$L^{-1}T^2$	L	ML^2Q^{-2}	Henry	L
Dielectric Constant	Dimensionless	$L^{-2}T^2$	$M^{-1}L^{-3}T^2Q^2$	Farad/metre	K
Magnetic Field	$M^{1/2}L^{1/2}T^{-2}$	$M^{1/2}L^{-1/2}T^{-1}$	$L^{-1}T^{-1}Q$	Ampere-turns/metre	H
Magnetic Potential	$M^{1/2}L^{3/2}T^{-2}$	$M^{1/2}L^{1/2}T^{-1}$	$T^{-1}Q$	Ampere-turns	
Magnetic Induction	$M^{1/2}L^{-3/2}$	$M^{1/2}L^{-1/2}T^{-1}$	$MT^{-1}Q^{-1}$	Weber/metre²	B
Magnetic Flux	$M^{1/2}L^{1/2}$	$M^{1/2}L^{3/2}T^{-1}$	$ML^2T^{-1}Q^{-1}$	Weber	
Magnetic Moment	$M^{1/2}L^{3/2}$	$M^{1/2}L^{5/2}T^{-1}$	$L^2T^{-1}Q$	Ampere-metre²	M
Magnetic Pole	$M^{1/2}L^{1/2}$	$M^{1/2}L^{3/2}T^{-1}$	$LT^{-1}Q$	Ampere-metre	m
Permeability	$L^{-2}T^2$	Dimensionless	MLQ^{-2}	Henry/meter	μ
Force	MLT^{-2}	MLT^{-2}	MLT^{-2}	Newton	
Energy	ML^2T^{-2}	ML^2T^{-2}	ML^2T^{-2}	Joule	
Power	ML^2T^{-3}	ML^2T^{-3}	ML^2T^{-3}	Watt	

magnetism. Unit pole in this system is so defined that the force between poles m_1 and m_2 is given by

$$F = m_1 m_2 / r^2$$

In other words the essential feature of the electromagnetic system of units is that the permeability of free space is identically equal to unity, whatever the units of mass, length and time. For material media the permeability is different from one, but is still dimensionless. On the other hand the dielectric constant is no longer dimensionless and is not necessarily equal to unity in free space.

To obtain the dimensions of electrical quantities on this system, the same equation as was used in 20.61, expressing the phenomenon of electromagnetic induction can be used. The unit of current is chosen so that the magnetic field produced is given by

$$H = (i \, ds \sin \theta)/r^2$$

without constants of proportionality.

20.63. *The ratio of the electromagnetic to the electrostatic unit of charge*

Consider the following ideal experiment. We require a source of positive electricity which can be used either to supply charge to a number of small conducting spheres, or to give a steady current of controllable size. In addition we have a magnetic pole, of unit strength on the electromagnetic system, i.e. a pole which repels an equal pole with unit force when placed at unit distance from it. We charge the two spheres until when placed unit distance apart the repulsion between them amounts to one unit. Each sphere then carries one electrostatic unit of charge. We now pass a current through a circuit of unit length and at unit distance from the pole and increase the current until the force on the pole reaches one unit. This is now unit current on the electromagnetic system. We now allow this current to flow for one unit of time into a third small conducting sphere. This sphere therefore carries one electromagnetic unit of charge. Finally we compare the amounts of charge on this last sphere with that on either of the others.

The reader will observe that the ratio may well depend on the choice of unit distance, unit force and unit time. The results of the experiment when C.G.S. units are employed is in fact 3×10^{10}; the electromagnetic unit is enormously larger than the electrostatic unit of charge.

We now ask what the ratio will be if we use other units such as those of the M.K.S. or F.P.S. systems. The experiment can of course be repeated using the new units but as we know the dimensions of charge on the two systems this is not necessary. Starting from the C.G.S. system let us go to a system in which the units of mass, length and time are greater by factors M, L

and T. Then since the dimensions of charge on the electrostatic system are $M^{1/2}L^{3/2}T^{-1}$ the new electrostatic unit of charge will be increased by this factor. Similarly the new electromagnetic unit will be increased by a factor $M^{3/2}L^{1/2}$. This it will be noticed is not the same factor and hence the ratio (R) of the e.m. unit to the e.s. unit alters ; in fact it changes by the factor $1/LT^{-1}$. This means that R changes in the same way as the *measure* of a given velocity when the fundamental units alter. But we have seen above that when C.G.S. units are used R has the same numerical value 3×10^{10}, as the measure of the velocity of light. It follows therefore that whatever fundamental units are used, R will always be equal to the measure of the velocity of light.

This result is sometimes expressed as follows :

$$\frac{\text{Electromagnetic unit of charge}}{\text{Electrostatic unit of charge}}=\text{velocity of light in vacuo}$$

and the bewildered reader is left with the impossible task of fusing two separate mental pictures; the two charged spheres on one hand, and a ray of light travelling through space on the other.

The situation resolves itself however if we remember not to confuse measurements with the quantities measured. The ratio of the units in a given system is a number with the dimensions of a velocity, the measure of the velocity of light is also a number. Both numbers are dimensional, i.e. they vary from one system to another (e.g. M.K.S. to F.P.S.) but they vary in the same way, namely, like a velocity ; hence if the two are equal in one system, they are equal in all systems.

Finally, why the velocity of light, rather than any other velocity? The point is, of course, that light is an electromagnetic phenomenon; when this is realised, it is perhaps less mysterious that the ratio of the two units of charge should be equal to the measure of the velocity of light.

20.64. *The Gaussian system of units*

This system would probably have remained unchallenged but for the discovery of electromagnetic induction and the subsequent technical importance of this phenomenon. In the Gaussian system all electrical quantities are measured in electrostatic units and all magnetic quantities in electromagnetic units. Thus the dielectric constant and the permeability of free space are both equal to unity and both dimensionless in this system. This is an advantage to the physicist but is not of value to the engineer who rarely if ever uses the inverse square laws. The disadvantage of the system is that the laws of electromagnetic induction, i.e. those in which magnetic quantities are related to electric quantities must contain proportionality constants involving powers of c, the ratio of the units

Thus Maxwell's equations for the electromagnetic field are

$$\operatorname{div} \mathbf{D} = 4\pi\rho, \qquad \operatorname{curl} \mathbf{E} = -\frac{1}{c}\frac{\partial \mathbf{B}}{\partial t}$$

$$\operatorname{div} \mathbf{B} = 0, \qquad \operatorname{curl} \mathbf{H} = 4\pi \mathbf{j} + \frac{1}{c}\frac{\partial \mathbf{D}}{\partial t}$$

E, **D** and ρ are regarded as electric quantities, **H**, **B** and **j** as magnetic.

20.65. *The M.K.S. system of units*

The engineer has a further objection to the Gaussian system. Not only does it simplify the two equations which he never uses at the expense of those which he does use, but also when used with C.G.S. units, the actual magnitudes of many of the units are inconvenient. The engineer, in particular, is not happy with numbers much over a thousand or much less than a tenth. He much prefers 132 Kilovolts to 132,000 volts, and 10 Megohms to 10,000,000 ohms ; this is quite reasonable ; there is obviously far less likelihood of mistakes if one refers to a current not as 0·000002 amps but as 2 microamps. He therefore strongly disapproves not only of the C.G.S. electrostatic unit of charge, and the C.G.S. electromagnetic unit of potential which are very small indeed, but of the C.G.S. system as a whole. The unit of energy on this system is the erg.—the amount of work done when a force of 1 dyne moves through 1 centimetre. This is absurdly small and huge numbers are required to deal with the outputs of even the smallest power plants.

The unsuitability of the C.G.S. system can be rectified by taking as the unit of energy the joule, i.e. 10^7 ergs. Since the dimensions of energy are ML^2T^{-2} we can do this by choosing a system derived from the C.G.S. system by increasing the units of mass, length and time by factors M, L and T such that

$ML^2T^{-2}=10^7$. It is not feasible to change the unit of time; which means in effect that we have to choose M and L so that $ML^2=10^7$. There are of course many possible solutions of this but the most satisfactory is probably the solution $M=10^3$, $L=10^2$. This gives rise to the M.K.S. (metre-kilogram-second) system.

The M.K.S. system gives rise to mechanical units of force, energy and power etc. which are much more comparable with engineering practice. It remains to consider how the electrical units appear. Consider first the M.K.S. electromagnetic system. The dimensions of current in this system are $M^{1/2}L^{1/2}T^{-1}$. Hence the unit of current is $(1000)^{1/2}$ $(100)^{1/2}$ C.G.S. e.m.u.'s, i.e. about 316. The C.G.S. unit however is itself rather larger than convenient and the practical unit of current, the ampere, is 1/10th of the c.g.s. e.m. unit and therefore 1/3160th of the M.K.S. e.m. unit, so this latter is clearly much too large.

Now consider the M.K.S. electrostatic system. The dimensions of current in electrostatic systems are $M^{1/2}L^{3/2}T^{-2}$ and therefore in going from the C.G.S. to the M.K.S. system, the unit of current increases by a factor $(1000)^{1/2}$ $(100)^{3/2}$, i.e. by about $3{\cdot}16\times 10^4$. As the ampere is about 3×10^9 times as large as the C.G.S. e.s. unit, the improvement is inadequate.

In other words the M.K.S. system is little better than the C.G.S. system in bringing up workable units of current. There is however a further possibility, and that is to abandon both inverse square laws and choose an entirely new starting point.

The most useful scheme, first suggested by Giorgi, for defining suitable electrical units appears to be that of introducing a fourth arbitrary unit, that of charge, say. The dimensions of all other electrical quantities will depend on the size of the unit chosen of course and so the dimensions now involve 4 numbers, M, L, T as before and a new number Q. This kind of procedure has already been adopted in defining the unit of temperature which as we have seen is in effect a separate independent unit.

The obvious unit to choose is of course the coulomb—defined as one-tenth the C.G.S. e.m. unit or more conveniently as that amount of charge which is delivered by a current of one ampere, flowing for one second.

The engineer's practical units, the joule, watt, ampere, volt, farad, henry then follow as the consistent units in a system of this type provided simply that we choose the metre, kilogram, second and coulomb as our basic units.

A further modification has been proposed which is frequently, but not necessarily, incorporated into the M.K.S.Q. system. Instead of defining fictitious isolated magnetic poles or dipoles strictly analogous to electric charges or electric dipoles, the definition of magnetic dipole is required to conform to the actual properties of dipoles formed by circulating electric currents of constant strength. Thus the torque on a magnetic dipole is required to be proportional to **B** (rather than **H**). To achieve this, magnetic pole and intensity of magnetisation are so defined that a pole of strength m traditional units is said in the new system to be of strength m/μ, and similarly for magnetisation. The corresponding law of force between magnetic poles is then $F=\mu m_1 m_2/r^2$ rather than the traditional $F=m_1 m_2/\mu r^2$.

Table V gives the dimensions of the principal electric and magnetic quantities on this new system. Notice that neither the permeability nor dielectric constant is dimensionless, and also that no fractional indices appear. The last column gives the name, where available, of the unit in the M.K.S. coulomb system.

20.7. B and H, D and E

The question of the units of magnetic induction and magnetic field causes a certain amount of controversy, particularly since these units require different names. On the Giorgi system of units confusion is bound to arise if one starts speculating on the intrinsic nature of these quantities ; if one confines attention to methods of measurement the difficulties evaporate.

In the electromagnetic system, the permeability of free space is equal to unity, and at any point in free space $B=H$. It is therefore reasonable to use the same unit for either quantity. The C.G.S. electromagnetic unit is the gauss and it would be legitimate to measure either induction or field in terms of this unit. In a material medium $B=\mu H$ but μ is dimensionless and it would be permissible to say, for example that $B=1000$ gauss and $H=1$ gauss in a given piece of ferromagnetic material. However, for better or worse, an International Conference decided by a narrow majority to call the unit of field the Oersted.

In the electrostatic system however the units of induction and field are different. Moreover unlike the electromagnetic system they vary in a different way if the units of mass, length and time are altered. In other words μ is not dimensionless.

Conversely electric induction and electric field have equal units in the electrostatic system, and unequal units in the electromagnetic system.

In a system with four arbitrary units such as the M.K.S. coulomb system, neither permeability nor dielectric constant is dimensionless, and neither of them will be unity in free space (unless of course the fundamental units of mass, length, time and charge are particularly chosen to achieve this). Hence in this system B and H have different units and likewise D and E.

It should be particularly noted that the discussion given above does not include any philosophical enquiry into the nature of induction and field. The distinction is drawn purely from consideration of the method of measurement.

The following Table VI summarises some of the characteristic differences between the four types of system in use. For fuller discussion of the equations involved, the reader must consult a text-book on electricity and magnetism.

There is no doubt that the Gaussian system which can of course be used with the metre and kilogram just as well as with the centimetre and gram, is the most generally satisfactory for the physicist. The four unit system, in particular the M.K.S. coulomb system, has, however, been widely adopted especially by the electrical engineer and is gradually supplanting the others.

The advantages are, of course, considerable and to the engineer, overwhelming ; for in this system the scale readings of standard electrical instruments, ammeters, voltmeters, wattmeters and so on, all belong directly and without further juggling with powers of 10, to a consistent system.

The disadvantage of this system to the physicist is that it complicates all equations except Maxwell's, which it simplifies very slightly by removing the factor c (a well-known and easily remembered number which always occurs in the combination $c\,\delta t$). To overcome this disadvantage *rationalised* systems have been introduced whereby the factors 4π are removed from Maxwell's equations. This is achieved by redefining dielectric constant and magnetic permeability so that their values are

TABLE VI

System	Electrostatic	Electromagnetic	Gaussian	M.K.S.Q.†
Inverse square law of electrostatics in free space	$F=\frac{q_1q_2}{r^2}$	$F=\frac{q_1q_2}{K_0r^2}$	$F=\frac{q_1q_2}{r^2}$	$F=\frac{q_1q_2}{K_0r^2}$
of Magnetism	$F=\frac{m_1m_2}{\mu_0r^2}$	$F=\frac{m_1m_2}{r^2}$	$F=\frac{m_1m_2}{r^2}$	$F=\frac{\mu_0m_1m_2}{r^2}$
Dimension of dielectric constant	—	$L^{-2}T^2$	—	$M^{-1}L^{-3}T^2Q^2$
Dimensions of permeability	$L^{-2}T^2$	—	—	MLQ^{-2}
Relation between D, E and P	$D=E+4\pi P$	$D=K_0E+4\pi P$	$D=E+4\pi P$	$D=K_0E+4\pi P$
Relation between B, H and I	$B=\mu_0H+4\pi I$	$B=H+4\pi I$	$B=H+4\pi I$	$B=\mu_0(H+4\pi I)$
Maxwell's equations for isotropic dielectric medium	div $\mathbf{D}=4\pi\rho$ div $\mathbf{B}=0$ curl $\mathbf{E}$ $=-\partial\mathbf{B}/\partial t$ curl $\mathbf{H}$ $=4\pi\mathbf{j}+\partial\mathbf{D}/\partial t$	div $\mathbf{D}=4\pi\rho$ div $\mathbf{B}=0$ curl $\mathbf{E}$ $=-\partial\mathbf{B}/\partial t$ curl $\mathbf{H}$ $=4\pi\mathbf{j}+\partial\mathbf{D}/\partial t$	div $\mathbf{D}=4\pi\rho$ div $\mathbf{B}=0$ curl $\mathbf{E}$ $=-(1/c)\,\partial\mathbf{B}/\partial t$ curl $\mathbf{H}$ $=4\pi\mathbf{j}+(1/c)\,\partial\mathbf{D}/\partial t$	div $\mathbf{D}=4\pi\rho$ div $\mathbf{B}=0$ curl $\mathbf{E}$ $=-\partial\mathbf{B}/\partial t$ curl $\mathbf{H}$ $=4\pi\mathbf{j}+\partial\mathbf{D}/\partial t$

† In this table unrationalised units are used.

respectively $1/4\pi$ and 4π times their values in the corresponding unrationalised system. The form of the inverse square laws and the units of displacement, pole strength etc. undergo a simultaneous change.

Example 1

What units of mass and length must be employed to give an electrostatic system on which the joule and the coulomb are the derived units of energy and charge?

Example 2

What units must be employed to do the same for the electromagnetic system.

Example 3

What unit of charge should be adopted in addition to the metre, kilogram and second if the derived unit of resistance is to be the 'B.A. ohm' which is 0·9866 of the M.K.S coulomb unit?

Answers: *Ex*. 1. $10^{25}c^{-4}$ gm., $10^{-9}c^2$ cm. ($c=3\times10^{10}$).
Ex. 2. 10^{-11} gm., 10^9 cm. *Ex*. 3. 1·0068 coulomb.

INDEX